Rand, Sweeny and Vincent's

Growth and Development
of the Young Child

Marian E. Breckenridge, M.S.
Physical Development and Nutrition, Merrill-Palmer
School, Detroit

Margaret Nesbitt Murphy, Ph.D.
Child Development and Family Life, Purdue University

Sixth Edition

W. B. Saunders Company
Philadelphia   London

Preface

When this book was first written in 1930 the field of child development was relatively new. Medicine, nutrition, psychology and education were opening their avenues of investigation of child development. Relatively little in terms of the knowledge of today was known about the normal, healthy child. That knowledge was scattered among a number of disciplines. Thus little appreciation of the interrelatedness of different aspects of development existed. Rigorous use of normals was advocated. Adherence to rigid schedules was the order of the day. Thus a rigidity in evaluating growth and development and in prescribing for the care of children existed.

From 1930 to the present there has been a growth in research and in the attempts to interpret research findings, to integrate them and make them useful to teachers and students in Child Development and Family Life. From the beginning the authors of this book have had as a major objective this interpretation and integration of research for its readers. The increase in the size of the bibliography from the first edition to this the sixth, from 165 references to 932 references, is indicative of the growth in the literature over the past twenty-seven years. The literature also indicates the growing tendency to share and relate information among the various disciplines.

With increase in knowledge, changes in focus and in practices in child development have occurred which are reflected in the changes in this textbook in content and in organization. The focus has changed from one of status to progress, with a decrease in emphasis on norms and an increase in emphasis on individuality. With the recognition of

iii

wide individuality in growth patterns has come an increased flexibility in prescribing for child care. Longitudinal studies of children throughout their developmental years have contributed to this knowledge of diverse growth patterns. The understanding of individual rates of growth plus the knowledge of the sequential patterns of development has reduced the sense of urgency in adults associated with children in promoting their growth. Further, it has given adults confidence in providing for children's needs and permitting each child to grow comfortably at his own pace. The multidisciplinary approach in child development, wherein the child can be viewed as a whole to which his discrete parts contribute and interact, has become recognized and accepted. This text has been concerned from the beginning with the value of focusing upon the whole child. The original organization on age levels was planned with this in mind. Later, when the organization was changed to permit a more logical and better integrated discussion of the various phases of child development, this concept of interrelatedness was continued through cross references and discussions in the text.

Efforts in the field of child development were early devoted to a description of growth and behavior. More recently the whys of growth and behavior have been sought. This has been made possible through a growing understanding of deep physiologic and psychologic needs. This understanding has led to the modification of the dogmatic tone of old precepts and tempered the rigidity of application. Along with this awareness of these needs of children has come an increasing awareness of the importance of emotional climate in the development of children, which has meant an increasing concern regarding attitudes and interpersonal relationships. The family, which has always been regarded as a primary influence in the life of the child by the authors of this book, is receiving much attention since it provides both a physical and psychologic environment which has great potential in influencing development. In relation to family and community influences the cultural patterns of the child's environment are receiving increased attention as significant influences in establishing habits and attitudes.

The authors of this revision aim to present an attitude or philosophy that can be used in the study of children, based on a few concepts which can be stated as follows: Children follow sequential patterns in the various aspects of their development. Each individual differs in his growth and development. This individuality is the product of the interplay of potentialities and environment. Various aspects of development are interrelated so that one aspect of development affects and in turn is affected at various times and to various degrees by other aspects of development.

Using these basic concepts the authors employ two approaches to the study of the child, namely those of status and progress, with particular emphasis upon the processes involved in the progressive changes observed as a child grows and develops.

The authors would like to suggest that the material in the book be used in a flexible manner so that the student will be able to view the child as a whole and see the interrelationships between his physical and psychologic development. Although the physical aspects of development are presented as a unit for the sake of clarity, they need not be studied as a whole and in the order presented. Sections on physical and psychologic development which are especially related to one another may profitably be studied together, as, for example, the development of nerves, bones, muscles and body balance, along with motor development. The study of the use of the hands might well precede the study of eating behavior. Study of the organs of special sense might accompany the study of perception. Because how the child feels is pertinent to various aspects of his growth, the section on components of personality might precede study of physical, intellectual and social development. Study of particular attitudes of parents in their relationships with children could accompany study of related aspects of development. Attitudes concerning discipline might be related to development of reasoning ability. Parents' affection for their child could be considered at the same time as emotional and social development.

The topics for study and discussion at the ends of the chapters are offered as a means of sharpening the student's awareness of the developing child and his needs by observation and by relating and applying knowledge of children to real situations. An annotated list of films is included from which the teacher may select those pertinent to the specific student group and likely to provoke thought and discussion.

The authors wish to express their appreciation and gratitude to Winifred Rand, Mary Sweeny, and E. Lee Vincent, the authors of the first four editions, for the soundness of their outlook. Appreciation and gratitude are also expressed to the many persons who have contributed to the fifth and sixth revisions in many ways—with critical reviews of the former edition, with information and with photographs, and in the preparation of illustrations and manuscript.

MARIAN E. BRECKENRIDGE
MARGARET NESBITT MURPHY

Contents

Chapter 4
**The Child's Physical Equipment for Growth,
Development and Functioning** **134**

Chapter 5
**The Child's Physical Equipment for Growth,
Development and Functioning (continued)** **191**

Chapter 6
Meeting the Physical Needs of the Growing Child **220**

Contents

Introduction

Whether as parents, potential parents, or teachers, or as others associated with children in professional and nonprofessional ways, people are interested in children. This interest varies in degree and kind. People want to know "how they tick" and why. They also have a sense of responsibility for providing a healthy environment for children. Confusion has resulted from the barrage of advice, the various theories of child care, the fads and old wives' tales. People are seeking answers to questions—some simple, some profound. In all areas there is a desire for more knowledge and understanding so that specific questions can be dealt with, facts and fallacies sifted, and confidence gained in one's ability to meet situations.

A person associated with a particular child wishes for further understanding of him as an individual and for increased ability to have satisfactory relationships with him. His questions concern the child's physical, intellectual, emotional, social, and spiritual growth. For example, the child's gain in weight, hours of sleep, play activities, feelings, reactions to adult suggestions, and interest in a world beyond his comprehension are only a few of the aspects which may receive attention. The person who thinks about the various phases of growth and development soon realizes they are interrelated in a complex way. He recognizes that knowledge of principles of growth is important, and is especially interested in knowing how these principles can be applied in an actual situation with a baby or young child.

What we know about children and their families, and what we hope for, for children and for ourselves in associations with them, and why, is a fascinating field of study.*

Topics for Study

1. To begin to be more aware of the interrelatedness and complexity of growth, briefly report one illustration of physical, intellectual, emotional, social, and spiritual growth noted in observation of one child or of a group of children.

* References concerning methods of observation are Almy[14] pp. 81-100, Hartley, Frank and Goldenson[337] pp. 339-350.

1

2. To begin to clarify your understanding of ways the adult and the situation affect the child, describe (a) what an adult said or did, and (b) what a situation provided which you considered related to each of the phases of growth listed.

3. Indicate questions concerning various phases of growth and factors affecting them which are of interest to you.

1

Current Concepts and Theories of Growth and Development

Changes in Emphasis

Interest in child development is a part of interest in human development. Both the narrow age range of childhood and the wide age range of the entire life span have been the subject of thought and writing for hundreds of years. Points of view on these have been expressed in philosophy, religion, literature and education. Increased attention to well substantiated factual material occurred in the field of child development, as well as in other fields, in the latter part of the nineteenth century and the beginning of the twentieth century. Psychologists, biologists and others began then in increasing numbers to provide findings, based on careful plans for thorough study, with as much objectivity as possible. In the first half of the twentieth century, individuals from these fields of psychology and biology, and from such others as nutrition, medicine, psychiatry, anthropology and sociology, began to show more interest in relating the findings from their various approaches. This drawing together of knowledge from different fields to provide an understanding of the child or of children from many aspects, is characteristic of the field called child development.

Today, in the second half of the twentieth century, those interested in child development and others are making particular efforts to state theories which seem appropriate in terms of current points of view and

3

knowledge.[65, 589, 732, 756] They are trying to pull from various sources general principles about human beings, their growth, development and behavior, and are attempting to assemble from these sources some overall statements which make sense in the light of present information. Explanations, as well as descriptions of the aspects of growth, development and behavior, are being included. Detailed definitions accompany statements of theories. Research is being conducted to check or amplify selected phases of theories, and to add to them. In the distant future, theories concerned with human beings and other animals, and those in the fields of biophysics, chemistry and botany, may seem more closely associated.

Factual material, which has been received over the course of a number of years of study, has led to emphasis on certain ideas or concepts concerning growth (increase in bodily dimensions) and development (the emerging and expanding of the capacities of the individual to provide progressively greater facility in functioning). Those which are frequently stressed today concern maturity, maturation, learning, emotional tone, and the developmental-dynamic aspects of the person. Statements of theory pertaining to these concepts are in the process of being formulated. They are, in a sense, hypotheses to be verified or revised through further study. Although additional research is certainly needed, there is enough basis for current emphases in concepts and related theories, to impel a person who wishes to be well informed to attempt to grasp them and their implications.

One current concept emphasizes maturation. In connection with child development, focus of attention is on *recognition of the child's stages of maturity* (his "unfolding" due primarily to intrinsic factors but affected by environmental factors). In the past thirty years, much knowledge has been provided which indicates that there are wide differences in the pace of growth and development in children who are to be regarded as normal.[81, 90, 288] There are slow growers, fast growers, and average growers. Some slow growers prove to be dwarfed; some fast growers prove to be gigantic. But many slow growers and many fast growers turn out to be normal well integrated people. Individuals arrive at the various stages of growth physically, intellectually, emotionally and socially, at different rates. For example, upright locomotion, or walking, is a step along the way toward greater maturity in motor control. Some normal children arrive at this step at eight months of chronological age, some at twelve months, and some at sixteen months. Figure 3, page 12, illustrates the variation in pace from one individual to another in eye fixation and horizontal following of an object. For some infants, the stage of maturity in which the eyes follow an object horizontally for a short distance was present at the end of 10 days; for all in the group studied it was present by the age of 60 days.

Furthermore, evidence indicates that the maturational pace may differ from one attribute to another in the same child.[247, 753] For example, the individual in Figure 1 showed certain language skills earlier than most children of his chronological age; his pace of growth and development in language was more rapid than that in gross motor responses.

Knowledge provided in the past thirty years also indicates a similarity in the patterns of growth and development over a period of time through which most children proceed.[286, 316, 528, 537] An example is the order of the appearance of the teeth. For most children, the lower front teeth appear first and are followed by the upper front teeth; the back molars appear last. For a few children this pattern may differ. Table 3 on page 212 indicates the pattern followed by the majority in this particular aspect of growth. This illustration concerning teeth pertains to physical growth. Likewise, in various types of behavior, the gradient of stages tends to be similar for the majority of children, although the chronological age at which the individual child arrives at a particular stage differs according to his pace. For example, Gesell's[290] description of the growth gradient of eye and hand coordination shows a pattern followed by most children.

Theories Concerning Maturity and Maturation. These theories, or over-all statements concerning maturational stages and the maturation process, pertain to physical aspects and to the development of various abilities. In his statements about physical aspects, Krogman[477] refers to the process of aging as maturation, and to "the termination of that process—whenever it occurs in the life cycle" as maturity:

"In a larger framework of biologic thought we would like to suggest that maturity is, in a sense, a climax of a biogenetic process; in this vein it may be considered as a never-ending series of climactic events in the life cycle of the organism. Therefore, the definition of maturity must shift with the stage or level of development unfolding that, in broadest aspect, we may call *organic growth*. Maturity, as a biological concept, thus becomes an aspect of the process of physical growth: it may be morphological, physiological, biochemical. It is rarely only one; it is generally all three, well-nigh inseparable."*

* Krogman[477] (p. 30).

In his statements of theory about behavior, Baldwin[65] refers to maturity as increase in competence. In his description of the psychological factors underlying the increase in competence of the child, four aspects of maturity are listed.

"The first of these, expansion of the psychological world, comprises the child's ability to notice obscure objects, to anticipate consequences, to strive for abstract goals as well as concrete ones, and to strive toward a remote future goal." ". . . as he matures, the child becomes able to respond to more and more objects and more kinds of objects." Secondly, as his psychological world expands, "his perception of the properties of the external world becomes more objective." A third aspect of change is differentiation; as he matures, the child becomes more able to make fine discriminations. "This flexibility of behavioral adjustment is achieved because many . . . actions are independent of one another and combinable in any desired way."* The fourth aspect of maturity to which Baldwin refers, i.e., emotional stability, is considered in the discussion of another concept in this chapter.

Other concepts, merely mentioned so far, reflect additional changes in emphasis. Maturity stages of the child are considered as the basis for the beginning of new learnings. Another prerequisite to smooth and successful learning, the emotional tone which facilitates use of the new inner resources, is stressed. The child's need for feeling secure and loved in order to respond successfully to inner and outer stimuli and to develop a well integrated personality is emphasized. Satisfaction of these needs begins early, and mother-child and father-child relationships are therefore considered extremely important. Emphasis of these points has been reflected in new ways of viewing individual differences.

Ways of Viewing Individual Differences

Shift from Age Scales to Maturity Scales.   With shifts in point of view have come changes in practice. Changes have taken place in ways of studying and recording growth. One of the important shifts in the past twenty years is from our previous dependence on age-scale standards (such as height-age, mental-age, and social-age) as a means of charting maturity as well as growth. Some age scales have been ex-

---

* Baldwin[65] (pp. 35, 36, 68, 110).

tremely valuable in giving us insight into quantity of growth but when applied too rigorously in individual instances they have led to misunderstandings about quality of physical, intellectual, and social growth.

Eventually age scales will probably be replaced by maturity scales which will be based on long time studies of children through their entire growth span. The steps of such scales will be steps or stages of growth and will be independent of chronological age. For example, we shall abandon attempts to set up social-age scales by studying typical social behavior of large numbers of subjects in each chronological age group. We shall continue and expand present efforts to study the pattern of development of social behavior in a number of individual children as they grow through the range of social behavior from infantile self absorption to the more mature stages of social cooperation. Thus, instead of comparing a three-year-old child with other three-year-olds, we shall study his current pattern of social behavior, review it in relation to the background in which he achieved it, and from this determine at what stage of his social development he is.

For example, if we measure a child who, upon entering kindergarten, stands around and does not adapt to the other children in cooperative play against an age scale, judging him only by observation of his present behavior and a checking of his behavior against the chronological scale, we might conclude that this behavior represents a frequently observed two-year-old type of inability to adapt to a cooperative situation.

On the other hand, if we view this child from the standpoint of his present stage of social growth, which can be interpreted only in terms of his maturity and his opportunities, we may see him in a different light. He may come from a pair of well adjusted but socially quiet and nonaggressive parents. He may have shown quite adequate early social adjustments to his parents and to the familiar children in the neighborhood, and at the same time have been somewhat reticent in a larger group of children or when faced with strange children. Given a little time, he may make satisfactory social adjustment to other children on a cooperative basis. In this light, we see this child as quite normally adjusted for a quiet, nonaggressive personality. His social adjustment is passing through a stage, or a maturity level, which is entirely satisfactory for his age and social experience. The later, more mature (young adult) level for this child will be an adequate social adjustment of the type his parents are making. We see him now as a child who will take a little time to effect a smooth adjustment to the larger group which he faces upon entrance to the kindergarten, and as a child who, for him, is adjusting satisfactorily. He is a five-year-old who has made satisfactory progressive steps in social growth of the quiet, nonaggressive, but adequate pattern. His channel of social growth is that of the nonaggressive personality. The channels of the aggressive personality and the highly aggressive personality are for children with somewhat different sets of social behavior steps.

The Concept of Growth Channels.   Social growth travels in certain channels, the successive steps or maturity stages of each channel having their own characteristics. According to this concept, a child is measured by his progress along his own channel of social growth rather than along a kind of "average" channel which implies that every child has the same kind of behavior steps.

The channel idea is demonstrated by such various devices for evaluating children's growth in height and weight as the Grid-Graph formulated by Wetzel,[890, 891, 892] the Bayley curves which are based on maturational status,[83] and percentiles[410, 821] as discussed in Chapter 4.

For another example of development along channels see Figure 58, Chapter 8.

Another use of the channel concept is shown by the Merrill-Palmer Logarithmic Developmental Graph* by which the developmental pattern of different attributes of a child may be observed. Figure 1 illus-

---

* On the Merrill-Palmer Logarithmic Developmental Graph[418] the age score, or indicator age, of any attribute is plotted against chronological age. For example, in Figure 1, at six months chronological age, the gross motor indicator age is seven months. The point on the graph representing this relationship is indicated by the dotted lines and arrows. Indicator age is determined by converting actual measurements or behavior of a child into an age by the use of norms. Indicator age is that age at which an actual measurement or behavior coincides with that which is most characteristic (the mean or median) for that particular chronological age. On the graph the diagonal lines represent proportions between chronological age and age scores. A one to one proportion, or a quotient of 100, is represented by the 100 line. When the age score and the chronological age are the same the point on the graph falls on the 100 line. In Figure 1 this is true when gross motor age is 24 months at 24 months chronological age. Above and below that 100 line are spaced other lines at 25 per cent intervals, thus forming channels. It is expected that a line representing a child's progress will parallel one of these channel lines. Permission to use this graph was obtained from Dr. C. G. Jennings, Merrill-Palmer School, Detroit, Michigan.

trates the use of this graph to demonstrate patterns of growth of different attributes for a single child, by plotting the scores for gross motor, fine motor, adaptive, language, and personal-social behavior according to the Gesell Developmental Schedule.

The Merrill-Palmer Logarithmic Developmental Graph

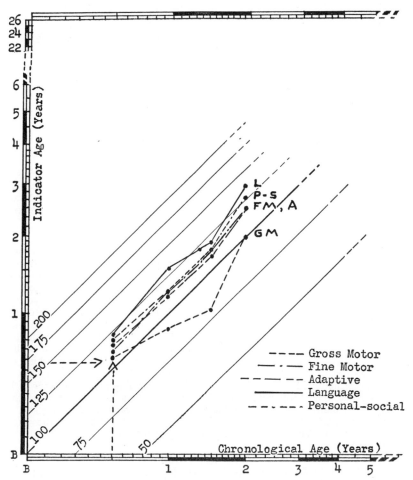

Figure 1. Gross motor, fine motor, adaptive, language, and personal-social behavior, determined by Gesell Developmental Schedules, of a boy from the age of 6 months to 2 years, showing different patterns of development in the five areas. Note greatest advance in language and least advance in gross motor.

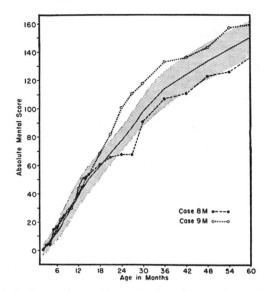

Figure 2. Individual curves of growth of intelligence in absolute scale units, showing contrasting patterns. (From Chap. 3, p. 31, H. A. Peterson, S. S. Marzolf and N. Bayley, Educational Psychology. New York, Macmillan, 1948. Also in N. Bayley: American Psychologist, vol. 10, p. 814, 1955.)

These scores have been plotted for a boy at six, twelve, eighteen, and twenty-four months. The graph reveals that this child is progressing at a more advanced level in some areas than in others. He is especially advanced in language and least advanced in the use of his large muscles. At eighteen months it was reported that in the use of his large muscles this child gave the impression of a child younger than his chronological age. He walked if both hands were held but preferred creeping as a means of locomotion. However, in other areas he seemed older than his chronological age. He used three-word sentences and referred to himself as "I." By two years he walked quite well and ran stiffly. Sometimes he walked up and down stairs while holding onto the rail. His fine motor ability, which was better than his gross motor ability, was indicated by holding a crayon with his fingers rather than with his whole fist, and also by building rapidly a tower of ten cubes. He had keen form perception. He occasionally helped to put away toys. He expressed many ideas with considerable skill. He could tell his own sex, the action of many of the objects pictured in a book, and named his own drawing, a "choo choo train." Thus he shows a pattern of growth in several areas which is unique for him.

Similar graphs for other children would reveal other patterns, as, for example, a child who is making rapid strides in motor development but who is slower in language and personal-social areas.

Another way of presenting information is suggested by Bayley in a

discussion of intelligence as measured by tests. She suggests trying "to present individual curves of growth in units that will emphasize a child's change in relation to himself. Growth curves will enable us to observe a child's periods of fast and slow progress, his spurts and plateaus, and even regressions, in relation to his own past and future."*
Figure 2 suggests attention to the rate and variability of children's test performances at different ages. Sixty-eight per cent of those of a particular chronological age, i.e., plus and minus one standard deviation, are included in the shadowed part. Intelligence test performance of two boys over a period of time, is graphed according to this way of viewing them. The boy, 9M, has a period of acceleration in his curve; the other boy, 8M, has a time of lag.

The Concept of Percentage of Terminal Status. Another method of expressing the growth accomplished by a given child at a given stage of development is in terms of percentage of terminal status (or mature development) he has achieved at the time measurement is made.[88, 597, 761] In using this method, terminal status, or the ultimate mature level of growth in any given growth area, is considered as 100 per cent. Any step on the way to this terminal status can be expressed in terms of the percentage of the total growth distance the child has traversed at the moment of measurement. The 100 per cent is the point at which the individual becomes mature in the function under consideration, regardless of the length of time it took him to reach that maturity. For example, in a study of eye fixation in infants Morgan and Morgan[597] found that certain types of eye fixation reach 100 per cent maturity within the first ten days of life (Fig. 3). The eye of the child is able to perform this phase of eye fixation at the age of ten days in the same way as it responds during the years of childhood.

Among 999 children studied at the Brush Foundation in Cleveland, Ohio, terminal status in stature (or adult stature) was achieved in boys as early as fifteen years and as late as twenty years; in girls, as early as fourteen years and as late as eighteen years. Most children have proceeded 90 per cent of the distance to adult stature at puberty.[761] For percentage attained during the early years see p. 136.

It is clear[316, 843] that although a child's stature is actually determined by the length of his legs and spine, his skeletal age or the speed of maturing of those bones is not closely dependent on his growth in size.

* Bayley[87] (p. 814).

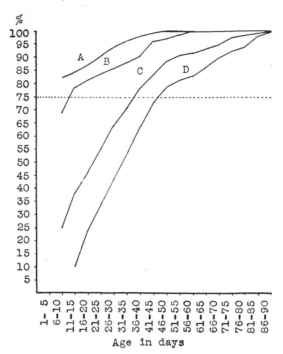

Figure 3. Fixation and horizontal following. A, Fixation curve indicates that infants passed 75 per cent criterion mark in less than ten days of life. B, Horizontal following a short distance. C, Horizontal following all the way and reverse. D, Continuous horizontal following. (Morgan and Morgan: Journal of Pediatrics, vol. 25, p. 172, 1944. C. V. Mosby Co.)

Some girls and boys attain puberty at the age of eleven and thirteen years, whereas other girls and boys have gone only the same distance in the life span at the age of sixteen and nineteen years.[88]

A girl, for example, who achieves biological sexual maturity at eleven years has arrived at 100 per cent of maturity in this area at that age; if studied at nine years of age, she probably would have achieved 90 per cent of the maturing in this function. Another girl at nine may have achieved only 60 per cent of her maturing in this area, because her 100 per cent level will not be achieved until sixteen years of chronological age.

In order to achieve 100 per cent maturity by age eleven years, a large girl would have to achieve more tissue growth in the same length of time as the small girl who achieves 100 per cent maturity at age eleven years. The sizes of the two girls will be confusing if they are used as maturity indicators.

The concept of maturity levels and maturity scales or of maturity and learning levels and scales may, of course, take some other form than those discussed in this chapter. We may be reasonably sure, however, that the idea of stages of a gradient as a basis for grouping children to be studied will in time replace concepts based on chronological age levels.

The Old, "Normal Weather" Theory of Growth Standards. Let us consider the practical difference between use of age-scale standards or of some other evaluation devices in studying child development. In the earlier days of the child development movement, children were studied in the mass. Measurements, both physical and mental, were taken on large groups of two-year-olds, three-year-olds, or five-year-olds. Averages were then taken, and "growth curves" plotted. From these curves one could supposedly tell whether any given child was maturing as he should, the assumption being that the averages of thousands of children must surely tell us what any given child ought to be like. If he were as tall as or as smart as the average, all was considered well. If he were taller than or smarter than the average, everyone rejoiced and felt sure of his success in life. If, on the other hand, he were shorter than or had fewer words in his vocabulary than the average child of his age, he was considered "retarded." This is in some ways like observing the weather over a period of seasons and setting up a "normal" weather for the given season, with days above normal being considered superior, and those below normal being considered inferior.

Children May Be Different Yet Normal. We now realize that within the scope of development there are wide ranges of individual differences. Many children who appear to be slow to begin certain areas of development later prove to be thoroughly proficient. It is also true that a child may develop one or some skills at a faster pace than others. Some children seem to bend their major growth energies to practice in motor skills, others to language skills, and others to social skills. No one of these patterns is to be preferred to the others. It will not benefit any child to compare him constantly with average age standards, with his brothers and sisters, or with neighbor's children. He is to be examined in terms of himself, for unless significant events or severe illness interrupts his progress, his own rate of progress follows the law of his own growth symmetry.

A   B

Figure 4. A, This child, at sixteen months, is taking his first hesitant steps. This is two or three months later than the average walking-age. B, At twenty-two months this same child is adept on his tricycle. This is two or three months in advance of the average tricycle-age.

A New Viewpoint Is Necessary. Since it is a fairly new idea to parents to be told to evaluate a child in terms of his own growth symmetry, let us summarize some of the things that have happened in practice when average age-scale standards were depended on. Using the average standard, parents believed that if a two-year-old child were 37 inches tall, he was superior in some way to other children. By the same reasoning, if he failed to walk until sixteen months, his parents worried about him or felt ashamed of him. Thirty years of records on the same children have shown us the error of regarding children in this manner.

The old philosophy, with its assumption that there was virtue in the early acquisition of growth steps, created in adults an urgency to try to "train" children as early as possible. Pressure has been exerted to get infants to give up the bottle as early as possible, to become reliable for the toilet, to dress themselves, and to pick up their toys before they are really ready to perform these tasks. Independence of the mother was fostered regardless of the child's degree of social and emotional maturity.

In current practice we have much less forcing of learning, and much more waiting for the child to reveal his maturational readiness for experiences. We find evidence suggesting alertness to the child's readiness in the sense of providing environment essential for learning.

Ways of viewing individual differences, such as those referred to here, reveal interest in the child's own changes with an acceptance of the interrelationships of growth, maturation and learning, when development occurs. This approach is clarified further in the presentation of detail concerning the following concepts.

Development Through Maturation and Through Learning

Maturational Readiness Essential to Learning. To refer to the "never-ending series of climactic events in the life cycle"[477] and to the "increase in competence"[65] is to refer to the child's use of his emerging abilities. In this use, he is learning (acquiring behavior primarily through his interaction with the environment his own body provides and with the environment outside of himself). *Recognition of relation of maturation and learning* represents the focus of a second current concept of growth and development. This focus has gained support from studies relating the child's ease of learning responses to his stages of maturity.[293, 536] Additional research is needed to provide more factual material concerning maturation and learning in children. In the meantime, statements such as the following seem sound in the light of current, admittedly limited, knowledge: Whether the behavior pertains to chewing, walking, grasping, perceiving, using words, adjusting to a group away from home or some other activity, stages of maturity make possible a particular response; the extent to which the stages are "well consolidated" affects the ease or difficulty with which related learning takes place. When structural and functional readiness are present, satisfaction in learning is inherent. When "forced" before he is ready, the child simply does not learn, is unskillful, may require a longer time to learn the behavior or may show undue strain.

This principle of the need to pace our expectations to the natural growth of the child may be illustrated by the results of giving a young infant solid food too early. In such a case digestion of food does not take place because the stomach of the infant is not yet structurally and functionally mature enough to handle solid food. The infant either vomits or passes the food mechanically through the alimentary canal in undigested form.

In the same way, a young child cannot learn to feed himself until he has achieved such maturity stages as:

Ability to sit up while making controlled movements of hands and arms.

Ability to coordinate hand and mouth with fair smoothness.

Mastery of sufficient finger control to permit easy holding of the spoon.

Emotional maturity to permit him to surrender at least part of his complete dependence upon his mother.

If we try to force learning before the child is ready, he will behave as he does with solid food which is given too early. He may resist openly, fighting against the attempts to teach him. This is analogous to the vomiting. Or he may appear to learn the task only to relapse later, which is analogous to passing the food through the alimentary canal in undigested form.

Maturity Indicators.   We are hoping to learn more about the way to tell when children are ready for given experiences. As in the illustration of readiness required for the learning of successful self-feeding, certain capacities like those listed above should be present before we start to teach the child to feed himself. In time, it is hoped, we shall know just what stages of development have been accomplished before control of elimination can be established. Guidance in self-feeding or in learning control of elimination is begun not according to any chronological age. These and other aspects of teaching are begun only when the child has accomplished the needed preliminary growths and learnings. *The list of the stages of growth and the accomplishments in learning necessary before a child is ready to undertake any given piece of learning is called a list of maturity indicators.*

An example of a maturity indicator series is the following list related to adjustment on entering school regardless of whether a child is five years old or six years old as required by law:

1. Toilet independence.
2. Ability to put on and take off outer clothing, like play suits, galoshes, and the like.

3. At least some immunity to usual childhood diseases.

4. Ability to understand and speak the language of the school with at least fair fluency.

5. Willingness to leave his mother for the requisite number of hours per day.

6. Ability to cooperate with another authority besides his mother.

7. Ability to share adult attention with other children.

8. Physical stamina sufficient to withstand the strain of school attendance several hours per day, five days per week, thirty to thirty-five weeks per year.

9. Ability to sit still and to attend to ideas or hand work for at least ten or fifteen minutes at a time.

10. Ability to accept the cultural pattern that school is "the thing to do."

11. Sufficient form discrimination to permit differentiation of letters and words in reading (for first grade).

12. Ability to take a working place as a participator in a group as large as the school assigns to each grade.

13. Ability to accomplish other intellectual tasks at about the level of most children of five years (for the kindergarten) or six years (for the first grade).

There would, of course, be other such maturities necessary to success in school. This is merely a suggested list of maturity indicators for school entrance. In our culture the great majority of children have accomplished these maturity levels at around six years of chronological age. Many have accomplished them earlier; many do not achieve them until later. It is one of the mistakes of our "average-age-standards" if we require children to enter at six years and then fail to recognize the range of their behavior in these responses.

Relation of Maturity Concepts to Educational Practice. This increasing awareness of the importance of regulating educational experience in terms of maturational readiness of the child does not mean less appreciation of the importance of setting the environmental stage in the school objectively. It does mean, attempting to stabilize educational practice so that it does not swing too far on the one hand in the direction of doing nothing until each child aggressively seeks an experience, nor too far on the other hand in the direction of forcing adult-conceived ideas upon children, regardless of their developmental readiness.

Judgment of Readiness, Pending Development of Maturity Indicator Scales. At the present time maturity indicator scales in many areas of growth are available.[82, 290, 527, 753] However, in still many areas we are only now coming to develop this information. This need not bewilder a parent or teacher unduly, since the child himself tends to indicate to us when he is first ready for any given experience. He does so in one way by the eagerness with which he seeks new function, seizing with zest on each new opportunity for activity as it is available. McGraw gives us insight into this. "Whenever any function or aspect of a function emerges, the child exhibits an indomitable urge to exercise it. The baby who has just acquired the ability to roll over can hardly be kept on his back; the infant who has just learned to pull himself up by grasping the bars of the crib does so repeatedly, though once up, he stands and cries, because he has not at the same time achieved the ability to let himself down. Many times I have seen a baby struggle again and again to stand on his feet in order to walk a few steps for a lure, although he could have crept for it with great ease."* As adults we have mainly to see that a growth environment is provided. This would be one which offers opportunities for the next steps in growth. When the child is ready he will, as a rule, reach out and take advantage of them.

A child may indicate his readiness for new experience in other ways than eagerness to use opportunities and to exercise a new skill. If an appropriate growth stimulus or opportunity is not available when he is ready for one, he may show his need for new experience by boredom with his present regimen. He may fret and appear restless, staring out of the window, or whining, "What can I do now?," or wandering aimlessly about the house and yard. Or he may become destructive, banging or taking apart the toys which are no longer challenging to him.

On the other hand, if his learnings are being forced he may display temper tantrums and negativism. If he does not do this he may indicate his distaste for the activity being forced upon him by escaping into activities of his own devising. If his imagination is sufficiently developed his escape may take the form of psychological withdrawal into a world of fantasy.

If we are sufficiently aware of the leads the child gives us, we can

---

* McGraw[540] (p. 128).

usually gauge our expectations so that he is neither understimulated nor overstimulated in learning. If, too, we know enough about the progress of children through the various maturity stages in each of the basic patterns of growth, our understanding of and adjustment to children will be much more comfortable for them and for us.

Theories Concerning Maturation and Learning. Thoughts such as these just presented suggest implications of a concept that maturation and learning are related. They provide background for consideration of theoretical statements. Theories pertaining to the concept of relation of maturation and learning refer to timing and to the influence of stimulation. According to Baldwin,

"Elapsed time, whether or not it includes practice, is accompanied by improved performance, although not as much improvement as if the time had been spent in practice. In many activities, however, there must be some practice of a skill before a certain point in time if the maturational potentialities are to be realized."*

Theories Concerning Learning. Learning is, of course, influenced by many other factors in addition to maturational readiness. Specific factors have been the subject of research which provides a great deal of information on particular influences on learning, those within the person at the moment and within his present setting, as well as those which have come from his previous experience.† Less information is available on the influence of the interrelationships of various aspects of the individual and his experience as he learns. The countless possibilities for study are realized when *recognition of the complexity of the learning process* is referred to as the focus of a third concept of growth and development. To mention a few of the carefully defined terms pertaining to learning theory is one way of suggesting the complexity of detail to be considered, if one attempts to study the child's development through learning. Considering the dynamics of the learning process means giving attention to the continuous interrelationships in the individual of drive (motivation), cue (stimulus), response (act or thought), and reinforcement (reward). These four factors are essential in learning (acquiring behavior through experience).‡ In defining drive, Dollard and Miller say:

* Baldwin[65] (p. 398).
† Chapters 3, 4 and 5 of Dollard and Miller,[222] Martin and Stendler,[559] Mowrer[602] and Ausubel[57] provide detail about theory of learning and bibliographies.
‡ These four factors in learning are referred to on pages 25 and 26 of Dollard and Miller.[222]

"Strong stimuli which impel action are drives . . . While any stimulus may become strong enough to act as a drive, certain special classes of stimuli seem to be the primary basis for the greater proportion of motivation. These might be called the *primary* or *innate* drives . . ." *Secondary or learned drives* "are acquired on the basis of the primary drives, represent elaborations of them."*

According to Mowrer:

"The so-called secondary ('psychogenic') drives . . . once learned . . . serve to motivate and, when terminated, to reinforce behavior, just as the primary ('viscerogenic') drives do." He refers to *two basic learning processes*: one *problem solving*, which occurs when a drive (primary or secondary) is reduced; and the other *conditioning*, which occurs on the basis of sheer contiguity or double stimulation and which accounts for the acquisition of the secondary drives."†

In discussing anxiety as a *reinforcing* agent, Mowrer says:

"The truth of the matter seems to be that all (problem-solving) learning presupposes (a) an increase of motivation (striving) and (b) a decrease of motivation (success) and that the essential features of the process are much the same, regardless of the specific source of motivation or of the particular circumstances of its elimination.

"There is, however, one practical consideration to be taken into account. Although learning through 'punishment' does not seem to differ basically from learning through 'reward,' interpersonal relationships are likely to be affected very differently in the two cases. If the method of 'reward' is employed, interpersonal relationships are likely to be made more positive (i.e., approach tendencies will be strengthened); whereas, if the method of 'punishment' is employed, interpersonal relationships are likely to be made more 'negative' (i.e., avoidance tendencies will be strengthened)."‡

The repertoire from previous experience, upon which the individual draws as he meets situations, represents another complex aspect in the study of his learning. Mowrer says, "Still greater orderliness can be introduced by making a systematic distinction between learning, as defined by two-factor theory (problem solving and conditioning), and a process which is variously known as *insight, reasoning,* or *thinking.*"§

It is not enough to consider cognitive aspects of the person, i.e., what he knows; it is also important to consider emotional aspects, i.e., what he feels.

Emotional Tone and Development

Increased Emphasis on Emotional Tone.   Emotional tone, which facilitates use of the new inner resources arising from maturation and

---

* Dollard and Miller[222] (pp. 30-32).

† O. Hobart Mowrer, Learning Theory and Personality Dynamics. Copyright 1950, The Ronald Press Company (p. vi).[602]

‡ Ibid. (pp. 24, 25).[602]

§ Mowrer[602] (p. 318). (Parentheses are ours.)

learning, is another factor emphasized today. *Recognition of influence of emotional tone on development* represents the focus of another concept of growth and development. It is considered especially important in personality development for the child to have, in infancy and in the preschool years, a sense of trust, a sense of autonomy, and a sense of initiative. To these, as he grows older, the child adds a sense of accomplishment and identity, and as he grows into adulthood he adds more of a sense of intimacy, a parental sense, and a sense of integrity.* Current thinking stresses the child's need for these feelings or "senses." With these feelings more of his responses are of the accepting or pleased kind with regard to himself and his world, rather than of the rejecting or displeased kind. Having the balance on this side means having emotional tone conducive to growth.

Parental Attitudes Conducive to These Feelings. Feelings such as these are considered to be to a great extent a reflection of the child's being loved, having his basic needs met, and being given opportunities to use his emerging abilities.[140, 301, 367, 733] This is more likely to happen when the child is "close" to someone, in the majority of instances to his mother, soon after birth, and to both his mother and his father as he grows older. But the closeness alone is not the explanation of the child's feelings. It is the feeling of being loved, cared for, and understood by a particular person, an association which a hospital or institution has difficulty providing for a child. The parents need to sense what the child is ready for, in terms of maturation as previously discussed. They also need to sense what he is ready for, in terms of basic needs such as food, warmth, activity, and rest, and also, for example, in terms of trust, autonomy, and initiative. It is fairly new for parents to be told to try to figure out what the child is seeking, and to give it to him if it seems related to a basic need. This attitude leads to change in practice. When the baby cries the mother tries to decide whether or not it is a hunger cry, and if it seems to be, she feeds him. If the child of preschool age wakes at night the parents try to decide whether or not it concerns his sense of trust, and if it seems so, they give him the reassurance he needs.

Practice of this kind is in contrast to earlier practice when a child, despite crying, was not fed until the hour recommended for children of his age. If he came into his parents' room at night, he was sent back

---

* These components of a healthy personality described in the Midcentury White House Conference Fact Finding Report[915] are discussed in further detail in Chapter 10.

to bed to remain in his room alone and "go to sleep." In these earlier practices, establishment of habits was emphasized, in the effort to have the child do what it was hoped would be repeated, i.e., eating at scheduled times, and sleeping through the night in a room alone. This earlier point of view has been "characterized as follows: Bodily and mental health is based on an orderly, strictly scheduled existence from early childhood onwards. . . . When babies or children cry without recognized legitimate cause it is best to let them cry it out. It is the responsibility of adults to teach children what is 'right' and what is 'wrong' in regard to meal times, sleeping hours, play interests and most other activities."* The expectation was "that bigger and better children could be produced—much like automobiles or washing machines—through specific, rather mechanical, prescribed procedures."*

Although more self-expression on the child's part goes along with the newer point of view, his not being the "slave of his own whims" and his learning "limits" and progressing from a less mature to a more mature stage are also implied. To encourage learning on the child's part adults are thinking not only about habits formed through practice with satisfaction, as in the past; they are also thinking (as suggested in the previous section on learning) about primary and learned drives and expectations with regard to how his needs will be met which the child is building up. In use of knowledge about how learning takes place, more attention seems to be focused at present on the drives or motivations of the person. If the child's ease of gaining satisfactions is decreased, his anxiety is increased. For example, in a theoretical analysis of the origin of dependence on adults in certain nursery school children, Sears said if the mother's "rigidity of scheduling of feedings and her method of handling the weaning process are such as to decrease the child's ease of gaining satisfactions, he would be expected to suffer, over the long term, an increase in his anxiety with respect to both food-getting and control of his mother. The increased strength of total drive produced by this anxiety would strengthen the motivation underlying the behavior that has as its aim the controlling of the mother, i.e., the dependency behavior."†

This quotation is included here because it suggests the complexity of research needed in relationship of emotional tone to growth. To find "channels" along which individuals grow, according to temper-

* Escalona[246] (p. 158).
† Sears[731] (p. 401).

ament and the tender loving care they do or do not receive, is an area of particular interest in research today.[140, 247, 733, 756] Emphasis on environment, which statements in the area of adult-child relationships sometimes imply, needs the balance of a reminder that "the child is not . . . a simple passive creature molded exclusively by external forces; he is very much a creature in his own right, moving through his own experiences and creating his own world. This is not to deny the value of nurture in creating the best possible world for children . . ."*

Indicators of Feelings. At present, it seems hopeful to look for indications of the child's feelings, even though detail as to what to look for and how to interpret it has not yet been provided by extensive research. We have suggestions of questions to ask in trying to find out what the individual child's feelings are. Does he feel well fed, able to rest, and able to be active? Is he trustful, autonomous (decisive where he is able), and able to explore his world? But the approach hinges on knowing what to look for as indications of these feelings and others. We find clues in his everyday actions over a period of time. We look at the child's behavior, discover his interests, and see signs of tension or freedom from tension. These clues, or implications of the child's behavior for the adult, are discussed in connection with various aspects of behavior, i.e., physical, motor, language, imagination, reasoning, emotional, social, and spiritual growth, in the following chapters. Attention to what the child says and does in these various and interrelated phases of growth can disclose a great deal about his feelings. Studies of children's acceptance of routines, of their play, and of their social relationships are beginning to provide details as to which responses should be the focus of attention.[337, 745] Projective techniques also provide detail.[598, 612] Well formulated lists of indicators of feelings are not available at this time.

Theories Concerning Emotional Influences. A variety of hypotheses concerning emotional tone, its indicators and bases is in the process of being checked. Drive, cue, response and reinforcement are dealt with in terms of how the person feels (tense or relaxed, "pressed," "anxious," "under stress," or free) and why. Basic needs, values, "conscience," concept of self, relatedness of the person and his world, are terms used especially often. The complexity of these areas

* Anderson[39] (p. 416).

has already been suggested in the quotation from Sears.[731] Another illustration of statement of theory is as follows:

According to Allinsmith, human behavior represents "a compromise among forces influencing the individual. In the first months of life, there are only two major forces—the child's own impulses, and external reality.* After the first few months, a third force begins to affect the individual, and thereafter the three interact to produce behavior. This third force consists of those social demands which were originally part of external reality but which have been *internalized* as part of the person's demands on himself." Allinsmith continues by saying that in the course of experience, each individual learns to make compromises among forces and to use techniques relieving tension which "work" for him. "The extent to which an individual is symptom-free and capable of meeting life effectively depends upon the ways the individual has learned to solve conflicts in the past, and upon . . . capacity for tolerating anxiety instead of resorting to defensive measures."†

Statements of theory concerning relation of mood and body chemistry have been in the process of formulation for a number of years.[153, 229, 587, 744] Their connection with the constitutional aspects listed in the following section, as well as with experience, represents another field of interest in research today.

Developmental-Dynamic Aspects of the Individual

A fifth concept concerning growth and development, which is, in a sense, a synthesis of emphases today, might be described as *reference to the individual child's "developmental-dynamic" aspects*. This has two ramifications. First, it means considering growth and development of the individual child with his particular constitution and experience by using each of the four previously mentioned concepts, i.e., recognition of stages of maturity, relation of maturation and learning, complexity of learning, and influence of emotional tone, and by using the concepts in an interrelated way. Secondly, it means considering the child at his present time (cross-sectionally), and over a period of time for him, past, present and future (longitudinally). This is intended to convey an idea of sequence and motion. Reliance on this fifth concept is evident in the chapters which follow. Although information is inadequate for its complete use, steps in the direction of it are presented.

* In a footnote, Allinsmith says "We are leaving out of consideration the individual's perceptive capacity and the degree of his psychological and physical maturity. These of course influence behavior but they are not motivational forces."
† Allinsmith[13] (pp. 3, 6, 11).

Current interest in such an approach is revealed in the following examples of statements of theory or wish for it: *

On the subject of constitutional aspects of the individual, the Fact-Finding Report of the Mid-Century White House Conference on Children and Youth[915] refers to the need for additional factually tested knowledge. Aspects listed as appearing to be constitutional are: activity and vigor, general and specific sensitivity, tempo and rhythm, bodily resilience and vulnerability, intellectual endowment, and pattern of development.

"Constitution is currently conceived as the sum total of the structural, functional, and psychological characters of the organism. It is, in large measure, an integral of genetic potentialities influenced in varying degrees by internal and external environmental factors. It is not a *biological given,* a structure destined to function in a predetermined manner. Rather it is a *process,* a series of operative questions that even by the time of birth have not become final declarative answers.

"What is given is the genotype, the complex of genetic potentialities with which the organism is endowed. Each individual's genotype is a unique physicochemical system comprising particular kinds of potentialities that have definite limits. . . . The manner in which the genotype functions depends in part upon the environment in which it undergoes development."†

On the subject of early experiences (including what is done and who does it), Martin writes as follows:

"An admission that the events we study are unique, unreproducible and nondeterminable does not preclude scientific activity, no more than the same admission does in the case of the physicist or the astronomer. But we first seek regularity and orderliness, in whatever degree they may exist, within the individual event, which for us is the effect of a particular training agent and practice upon a particular individual under given conditions. As we accumulate data about a number of such individual events, it may be possible to discover, through a study of similarities and dissimilarities among them, certain principles or laws, statistical in form, that may apply to all. We will not enhance the probability of discovering such regularities by losing the individual event in a sea of mass statistics."‡

On the subject of a material factor, food, Hunscher makes the following statements concerning the life cycle and its diet:

"We know a great deal about how children grow and we know a great deal about what they eat, but we lack in the combination or relationship of the two as life and growth progress in sequential and consequential evidence. . . . We are, in this field of nutrition, seeking to know to what extent the feeding is providing adequate constituents for the construction of the body as it grows in its functioning indi-

* References for the quotations which follow include bibliographies on related theory and research.

† Witmer and Kotinsky[915] (p. 30).

‡ Martin[558] (pp. 40-41).

vidual way. The importance is in enough of the constituents, measured by balances or otherwise, to influence growth rather than the amount per se in a given chronological age period in the average child."*

On the subject of biochemical individuality, Williams says:

". . . each human being possesses a highly distinctive body chemistry. While the same physical mechanisms and the same metabolic processes are operating in all human bodies, the structures are sufficiently diverse and the genetically determined enzyme efficiencies vary sufficiently from individual to individual so that the sum total of all the reactions taking place in one individual's body may be very different from those taking place in the body of another individual of the same age, sex and body size.

"The genetotrophic principle . . . is a very broad one encompassing the whole of biology. It may be stated as follows: Every individual organism that has a distinctive genetic background has distinctive nutritional needs which must be met for optimal well-being. . . .

"If during embryonic development, a particular ovum has needs which cannot be satisfied in the environment provided, then it either dies or its organs and functions fail to develop in a well-rounded fashion. If, during childhood, the individual has nutritional needs which are not fully satisfied, his metabolism is altered accordingly; he becomes a prey to infections and his growth becomes retarded or distorted.

"If this principle is valid we may by a slight extension say that it should be possible, theoretically at least, to meet the needs of almost any developing ovum, even though these needs are unusual, *provided the needs are known*. In case these needs are known and can be consistently met throughout life, then development proceeds in a regular fashion regardless of the presence of untoward structures and partial genetic blocks which augment special needs."†

An inclusive statement has been written by Anderson:

"In considering the content of child development we need some conception of the nature of the growing human person or a theoretical model against which to orient our studies. The growing person is an ongoing manifold moving through time with a multidimensional head much as a tunnel-making machine moves under a river. Viewed from the moving front or the present moment of time this consists of many irregularly shaped structures of various sizes with a complex series of interrelations. At the boundaries there are complex relations to the external world which involve a continuous intake and outgo on both a physiological and a psychological level, an interchange which maintains a dynamic or ongoing equilibrium.

"Viewed as a whole, the system is asymmetrical and open-end. Its basic organization is hierarchical in the sense that as-it moves forward in time new properties and qualities emerge at successive levels of integration. These need study and analyses in and for themselves. An analysis at one level, however adequate, cannot explain the properties of a higher level."‡

* Hunscher[377] (pp. 105-106).

† Reprinted with permission from R. J. Williams, Biochemical Individuality, 1956, John Wiley & Sons, Inc. (pp. 166-168).

‡ Anderson[36] (p. 190).

With this model as a base, Anderson considers scientific literature of eight broad classes as pertinent: space-time form studies, longitudinal slices, cross section studies at successive levels, cross section studies at one level, short-period function modifications, genetic determinism, environmental impingement and determinism, and construct determinism or study of effects of one phenomenon generalized.

In its attempt to present information from these various angles, this book is organized in accordance with the fifth concept mentioned in this chapter: a developmental-dynamic concept. Consideration of particular systems and of that which is not "interrelated" and "individualized," as well as that which is, has been recognized as appropriate. This means what Sigel refers to as thinking of the " 'whole' child as an organization of a number of systems, which function at varying degrees of autonomy and interrelatedness."* Particular attention is given to the physical system (process and content) in Chapters 3, 4, 5, 6, and 7, to the psychological system in Chapters 8, 9, and 10, and to environment outside the person (exogenous) in Chapters 2 and 11. Information on the interrelatedness of the systems has been included when available. Each system can be dealt with according to a developmental-dynamic concept.

Outlook on Child Development. Statements of concept and of theory quoted in this chapter have been accepted as the ones in the light of which the content of the following chapters will be selected and organized. Content fits into a framework such as the following which was suggested by one group of students. They considered it a useful outlook in tying together details on child development. It provides a view in thinking of information and questions, whether they concern the child development field or the individual child.

Conceptual Framework in the Study of Child Development

into which theories and details of information fit
through which questions can be considered.

Introductory Statement: The conceptual framework is in essence an attitude or philosophy used in the study and understanding of the individual child. This attitude is based on the following assumptions and concepts:

Assumptions: Two assumptions underlying the concepts are:
1. Each individual differs in his growth and development
2. Constitution and environment or setting influence (or explain) individual growth and development

* Sigel[756] (p. 242).

Concepts: Concepts pertain to:

1. Physical aspects and behavioral aspects of development (at a particular time and over a period of time, on the surface and within the person)

⎧ Body structure and function
Habitual responses pertaining to eating, sleeping, elimination
Motor behavior
Sensory judgment
Language
Reasoning
Imitation
Imagination and creative activities
Emotional behavior ⎰ feeling tone
　　　　　　　　　⎱ seeking what is needed
Social behavior
Spiritual response ⎭

2. Processes of growth and development

⎧ Biologic—change in and use of physical equipment, physiological processes, use of nutrients, biochemical processes
Psychologic—change in and use of psychologic equipment (including intellectual, social and emotional processes) ⎭

⎱ through processes of growth, maturation, maturation and learning, learning ⎰

through aspects of constitution such as:

   (1) endowment
   (2) bodily functioning and environment within the person

and environment outside the person such as:

   (1) provision for meeting basic needs
   (2) provision for use of emerging abilities
   (3) relationships within family
   (4) relationships outside family
   (5) material factors

Topics for Study and Discussion

1. Make a survey of the content of child care or child development articles in a woman's magazine or in a professional journal for a year in each of the periods, 1900 to 1910, 1920 to 1930, 1945 to 1957. Discuss the differences in content and philosophy of child care as reflected in these articles.

2. Observe several children of the same chronological age for similarities and differences in motor ability, in size, and in other attributes of development. Dis-

cuss the results of this observation in relation to the use of norms and environmental needs. Also, attempt to use a point of view which recognizes maturity indicators in considering what each child seems ready for.

3. As a basis for discussion of learning to use emerging functions, observe a child who is suddenly aware of the emergence of a new skill. Record his behavior and any indications of his feelings.

4. Observe a mother and her infant and note how she is providing for the infant's need of love and security and how the infant responds.

5. Illustrate meanings of a developmental-dynamic concept by use of observation of one child, or several, to provide examples of behavior and pertinent questions about the behavior from a developmental-dynamic point of view.

Selected Readings

Anderson, J. E.: Dynamics of Development: Systems in Process in The Concept of Development: An Issue in the Study of Human Behavior. Ed. D. B. Harris. Minneapolis, Minn., University of Minnesota Press, 1957.

Gesell, A., and Ilg, F. L.: The Child from Five to Ten. New York, Harper & Brothers, 1946. Chap. 2.

Senn, M. J.: Fads and Facts as the Bases of Child-Care Practices. Children 4:43-47, 1957.

Stendler, C. B.: Critical Periods in Socialization and Overdependency. Child Development 23:1-12, 1952.

Supplement: Chicago Conference on Child Development, 1955. Child Development 27:179-286, 1956.

Symposium: Concept of Maturity from Anatomical, Physiological and Psychological Points of View, by L. K. Frank, W. M. Krogman, W. W. Greulich, D. Wechsler, and S. Wishik. Child Development 21:21-60, 1950.

Symposium: Child Growth and Development, by A. H. Washburn, L. W. Sontag, J. D. Boyd, and H. C. Stuart. The Child 16:50-63, 1951.

2

The Home and Family
as a Background for Growth

Importance of Home and Family

Recognition of the Importance of the Family. One way to begin to clarify understanding of the home and family as background for the child's growth is to consider their *uniqueness* for each child. Brief descriptions of different families will make evident a few of the unique elements of relationships alone. For example, in the families whose descriptions follow, the daughters were of similar age. Mary's mother had a gay, friendly manner, and gave an impression of being leisurely. Her father seemed matter-of-fact. Their children were encouraged to be self-reliant and "individual." Mary was the fourth child in a family of five, all of whom were girls except the oldest. Her play at home involved attempts to do what the older children were doing; one day their football play appealed to her; another day it was tap dancing.

In Ellen's family, the mother seemed quiet and calm. In home management, she planned so that routines and activities proceeded smoothly. The father liked logical thinking. He encouraged Ellen's interest in facts, in stories, and in music. From the time she was a baby, Ellen was taken with her parents whenever they went away in the evenings, as they occasionally did. She was able to go to sleep at the friends' house and remained in bed there until her parents took her home with them. As the older of two girls, she enjoyed helping her mother in taking care of the baby. In Mary's and Ellen's families some of the aspects usually considered in study of families, such as socioeconomic factors, education of the parents, and place of residence, are similar. Both parents are in the home, and the children are not having behavior difficulties. The aspects of the two families described represent details useful in gaining a picture of the child's setting; they are not to be labeled as being either commendable or questionable.

When uniqueness of each family is considered, not only with regard to relationships of the people, but also with regard to traditional socioeconomic and cultural pattern, additional variations are evident. Davis and Havighurst describe one family, called the Washingtons, as follows: " 'Meal-time' or 'bed-time,' and other similar restrictions mean little or nothing to the Washington children. They may play on the streets after dark; they do not have to go to bed until the adults go. They eat their meals whenever they wish to and—best of privileges to the child—they do not *have* to eat if they do not want to.

"At *two* years, the Washington twins were crossing the street alone; at *three* years, they often roamed three or four blocks from home. At *three,* also, they crossed the carline alone to spend their own pennies at the candy store."*

In describing the Brett family, Davis and Havighurst refer to the fact that their diet is wide and varied and to the fact that each child has a room, and goes to bed at nine o'clock. They have a great variety of toys. Mrs. Brett "keeps her children in their playroom or in their spacious yard. Nor does she allow them to stay in the yard after six, even in summer."† Again, without judging, without implying that similar aims or procedures are appropriate for all families, it is possible to look at these facts about the Washingtons and the Bretts, and to use them and many others in attempting to understand the children.

In looking for facts about families to use in our understanding of children, reference to what the family provides, its nature, its growth and explanations of its influences is useful. Information in the following pages is illustrative but not complete. It clarifies a *concept of the family as based on close relationships of persons* by birth or marriage: (1) *providing a biological, social and cultural heritage, and an emotional and physical climate;* (2) *having the nature of a growing organism*

* Davis and Havighurst[189] (p. 20).
† Op. cit. (p. 23).

in the sense of growth and development of each of its members and also of growth and development as a unit; and (3) *having growth* in the sense of orderly change. This concept makes possible use of the ideas about growth and development included in Chapter 1. The family's aspects (form and dimensions) and processes are influenced by factors such as those mentioned in the following sections of this chapter. Here, and in later chapters, references to statements of theory and current research stress the great influence of the many ramifications of the family upon the child's development.

What the Family Provides

Biological, Social and Cultural Heritage. Biological heritage, in the sense of inherited characteristics, or form, such as eye color and body build, is discussed in Chapter 3. Another biological aspect concerns *chemistry of the body, enzymes, and metabolism,* which affect behavior. Scheinfeld,[723] in considering individual differences with respect to body functioning and well-being, refers to the point of view of Roger J. Williams, the biochemist, that "every individual inherits a distinct 'metabolic personality' which governs not only his chemical workings in many ways, but also affects almost every aspect of his behavior and social relationships."* He also refers to Ginsberg who

"suggests, on the basis of recent findings and theories, that the manner in which genes influence behavior may be, in part, through the enzyme control of metabolic and energy-yielding processes in the nervous tissues, with variable effects on the nerve impulses and motor reactions. This might apply principally to the production, conversion and supply of various forms of proteins, carbohydrates, glucose, etc., to the nerve tissues, with specific variations in metabolic activity, as governed by different genes and/or gene combinations, leading to some of the differences in nervous reactions and behavior patterns characterizing different species and individuals. (*Genetics and Social Behavior,* Jackson Memorial Laboratory Lectures in honor of Dr. C. C. Little, 1949.)"*

A biological basis for difference of one individual from another in *selection of parts of the environment to react to,* is suggested by Plant.[665] He says, "Between the need of the child and the sweep of social pressures lies a membrane—a sort of psycho-osmotic envelope. . . . One should never think of this as a tangible, material structure. It is rather a property of that part of the personality which is in

* Scheinfeld[723] (p. 402).

touch with the environment. If one must neurologize, then the envelope is certainly to a large extent a cortical structure. . . . Moreover, it seems to grow in efficiency and complication as the individual grows from childhood—and this at least parallels the growing use of cortical structures. . . . Normally the personality has the ability to shut out large sectors of its environment and to translate those parts that it takes in into usable or understandable material. It is the part of the personality where this selection occurs that I call the envelope."*

In referring to bases of behavior some writers would add to a consideration of differences in body functioning and in selection of parts of the environment to react to, description of heritage in another way. For some, emphasis would be on the biological side in terms of racial and familial stock; for others, emphasis would be on the cultural side in terms of learned behavior.

Social and cultural heritage† provided by the family has several aspects. The child's heritage is affected by attitudes and experiences of the many generations which have preceded him. According to where he is reared, the material equipment, ways of doing things, ideas, habits, and values will vary. It is as a part of this culture that social organization is best understood. For example, Bossard contrasts *family culture patterns* of southern Italy and of Sweden. And, in stressing that in different regional areas the values transmitted by the family may differ, he refers to "the child of North Carolina piedmont parentage who is thrust overnight, as it were, into the school and social life of a second-generation Irish or Portuguese section in New England. Such a child appreciates . . . the reality of differences in the regional culture."‡

In addition to the social and cultural influences from the past, there are *attitudes of the child and his family reflecting more immediate experience and setting.* How subtle some of these influences are is suggested by a number of studies.§ For example, Allison Davis‖ stresses

---

* Plant[665] (pp. 2-3).

† References to studies of children in other cultures are Dennis (ed.),[208] Haring,[330] Martin and Stendler[559] and eds.,[560] Mead,[566] Mead and Wolfenstein,[567] Whiting and Child.[898]

‡ Bossard[121] (p. 130).

§ References concerning socio-economic differences in child rearing are Davis and Havighurst,[189] Havighurst and Davis,[344] Klatskin,[456] Maccoby and Gibbs,[521] Sears et al.[733]

‖ *Proceedings of the Midcentury White House Conference on Children and Youth*[584] (pp. 77-83).

effects of the family's having been hungry, cold and without adequate shelter and light, its having been uncertain that basic needs would be met. Then, when these needs can be met, for the child and the adult to want a great deal, is explained by Davis in terms of a learned fear of deprivation. In other families where anxieties such as these were less pressing, he found that children had more pressures from their families for early and rapid attainment and for conscientious work habits, which made them work harder in school.

Whether a child and his family live *on a farm, in a rural, nonfarm area, or in an urban situation* has been receiving more attention recently. For example, Stott mentions differences between only children who were town and city children and those on isolated farms who had few contacts with children of other families. In a study of Nebraska families he found "the farm and small town parents were inclined to favor strict disciplinary control of adolescent children while the city parents tended more toward leniency and freedom. The most striking difference of all was that between the town and the city fathers. The latter most strongly favored leniency."* In Ohio farm families studied by Hoeflin,[364] child-rearing practices with preschool children were more in accordance with currently recommended procedures than not; no significant relationship between socioeconomic status and child-rearing scores was found.

Setting, in the sense of the psychological habitat of a child, has been studied intensively by Barker.[71, 73] In a town with a total population of 750 he considered such community behavior settings as the Midwest Hardware and Implement Company, Women's Club I Meeting and Trafficways, and such family behavior settings as Home Meals and Home Outdoors. Participation in the various situations and the richness of this participation are emphasized in relation to the child's behavior, social action and interaction.

A sociologist recently stressed the influences of the world situation with its urbanization, industrialization and military service on families and children, by indicating the following related questions:

"1. The relativity of morals and the search for standards—How to teach the child to be familiar with many standards and accepting of them without leaving him no standards at all?

---

* Stott[816] (p. 81).

"2. Threat of total war—How to provide children and youth with security which makes them adequate, happy adults at the same time that preparation for war is necessary?

"3. Depersonalization of relationships—How to provide satisfying personal relationships when children and parents are in the situation of not really knowing others, or being known by them even when in a group? How within our kind of society are we going to provide children (and adults) with kinds of intimate personal relationships which make 'escapist' behavior unnecessary?

"4. Disruption of the kin group—How to enable young unstable families, apart from the example and help of older members of their families, to continue to grow in their security, their moral and ethical values?"*

Effects of war and the threat of war vary according to circumstances in which individual families find themselves. During World War II in England, where rationing was carefully planned, the general population, including the children, was adequately fed. The working class was better fed than formerly.[365] Some of the effects in other places where there was profound starvation are discussed in Chapter 3.† A number of studies present contrasts according to the particular country in which the family lived.[209, 210, 500, 569]

In one review of research on war and the family it was stated that "war had created no essentially new problems for children, but had intensified the old and made more clear the role of parental attitudes and intrafamilial problems in determining behavior."‡ Peacetime generalizations concerning the importance of family ties and the influence of parents' emotions on children's reactions were supported in findings of Jersild and Meigs.[429] Strain of separation from parents by evacuation in England was stressed by Freud and Burlingham[271] and others.[119, 850] In the United States, threat of separation as well as actual separation from the father caused anxiety.[105, 162, 188, 386] Constructive as well as destructive influences of wartime situations in families have been reported.[423, 500, 509] Levy[509] found families drawn more closely

* Gerald Leslie, Parent-Teacher Institute Talk, Lafayette, Indiana, November 1955.
† For a discussion of observations of the effect of war on physical development, see Keys and others,[454] Chap. 45.
‡ Kelley and Nesbitt[449] (p. 72).

together by such factors as increased interest in the home on the part of fathers and sons, by privations shared together, and by more plentiful employment.

In studies of families after return of the father from service or employment elsewhere, and after the mother's employment away from home decreased or was discontinued, findings again varied according to circumstances of the particular family. Hill[360] discussed the process of family reorganization after return of the fathers from service as follows: Some "had settled down to their former pattern of family life. . . ." Others ". . . were completely adjusted except in regard to the children's acceptance of the father's discipline. . . . In other families old . . . troubles . . . were being revived; . . . there were . . . arguments over what kind of job the husband should have, whether to buy a house or a car or just save, and so on. . . ."*

In describing children born during the years of World War II, Hymes[385] commented on "the cold shoulder that Joe felt; the too high standards that plagued Francie; the love that smothered Dennis; the worry in Martha's home; the way that Jerry was spoiled; the out-again-in-again of Sammy's early life."† Children of veterans enrolled in college, when studied in University nursery school and play group situations, seemed exceptionally well adjusted, resilient, happy to come to school, and willing to share equipment and to accept the necessary routines.[133, 773]

Realization that economic security is not the most important objective, and that a new security is found in deeper personal relationships within the family, recognition of relationships as more important than housekeeping standards, willingness of husbands to share home responsibilities, wives' acceptance of what they do in the home as of importance for members of their family and also for the community, are a few of the aspects of the family receiving consideration as strengths in the present situation.[21]

In referring to the setting in which families in the United States find themselves today, Margaret Mead stresses rapidity of change. She says:

"American children are growing up within the most rapidly changing culture of which we have any record in the world, within a culture where for several generations, each generation's experience has differed sharply from the last, and in which the experience of the youngest child in a large family will be extraordinarily dif-

* Hill[360] (p. 254).
† Hymes[385] (p. 9).

ferent from that of the first born. Mothers cannot look back to the experience of their mothers, nor even to that of their older sisters; young husbands and fathers have no guides to the behavior which they are assuming today. So long-standing and so rapid have been these processes of change that expectation of change and anxiety about change have been built into our character as a people. Our homes have become launching platforms from which our children set out on uncharted seas, and we have become correspondingly more anxious that they should be perfectly equipped before they go."[*]

Environmental Opportunities for Growth, through Emotional and Physical Climate. Paralleling recognition of the family's provision of biological, social, and cultural heritage is recognition of the family's influence on the child's feelings. *Emotional climate of the kind which tender loving care provides* is receiving much emphasis today.[123, 140, 247, 733, 745, 781] For the infant, the preschool child, the older child, the adolescent, and the adult, the form of family care differs according to maturity. But at every age the attitudes of acceptance and understanding and of attempting to meet basic needs, which underlie the different forms of care, are sensed; their presence provides an atmosphere considered important. How the child feels about himself and his world seems to be a reflection of his emotional climate. How the mother and father feel about the child and about what he does seems to influence this climate more than their specific words or actions.

Parents who want to recognize the child's basic needs, and so to contribute to his contentment and his feeling of harmony with his world, are found everywhere. Doing things differently in different families may still have this effect. Maloney[551] attributed emotional stability of Okinawans to their being "well mothered"; as babies they were fed when hungry, and were strapped to the mother's back when she worked in the fields. At the age of three they were entrusted to the care of the next elder sister. A visitor in Mexico is apt to comment on the closeness of the mother and her child. An American pediatrician, Spock,[792] says: "what good mothers and fathers instinctively feel like doing for their babies is usually best after all. Furthermore, all parents do their best job when they have a natural, easy confidence in themselves. Better to make a few mistakes from being natural than to do everything letter-perfect out of a feeling of worry."[†]

Although in Okinawa and in Mexico, and among grandparents in the United States, for example, such naturalness has been "just there"

[*] *Proceedings of the Midcentury White House Conference on Children and Youth*[584] (p. 84).
[†] Spock[792] (p. 4).

and did not need to be written about, we feel impelled to write about it now to balance previous writing about something different. Behaviorism, widely accepted by psychologists in the 1920's, stressed environmental influences on learning (Watson[882]). Parents were made aware of ways of controlling experience to cause learning and habit formation (Blatz and Bott[116]). From the psychoanalytic point of view, which began to be popularized in the 1920's, childhood experiences, the unconscious, a few drives such as those connected with sex and will to power, were considered basic in the child's adjustment (Adler,[2] Horney,[371] Isaacs[402]). Parents were made aware of something deep beneath the surface, not easily revealed in behavior. Those writing from child development points of view during these years referred to learning and habit formation and to a number of different drives or needs, along with an emphasis on the influence of the child's physical growth and health. Relation of physical and psychological aspects was considered (Aldrich,[6] Breckenridge and Vincent,[131] Olson[640]). Patterns of growth due primarily to innate factors were described (Gesell[285, 292]). Previously recognized in all of these approaches, but highlighted today, are the feelings of parents and children. Emotions and their expression are receiving much attention (Baruch,[77] Read[684]). Integration of this interest, the current interest in dynamics in psychology and physiology, and the earlier emphases referred to, such as those on learning, drives, interrelationships and patterns, is at present progressing.

More detailed consideration of parent-child relationships and related research is in Chapters 10 and 11.

Consideration of *physical climate,* as contrasted to emotional climate, focuses attention on material aspects of the home affecting the child's growth. These material aspects pertain, first of all, to food, warmth and shelter, and then, in a secondary sense, to opportunities for the individual to "unfold" in a way that involves use of his abilities. Sunshine, fresh air, opportunities for rest, sleep, and exercise, safe milk supply, satisfactory system of sanitation and protection against disease are of primary importance. The child's use of his abilities is considered to be affected by both physical and emotional climate. Evidence of the influence of any particular material factor at a level different from one of survival or physical health is not clear-cut. Again, the many differences between families warrant emphasis on the multiplicity of variables affecting growth rather than a cause and effect connection between such specific factors as specific foods, living arrangements, space, play opportunities and growth. Whatever the particular physical aspects of the home, the adult who keeps the essentials in mind, and uses ingenuity to provide them, has an advantage.

Values of space are well known. Housing research which provides detail concerning its influences on individuals is just beginning to be planned. To have research findings related to statements such as the following, lies in the future. In the meantime, listing possible influences may encourage thought concerning relation of behavior and situations. For the infant, a place where he can have fresh air and sunshine, and a small area for exercise may be sufficient, but the child who has begun to explore the world on his own two feet seeks more room. As children grow older they like space which is their own, where they can keep their own things and play their own games without running the risk of hearing frequent complaints because they are under foot. They are sometimes noisy in ways which can become a source of irritation to the individual family or to the nearby neighbors. Fear of annoying the neighbors or of what neighbors will say may affect a mother's attitude toward her child.

The family is made up of adults and children and the needs of the two differ in many respects. The problem often becomes one of adjusting to meet the needs of one without sacrificing the needs of the other. On the whole, the house is built for adults; the furniture and equipment are for adults, but children live in that house and the extent to which their needs are met is pertinent. Respect for furniture and walls is not inherent in children, and, although it has a function, a child misses something very important out of life if there are no chairs which he is allowed to tip over to make a train or to set up a house or tent by covering with an old blanket. Imaginative play is too important in a child's life to deprive him of it in his home. Adults' needs are also important. The mother who is in need of rest wishes for relief from too close proximity to the play of eager boys who become, for the time being, various kinds of airplanes traveling from city to city over land and sea.

Whether it is but a corner of a room or a lower drawer or shelf somewhere in the house, space within reach of the child's arms enables him to feel that this is his own for his own things. Not only providing the space but also respecting it and keeping it free from intrusion are important to him. He will not wish to have his things, no matter how absurd they may seem in the eyes of the unimaginative adult, ruthlessly cleared out. No things of his own, no space for his own things, no guidance in respecting the possessions of others, may make for difficulties in learning respect for property and respect for the rights of others.

Equipment of the home can aid in encouraging desirable habits. A child, for example, can hardly be expected to form the habit of clean hands before meals and of using his own towel if washing before dinner is either a matter of a hurried wash at the high kitchen sink at the hands of some grown-up when he comes in from play, or if the washing entails a long trip upstairs to a bathroom where nothing fits his size. The essential thing, if one would have children acquire the habit of cleanliness, is to provide a way for children to learn easily to wash themselves and reach their own towels, face cloths and tooth brushes. This can be done if there are low hooks or racks, a chair or box to reach the high bowl or a separate basin which can be set on a low stool. A place for hanging outdoor things on a hook within the child's reach will help him to assume this responsibility. Tables and chairs which will make the child comfortable rather than uncomfortable at meals facilitate the development of good eating habits.

Equipment that makes "helping mother" in household tasks pleasurable and within the realm of possibility is well worth having. The preschool child has the skill and the strength to help in many ways. He can empty waste baskets and ash trays, assist in wiping some of the dishes, and use a small mop or broom. One will not expect a performance that is equal to the adult's. But the child is learning to share, to acquire skills and standards, and such learning at an early age far outweighs any inadequacies in the results he achieves.

The "grown up" bed instead of the crib may actually serve in promoting growth in self-reliance. "Things" which are not too precious in the eyes of the mother, so that she may be able to bear with serenity some possibly inevitable destruction or marring, may well be used for a few years instead of more highly valued furniture or equipment.

The economic factor in family life is an extremely important factor. Although family life may be successful in its main elements, it cannot be denied that poverty and wealth inject certain difficulties into the family situation that sometimes are a predisposing factor to the family breakdown.

An income which is so small that it has no amount to allot to that essential, recreation (which is in truth re-creation), or which allows no margin for meeting the emergency of sickness or for saving, puts upon those responsible for the care of the children (especially if they are carrying that responsibility conscientiously) a burden which is difficult to bear without worry. Worry means a stress or strain which makes for tension and thereby destroys a certain serenity important to family life. Wise planning and an ability to differentiate between essentials and nonessentials of life can do much to alleviate some of the difficulties of maintaining a satisfactory family life on a limited income. There are indeed certain values to be gained from life in a family where there must be careful money management. A spirit of cooperation and helpfulness, a self-reliance, a willingness to do without, a willingness to give up in order that some one else may have, may be fostered more easily in the home where the income seems to need stretching than in the home where the economic situation is such that these traits are not naturally required. The difficulties of having too little are obvious, and are often very great when the discrepancy between income and standards of taste and living is wide, but the difficulties of having too much, though less obvious, are nevertheless important. The home in which there is plenty of service, and the home in which it is economically easy to provide the child with everything that he needs, may mean for the child that he has no chance to learn to wait on himself. He may come to overestimate the importance of self because not only is his every need supplied but his every desire is gratified.

It is not possible to translate the term "sufficient income" into dollars and cents, for many factors enter into the decision. Time and place, the cost of living, and standards of living (a product itself of many different conditions) make "sufficient income" almost an individual matter. The children must be sheltered, clothed, fed, protected against disease, cared for if sickness occurs, and educated to meet life as successfully (not used in the material sense) as possible; but so varied are the individual interpretations as to how this should be done that it makes a definite statement impossible.

Nature of the Family

The Family as a Growing Organism. A concept of the family as involving growth and development of each of its members and also growth and development as a unit can be useful. In clarifying these aspects of the family, definitions of an organism and of growth add detail with which a parallel can be drawn. An organism may be thought of as having a very complex structure and parts which function not only in terms of their distinct special character but also in terms of the whole. Growth means increase in size and complexity. Both terms apply to individual family members in a literal sense and may be used to apply in a parallel sense to the family as a unit.

For a time, writing on the subject of the young child seemed to be describing a "child-centered family." Adaptations of parents to a particular child's needs occasioned more discussion than needs of the adults and the other children. When the family is thought of as a growing organism, needs of the family unit as well as of each family member are more likely to be recognized. The currently popular term, "family-centered family," conveys this meaning. The family unit, or organism as a whole, as well as its parts (i.e., the baby who is hungry every three hours, the mother who feeds him at those intervals, and the older child who watches her feed him), warrants thought. The four-year-old who asks his father to play with him when he comes home in the evening, the father who sits down to read the newspaper, the mother who is preparing dinner, and the grandmother who is ill, are parts of the family "organism."

The family is a complex structure. Interaction between various members includes parent-to-parent, child-to-each-parent, and child-to-child reactions. In referring to dynamics of family interaction, at a particular time and also in the course of years of change, Lawrence Frank considers "dynamic, circular processes wherein each participating entity is at once helping to create and maintain the larger pattern or organization which is also reciprocally directing, influencing, and guiding what he or she is doing."*

Growing individuals who compose a family are parts of its continual change. One way of describing the family's life cycle is to refer to stages in a chronological sequence and to developmental tasks of children and their parents at the different stages. Developmental tasks[343] are actions and feelings important for the person at a particular stage if he is to continue his growth. Such an approach is presented in Figure 5. Stages in the family life cycle are listed in the column on the left, but developmental tasks and what other family members do about them are not included. Arrows suggest that adjustments are in several directions, not only in the direction of parent to child but also of child

* *Dynamics of Family Interaction*[619] (pp. 1-2).

to parent, family unit to members, and vice versa. Child to child adjustments are not shown in this figure. If this detail were used in an attempt to understand an individual family, the form it might take is illustrated by the following quotation concerning one of a number of developmental tasks of parents of preschool children. The developmental task is stated to be:

"To recognize the rapidly changing nature of childhood, and to get used to and prepare to meet the onrush of stages of development, while being aware as well of the need of waiting upon maturation. To accept the child's increasing range of skills and physical activity, and to find satisfactory roles in which physical help is gradually diminishing and other kinds of help gradually increasing. To avoid unnecessary worry and fear, whether in connection with a child's physical competence or growing social interests."*

STAGES IN FAMILY LIFE CYCLE	Developmental Tasks of Children	Developmental Tasks of Parents		Challenges, Hazards, Crises, Problems which Arise for Each Stage	Implications for Services Needed, Aids, Education
		Mother	Father		
Early Marriage and Expectant Family					
Child Bearing Family^A (Birth to 30 months)					
Pre-School Family^B (2-1/2 to 5 years)					
School-Age Family (5 to 12 years)					
Family With Teen-Agers (13 to 19 years)					
Family as Launching Center (early twenties)					
The Aging Family					
Families in Crises					

Figure 5. Summary chart depicting interrelations of developmental tasks throughout the family life cycle. (Adapted from *Dynamics of Family Interaction,* National Conference on Family Life, Report of Committee, submitted by E. Duvall and R. Hill, mimeographed, 1948 (p. 10). Arrows have been added to illustrate (A) adjustments of family members, and (B) adjustments in family unit. A and B should be superimposed.)

* Op. cit. (III-8).

More specific description of this task might be:

"One of the perpetually surprising features of family life is the fact that it never stays put. No sooner has a fence been built to keep a 2-year-old out of the street than he's a 3-year-old, capable of understanding why he must keep to the sidewalk. The period of teaching the youngster to keep dry is succeeded by one of helping him to get used to sharing his parents with a new baby. Just as a child has reached a stage when his mental growth has made him an increasingly interesting companion, he is snatched away by the school, and his parents begin to be outsiders, unaware of what is happening to him during a big share of his waking hours."*

Tasks and challenges such as these just quoted for parents are related to developmental tasks of the preschool child. What the child does in his early years and what his family and others do, as he and they grow, are discussed in the following chapters.

Growth of the Family

With an introduction to knowledge of (1) what the family provides in terms of biological, social and cultural heritage, and in environmental opportunities for growth, and (2) the nature of the family as a growing organism, another step in understanding the home and family as background for development relates to (3) growth of the family. Its aspects in the first three stages of the family life cycle of Figure 5 will be considered. In the first stage, early marriage, the *husband and wife bring to the family two individual personalities*. Their biologic heritage has meaning for themselves and for their children. Their health† and vitality can include assets and liabilities. Their intellectual ability involves not only knowledge in many fields and experience in its use which both bring to their new family unit but also their potentialities for learning from this new experience. In addition, each person has feelings and attitudes which may be quite similar or different.‡

These two individuals in establishing a home set up an environment

---

* *Dynamics of Family Interaction*[619] (III-8).

† As defined in the constitution of the World Health Organization, "Health is a state of complete physical, mental and social well-being and not merely the absence of disease or infirmity . . . the ability to live harmoniously in a changing total environment is essential to . . . development"[382] (p. 11). Another description of a concept of health: "Health is obviously a process, not a state . . . health is conceived of as functioning to the best of one's capacity in the general areas of work, play, sex and family life"[759] (p. 14).

‡ See Bowman,[124] Christensen,[164] Foster,[266] Duvall and Hill,[233] Glick,[299] Koos,[472] Landis and Landis,[491, 492] and Seeley, Sim and Loosley[739] for further discussion of marriage and family relationships.

with both physical and emotional climates. They do this consciously and unconsciously, with some elements within their control and others beyond their control. Not only their roles as husband and wife, but also housing, family health habits, establishment of food habits, home management and routines, and planning for children, are all in the process of becoming one kind or another, in this early stage of the family.

Housing. The place in which the family lives is important to its total well-being. Good housing facilitates good family living; inadequate housing places a strain on families. Lack of space and privacy is hard on children and their parents. Conflicts and tensions which may jeopardize emotional security may develop easily. Health hazards are created. These are intensified when lack of space is accompanied by substandard housing and surroundings which make it impossible for the basic needs of individuals to be met and which are breeding places for disease. Children who live in slum areas with crowding, poor houses, and other deprivations which accompany such conditions, and

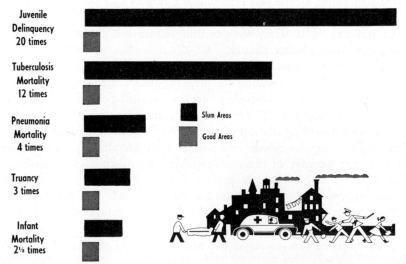

POOR HOUSING MEANS POOR CHANCES FOR CHILDREN

A comparison of 4 slum areas and 4 good areas in Chicago shows these conditions:

Juvenile Delinquency 20 times

Tuberculosis Mortality 12 times

Pneumonia Mortality 4 times

Slum Areas

Good Areas

Truancy 3 times

Infant Mortality 2½ times

Figure 6. (Chart 28, reproduced from Children and Youth at the Midcentury; A graphic presentation of social and economic facts important in the lives of children and youth. Raleigh, N. C., Health Publications Institute, Inc., 1951.)

are related to low income, are more likely to have serious health and social problems than children living in good areas. Figure 6 shows that poor housing means poor chances for children as demonstrated from figures from the Chicago Housing Authority. Rates of juvenile delinquency, truancy, infant mortality, and tuberculosis and pneumonia mortality among children are higher in slum areas than in good areas.

Another study in Chicago,[275] comparing infant mortality in public housing projects and in areas surrounding the projects, demonstrates that babies living in those projects have a better chance for survival during the first year than those of families of similar income living in areas nearby. The infant mortality rate* under one year of age among the white families in the project was 16.0; in the surrounding areas it was 33.6. The rate was 35.0 among Negro families living in the project and 53.9 in the surrounding areas.† The mothers in these housing projects no longer are frustrated by unhygienic living, such as the reported conditions in the slum area adjoining one of the Chicago Housing Authority's projects. "Rats, mice, roaches and other kinds of vermin infest more than half the buildings; stoves and makeshift arrangements are the only means of heating for nearly 85 per cent; almost seven-eighths of the individual flats are dilapidated or are in dilapidated structures; a little less than half the houses lack bathing facilities; toilets in good condition amount to less than one per dwelling for every other building."‡ It is no wonder that babies not subjected to these conditions have a better chance.

The basic principles of healthful housing[667] may be grouped under four broad headings: meeting the physiological needs and the psychological needs of the individual, protection against contagion, and protection against accident. The first category, meeting physiological needs, covers the areas of regulation of temperature, ventilation, light, protection against excessive noise, and provision of adequate space for exercise and for the play of the children. Meeting psychological needs includes provision of adequate privacy for the various members of the family, provision of opportunities for normal family life, provision for facilities which make possible the performance of tasks of the house-

---

* Number of infant deaths per 1,000 babies.

† This difference between Negro and white babies suggests that even though Negro and white families move out of slums to better quarters, the Negro baby does not immediately have an equal chance of survival because of general economic and social disadvantages.

‡ Fuerst and Kaplan[275] (p. 178).

hold without undue physical and mental fatigue, provision of opportunities for normal community life, provision of facilities for maintenance of cleanliness of the dwelling and the people in the family, and concordance with the prevailing social standards of the local community. Protection against contagion involves safe and adequate water supply, adequate toilet and sewage facilities, absence of vermin, sanitary conditions in the vicinity, provision of facilities for keeping milk and food fresh, and provision of sufficient space in sleeping rooms to minimize the danger of infection by contact. Lastly, protection against accidents includes a safe dwelling, elimination of fire hazards, protection against the danger of electrical shocks or burns, protection against falls and other mechanical injuries, and protection of the neighborhood against the hazards of automobile traffic. Housing which conforms to these basic principles provides an environment for healthful living.

The home which the husband and wife choose for their family has to be selected realistically according to their income, availability of houses or sites for building, and personal preferences. A couple may start their married life in a small apartment and gradually make plans for a home for their family. They may have little choice because of limiting circumstances but through ingenuity can often make a seemingly impossible spot into a comfortable home. Planning houses for families, as discussed by Gutheim,[322] requires long-range planning as well as planning for immediate needs. This means planning homes which are so arranged that they will be adequate for the "crowded years," when the children are young and around the house, and for the "peak years," when all the children are in school, and which can still be rearranged to fit the needs of the parents when the children have grown up and left home. Gutheim recommends that the house be flexible in plan and arrangement. Ideally, it has characteristics such as the following. It changes as the children grow. It changes as human needs change. It changes from time to time with different activities. It is planned to minimize waste of space and to make each action efficient, each trip short, and to reduce steps. It is zoned for centers of family living with places for noise and places for quiet, places for getting together and places for being alone. In other words, the house fits the family needs; whether it be quiet for father after a hard day, peace of mind for mother as she works and supervises the children at the same time in a work center planned for children's play space as well as work space, and privacy for the older children when the young ones bother them. So houses can be planned for the modern, democratic family, to meet the needs of all and facilitate day to day living.

Health Habits. Health habits comprise the daily way of living by which the physical needs of the body are met. They are, therefore, important in maintaining the health of an individual. Health of each member of the family is important for the group. Healthy parents are in a better position to provide good care for their children. Hungry parents, sick parents, or constantly fatigued parents are handicapped in providing good care for their children. Routines should be such that they contribute to a state of surplus energy and vitality, which are characteristics of a healthy person.

The man and woman when they marry bring to this new family a set of health habits and attitudes which are firmly established. Each has a pattern of living in the area of physical health habits, including eating, sleeping, activity, and elimination. If these habits are similar, fewer adjustments are necessary. If they differ considerably some adjustment on the part of one or both must be made in some of these routines. In any case, it seems advisable in planning for their life together to take an accounting of their health habits and attitudes and include an evaluation of them in making an over-all plan for marriage and family life. If a woman has a regimen which is satisfactory for her, she will not have to make any radical changes when she becomes pregnant. These habits and attitudes are also part of the environment which these potential parents set up for their children, and they will have a significant effect on the habits and attitudes established by their children.

These habits have been built up by the individual over the years and have been determined by circumstances, understanding of the body's needs, and the feelings of the individual. Some people are neglectful in providing for their physical needs; some people are overconcerned; others have learned the routines which are satisfactory for themselves and follow them in a comfortable manner. These latter individuals can more easily establish family ways of living that will meet the physical needs of each member of the family and create wholesome attitudes toward fulfilling these needs.

Food Habits. Of the health habits, food habits will be dealt with individually (1) because of the importance of food in sustaining life and providing for growth and development and (2) because there is a multiplicity of factors contributing to them. An individual's attitude toward food is an expression of his total personality. Understanding an individual's behavior in respect to food means understanding the many facets of his personality. A person who tends to be inflexible in other areas of life will tend to be inflexible in eating behavior; a person who is flexible and faces change with ease will tend to be more accepting of a variety of foods and new ones. People have strong feelings about food. Each person enters marriage with a very definite pattern of behavior in respect to food and the two set up an environment relating to food which will influence the feeling and behavior of their children toward food.

Food with man is not just food. "It is the crossroads of emotion, religion, tradition, and habit. That to which we are accustomed seems natural, while the strange seems unnatural and undesirable."*

Emotions affect what one eats and how one feels about it. People primarily select food on the basis of what they like. Intellectual conviction of the value of food is of secondary importance. People eat for satisfaction, namely, relief from hunger. Generally this hunger is physiological. However, an unsatisfied psychological hunger is sometimes met by eating. Thus a lonely or unhappy person may use food as a substitute for an unfulfilled need. A person may eat too little or too much when he is anxious or worried. Pleasant or unpleasant experiences around a food may strongly affect later feelings about that food. Food well prepared, served in an appetizing fashion, and eaten in good company will create pleasant memories and lead to later enjoyment of the same food. Conversely, food of poor quality, unpleasant surroundings, and unhappy interpersonal relationships will lead to unpleasant memories and possible rejection of that food later. Unhappy mealtime experiences that are unrelated to the food served may lead to later disinterest in food in general. Thus emotions are a potent force in molding food habits.

Religion, with its taboos and rituals surrounding food, affects the food habits of many. The dietary laws of orthodox Jewry, fasting of Catholics during Lent, and the exclusion of animal foods by the Hindus are cases in point.

Tradition, which includes all the social and cultural factors, has a strong effect on the foods selected, food preparation, and behavior associated with eating. The food preferred by a man in the British Isles would not satisfy one from Italy. Meat, boiled potatoes and vegetables,

* Graubard[312] (p. 19).

and porridge are acceptable to the British; spaghetti with cheese and a well seasoned sauce is a main stay of the Italian diet. American families reveal the heritage of food patterns. Families of Polish extraction will serve one kind of food; a Chinese family will serve a different kind; a Middle East family will serve yet another kind. Sometimes this cultural heritage has remained only as a remnant; sometimes it remains as a strong influence.

Food is often chosen because of its prestige value. Certain foods, to some, may carry a connotation of wealth and position. In every society some foods are rarer, finer, more delicate, more desirable, more expensive than others. Social groupings tend to express themselves in food. That foods carry a status value is indicated by the fact that most families have company foods which are served when guests are present, and other foods which the family will eat and enjoy themselves but would be unwilling to serve to guests. The stubbornness with which the American public has clung to white bread, despite the educational campaigns to encourage the use of dark breads, is perhaps explained by the long history of prestige value of white over dark bread which came from Europe where white bread, plentiful white sugar, and meat every day were symbols of high social status. In addition to foods themselves, the way food is served and behavior at mealtime also indicate social heritage and social status.

As said earlier, we like that to which we are accustomed. Thus custom is a strong force in determining our food habits. The food patterns of an individual who has grown up in a family where there has been a wide experience with different foods will differ greatly from those of one who has had a narrow experience with foods. A person who has lived in a low income family will have had experiences different from one whose family had and spent plenty of money for food. One who has grown up in a family in which food was merely a means of satisfying hunger will have attitudes toward food quite different from one whose family enjoyed food and made mealtime a social time, or a time for consolidating family ties. One who grew up in a family where the food was planned around someone in the group who required a special diet because of some chronic illness, such as diabetes, may look upon food differently from another whose family dietary was not focused on one person. One individual may have learned to look on food with boredom; another may have acquired a deep interest in food. Thus many individual patterns result from habits which have accumulated during the growing years. The manner in which differences are reconciled at marriage depends on the two people and the circumstances facing them. In the food pattern they establish for the new family, the couple will determine to a large degree how their offspring will feel about food and whether they will be well-fed or misfed.

Different people have different patterns of distributing their food intake during the day. In the United States the custom of three meals a day is general. Some distribute their food intake fairly evenly among the three meals. Some have no breakfast; some have a light breakfast, light lunch, and heavy dinner, thus counting on the night meal to provide the major portion of their nutritional needs. It is believed that more even distribution through the day provides for better physiological function than a very uneven distribution. Studies of the effects of different types of breakfast indicate that the habit of a skimpy breakfast is not the best pattern for promoting individual well-being.

In one study[855, 856] people were fed different types of breakfast: (1) coffee and cream, (2) a 400 calorie meal of fruit, toast, butter, milk and coffee, and (3) an 800 calorie meal of fruit, cereal, cream, egg, bacon, toast, jam, milk, and coffee, and (4) no breakfast at all. This study revealed that going without breakfast or having only coffee in the morning tended to decrease maximum work output and increased neuromuscular tremor during the morning as measured under laboratory conditions. Improvement of these functions was noted after subjects had had breakfast. Another study[642] of blood sugar concentrations after subjects had had various kinds of breakfasts disclosed that when only coffee was taken the blood sugar levels dropped below the fasting level and some of the subjects often reported hunger, weakness, headache and lassitude. When a protein food such as milk or eggs was included, the blood sugar level dropped more slowly. A sense of well-being was consistently reported after breakfasts that provided larger quantities of protein-rich foods. It was even found that the breakfast meal may influence blood-sugar levels in the afternoon. Other evidence of the value of a good breakfast comes from an experiment[504] in which the total amount of protein remained the same each day but was varied in its distribution among the three meals. The women subjects in this experiment retained more nitrogen (which meant they had more available for repair and growth of body tissue) when some of the protein was supplied in the breakfast meal.

It is evident that a breakfast of fruit juice, toast, and coffee is not as satisfactory a preparation for the day's activities as such a breakfast to which is added milk or eggs, or both. Since breakfast is as important a time, nutritionally speaking, as other mealtimes, family schedules need to be planned to allow time for this meal. Establishment of the pattern of a good breakfast early in the life of the family will contribute to the well-being of the husband and wife and later to that of their children.

Home Management and Routines.   One task of the woman entering marriage is the organization of her work as a homemaker. How she does this, of course, depends on her training and experience and on the circumstances of living. She may have had experience with household tasks. She may continue outside employment. She may share in the husband's work, as is the case in families living on a farm. On the other hand, her only responsibility may be keeping the home and providing for the needs of her husband. The relative simplicity of living at this time masks important problems of adjustment and serious preparation for later family responsibilities. Some women are aware that this period is a time of preparation for the years when the family is growing. This is a period of learning to live together. It is a period of discussion, compromise, sharing. It is a period in which an agreed-upon way of living evolves. Planning has an advantage in long-range living.

Family living is becoming for more and more couples a cooperative venture. The manner in which work is shared depends largely on the feeling of a man about his role in the home, and this in turn reflects his experiences in his home as he grew up. The attitude of the woman about her role and that of her husband is equally important.

Couples learn that it takes time to do the daily duties. One study in New York State showed that it took the average homemaker 6.3 hours a day for homemaking if she lived in the city and 7.0 hours if she lived on a farm.* It has been said that today people are more comfortable and cleaner, healthier, better looking and more stylish. All this takes more time and work. Many women do their own work and many still live in apartments or houses which had been planned without much thought of providing means for efficient living. These first years of marriage are the ones for mastering the art of homemaking, for learning effective and easy ways of performing the daily household tasks.

* 1952 data from New York State College of Home Economics. Courtesy of Dr. Jean Warren.

There are easy ways and hard ways of doing household work.* Learning the easy ways will help to accomplish the work with a minimum of strain on the body, and reduce fatigue with its accompanying nervous tension, irritability, and effect on disposition and appearance. Good posture in housework can be attained by (1) using one's body correctly, (2) having the correct heights for working surfaces, (3) using the correct tool, and (4) eating foods that build healthy muscle.[858] Such habits, plus that of resting briefly from time to time during the day, will reduce fatigue.

With the growth of the family, time required for homemaking changes. In the study in New York State mentioned above, the average homemaker with children who were less than eighteen years of age spent 8.1 hours a day in homemaking if she lived in the city and 8.2 hours if she lived on a farm. It is especially heavy when the children are young. According to one study[902] in families where the youngest child was under two years of age, the mother spent an average of more than nine hours a day in homemaking. In families when the youngest child was between four and nine, nearly 7½ hours were used. In older families with the youngest between ten and seventeen years, the time dropped to less than 6 hours. As life becomes busier and new problems arise, there is little time for replacing old, unsatisfactory habits with new ones.

As Gutheim[322] says, a couple needs certain "tools" for carrying through a plan for family living. These include a budget, a schedule, and a house plan. A plan for the house has been discussed previously. Effective use of money and time both for work and leisure by each person and by the whole family is extremely important. These "tools" can be used in such a manner that they do not become the masters of the users but are a means to providing a smoothly operating family.

Schedules will have to be changed from time to time, and major changes will take place as the family grows. Figure 7 shows how the woman's day changes in shape. In the early years it is shaped like a dumbbell, the crowded times coming in the morning and evening. In the middle of the day the woman is alone to do her housework and any other activities she might choose. When children arrive, a change takes place. The shape of the day now assumes that of an egg, since the mother is busy all day with child care and housework. She has to plan her schedule so that the care of the children and her housework

* See Posture in Housework.[858]

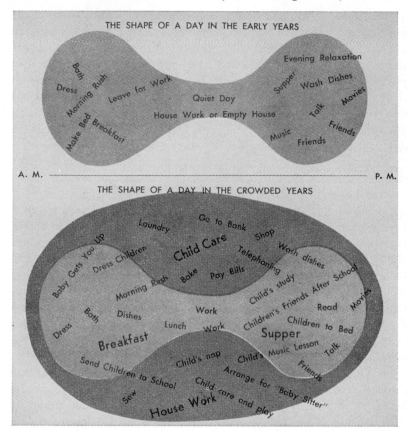

Figure 7. (Reproduced from Gutheim, F.: Houses for Family Living. New York, The Woman's Foundation, Inc., 1948.)

are synchronized. In addition, she needs to plan her day so that she is not so fatigued at the end of the day that she has no energy for enjoying life with her husband when he is at home. Planning and learning efficient ways of doing the daily jobs at the beginning of marriage now begin to pay dividends.

Planning for Children.   Most people want children. Having children is a natural part of life to many, and is a very important part of life. "Nothing in the life of a man or a woman is going to be as important to themselves or to society as their parenthood. It seems reasonable, then, that prospective parents should apply at least as much intelligence and foresight to this as to designing a home, buying furniture, planning a vacation or perhaps even choosing a career. Knowledge and thought can be applied to the production of a family with at least as much prospect of success as in the case of any other human activity."*

Planning for children may vary from discussions of how each feels about children and what they wish for their children, to a purposeful kind of planning including setting goals for themselves as parents, planning how they and their children will fit into a family group, and coming to some decision about the kind of philosophy to have as a basis for family living and the guidance of their children.

A question of the advisability of having children sometimes arises because of some undesirable trait that has occurred in the family of either or both husband and wife. Potential parents with this concern can obtain help in making their decision by consulting someone who understands the mechanics of heredity and can tell them something of the chances of such a trait occurring in their offspring. Doctors informed in the field of genetics can serve as such counselors. In some places there is a heredity clinic where potential parents can obtain expert information, after which they will be in a better position to make a decision. Often fears about the transmission of characteristics are not substantiated by fact and anxiety can be eliminated completely.

For some, planning may include planning in terms of the number of children, the spacing of these children, and the time of year when they will be born. Economic and health factors are often reasons for such planning. According to present knowledge it is considered wise to begin one's family in the early twenties, that is, in the early years of physical maturity. Research has shown that the risk of early mortality is higher for infants born to very young or old mothers than for infants born to mothers in their twenties.[857, 929] Eastman has said that the greatest asset a pregnant woman can possess is youth. Whatever advantage is gained by several years' rest between births is offset, and in some respects more than counter-balanced, by aging. "For the best maternal and fetal outlook we are inclined to believe that Youth is a better ally than child spacing."†

The desirable interval between children differs with different women, since there are individual differences in the length of time required for

---

* Rock and Loth[708] (pp. 3-4).

† Eastman[234] (p. 463).

a woman to recover from the strains of pregnancy and lactation. The interval depends on her general health and nutritional status, and the emotional influences in her environment. From one careful study[930] it seems that the rate of stillbirths increases when the interval between births is either too short or too long.* A woman's physician can tell her when she is physiologically ready for another child.

The preparation for children, whether done consciously or not, is important in terms of the well-being of the child. Preparation begins long before the time when pregnancy is recognized, even before the child is conceived. To begin preparation at that time may be late. Thus the concept of *preconceptional preparation* has emerged. Preconceptional preparation encompasses all in the life of a person which contributes to the creating of a healthy individual who has developed to the point of being physically and psychologically ready for parenthood. It means proper growth and development from birth to maturity in all its phases.

For the woman a healthy, well-nourished body is of paramount importance as she approaches her reproductive period, since the physiologic demands on her body during these years will be heavy. Growth of tissue continues during this time, both during the monthly reproductive cycles which culminate with menstruation and during pregnancy. It has been calculated[848] that between the ages of 15 and 45 years the weight of tissues produced in the physiologic growth required to provide for menstruation uninterrupted by pregnancy is about equal in amount to a woman's weight. If in those years a woman has six children and breast feeds each for nine months, the metabolic demand for tissue production is approximately double her adult weight. If she enters this period well nourished, her body is ready for the work demanded of it; if her body is not well nourished, due to faulty food habits or factors which interfere with the use of the nutrients supplied in the food or both, she enters this period with a handicap.

It is agreed that undernutrition, overnutrition and malnutrition† can

* See also bibliographical reference 857.
† Undernutrition is a condition due to inadequate food consumption in which the deficiency is quantitative rather than qualitative, i.e., a deficiency of calories with the nutrients fairly well balanced. Such was the condition in much of Europe during and directly following World War II, described in Studies of Undernutrition, Wuppertal, 1946-1949.[568] In overnutrition there is a quantitative excess of calories leading to obesity. In malnutrition there is a deficiency of specific nutrients, e.g., the deficiency of vitamin B complex found in the Japanese prison camps.[771]

influence the capacity to reproduce successfully.[901] However, to demonstrate the effects of nutrition upon reproduction is somewhat difficult because of the multiplicity of factors involved in the reproductive process and the difficulty in controlling the many variables in the life of a human being. It is not surprising, therefore, that results are sometimes conflicting. During the famine period in Holland in the winter of 1944 and the spring of 1945 when women were under nutritional and emotional stress, about 50 per cent of the women had cessation of menstruation (amenorrhea) and were presumably infertile.[766] Concurrently, the number of births nine months later fell to about one third of the usual number. With the return of food the amenorrhea disappeared. However, in Malaya another study[591] concluded that undernutrition in that situation did not affect fertility. Keys and his co-workers,[454] in an experimental study in semistarvation, found that during the period of severe undernutrition the young men produced sperm that were less mobile and which lived a shorter time. When the diet was restored to meet the needs of the men, the sperm returned to normal. Many studies* indicate that nutrition plays a role in the health of both mother and child. This role, however, may not always be a primary one in causing maternal and fetal complications as is indicated by the Vanderbilt Study.[534, 535] It is to be remembered that many factors contribute to complications in pregnancy.

In animals Warkany and his co-workers[878a] have demonstrated that certain congenital malformations may result from maternal dietary deficiency. If it is found that such a relationship exists in man, and that conditions in human mothers bearing malformed infants are similar to those in animals, the first two months, when the organs and systems of the embryo are being formed, is the crucial time, and deficiencies then may result in abnormalities. If a woman waits until she knows she is pregnant to practice satisfactory food habits it may be too late, since most women are not immediately aware that they have become pregnant.

Unfortunately, nutritional deficiencies, especially those which have persisted over a long period, cannot be remedied in a short time. More time is required for an individual to recover from a long-standing deficiency than from an acute one. For example, Stearns,[799] in discussing calcium metabolism, points out that recovery from chronic substandard nutrition is not a matter of days but of months. It is, therefore, advantageous for a woman to enter her child-bearing years with bones

* Burke et al.,[148] Ebbs and Tisdall,[236] Dieckmann,[217] Smith,[770] Tompkins.[845]

well stocked with calcium, since bones store calcium to be used when necessary.

Dietary deficiencies in adolescence may therefore contribute to a lack of nutritional readiness for pregnancy. This may be true especially today in the United States where the child-bearing years begin earlier* due to the current trend of earlier marriages and earlier parenthood.

For both the man and woman, satisfactory development of a well-integrated personality through the orderly acquisition of the successive steps in the process of maturing is important.

Thus preparation of children for the time when they will be parents means building sound minds and bodies, making available to them the necessary foods, helping them to learn about the needs of their bodies, and giving them the opportunities to develop satisfactory food habits through the enjoyment of foods which will meet their needs. It means supervision of health. It means as Spock says ". . . a fundamental reemphasis on all childhood education, in which human feelings and family relations will become the core. The result to be hoped for is that the idea of eventually being a father or being a mother will sound like an exciting aim throughout childhood."† It means growing up in homes and communities where children can have love, security, a chance to share and to understand and accept themselves and others: in fact, a wholesome life.

There is growing interest in preparation for parenthood. In addition to the long range program of providing for optimum growth of individuals, there are community facilities for young people to gain knowledge and receive help with their personal problems. In an increasing number of communities opportunities are available for young people to gain insight and knowledge which will prepare them for parenthood. Such opportunities include medical and psychological counseling for adolescents, engaged couples, and young married couples, courses in education for family life in high schools, and discussion groups for those anticipating marriage or those recently married. The churches, the schools, the colleges, social agencies, and the medical profession are all participating. Thus a couple can enter into parenthood with better understanding of what is ahead and confidence in their ability to meet the future.

---

* According to the Metropolitan Life Insurance Company[578] one-third of the brides and about one-fourth of the mothers bearing a first child are less than twenty years old.

† Spock[794] (p. 74).

As stated earlier, planning for children, for some, may include planning for the size of the family. Some people do not believe in so regulating their families; some people do. It is evident without consulting statistics that families range in size. In some there are many children; in some there are few. As shown in Figure 8, half the children under eighteen years of age in 1949 were in families of three or more children. Of the thirty-nine million families in the United States, over two-fifths had no children under eighteen. Of the twenty-three million families with children, about 40 per cent of the families had one child under eighteen, about 30 per cent had two, and about 40 per cent had three or more.*†

There tend to be more children in low and moderate income fami-

HALF THE CHILDREN ARE IN FAMILIES OF THREE OR MORE CHILDREN

These families with 3 or more children care for 23 million children under 18

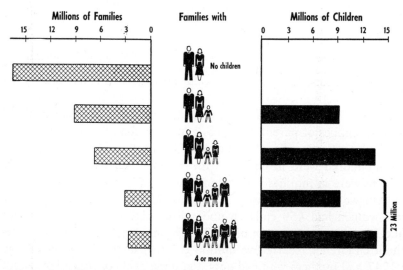

Figure 8. (Chart 11, reproduced from Children and Youth at the Midcentury; A graphic presentation of social and economic facts important in the lives of Children and Youth. Raleigh, N. C., Health Publications Institute, Inc., 1951.)

* Figures from Census Bureau.

† 1954 figures show somewhat similar differences. At that time over half the children under eighteen years of age were in families of three or more children. Forty-one per cent of the families had no children under eighteen. Of the families with children 35 per cent had one child under eighteen, 33 per cent had two, and 31 per cent had three or more.[433]

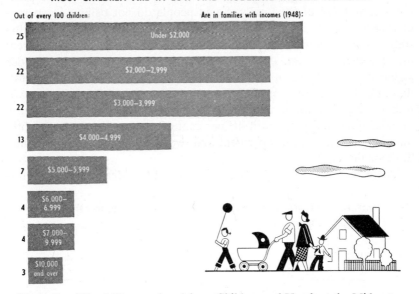

MOST CHILDREN ARE IN LOW AND MODERATE INCOME FAMILIES

Out of every 100 children: Are in families with incomes (1948):

25   Under $2,000

22    $2,000–2,999

22    $3,000–3,999

13    $4,000–4,999

7    $5,000–5,999

4    $6,000–6,999

4    $7,000–9,999

3    $10,000 and over

Figure 9. (Chart 22, reproduced from Children and Youth at the Midcentury; A graphic presentation of social and economic facts important in the lives of Children and Youth. Raleigh, N. C., Health Publications Institute, Inc., 1951.)

lies than in high income families, more in farm than in urban families, more in families of parents with less education than in those of parents who had more education. As shown in Figure 9, in 1948 25 per cent of the children were in families with incomes under $2,000, over 69 per cent were in families with incomes under $4,000, and less than 20 per cent were in families with incomes of $5,000 or more.*† In 1947 farm women had 459 children under five years per 1,000 women of child-bearing years; women of similar age in urban areas had 321 pre-school children.* Nearly five million children under five years of age in 1947 had mothers who had only a grammar school education; about eight million had mothers who had completed 1 to 4 years of high school, and about one and one-half million had mothers who had com-

* Figures from Census Bureau.
† In 1954 as compared with the national average family income of $4,173, families having four children had an average income of $3,949; families with five children, $3,155; and families with six children or more, $3,252. Preliminary data from Census Bureau.[433]

pleted at least one year of college.* Of the 30 per cent increase in fertility rates between the years 1940 and 1947, the largest increase was found among mothers who had graduated from college,* as shown in Figure 10. This was due to the very high marriage rate among that group in 1940. Even with this increase, the mothers with less education continue to produce a larger proportion of the children. It is said that for the college population to replace itself, each college graduate would have approximately 2.15 children.[668]

According to an annual survey[668] of the birth rates of college graduates from a large number of representative colleges, the twenty-five-year graduates (class of 1931) come closer to the replacement level than ever before, having 2.09 children for men and 1.55 for women. In 1956 the average rate for ten-year graduates was higher for women at 1.70, and 1.90 for men, not far behind that for the men of the 1931 class. These figures plus census figures indicate that college graduates

MOTHERS WITH MOST SCHOOLING SHOW GREATEST INCREASE IN FERTILITY

Increase in children under 5 per 1,000 women of childbearing age has been greatest for those with college education

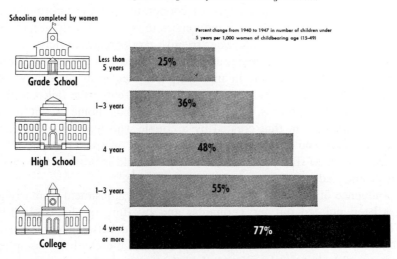

Figure 10. (Chart 10, reproduced from Children and Youth at the Midcentury; A graphic presentation of social and economic facts important in the lives of Children and Youth. Raleigh, N. C., Health Publications Institute, Inc., 1951.)

* Figures from Census Bureau.

have participated in the nation's baby boom to an even greater extent than other groups in the population. Thus, while the differential levels by educational levels still exist, they have declined. More time is needed to measure and evaluate this trend.

Adjustments of Family Members to Each Other. Some suggestion of the rapid change and growth of the new family is gained from the terminology of Figure 5 on page 43; the cycle proceeds from an expectant family, to a child-bearing family with children from birth to thirty months, to a preschool family with children two-and-one-half to five years of age. *Adjustments are made as the family changes.* Children and family routines are fitted together. Changes take place in interactions between various members, between the parents, between the child and each parent, and between one child and another.

Whether the family is rural or urban, and whatever the income, ways of daily living, and number of children, *relationships of parents to each other* affect adjustment of the child. For example, Baruch[79] found tensions in interparental relationships coexistent with less satisfactory adjustment of the children. Factors which she listed contributing to interparental tension were sex, ascendance-submission relationship, lack of consideration, sympathy, lack of cooperation on the upbringing of the child, inability to talk over differences to reach mutually acceptable solutions, expression of affection, friends, work, relatives, leisure pursuits, criticalness of the mate, and finances. She wrote, "The children, when they arrive, enter life in an atmosphere created by the two people who are their parents. When, as people, the parents have failed to find a measure of happiness, the atmosphere of their home is apt to be quite different from that created by a couple who have found in each other stability and strength. The relationship of one parent to the other is the essence of that climate into which the child is born and in which his primary adjustments to living must be made."*

Influence of their childhood home on adults' adjustment in marriage has been pointed out by Terman[835] and by Burgess and Cottrell.[145] The happiness of parents, the affectional bond between parents and children, the lack of conflict, the happiness of the children, discipline that was firm but not harsh were found important when attempts were made to predict success in marriage. Home atmosphere has an effect not only on the child's adjustment in the present but also on his later

* Baruch[78] (p. 60).

adjustment as an individual and as a husband or wife establishing a new family.

The child's *position in the family* has some effect on the way his personality will develop. Whether he or she is an oldest child, a youngest child, the older or younger of two of the same or opposite sex, an only child, an only boy in a family of girls or an only girl in a family of boys, or a member of a family in which all of the children are of the same sex, all tends to influence the experience the child has and the attitudes and feelings the child develops as his personality grows. It matters, too, what his appearance and abilities are in relation to those of his siblings since these facts also influence what the child experiences and hears about himself, and what is conceded to or expected of the child by himself and by others.

Research suggests that the influence of the child's position in the family on his growth and development is complex, and that there are variables within a particular position which have significance.[464, 465, 466, 468, 469, 496, 731, 733] Knowledge of what is apt to happen in parental practice in particular ordinal situations comes from such findings as those of Sears.[731, 733] From the practices of mothers whom he studied, he found that in feeding, "the later the child in birth order, the less likely he was to be breast-fed;" in regard to permissiveness for quarreling among siblings, "*older* children were given more freedom than younger ones;" in restrictions and demands, "there was some tendency for second or later children to be held 'under wraps,' more with respect to making noise or interrupting adults at the table." There also was "the stronger tendency to keep close track of the child, among mothers of *only* children. On the demand side of the matter, there was a definite tendency for the *older* and *middle* children to be assigned more tasks and chores than were the *younger* children."*

How the characteristics of their siblings affect children's personalities is seen from such studies as those made by Koch. Ratings of children concerning work attitudes,[465] emotional attitudes,[466] characteristics of their playmates,[469] attitudes toward their peers[464] and toward adults[468] were related to certain sibling characteristics: such as being the older or younger of a two-child family of the same or opposite sex with age differences of under two years, from two to four years, and from four to six years. In a number of instances Koch refers to "the variable, sex of sib, in relation to sex of child" as seeming to be "an important con-

* Sears[733] (pp. 411 and 412).

ditioner of many of the group differences in personality. . . . The girl with a younger brother, for instance, apparently stimulated by sex rivalry, presents a picture of greater dynamicness than the girl with a younger sister."* She also refers to the two-to-four-year spacing by saying it "may be a rather stressful one."† Her discussions of these and other findings emphasize an approach of attempting to understand why.

Social situations arise from being the only, oldest, middle, or youngest child in a family. Statements related to such particular situations as the following, can provide a framework for viewing qualities in the individual and in his relationships.

THE OLDEST CHILD.   The oldest child has had at least a year or so in the family as the only child, after which he is forced to yield part of the attention and affection of his parents to a younger child. The extent to which he feels prepared to share his place willingly with the new baby and how comfortably he finds himself shifted to a position of older brother will affect his ease of acceptance of his new situation. If he finds only that the arrival of a new baby means complete displacement for him, the change will cause him much emotional strain.

The oldest child, having been the first child, may have served as practice material for his parents. In some families the oldest child remains the favorite. In other families he becomes a substitute parent for younger children and shoulders responsibility early.

THE YOUNGEST CHILD.   The youngest child in the family has no occasion for giving place to a successor and thus may remain the baby of the family. He may be deprived of the privilege of carrying a normal burden of responsibility, and may grow up dependent. Or, with all the older members of the family not only to wait on him but to "boss" him, he may be subject to constant and inconsistent commands.

THE MIDDLE CHILD.   The middle child or children being neither oldest nor youngest, may slip into the background of parental attention and affection. They may spend their energies trying to imitate the behavior or win the approval of the older brothers and sisters.

Some parents make special efforts to plan occasions when one child has their companionship without the presence of the other children. This experience of being alone with his mother or father instead of one of a group can be especially valuable for the middle child, but it has advantages for each child, whatever his position. One child of a family

* Koch[465] (p. 303).
† Koch[464] (p. 40).

of several may go along one time and others at other times, as the mother does her marketing or as the father buys supplies for house repairs. A cooperative arrangement with the other parent, a neighbor, or a grandparent, may be needed for care of the other children, but it can seem worth the extra arranging, from each child's point of view, and from the parent's, the grandparent's and the neighbor's point of view.

THE ONLY CHILD. Studies differ radically in their findings about "only" children.* There is a popular belief that an only child will inevitably turn out badly because he is always spoiled. The truth is, however, that they often turn out well. It is true that the two parents have only one child upon whom to lavish all of their attention and affection. They may find it difficult to deny any of his whims or to discipline him for undesirable behavior. More situations involving this give and take of life tend to be present in large families. Brothers and sisters may provide this experience of adapting to others and being adapted to by others; parents may also provide it.

THE ONLY BOY OR ONLY GIRL. The only boy in a family of girls and the only girl in a family of boys may be in some degree selected for special treatment by the other members of their families. Such a child may receive an undue share of attention and affection, to the extent that he or she may get the idea that there is something particularly sacred about the sex to which he or she belongs. Or, children of each sex may learn a fundamental consideration for the viewpoint and the happiness of the other.

ALL BOYS, OR ALL GIRLS. Families made up of boys only or of girls only tend to have fewer experiences with children of the opposite sex, and may not be introduced often enough and for long enough periods for close acquaintance to follow. Acquaintance with members of the opposite sex may be provided which develops a natural social ease and gives in early childhood the knowledge of differences of the sexes which is frequently of interest to children before school age.

DIFFERENCES IN ABILITY AND APPEARANCE. Differences in ability and appearance may produce differences in the amount and quality of attention and affection given to children. A single less capable child in a family of more capable children, a single slow child in a family of children who learn quickly, or a single child of less appealing appearance in a more attractive family may experience unfavorable contrast. If such

* A review of these findings can be found in Breckenridge and Vincent.[131]

contrast becomes disturbing to the child, the resulting sense of inadequacy may prove disastrous to his personality growth, and may keep him from developing to the maximum whatever ability or qualities he has. Attempts to avoid inadequacy feelings need not, however, develop into situations in which weaknesses of body or mind serve as excuses for lack of wholesome effort toward achievement on the part of each child in the family. Even though a child may be handicapped by a crippled body he grows through making an effort to carry his share of family responsibility. Otherwise his limitations may serve as a means of attracting attention or as a ready excuse for not using abilities he has. On the other hand, a child who is more competent also grows through the use of the various abilities he has.

How to Meet These Differences. These differences can be met through the child's understanding and acceptance of himself and of others. Each child in the family can receive praise according to his effort as well as according to his product. Each child can come to recognize his capacities as well as his shortcomings, and develop a sense of responsibility for contributing, first to the family and later to society, the best that he has to give. He can grow up with a joy in accomplishments reasonably possible for him.

Regardless of sex, age, ability or appearance it is possible for there to be no obvious favorites in any family. This does not mean, of course, that all members of a family can or do love all other members with equal intensity or with equal understanding or rapport.* It does mean, however, that each member of the family shows reasonable respect and consideration for all the other members of that family.

The Adopted Child. Perhaps a word should be said here about the adopted child. If taken early in life, preferably in infancy, an adopted child can be given as much affectional security as can own children. In many cases adopted children are far more secure affectionally than are some own children, since the adopted child is unquestionably a wanted child, whereas not all own children are.

One thing seems clear to students of child development and to social workers who handle adoption cases. Adopted children who know they are adopted from the beginning of their adoption will not experience shock concerning this fact. Infants, naturally, cannot understand this; but there should be no time in any adopted child's life when he is not

* References on relationships of brothers and sisters are McFarland,[533] and Neisser.[624]

aware of the fact that he is a foster child, and, because of this, an especially cherished child.* Only in this way can one avoid the disaster of the fact being discovered by accident, on marriage, or on application for a passport for travel. Otherwise, the child could believe that he was not told frankly and simply about being adopted because there was something to be ashamed of in the fact. The secrecy can be interpreted by him as the result of shame by the foster parents. If it were all right, he thinks they surely would not have hidden it from him. Nothing reassures the adopted child more than to have the fact of his adoption openly accepted as something cherished and precious to all concerned.

Love is not an automatic product of birth by blood. Some blood relatives dislike each other cordially. Love is, rather, the product of long association, shared interests, mutual services and abundant memories of happy times together. Adopted families often have these interests and memories even more than own families.

Differences in Family Patterns

Points previously discussed in this chapter are indicative of the many ways in which each family provides for each child a background not exactly duplicated by the background of any other child. Some families are rural and others are urban. In those where the mother is not employed outside the home, the amount of time she spends at home and with her children varies according to her other responsibilities and interests. In some families *both parents are employed outside the home*. One out of five mothers with children under eighteen years of age worked outside the home in 1949. Of the twenty-one million mothers with children under eighteen years of age, over four million worked outside the home. One and a half million of these had children of preschool age.† Three years later "available census figures show

* Books which help foster parents to present this to preschool children are Wasson, V. P.: The Chosen Baby. Philadelphia, J. B. Lippincott Co., 1939; and Rondell, F. and Michaels, R.: The Family That Grew. New York, Crown Publishers, 1951. Other books of help to foster parents are Brooks and Brooks;[141] Prentice;[672] Rondell and Michaels;[711] also helpful are pamphlets put out by the New York Committee on Mental Hygiene: About Foster Children (for social workers, nurses, foster parents) (price, 25c); To Foster Parents: This is Your Foster Child (price 10c), 1944. Additional pamphlets are Children's Bureau Folder No. 13, When You Adopt a Child, 1947, and Public Affairs Pamphlet No. 173, So You Want To Adopt a Baby, 1951.
† Figures from Census Bureau.

that early in 1952 over 5¼ million women workers had children under 18 years of age and, of these, 2 million had children under 6 years of age."* "Most mothers who work do so because they have to. Frequently their earnings are the family's only support or are needed to help in maintaining the family. This is particularly true of mothers who head broken homes."† For the mother who prefers it, her presence at home with her infant or child of preschool age is considered important enough that many social agencies wish they could arrange it.

In some instances, the mother's reasons for working outside the home are not primarily economic. Her own needs, personal and professional, and the needs of the family, as she and her husband see them, may lead to such a choice. Emphasis on quality of her relationship with her children, rather than quantity, may serve as a guide in making such a decision. To put a premium on amount of time spent with a child, without reference to what it involves, is questionable.

For the child whose mother works, arrangements for care which provides climate conducive to growth are important. Qualifications should be high for the person who comes into the child's home, or in whose home he stays while his mother is away. Day nurseries and nursery schools as community services, with educational values for the child and his family when he is away from home, are discussed later in this chapter.

Instead of full-time employment, some mothers of young children find part-time employment outside the home more satisfactory from many points of view. Others arrange to supplement the family income through business activities which can be carried on at home.

A child may be living with *only one parent* for a number of different reasons. One out of eight children was not living with both parents in 1948. "About two million children under 18 years were living with neither parent and nearly four million children with only one parent. Among children living with only one parent, approximately 1,500,000 had a widowed parent, 900,000 had a divorced parent, and 1,500,000 had a parent away from home. Absent parents included those in the armed forces, those employed away from home, those severely ill and cared for outside of the home, or those who had left the family by

* U. S. Dept. of Labor[863] (p. 2).
† Midcentury White House Conference on Children and Youth Chart Book,[582] Chart 12.

separation. Among the 39 million children living with both parents, including step-parents and adopted parents as well as natural parents, nearly six million had at least one parent who was remarried."* Generalizations on the effect of situations such as these are inappropriate, since so much depends on the adjustment of the individual parent with whom the child lives.†

A study by Sears, Pintler, and Sears,[735] conducted during World War II, suggests effects on the young child of the father's absence. Boys three, four, and five years of age, from homes where the father was absent, portrayed much less fantasy aggression than boys from homes where the father was present. How the father's role contributes toward the sex-typing of boys in respect to their expression of aggression was not discovered. The father's providing a more aggressive model and a more permissive environment for aggression than the mother, the father's greater aggressiveness operating as a frustration to his son, are possible influences suggested by those conducting the study. In a study by Stolz,[811] when fathers were away from home at the time of and for more than 10 months following the birth of their first child, the children had more difficult adjustments in their early years after the father's return than those in families where parents were not separated by war for their first-born's first year.

A family may include *three generations.* Again, generalization is inappropriate concerning effect on the child in the situation. Whether the grandparent lives with the family or the family lives with the grandparents, characteristics of the individuals are the most pertinent elements. Ellenwood[241] describes the particular individual of one family this way: It is necessary for grandmother "to be so many people. . . . She is a mother who must gracefully relinquish her authority. . . . In addition . . . she is a mother-in-law . . . she has to carve a relationship with a person whom fate picked out of the mob. . . . Then, she is a grandparent. . . . Always in between Grandma and the baby hover the forbidding parents. . . . And so many rules have completely turned around since Grandma brought her baby into the world!"‡

---

* Midcentury White House Conference on Children and Youth Chart Book,[582] Chart 13. Figures from Census Bureau.

† References on bereavement, divorce, and family crises are Hill,[360] Koos,[472] and Waller.[876]

‡ Ellenwood[241] (pp. 101, 103, and 105).

Family Use of Community Services

Thought about family setting, leads to thought about *community influences*. Again interaction is evident. What the family provides and what the community provides are related. Some of the influences of the family on the community and of the community on the family concern attitudes. How the child feels about his particular heritage and situation has a connection with attitudes of those in his community. However, his interpretation of their reactions to him and his family will be influenced especially by his parents. The child who is different, physically or intellectually, whose economic status is above, below, or similar to that of the community in which he lives, and the one who belongs to a minority or majority group, will tend to reflect parents' adjustments to these facts. The child's adjustment to the realities and the reaction of other children and their families to them will depend on what his parents feel, say, and do. How his family responds can affect community attitude.

Statements such as these expressing convictions about the great extent of the family influence are made with awareness of the fact that what a family contributes to the child's outlook varies immeasurably. Some of these variations are due to differences in resources on which the parents rely, consciously and unconsciously. For some, modern means of communication, such as newspapers, movies, radio, and television, may be especially influential. For others, use of additional sources of information in the present and from the past may be more extensive.

In addition to sources from which the family receives its points of view, services which the community provides affect the child and his family. Health and recreational facilities, schools, and churches, social agencies, and special facilities for those with particular situations or difficulties, are a few of the community services affecting a large number of families. The form these services take as they attempt to meet needs of young children and their families varies with the locality; different communities make different plans.

Community Health Services for Families.   The community can serve a family in many ways. It can provide a healthful environment which includes sanitary measures to provide safe water, sewage disposal, garbage disposal, and other public health measures to prevent the spread of disease, abatement of noise, safety measures to prevent accidents, and space for outdoor play and recreation. It can provide a shopping center in which a good variety and quality of foods are available. It can provide medical care and health education in its doctors, dentists, clinics, public health nurses, nutritionists, and hospitals. Some communities have a good plan for protecting the health of their people; other communities are lacking in this respect. Since it is to the advantage of society to keep people well, it is a wise community which provides adequate facilities for health protection. Many cities have well-organized health centers under departments of health which give public health services to individuals. For example, a New York City health center may provide facilities for promotion of child health, care of dental, chest, and venereal diseases, eye examination, school services, plus health education, public health nursing, nutritional instruction and certain aspects of communicable disease control. Counties may have mobile units, or a center where people can come for help and from which health officers, public health nurses, and nutritionists perform their functions. Child health conferences may be held at regular intervals. In one county buses bring in mothers and babies on the appointed day of the conference. The mothers bring their lunch and spend the day, so the event has a social as well as a health value. Public health nurses visit in the homes. Often, because she is the only professional contact with the family, the public health nurse acts as a counselor in many ways and assumes the role of a family social worker.

Health insurance plans, as for example the Health Insurance Plan of Greater New York and the Kaiser Foundation Health Plan in Oakland, California, provide prepaid maternity care and medical care in case of illness, and, in some cases, health examinations as well.

Health services in the past have been more readily available to urban than to rural communities. This inequality has been erased in areas in Western Canada where the Manitoba Health Plan[409] came into being as a result of the passage of health legislation by the three Prairie Provinces. This plan provides for rural health units which are wholly tax supported, one-third of the cost being raised by the community and two-thirds provided by the provincial government. This health plan "is neither health insurance nor state medicine. It provides health services to the family as a tax-supported community utility, with citizen participation."* By 1956, 75 per cent of Manitoba's population had been

* Jackson[409] (p. 54).

provided with a full-time preventive service.* The organization of the services under this plan is such that the family is used as the unit for the provision of health care. "The public health nurse, the backbone of any worthwhile health effort, through her home visiting must consider her duties and responsibilities from the standpoint of the family. Prenatal care, postnatal care, infant care, school health services and general health education are integrated to form a family service. The sanitary officer, particularly in a rural area, is concerned with the family environment, because, with the wide spread electrification of rural areas, complete modernization of farm homes is rapidly increasing and this emphasizes the family and its home as a unit in health administration. In diagnostic facilities,† it is the head of each family who gets the necessary card of identification that entitles him and all members of his family to the services available. The same applies, of course, to the prepaid medical care program. Even in the taxation under medical care, the rate of taxation is usually decided on the number of families in the area being served."‡

This is one indication that the concept of the family as the "unit of health"§ is growing in importance and being considered in planning community health services. The Pioneer Health Center in London, later known as the "Peckham Experiment,"[60, 654] was the first group which offered a community service built around the concept of "family health." Here the health service was part of a family club, of which doctors and nurses were ever present members and which provided for the social and recreational needs of families as well as the physical needs.

In this country an experiment in family health services is being

* Communication from Division of Health and Welfare Education, Department of Health and Public Welfare, Winnipeg, Manitoba.

† Laboratory and X-ray facilities is the most commonly used term today.

‡ Jackson[409] (pp. 53-54).

§ Health is a collective as well as an individual characteristic. "The acceptance of the family as the unit of health leads to the concept of 'family health.' 'Family health' is not just an arithmetical mean of the health status of the various family members. It is something more. It is the aggregate of the physical, mental and moral well-being of all members including their adjustment to group life and to other environmental and biological conditions which the family must meet as a unit. A family with a seriously handicapped or chronically ill member might occasionally have to be considered as 'healthier' than one without any member suffering from overt disease. In striving for 'family health' unity and 'esprit de corps' are strong assets; disharmony and tension—often concomitant with life in a social unit as a family—equally strong liabilities." Dublin and Fraenkel[226] (pp. 26-27).

carried on in New York City.[226, 585] The Family Health Maintenance Demonstration,* a five year research program, is concerned with family health maintenance which includes physical, social and emotional health. An integrated preventive and remedial service is offered by a team comprised of physician, public health nurse and social worker. The program for the family includes (1) an initial inventory including both an inventory of biological and social characteristics of the family as a group and an inventory of the physical and psychological characteristics of each individual, (2) periodic re-evaluations, (3) guidance and (4) health education which acts as a thread interwoven into the total program. This program provides for a community health service based on the sound concepts of considering the individual as a whole and as a part of an interactive group, the family.

Some programs have local tax support; others have state and federal subsidy. Furthermore, other plans involve use of funds of private agencies for health services. Community fund agencies, and local and national organizations sometimes take responsibility for particular kinds of health care. Interest of physicians in what the community provides is illustrated by the nationwide study of the American Academy of Pediatrics concerning child health services.[18]

The Day Nursery and the Nursery School. In the days when it was generally accepted that the mother who was in economic need should work outside her home to support her family, the philanthropically minded saw the Day Nursery as the solution and in the latter part of the last century the Day Nursery sprang up in many communities. Its purpose was to care for the children of working mothers, often from infancy to school age, during the hours of the day when the mother must be at work. As the philanthropically minded grew into the socially minded some questioning arose as to whether or not removal from the home was the best solution for this problem. For a special group another solution was devised, through legislation† providing for aid to dependent children, which made it more possible for the mother

* The demonstration which originated in the Community Service Society has as its participants the Community Service Society, Montefiore Hospital, College of Physicians and Surgeons of Columbia University and the Health Insurance Plan of Greater New York. One hundred and fifty families who are insured under the Health Insurance Plan of Greater New York participate.

† Information on types of legislation, public agencies, trends in family, child population and employment of women is in Planning Services for Children of Employed Mothers.[863]

to stay at home and care for her own children instead of putting them in the care of someone else for part of the day. This legislation, together with the development of higher standards for day nursery care, slowed up to some extent the theretofore rapid increase of Day Nurseries.

Shortly after World War I another institution appeared, coming to us from England, namely the Nursery School. The term Nursery School meant a *learning* place for *young* children. Its program recognizes the period between approximately two and one-half or three years and five years as an age when much important learning takes place through group living for part of the day with other children of fairly similar age under the guidance of well-qualified people. The Day Nursery was at first principally a custodial institution, the Nursery School is primarily an educational institution. During the years both ideas have been modified, the Day Nursery having been definitely influenced by the Nursery School philosophy. The Day Nursery has expanded its concept of what care of children means; it has become increasingly aware of its responsibility for the total development of the child and has instituted a more varied program for the children under school age who are in its care. The Nursery School has frequently been a partial solution for the business or professional mother as it has cared for her child under five for possibly six hours in the day.

With establishment of nursery schools with high standards, the possibility of their supplementing the child's experience at home has been recognized.* Parents enroll children because of educational values; absence of the mother during the day is not the basis for their decision. The school situation includes equipment and activities scaled to the child's size and abilities. Physical activity is provided for.

"The well-planned nursery school offers a myriad of opportunities for investigation, experimentation, problem-solving, imaginativeness and creativeness —activities which require children to develop their intellectual powers. . . .

"In a preschool group the child spends his time with others who have needs and desires strikingly similar to his own. Furthermore, they express these needs and desires at the same time and in the same ways that he does. Here then, is a rare opportunity for him to learn the importance of the other fellow; to learn to share materials, attention and space with him; to learn how to live in a group that is different in structure from the family group. Here too, the child learns to accept other forms of authority, perhaps different from those he finds in his family."†

* References to research on effects of nursery school experience are in Essentials of Nursery Education[618] and in Jersild.[421]

† Essentials of Nursery Education[618] (pp. 7-8).

Qualifications of the nursery school teacher, health policies, number of adults in proportion to number of children, educational methods, and physical set-up, represent a few of the bases for selecting a day nursery or nursery school.*

Where nursery schools have not been readily available, groups of mothers have experimented in different ways of providing group experience for their children. For example, one group of rural women who attended an adult meeting once each week arranged to have their children play together on that afternoon under the guidance of a well qualified nursery school teacher. In a number of communities, three or four mothers have tried taking turns having their children meet at different homes perhaps two mornings or two afternoons each week. The mother at whose home they played was responsible for their activities. When cooperative play groups and nursery schools have been established, a trained teacher has given continuity to the program. She has been assisted by parents of children enrolled.† In any of these programs, and also in church school programs, careful study of their values is an important part of the community's approach to them.

Community interest in growth and development of infants and young children and provision of educational opportunities for parents have sometimes paralleled each other. Preparental education and parent education have taken a number of forms and have been provided in a variety of settings.

Methods of Study of the Family

Any consideration of the family and factors influencing it leads to the wish for more specific information. Longitudinal studies of families are beginning to be attempted. To consider the family at the time of marriage and then to study its development and the development of each member seems to be a way to learn more about interrelationships. This approach is another step intended to increase understanding of individuals through time instead of centering on cross sections of time. At first, in studies of children, cross sections were considered; data

* References on day nurseries and nursery schools are Allen and Campbell,[19] Forest,[263] Green and Woods,[314] Landreth and Read,[493] Moustakas and Berson.[599, 600] Read,[684] Forty-sixth Yearbook of the National Society for the Study of Education, Part 2,[620] and Updegraff.[866]

† References on cooperative nursery schools and play groups are Armbruster,[47] Read,[685] Taylor,[827] and Wagoner.[873]

concerned large groups at a particular point in time. Then, in longitudinal studies, particular phases of growth received attention; height and weight, motor ability and language were studied as the children grew older. In later longitudinal studies, attempts were made to consider various phases of growth of the same person, i.e., the "whole child" (with a realization that this could never be completely accomplished).* Now it is recognized that not one member but the various members of the family need to be studied as the family grows. Interest in study of the child and his family seems to be expanding to include interest in the family group and its dynamics.†

Topics for Study and Discussion

1. After a visit to a home where there is a baby, or a preschool child, or both, discuss the child's responses to space, equipment, routines (his and those of other family members), and people. Or, if observation in a home situation is not possible, some of the responses could be noted in other situations, such as shopping, riding the bus, or arriving at, leaving, and attending nursery school.

2. Using as a guide the categories of Figure 5 concerning the family cycle, describe developmental tasks of the father, mother, child or children, and the family as a unit, for a particular family (a real family or an assumed one).

3. Describe services of the community in which you live which concern children and their families.

4. Have a panel discussion of three mothers or fathers, one the parent of a young infant, another the parent of an infant and a preschool child, and the third a parent of preschool and school-aged children, in which they discuss a day in their lives—their jobs and their activities with their children.

Selected Readings

Bacmeister, R.: Growing Together. New York, D. Appleton-Century, 1947. Pp. 179-290.

Baruch, D.: Parents and Children Go to School. New York, Scott, Foresman & Company, 1939. Chap. 5.

Child Study, Vol. 34, No. 3. Summer 1957 issue, The Man in the Family.

Gruenberg, S. A., and Child Study Association, editors: Our Children Today. New York, Viking Press, 1952. Chap. 1.

Gutheim, F.: Houses for Family Living. New York, The Woman's Foundation, Inc., 1948.

Herbert, E. S.: When the Homemaker Goes to Work. Journal of Home Economics 44:257-259, April, 1952.

* Methods of studying children are presented in Anderson,[38] Olson,[640] Chap. 1, and Stott.[813]

† Methods of studying families are considered in Foote and Cottrell,[262] Hill,[361] Rockwood,[709] and Stott.[812, 815]

Leverton, R. M.: Food Becomes You. Lincoln, Neb., University of Nebraska Press, 1951.
Metheny, E.: Body Dynamics. New York, McGraw-Hill Book Co. Inc., 1952.
Midcentury White House Conference Fact Finding Report. Part II, in A Healthy Personality for Every Child. Raleigh, N. C., Health Publications Institute, Inc., 1951; or in Personality in the Making (H. Witmer and R. Kotinsky, editors). New York, Harper & Brothers, 1952.
Neisser, E. G.: Brothers and Sisters. New York, Harper & Brothers, 1951.
Waller, W.: The Family, revised by R. Hill. New York, Dryden Press, 1951. Chap. 2.
Wolfenstein, M.: Fun Morality: An Analysis of Recent American Child-Training Literature. Chap. 10, Childhood in Contemporary Cultures (M. Mead and M. Wolfenstein, editors). Chicago, University of Chicago Press, 1955.

3

Life Begins

When Life Begins

When a new life begins it both initiates a new life cycle and contributes to the life cycle of its parents. If it is a first child it initiates a new phase, parenthood; if it is another child it initiates an enlargement of parenthood.

This new life will have its own unique pattern of development which will be determined by the potentialities given by the parents, the conditions in utero, the kind of home into which it is born, the manner in which its needs are gratified, and the feelings and attitudes of people in its environment. Consequently the home and the parents will have a profound influence upon the development of this child.

Inheritance and Environment. At the time of conception the new organism receives, in equal parts from each parent, the requisite number of chromosomes containing a large number of genes. This genetic material is present in every functioning cell (except mature red blood cells) and plays a role in all cellular activity. These genes determine the complex of potentialities for the individual. To what degree these various qualitative and quantitative potentialities are expressed depends on the interaction of the genes with their cellular environment. This cellular environment, in turn, is influenced by the larger environment within and without the organism. Thus the uterine environment before birth and the many facets of the external environment after birth play important roles. Hence the two factors of heredity and environ-

78

ment must be considered together in order to understand the developing organism.

The dynamic relationship between these two factors may be seen by the influence which the genetic endowment may have on a child's use of his environment. This can be illustrated by the difference in the use of their environment by two children of differing intellectual potential. Given the same environmental opportunities, and all other factors being constant, the one with a higher intellectual endowment will tend to exploit his environment more completely than the one with a more limited potential. Thus the very bright child may learn more from a meager environment than a less gifted child may from richer surroundings.

The complexity of the problem of what is inherited and what is acquired is indicated by the fact that the same trait may be an expression of different relationships between these two factors. This can be illustrated in considering the trait of height. A child may be short because he stems from a family of short people. In such a case no attempts to increase this child's rate of growth will be successful. Shortness may in other instances be due to failure to utilize fully his potential for height, as an example, in the case of an endocrine disturbance or in environmental deficiencies producing malnutrition when the materials for growth have not been made available to the body. Many children never achieve optimum growth in one or many of its phases because of environments which afford limited opportunities.

Although the genetic makeup of an individual is not changed (except in rare cases of mutation), the dynamic relationship between heredity and environment throughout the life span of an individual calls for a realistic rather than a fatalistic approach to the subject of heredity. It is important to provide each individual with an optimal environment. Much is known about the effects of environment on health and development. This knowledge has been used in providing satisfactory living conditions. However, different children will thrive differently in differing environments. What is "best" for one may not be the "best" for another, since each individual, except in the case of identical twins, has a different assortment of genes and, therefore, reacts to environment in his unique way. In providing for the health and growth of an individual the strengths and weaknesses with which that individual is endowed must be considered.*

* For further discussion, see Stern[807] or Scheinfeld.[723]

Health of the Mother.   Pregnancy is a normal physiologic process to be experienced joyously and, for many, with an increased buoyancy of health. It is a period of growth both for the mother and the child. To provide for this growth physiologic adjustments occur, and greater demands are placed on all organs and systems of the maternal body. A woman who begins pregnancy with a healthy body, that is, one that functions adequately and whose tissues are well stocked with the necessary nutrients, is well prepared to meet these demands. The importance of preparing for pregnancy, mentioned in the preceding chapter, is discussed here in more detail. The mother whose pelvis has been free from rickets or other bone deformities is much more likely to go through a normal, uncomplicated delivery. If she comes to pregnancy with rich stores of calcium in her bones, it is much easier for her to keep, with a good diet, adequate supplies of calcium both for her own and for her child's needs.* A good background of nutrition and general health also provides for a good retention of nitrogen[376] from the protein eaten, which is so necessary for prenatal growth and later for lactation. The woman who begins pregnancy with a normal hemoglobin level stands a better chance of keeping it high. Normal body weight for body size is another asset. There is some evidence[846] that a woman who enters pregnancy markedly underweight has a greater hazard of giving birth to her child prematurely than one who is of normal weight or overweight. Also, while she is less likely to develop toxemia than the overweight woman, when she does it tends to be more severe.[845] In a more general way, the woman whose habits of eating, sleeping, exercising, eliminating and posture are optimum and so long practiced as to be almost automatic has fewer changes to make in her habits in a period which requires a great many adjustments at best. Buoyant health means better general resistance to infection, fatigue and other physical hazards which may beset her path. Because of her good health she also finds a good emotional adjustment easier.

Similarly, the woman's life-long mental, social and emotional development and habits are of great importance to her in her adjustment to the changes involved in pregnancy and in the birth and care of her child. If she has grown in emotional maturity to the point where she is emotionally ready for parenthood and, in cooperation with her hus-

* Experiments have indicated that better retention of calcium is found in individuals who have previously had ample calcium in their diets (Stearns[799]).

band, is ready to give her energies to the creating and guiding of another generation, she will be able to cope with the adjustments required of her. Since the interaction between mind and body is so close, her emotional maturity is important for her own physical well-being and consequently for that of her child. It is also essential for the peace and happiness of her husband.

Role of the Father. The father's influence on the unborn child, once the child is conceived, is indirect as he contributes to the well-being of the mother. However, as a member of a growing family, he is very important. It is obvious that good physical health will be an asset for any man with a family. It is also important for a man to have grown psychologically through the series of steps in the development of a healthy personality* so that he is ready for parenthood. Such readiness involves the desire for children whom he will consider as a trust and not as an extension of himself.

If he understands himself, has a true appreciation of others, and can share with the others of the family in a warm, spontaneous manner, he should be able to meet with confidence whatever problems arise during the pregnancy of his wife and lend her the necessary support. Many men are interested in learning what takes place in pregnancy and how the child grows. Equipped with knowledge about pregnancy a man can more easily play a supportive role. If there are young children in the family, this is a time for the father, if possible, to participate more actively in the children's routines and activities, which will relieve the mother and at the same time increase the bond between father and children.

Adjustments to Pregnancy

Young Family Adjustments in Preparation for the New Baby. Whether the pregnancy is planned or unexpected, comes early or later in marriage, and is a first or a subsequent one, there are various adjustments which both the man and woman must be prepared to make. A planned pregnancy may mean that various adjustments have been made prior to this time, making the couple ready for the adjustments which are specific to pregnancy. They have had time to anticipate and plan for the changes which may have to be made in their lives with the coming of a baby. However, many people who do not believe in

* For discussion of the development of a healthy personality see Erikson.[244]

planning pregnancies make the adjustments with ease. If the woman becomes pregnant very soon after marriage, she will be required to make the many adjustments to marriage at a time when she may be suffering from some of the physical disturbances that occasionally accompany pregnancy. This may put a rather heavy burden on both the man and woman. Superimposed on making the early marital adjustments is the realization that there is to be a new member in their family who will absorb a great deal of time and who may require an entirely different mode of living from the one currently followed. However, many young couples manage very well to make the adjustments of a pregnancy in the first year of married life. In subsequent pregnancies family adjustments will involve the children as well as the parents. The ease of adjustment depends on the emotional maturity of each. Unresolved emotional problems, even if unrecognized before, may very well become intensified at this time.

Although the adjustment will differ somewhat both in degree and kind, depending on the circumstances, the planning and preparation can be of such intense and mutual interest as to draw the parents into a closer sympathy and understanding and to make them look upon this period as one of deep joy. However, when both husband and wife have some realization of what adjustments are to be made they are better equipped to make them successfully and less likely to think of them as difficulties or problems.

Financial Considerations.   Both husband and wife must realize the importance of adequate care for the woman and the expense which it entails. The selection of the physician who will care for the woman during pregnancy and at the time of birth is extremely important. They will want to select a physician whose fee for service will be compatible with their income and at the same time one who has the medical qualifications. They will want one in whom they have complete confidence and with whom they can feel free to discuss all problems, both physical and psychologic, which may arise. They may be financially able to secure one of the best obstetricians in the vicinity, or it may be necessary to secure the best available obstetrician at the lowest possible cost. Economy may necessitate attendance at a special clinic for pregnant women, thereby securing the services of well-trained physicians at little or no cost, and going into a hospital ward rather than into a private room when the baby is born. The important thing is for the husband and wife to choose wisely a physician whom they know is well trained, preferably an obstetrician, or a general practitioner who is skilled in obstetrics.

The parents must, of course, plan for the baby in accordance with their pocketbook. In talking with their physician they must be quite frank and ascertain what his charges will be, and if his charges are more than they can afford, they should say so frankly. There need be no sense of shame in saying that one cannot afford a certain charge, and one finds that the best physicians prefer this honest acknowledgment on the part of a patient. If the charge which an older man with years of experience makes is too high, such a physician may refer the patient to a younger man who, though well trained, has not had the experience which would warrant the higher fee of the older man.

It may be that the husband and wife in deciding to go to a specialist for care during pregnancy and the obstetrical period will have to withstand the prejudice of an older generation who considers such precautions and additional expense unnecessary, but they can fortify themselves with the facts and statistics which show that good prenatal and obstetrical care saves the lives of mothers and babies.

Between 1930 and 1934 the maternal death rate in the United States dropped only 12 per cent, but during the next five years, after enactment of the nationwide program of health services for mothers and children under the Social Security Act, the maternal death rate fell 32 per cent. The death rate for all causes for persons of all ages during the same period dropped only 5 per cent.[177] The maternal death rate has dropped from 60.8 per 10,000 live births in 1915, to 20.7 in 1945, to 9 in 1949,[251] to 6.1 in 1953, the lowest ever recorded for the United States.[861] The average rate for nonwhites, 17.7 per 10,000, is greater than that for whites, 4.6 per 10,000.[861] The New York Academy of Medicine, in a study of puerperal deaths in New York City from 1930 to 1932, found that 1343 of 2041 deaths, or two out of three, were preventable, two thirds of them through better care on the part of the attendant, and one third through better care on the part of the woman herself and better use by her of available facilities.[368] The leading causes of maternal deaths are infection, toxemia, and hemorrhage, trauma and shock, the last three usually being grouped together.

The maternal death rate for all races varies from state to state. From 1952 to 1953 the lowest rate of 2.8 per 10,000 registered live births was recorded for Washington; the highest, 18.4 per 10,000, for Mississippi.[861] There is still need for more to be done to protect the lives and health of mothers.

The United States has also succeeded, through good prenatal care and public health education, in greatly reducing its infant mortality rates. The rate for the first year has dropped from 99.9 per 1000 registered live births in 1915, to 64.6 in 1930, to 38.3 in 1945, to 31.3 in 1949, and to 27.8 in 1953.[251, 860] The drop in mortality of infants during the first month of life has been considerably less than that of infants between one month and one year. In 1953, with a mortality rate for the first year for all races in the United States of 27.8, the rate for infants under twenty-eight days was 19.6, and for those between twenty-eight days and one year, 8.2.[860] These figures suggest the need for more extensive research on the causes of death in the first days of life. It has also given considerable impetus to the growing awareness among obstetricians and professional workers in related fields that adequate obstetrical care involves both preconceptional and prenatal care if the life and health of the infant as well as that of the mother are to be protected.

Changes in Living Conditions. The arrival of the new baby may necessitate a change in living because the living quarters seem too small to add a third person whose regimen is to be so different from the regimen of his parents. It is generally advised that a baby sleep in a room by himself if possible. In this way he can live in accordance with his schedule without interfering so much with the normal activities of the family. Their movements and the lights in their room will not disturb his sleep. Parents also can relax and rest better if the baby is not in their room. If things needed for the care of the baby are kept in his room, and if the bathroom is near by, the many necessary things which must be done for the baby can be done with the least effort, an important consideration for a woman who may have many other household duties besides the care of the baby. If moving is to be done, it should be planned with the advice of the physician at a time and in such a way as to avoid overfatigue for the wife. When necessary, however, parents who must continue to live in small apartments or small houses can, with ingenuity, rearrange the living space to meet the needs of the infant and themselves. The experience of families of service men during World War II demonstrated that young families with infants can adapt themselves to a variety of circumstances.

Changes in Habits of Living. Both husband and wife must realize that a baby will make a great difference in their household. They will not be free to come and go as independently as they did before. The night's sleep will probably be interrupted because the baby must be fed for a time once or twice during the night. The late Sunday morning sleep may also be interrupted. These adjustments are a small price to pay for the joy of having a baby, but prove irritating to some young people if they do not appreciate them in advance and accept them as part of the experience.

Preparation of Parents for These Adjustments. Parents will make the adjustments described above and any others necessary with much more ease if, before the coming of the first baby, they have had some instruction in what to expect and some experience in child care. Prospective parents may receive information and have their questions answered by the doctor during the mother's visits to his office. The husband may occasionally accompany his wife or he may seek an appointment with the doctor alone to learn about pregnancy and the needs of his wife, so that he may be more understanding and supportive. In many communities there are classes for prospective mothers conducted by public health clinics and sometimes classes for prospective fathers. Better still, discussion groups for both husbands and wives are sometimes available.*

Of the many available classes in infant care, some are excellent and many are good, but too often they give class instruction without observation of babies or practice with them. Thus these classes frequently engender anxieties in parents by making them aware of all there is to know about infant care and the hazards of ignorance, without giving them the assurance and security in their own competency which comes only through practice. A few generations ago a large majority of the young people grew up in large families and usually had much practice either with their younger brothers and sisters or, if they were younger children, with their nieces and nephews. In many ways they were better off with practice and without instruction than youth today, who may have instruction but frequently do not have practice. Some high school and college students gain experience in caring for babies through the

---

* Such experimental groups have been conducted at the Merrill-Palmer School in Detroit in cooperation with obstetricians. A class consists of patients of an obstetrician and their husbands. The discussions are conducted by the obstetrician and members of the staff of the school. The department of health in the city as well as some hospitals have also established classes for both prospective parents.

practice of "baby sitting" for parents while they are away for the evening or part of the day.

In an age when we offer in our schools and colleges special training for almost every other vocation or profession, we still offer too little in the way of special education for life's most important profession, namely parenthood. Educators are becoming aware of this lack. More and more high schools and colleges are attempting to educate both boys and girls for their future roles as parents. In the meantime, as these programs are developing and becoming more widespread, if adequate instruction and experience for prospective parents is not available through some Child Center, a very practical procedure is to ask the family doctor, a pediatrician, or a pediatric clinic to recommend a few good books which can be studied by both father and mother. Often there are friends who have young children and who will be glad to demonstrate for the prospective parents at least such procedures as bathing and feeding. After the parents-to-be have practiced a little, they may even take over occasionally while the parents enjoy a little freedom. Another place in which practice may be had is in an orphanage or a home for illegitimate children. Such places are usually short of helpers and will gladly give instruction in return for some volunteer help. While such experience may not be as good as that obtained under the constant supervision of a trained instructor, the opportunity to learn to handle and care for babies without fear is an invaluable experience which will not only make the new father and mother feel that the care of their own child is easier, but will actually make it easier, for tension or lack of it in the infant is very apt to be a direct reflection of the degree of insecurity or security of his parents in their own feelings of adequacy in respect to his care. Parents with some previous experience in child care are aware not only theoretically but practically of the "nuisance value" of children and also of the overbalancing pleasure in their society. Consequently, they are prepared to accept the former in their own children without irritation and frustration and, through the waiting period, to anticipate their child with pleasure.

Diagnosis of Pregnancy

The medical preparation for safe pregnancy with optimum health and comfort for the mother and optimum environment for the developing embryo and fetus begins, as was said previously, with the beginnings of the lives of both parents. The more immediate medical preparation should begin preferably with thorough premarital examinations of both the man and woman contemplating marriage, and certainly with thorough preconceptional physical examinations of both partners. Every married woman should know the probable signs of pregnancy in order that she may know when she becomes pregnant. When she suspects that she is, she should go at once to her physician. She can learn from her physician whether or not she is pregnant and, if she is, can begin intelligent care under his supervision at once.

Probable Signs and Symptoms. CESSATION OF MENSTRUATION. If the married woman who has previously menstruated regularly goes more than ten days beyond the expected date without menstruating, she has good reason to suspect that she is pregnant, although this is by no means positive proof that she is. Many other causes than pregnancy can account for cessation of menstruation and, conversely, it is not uncommon for a woman to have one or two menstrual periods, usually very short, after conception has occurred.

CHANGES IN THE BREAST. Other indications of pregnancy which a woman notices about the second month are an increase in the size and firmness of her breasts and the greater prominence of the veins of the breast. The nipples become darker and more prominent, and the areolae (the dark circles around the nipples) increase in size and also darken, particularly in brunettes. There is often a pricking or tingling in the breasts even before they increase in size. Sometimes they become very tender soon after conception and may remain so for some time. Later on in pregnancy some protuberances like miniature nipples appear in the areolae. Change is more pronounced in women pregnant for the first time than in women who have had previous pregnancies.

INCREASED FREQUENCY OF URINATION. Early in pregnancy there may be an increased frequency in the desire to urinate due, not as so many women think, to kidney trouble, but to the stretching of the base of the bladder by the growing uterus. This causes a sensation like that of a full bladder. Since the need for frequent urination is so often a sign of some nervous tension, it cannot by itself be considered a sign of pregnancy. It is simply additional evidence when other signs of pregnancy are also present.

OTHER SIGNS AND SYMPTOMS. Some women, beginning usually

about two weeks after the first missed menstrual period, may have waves of nausea without vomiting for a few hours in the morning and some may actually vomit. This is commonly called "morning sickness." However, this sign, unless accompanied by other symptoms, is of no diagnostic value as it may also be a symptom of many other conditions. Extreme fatigue is sometimes another symptom of early pregnancy.

When basal temperature has been taken daily prior to and following conception the *pattern of basal temperature* can serve as a suggestive sign of pregnancy. A level of 98.8 to 99.9° F. sustained for more than sixteen days after ovulation is highly suggestive of pregnancy. Such a diagnosis is correct in at least 97 per cent of cases.[76, 649]

The woman herself may be aware of the *enlargement of her abdomen* by the end of the third month, when she may be able to feel a softness just above the pubic bone. By the end of the fifth month, when the uterus will have enlarged and pushed up in the abdomen to the level of the navel, the enlargement will be quite obvious. By this time, too, the pregnant mother will usually have felt tremulous movements of the fetus low in the abdomen.

Any woman for whom pregnancy is a possibility should, after experiencing any of the above signs, see her physician in order that he may make a definite diagnosis as promptly as possible. If several of these signs are present, the physician will be helped in making his diagnosis. However, since no one of them is definitely diagnostic of pregnancy, he will also want to examine the patient for other more positive signs.

PELVIC EXAMINATION. After he has made a professional examination of the breasts to corroborate the changes which the patient has probably observed herself, the physician will also do a simple, painless pelvic examination. First he will inspect the mucous membrane of the vagina, which, ordinarily pink in color like mucous membranes elsewhere in the body, early in the first pregnancy takes on a bluish cast.* He will also palpate the uterus to determine its size, shape, and consistency.

Positive Signs. FETAL HEART SOUNDS. Detection of the fetal heart beat is an absolute sign of pregnancy. This is frequently possible by the middle of the fifth month, the sound being detected by the doctor with his stethoscope, or sometimes by placing his ear against the

---

* After the first pregnancy this change in color may persist, to a degree at least, so that this sign is less significant in a subsequent pregnancy.

abdomen. Through fetal electrocardiography this is often possible even earlier in pregnancy.[108, 283] However, its use in early pregnancy is still limited. The technique requires further refinement to meet the criteria of a clinically useful test.[107]

FETAL MOVEMENTS. While the mother may sometimes mistake movement of gas in the intestines for fetal movement, the physician examining the abdomen will not be mistaken if fetal movements are felt, since his experienced hand can detect the difference. Such movements also constitute a positive sign of pregnancy and may be felt fairly early in the fifth month. However, by this time the physician is usually so sure of his diagnosis as not to need such confirmation.

X-RAY DIAGNOSIS. Occasionally x-ray is used in diagnosing pregnancy. Again, however, since the skeleton of the fetus rarely shows up before the middle of the fourth month, this test is usually not necessary and is not often used.

Legally, any one of these three is acceptable as a positive sign of pregnancy, that is, the detection of fetal movements, or of fetal heart sounds by the trained examiner, or detection of the fetal skeleton by x-ray.

LABORATORY TESTS. If very early diagnosis is imperative for medical reasons, certain laboratory tests may be used, such as the Aschheim-Zondek and Friedman tests. In most cases such a test is unnecessary.

Physical Changes During Pregnancy

Although there may be various discomforts during pregnancy and occasionally serious complications, for the healthy woman this is more often a period of increased well-being and of even more vigorous health than usual.

Increase in Weight. An average, normal woman increases in total weight during pregnancy about 24 pounds: * According to Chesley, as quoted by Greenhill,[315] about two thirds of these women can be expected to gain from 13 to 35 pounds. This weight increase represents the weight of the fetus, the placenta, the membranes and the fluids, the growth of the breasts, and some gain in the other tissues of the body because of improved appetite and digestion. Nature stores up materials during this period to provide, not only for the growth of the fetus, but also for energy during labor and for later lactation. During the first

* See Greenhill,[315] Moyer et al.,[604] Tompkins.[846]

third of pregnancy a woman will gain about 2.5 pounds; during the second third of pregnancy about 10.8 pounds; during the last third of pregnancy about 11.2 pounds.[315] The gains in the first two thirds of pregnancy are due chiefly to gains in the tissues of the mother; in the last third the gains are due chiefly to the growth of the fetus and the uterus. The weight is carefully watched by the obstetrician and not allowed to become excessive, since excessive gains may mean retention of fluid in the tissues which is a warning of possible danger.

Tompkins[846] points out that too little gain may also be a hazard. He found that failure to gain an average amount, especially in the first two thirds of pregnancy, increased the likelihood of premature birth. Premature births were nearly three times as frequent among women who gained less than the average from the first visit to the clinic to the end of the second trimester, as among the women who had an average or greater than average gain. He concludes that early metabolic and physiologic stabilization of a woman, with a steady gain in weight at an average rate, can contribute significantly to a reduction in premature labor, the highest single cause of infant loss.

The Uterus. This organ, situated within the pelvis, must stretch from a small, almost solid organ, shaped something like a pear and approximately three inches long and weighing about 1.5 ounces, into a large muscular sac, weighing about 1.5 pounds, which will hold a seven or eight pound or even larger baby, a placenta weighing about one and one-quarter pounds, about twenty inches of umbilical cord, and an amniotic sac containing a quart or more of amniotic fluid by which the baby is completely surrounded. The uterus has increased in capacity from 2 cc. to 4000 cc. in order to do this. Through hypertrophy of its muscle walls, the uterus must have, when the time comes, power to contract with such force that the baby and placenta will be expelled through the vagina into the world. The most rapid increase in weight of the uterus occurs during the first half of pregnancy. Its increase in weight is due partly to growth of new muscular tissue and partly to increase in size of the muscle already present. A woman, to accommodate herself to the change in size, weight, and position of the uterus and its contents, sometimes noticeably changes the way she carries herself, tending to throw her head and shoulders back.

Because the uterus is attached to ligaments which are fastened to the pelvis and is not fixed in a stationary position, it pushes upward into the abdominal cavity as it grows. By three months it is halfway to the umbilicus, by five months at the umbilicus, and by nine months it reaches the tip of the sternum. During the last two or three weeks of gestation the uterus drops back toward the pelvis again, and the change in the contour of the body indicates to a woman that she is drawing near the end of her pregnancy.

The Mammary Glands. The breasts, or mammary glands, are skin glands which have undergone highly specialized development. The early cell mass undergoes a process of multiplication and ramification into a fairly complex duct system. Later, actual secreting glandular cells develop. One of the first signs of oncoming puberty in the female is increased activity in the breasts, with increased growth in the duct system, due to increased ovarian secretion and increased deposits of fat. Relatively little growth of glandular tissue, or the secreting alveolar cells, occurs until pregnancy, when an extensive differentiation of the glands occurs. This development and the subsequent secretion of milk involves an interaction of the hormones of several endocrine glands, namely the pituitary, ovaries, and adrenals, and of the placenta.[854] Figure 11 shows some of the most generally accepted concepts of the endocrine interrelations concerned with the growth and secretion of the mammary glands. In addition to the interaction of hormones, complicated neural and nutritional mechanisms are involved in milk secretion.

By the twelfth week of pregnancy colostrum, a yellowish fluid, may be secreted. Lactation does not occur, however, until after delivery.

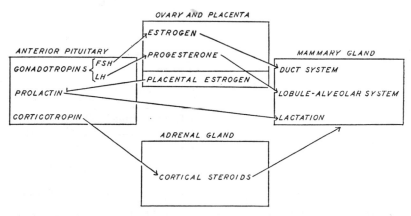

Figure 11. Schema illustrating source of the hormonic interrelations involved in mammary differentiation and lactation (Turner, C. D.: General Endocrinology).

Other Changes.   The basal metabolic rate of the pregnant woman is increased as the thyroid gland becomes more active. This accounts in part for the increased feeling of well-being and increased energy which frequently accompanies normal pregnancy. Various other endocrine glands, as the cortices of the adrenals and the anterior lobe of the pituitary, become more active also.

Various physiologic adaptations take place to meet the needs of the growing organism* which means alterations in all functions of the body and possible instabilities in functions. There is a slight decrease in hemoglobin which can be attributed in part to an increase in blood volume, rather than to an actual decrease in the amount of hemoglobin. Skin glands, the skin being an important excretory organ, increase their activity, and perspiration may increase. Especially during the later part of pregnancy there is a normal increase in the vaginal secretion. Because of its antiseptic qualities this is looked upon as an additional safeguard during delivery. Changes in pelvic joints increase the capacity of the pelvis and make the passage of the child at delivery somewhat easier. There may also be a more luxuriant growth of hair, and often hair which has been lifeless before pregnancy takes on a much healthier appearance.

Development of Embryo and Fetus

Development of the infant in utero requires about 9½ lunar months, or 266 days, after fertilization of the ovum. Since exact knowledge of the time of fertilization is usually impossible, the first day of the last menstrual period is used in calculating the date of birth. The majority of babies are born about 280 days from the first day of the last menstrual period. About 95 per cent of all babies are born within two weeks of the 280 days.

During this period the infant grows from a single cell (the fertilized ovum), which is almost invisible to the naked eye, to an infant weighing about 7½ pounds. During prenatal life the weight of the body increases several billion times, whereas from birth to maturity the increase is only twentyfold. Although actual weight gains are greater in the latter months, the proportionate growth is much more rapid in the early months of fetal life, as indicated in Table 1.

* For biochemical changes see Macy and Mack[546] and Macy et al.[549] For functional changes see Greenhill.[315]

Table 1.   Relation of Age and Weight in the Human Embryo*

Age of Embryo	Weight in Grams	Ratio of Increase Each Month When Value at Start of Month Equals Unity
Four weeks	.02	40000.00
Second lunar month	1.	49.00
Third lunar month	14.	13.00
Fourth lunar month	105	6.50
Fifth lunar month	310	1.95
Sixth lunar month	640	1.07
Seventh lunar month	1080	0.69
Eighth lunar month	1670	0.55
Ninth lunar month	2400	0.43
Full term (266 days)	3300	0.38

* Taken from Arey, L. B.: Developmental Anatomy.[46]

Occurring along with the rapid increase in size are the changes due to the process of differentiation, namely, the emergence of tissues, organs, and systems, and their sequential development.

Maturation of Germ Cells.   Each cell of the body has in its nucleus forty-eight chromosomes on which are carried the genes, or determiners of heritable traits. This is as true of immature germ cells as it is of other cells of the body, but mature germ cells have only twenty-four chromosomes. If two germ cells, each with forty-eight chromosomes, united, the new individual thus formed would have ninety-six chromosomes in each of his cells, and a new species would be initiated. Nature has provided for the maintenance of the species man by a process of division of germ cells which results in only twenty-four chromosomes in a mature germ cell. In this way the paternal germ cell and the maternal germ cell each contributes twenty-four chromosomes to the new being whose life begins when the ovum, or female germ cell, is fertilized by the spermatozoon, or male germ cell.

While the ovum is still in the ovary, it divides into two cells each with twenty-four chromosomes. The forty-eight chromosomes in the immature cell are arranged in pairs, and each of the new cells contains one from each pair. One of these new cells contains most of the cell cytoplasm and is much larger than the other cell. Each of these cells again divides, this time with the usual type of cell division in which the chromosomes divide longitudinally. Again one larger cell and one very small cell result from the division of the cell which carries most of the

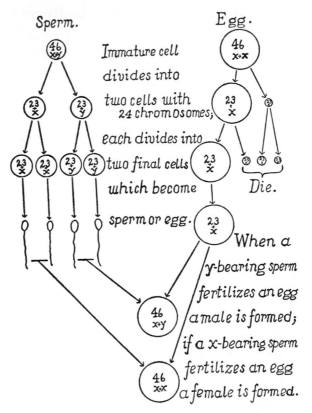

Figure 12. Maturation of sperm (on left) and egg (on right), and their fusion to form a male or female individual. The forty-eight chromosomes of each immature cell are indicated as 46 plus X-Y in the male, or 46 plus X-X in the female. (Gilbert, M. S.: Biography of the Unborn. Baltimore, The Williams & Wilkins Company.)

cytoplasm of the original immature cell. Thus there results from these two divisions one larger cell, the mature ovum, and three small cells, called polar bodies, which soon die. Actually the larger cell is extremely small, with a diameter of about 1/125 inch.

Division of the immature sperm cell is similar to that of the immature ovum except that in the division of the sperm cell four mature spermatozoa are formed. Each of these cells measures only about 1/450 inch in length.

Determination of Sex. Each set of the original forty-eight chromosomes in each of these immature germ cells contains one pair which is responsible for determining sex. In the female the two chromosomes of this twenty-fourth pair are alike and are usually designated the "XX" chromosomes. Thus the mature ovum always contains one of these X-chromosomes. In the male, however, the members of the twenty-fourth pair are unlike and are designated "XY." Division of the sperm cells will produce spermatozoa with the Y-chromosome or with the X-chromosome. The sex of the new individual, conceived when a mature spermatozoon penetrates and fertilizes an ovum, will depend on whether this spermatozoon carries a Y or an X chromosome. If it carries a Y, the twenty-fourth pair in the new being will be XY, and a male baby will result; if it carries an X, the resulting twenty-fourth pair will be XX, and the new child will be female (Fig. 12).

Fertilization. About every twenty-eight days during the child-bearing period of a woman's life, an ovum matures. It is swept into the fallopian tube and passes along this tube on its way to the uterus. If sexual intercourse occurs about the time the ovum is expelled from the ovary, spermatozoa pass through the vagina, uterus and tube to meet

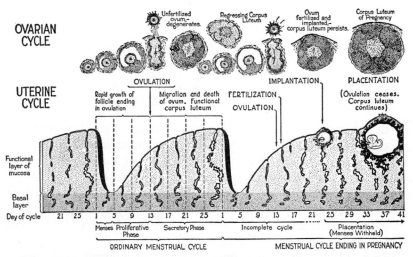

Figure 13. Graphic summary of changes in the uterine mucosa during an ordinary menstrual cycle and a subsequent cycle in which pregnancy occurs. (Modified from Schroder.) The correlated changes in the ovary are suggested above in their proper relation to the same time scale. (Courtesy of Patten, B. M.: Human Embryology, ed. 2. New York, Blakiston Div., McGraw-Hill Book Company, Inc., 1953. Fig. 24, p. 43.)

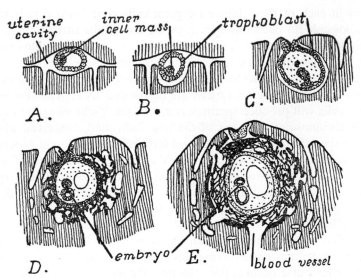

Figure 14. Diagrams to show implantation of egg in wall of the uterus. The uterus is marked with parallel lines. A, B, C are hypothetical stages; D, E are the youngest human embryos known.

A. Egg lies in cavity of uterus.

B. Egg lies in small pit in uterine wall.

C. Egg enclosed in small cavity within uterine wall.

D. Trophoblast of egg destroys uterine tissue. The embryo now consists of two small vesicles.

E. Spongy trophoblast processes invade the uterine tissue farther and open blood vessels of the uterus. (After Arey, from Wollard, in Gilbert, M. S.: Biography of the Unborn. Baltimore, The Williams & Wilkins Company.)

the descending ovum. When a spermatozoon penetrates the ovum, fertilization occurs. While usually only one ovum a month is matured, nature lavishly multiplies the possibilities of its fertilization by producing about 200,000,000 spermatozoa in each ejaculation. These have long thin tails which give them the power of relatively swift locomotion, and dozens of them may meet the ovum descending the tube. Only one penetrates, however, for after one has fused with the ovum the fertilized cell repels any others.

Figure 13 illustrates diagrammatically what happens in the uterus and ovary when fertilization does not occur and what takes place when it does.

Implantation. Immediately after fertilization as the ovum descends the fallopian tube, the nuclei of spermatozoon and ovum fuse, and rapid cell division occurs, resulting in a clump of cells called the morula. It is probably seven to eight days after fertilization before the ovum begins to implant itself in the uterine lining. The ovum actually burrows through the uterine lining and embeds itself in the thick decidua, richly prepared for its reception (Fig. 14).

Period of the Embryo. In the meantime, the morula has become a blastocyst or hollow vesicle with an outer layer of cells, the trophoblast or feeding layer, and an inner cell mass which now undergoes rapid cell division and differentiation. This period of differentiation of cells' during which the various body organs and tissues are formed extends from about the end of the second week after fertilization until the end of the second month, and is called the period of the embryo. Diagrams drawn to natural size in Figure 15 give a visual impression of the growth which occurs in the early part of development. (See also Fig. 19.)

In the very early stages of this period the blastocyst becomes covered with branching projections called villi, and the whole structure is called the chorionic vesicle. The developing embryo is connected with the wall of this vesicle by means of the body stalk. As cells covering the villi destroy surrounding tissue, walls of the blood vessels in the decidua immediately surrounding the chorionic vesicle are broken down, and the vesicle is bathed by maternal blood which gradually assumes a definite course of flow. Late in the second month of pregnancy some of the villi degenerate, leaving only about one-fifth of the chorion covered. Those remaining, together with tissue developed from the decidua, develop into the placenta, or "after birth." The body stalk becomes greatly elongated, and through the resulting umbilical cord run three blood vessels. Two arteries carry blood from the infant to the placenta, and the one vein carries oxygenated blood from the placenta to the infant.

The amniotic sac, appearing early in gestation as a transparent, nonvascular membrane, completely envelops the embryo, except at the point where the umbilical cord projects through it to the placenta. The amniotic fluid within this sac acts as a buffer to protect the developing embryo and fetus from jars and shocks experienced by the mother. It also helps provide an even temperature for the developing organism and serves to prevent adhesions between the skin of the fetus and the amniotic membrane (Figs. 16, 17 and 20). By the end of the period of the embryo, two months after fertilization, the cells of the three germinal layers, the entoderm, ectoderm and mesoderm, have under-

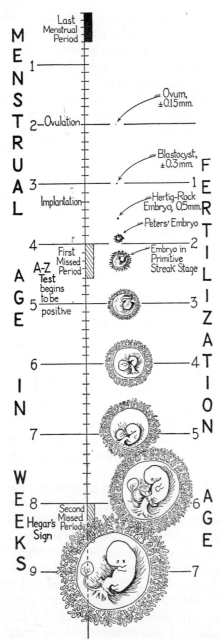

Last Menstrual Period

M E N S T R U A L

1

2 – Ovulation

Ovum, ±0.15mm.

3

Implantation

Blastocyst, ±0.3mm.

Hertig-Rock Embryo, 0.5mm.

Peters' Embryo

4

First Missed Period

Embryo in Primitive Streak Stage

A G E

A-Z Test begins to be positive

5

6

7

W E E K S

8

Second Missed Period

Hegar's Sign

9

F E R T I L I Z A T I O N

1

2

3

4

5

A G E

6

7

Figure 15. Diagrams showing actual size of embryos and their membranes in relation to a time scale based on the mother's menstrual history. A-Z, Ascheim-Zondek. Heger's sign, softening of the muscle in the lower segment of the uterus. (Courtesy of Patten: Human Embryology, ed. 2, New York, The Blakiston Company, division of McGraw-Hill Book Company, Inc., 1953. Fig. 105, p. 190.)

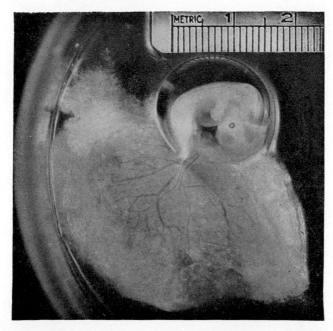

Figure 16. An embryo of about 4 weeks showing blood supply from the chorion (placenta). (Davis and Carmon: DeLee's Obstetrics for Nurses.)

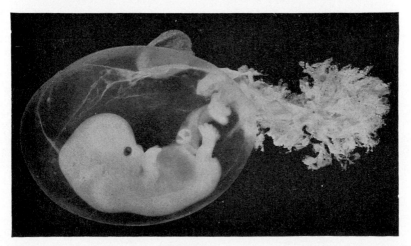

Figure 17. Embryo within amniotic sac at end of the eighth week. A small fragment of placenta is attached. (Davis and Carmon: DeLee's Obstetrics for Nurses.)

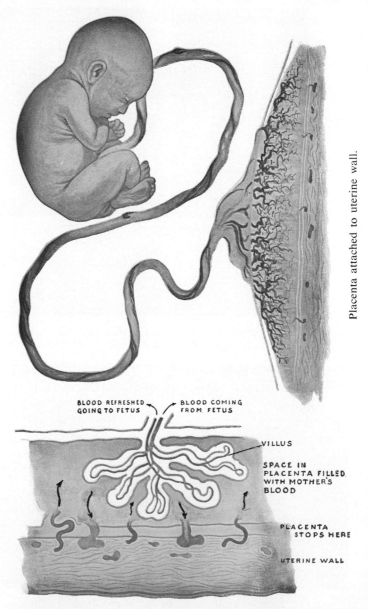

Figure 18. Relations of maternal and fetal circulations. Purely diagrammatic.
(Davis and Carmon: DeLee's Obstetrics for Nurses.)

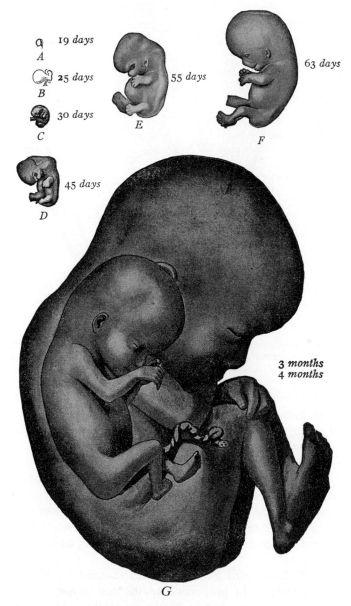

A 19 *days*

B 25 *days*

C 30 *days*

D 45 *days*

E 55 *days*

F 63 *days*

3 *months*
4 *months*

G

Figure 19. Graded series of human embryos, natural size. (Arey: Developmental Anatomy.)

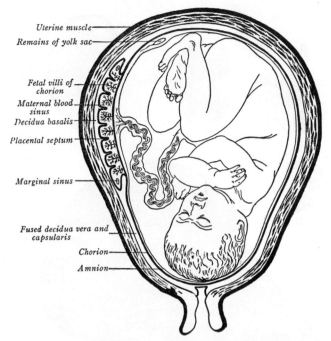

Uterine muscle
Remains of yolk sac
Fetal villi of chorion
Maternal blood sinus
Decidua basalis
Placental septum
Marginal sinus
Fused decidua vera and capsularis
Chorion
Amnion

Figure 20. Diagrammatic section of uterus illustrating relationship of advanced fetus to placenta and other membranes. (Ahlfeld, reproduced in Arey, L. B.: Developmental Anatomy, ed. 5, 1946.)

gone rapid division and differentiation, with the result that there is now a miniature baby, with heart, lungs, brain, spinal cord, head, face, organs of sense, arms, legs, hands and feet with stubby fingers and toes, and other essential parts.

Period of the Fetus. A few parts of the body, such as the differentiated external sex organs and finger and toe nails, develop after this time, but for the most part growth during the rest of pregnancy consists of growth in size and increase in function rather than differentiation of parts. This later phase of prenatal development, from the end of the second month until the birth of the baby, is usually called the *fetal period*.

By the end of the third month the fetus resembles a human being, but the head is large in proportion to the rest of the body. By six months the body is lean but in better proportion. At this time the vernix caseosa, a mixture of cells flaked off from the skin and fatty substance secreted from the sebaceous glands, which presumably acts as a protective covering to the skin, begins to form. By seven months the fetus resembles a "dried up, old person with red wrinkled skin." In the eighth month subcutaneous fat begins to be deposited and this continues so that the body continues to round out until birth. Bones begin to calcify toward the end of the second month. Enamel and dentine of the teeth begin to form early in the third month.

During the greater part of fetal life all the organs carry on to some degree the processes that will be necessary for the maintenance of life after birth, even though these functions are not essential until birth. From an early age the fetus swallows amniotic fluid and this fluid is absorbed from the walls of the digestive tract. Enzymes are secreted into the digestive tract. Bile is produced and liberated into the intestine as early as the third month. There is some peristaltic activity. Muscular activity begins early. Spontaneous movements of arms and legs begin the fourth month and become vigorous during the fifth month, at which time the mother is usually aware of fetal movement. The fetus has periods of activity alternating with periods of rest.*

The fetus takes very small breaths, which draw a small amount of amniotic fluid into the lungs, but there is no constant respiratory movement as there is after birth. The kidneys secrete urine. Meconium, consisting of waste products, accumulates in the intestines but normally is not eliminated until after birth. The endocrine glands begin to function and there is an exchange of hormones between the mother and fetus through the placenta. The beating of the heart begins during the first month of life, as pulsations in a rudimentary heart. Fetal circulation is established early.

The fetus must have achieved a certain degree of maturity to survive at birth. Organs and functions must have become sufficiently mature to meet the demands of postnatal life. If the fetus is immature it may not survive, depending upon the degree of immaturity, or it may survive only when specially fed, provided with special warmth, protected carefully from possible infection and given some additional oxygen to

---

* Fetal activity, studied from the sixth month, has been found to increase with fetal age up to the last fetal month,[628] to vary considerably from day to day,[451] to be more pronounced at the close of the day than in the morning,[332] to vary among individuals so that some fetuses may be very active and some relatively quiet,[628] and to differ in type. Three types, squirming, kicking and rhythmic series of quick convulsive movements, termed hiccups, have been described.[628] Kicking was the largest component of total activity, and hiccuping the smallest.

breathe.* Since immaturity is a hazard for the newborn, it is important that a fetus develop fully before birth and not be born prematurely.†‡

Prenatal Influences. The old concept of the fetus being a parasite, living a well protected life and taking from the mother, at her own expense if necessary, all that is needed for its development has been replaced by the concept of a dynamic relationship between mother and child, in which there is an interchange between the two and in which the well-being of the mother has a definite effect on the development of the child. Thus some discussion of prenatal influences is essential in understanding fetal development.

In appraising the effect of any one factor on the health of mother and child one must consider a multiplicity of factors and place each in its proper relationship to the others.§ Bearing this in mind, it would seem that *nutrition* can influence the development of the child.|| In some instances nutrition may be the limiting factor in the development of a healthy newborn; in other cases, the limiting factor may be of a non-nutritional nature. Hence, as stated in Chapter 2, it is not surprising that studies which attempt to evaluate causal factors in development differ. Conflicting results may arise from differences in the subjects studied, different circumstances of their lives, or from varying ways in which the data are analyzed.

Studies which attempt to determine the role of nutrition as a prenatal influence include those in which women on self-selected diets have been observed; those in which supplements have been given to improve a poor diet, and comparison between the supplemented and non-supplemented groups made; and observations of mothers and infants during periods of severe food shortage, as, for example, in Holland and in Leningrad during World War II and in Wuppertal, Germany, in 1946. In such studies, birth weight, prematurity and the health status of the infants observed by a pediatrician were investigated. It was

---

* Oxygen is now recommended to be used in minimal amounts to meet clinical needs since it appears that oxygen used in too large quantities is associated with retrolental fibroplasia, a condition in the retina of the eye which may affect eyesight.[230, 325]

† For further discussion of fetal development, see Arey,[46] Gilbert,[298] and Smith.[769]

‡ For discussions of the premature baby and the effect of prematurity on later development, see Breckenridge and Vincent,[131] and Dunham.[230]

§ For a discussion of prenatal factors see Montagu.[594]

|| For a review of studies see Josey,[440] Toverud, Stearns and Macy,[848] and Keys et al.,[454] Chapter 45.

found that birth weight was reduced during the famine months of late 1944 and early 1945 in Holland[766] and during the period of food shortage in Germany after World War II.[198] In the United States a group of underweight mothers had significantly lighter and shorter infants than mothers of approximately standard weight.[846] Burke and her co-workers in Boston found a relationship between protein intake and the size of the baby at birth.[149] However, this was not confirmed by Dieckmann[217] in Chicago. Macy[604] in Detroit, Sontag and Wines[783] in Ohio and workers in the Vanderbilt Cooperative Study of Maternal and Infant Nutrition in Tennessee[185] found no relation between maternal diet and birth weight. It would appear that severe deprivations are necessary to affect the size of the child. Prematurity occurred more frequently among the infants of the underweight subjects of Tompkins.[846] There was a positive relationship between poor diets and the incidence of prematurity in studies in Boston[148] and Iowa,[417] while Dieckmann[217] and the Vanderbilt Study[185, 534] found no correlation between the two. Supplementation of poor diets done in studies in Toronto,[236] and in England,[656] on the other hand, reduced prematurity.

Evidence that maternal diet affects the condition of the infant at birth has been presented by Burke and her co-workers.[148] They state that in 216 cases studied, every stillborn infant, every infant who died within a few days of birth with one exception, the majority of infants with marked congenital defects, every premature and every "functually immature" infant was born to mothers whose diets during pregnancy were extremely inadequate. Dieckmann[217] also found that pediatricians' ratings of infants correlated highly with the protein intake of their mothers during pregnancy. Supplementing inadequate diets reduced stillbirths and neonatal mortality,[70] and improved the general condition of the infants.[236] In this latter study, the infants of the mothers with supplemented diets also had a lower incidence of infection during the first six months of life.[236] In addition, evidence also comes from Leningrad:[43] during its siege in 1942 under such conditions as severe food restriction, the necessity for many women to do heavy work and the emotional stress of the bombardment, mothers gave birth to infants who showed lowered vitality. However, in contrast to this evidence, the Vanderbilt Study[534] found no relationship between the mother's diet and stillbirths or neonatal deaths.

In spite of the fact that nutrition was not found to be a primary cause of obstetrical difficulties in the Vanderbilt Study, the authors point out that diet during pregnancy is important. They also indicate that adding to an already adequate diet will provide no additional benefits. The diets of their subjects, although they were somewhat below the recommended allowances of the Food and Nutrition Board, were not disturbingly low. Their food intake showed frequent consumption of necessary basic nutrients, supplied by milk and eggs, green and other vegetables, citrus and other fruits. The range between diets which may be too inadequate to promote good prenatal development and those which are adequate for such development cannot be thought of as a narrow one.

We have pointed out that the severe deprivations which accompany war can affect the pregnant woman and her child. However, the effect of war upon mother and child depends upon the conditions under which she lives and the care which she receives. This was demonstrated in World War II. In Oslo, for example, a program of health supervision of pregnant women, begun in 1939 and continued throughout the war period, demonstrated the positive values of planning and supervising good nutritional care of the mother during wartime. This care was reflected in the health of the child.[847] Between 1939 and 1944, despite food shortages, the supervision in dietary management and the provision of supplements improved the nutritional status of the mothers. These mothers had markedly less stillbirths, premature births, and less infants who died during the neonatal period than did a similar group of unsupervised women; none of the babies had rickets and even milder pathologic bone changes disappeared.

Other factors influencing a woman's health, besides nutrition, have a bearing on the welfare of the infant. Hirsch,[363] for example, found that *hard work* during the last months of pregnancy increases the number of prematurely born infants and infants of low birth weight.

Evidence tends to show that maternal experience of deep *emotions* can affect the child. To be sure the "old wives' tale" of the effect of maternal impressions is not true because there is no nervous connection between mother and child. However, emotions, deep and prolonged, may so alter the body chemistry that the growing organism can be affected. Sontag[782] has reported increased fetal activity when mothers have been under deep emotional stress. The more active fetuses tended to weigh less at birth and had minimal amounts of fat storage. Some of the infants born to mothers subjected to such stimuli had feeding difficulties during the first month after birth. One study[699] showed a positive relationship between fetal activity and performance of the Gesell test items at 6 months of age. However, whether increased fetal activity has any effect on later development has yet to be determined.

Virus infection in the first six to ten weeks of pregnancy may interfere with normal fetal development. This statement is based on evidence that infants with structural abnormalties have been born to mothers who had German measles (rubella) during the first two or three months of pregnancy.*

There is a complementary action of the *maternal and fetal endocrine systems*. A maternal deficiency of endocrine secretions may affect the development of the fetus. For example, if a mother has an inadequate thyroid function, part of the secretion of the fetal thyroid will be used to support the "poor relation." Children of hypothyroid mothers have been known to have enlarged thyroids at birth.[782] Similarly, maternal diabetes affects the fetal pancreas, and its function at birth is greatly accelerated. Maternal diabetes also affects the size of the newborn, because of deposition of additional quantities of fetal fat.[782]

The incompatibility of an inherited blood substance, the *Rh factor,†* between mother and fetus will cause anemia in the late fetal months if the mother has become sufficiently sensitized to have produced antibodies which in turn will reach the blood stream of the fetus and cause destruction of the red blood cells. This can occur when the mother has Rh-negative blood and the fetus has Rh-positive blood. Sensitization of the mother may occur through blood transfusions with Rh-positive blood or through gradual sensitization by the fetus. This sensitization will not be sufficient usually to affect a first child. Later children may or may not be affected. Rh-negative women with Rh-positive husbands can be reassured about the outcome of a pregnancy because of the growing knowledge of how to avert serious effects upon the fetus.

Deep *x-ray* treatment during the early months of pregnancy can also affect fetal development. That *radiation* affects the developing fetus has been demonstrated in two studies, one in Nagasaki[928] and another in Hiroshima.[666] The infants of Nagasaki women who showed major radiation signs from the atomic bombing had a higher morbidity and

* For references of studies see Toverud, Stearns and Macy,[848] Krugman and Ward.[482]

† See Rapaport,[681] Scheinfeld.[723]

mortality than those of mothers who were beyond the radiation center.*
In Hiroshima in a study of anomalies occurring in children exposed in
utero to the atomic bomb, it was concluded that central nervous system defects can be produced in the fetus by atomic bomb radiation,
provided that exposure occurs approximately within 1200 meters of
the hypocenter. No effective shielding, such as concrete, protects the
fetus from direct irradiation.† *Certain drugs,* likewise, have deleterious
results.

Experiments have demonstrated that *anoxia,* insufficient oxygen,‡
is a specific cause of congenital deformity in mice.[389, 391] The nature of
the defect is determined by the degree of anoxia and the time during
pregnancy at which the mouse is exposed. Some fragmentary clinical
and epidemiologic facts are beginning to indicate that the experimental
findings in mice may apply to humans.[391] More study needs to be done
on humans before it can be said with any degree of certainty that harm
to the fetus will follow exposure to high altitudes. Ingalls points out
that it is an oversimplification to say that lack of oxygen causes defects.
Both genetic factors and environmental stress combine to form a specific defect at a particular stage of development.

In considering conditions which may be unfavorable to the growing
organism it should be remembered that such occur infrequently; ". . .
once implantation is well established the odds are overwhelmingly in
favor of a normal delivery and a healthy baby."§

Physical Care During Pregnancy

Nutrition.   Foremost in the general hygiene of the pregnant mother
is her nutrition. The mother's body can nourish the growing organism
only by means of the nutrients in her own blood stream. These nutrients
she obtains from her food through the process of digestion. They are
absorbed and carried by her blood stream to the placenta through

---

* Fetal mortality was 23.3 per cent in contrast to 2.7 per cent among the
controls; neonatal and infant mortality was 26.1 per cent, with controls 3.6
per cent; cases of mental retardation were 25 per cent and 0.

† Seven of 11 children of mothers within 1200 meters had microcephaly with
mental retardation. Nine of these 11 children had head circumferences that fell
below 1 s.d. of the mean for Japanese children.

‡ Mice were subjected to conditions similar to transporting them to the top
of Mt. Everest for five hours.[390]

§ Corner,[172] (p. [117]).

which they pass on their way to the fetal circulation. The richness of the maternal supply and the child's absorbing power are important factors in providing for his adequate growth and development. Some nutrients can be stored in the body and later used to meet an inadequacy in the diet. Such is the case of calcium which is stored in the bones and can be removed from them to meet fetal needs, if necessary. Other minerals also can be stored. However, certain substances, such as many of the vitamins, are not stored and the fetus is dependent solely upon the diet of the mother for meeting his needs. To provide for fetal needs and to prevent depletion of the maternal stores, an optimum diet in pregnancy is important.

The nutritional needs of the growing organism and the mother are the same in kind, that is, the same amino acids, minerals and vitamins, but different in amounts. Thus, the change in nutritional needs with the advent of pregnancy is one of increasing amounts as the fetus develops.

A woman knows before she becomes pregnant what she can digest, what she prefers, and what she has to add or eliminate from her diet in order to keep her body in optimum condition, which means her weight is correct for her build and her health is optimum. When she becomes pregnant, she needs to scrutinize her dietary habits to see that they will provide the nutrients essential for the growing fetus and for her own well-being.

As has been said before, all of life up to the time of pregnancy is in a certain sense a preparation for pregnancy. When she knows she is pregnant, a mother does not try to obtain a nutritional "trousseau" by drinking large quantities of milk, by taking calcium preparations, and eating unusual quantities of leafy foods, but gradually increases her diet according to the needs of the fetus. If the woman before conception has been accustomed to eating a well balanced, adequate diet she need only be concerned about the quantities the fetus requires. Increase in her weight is one indication of the growth of the fetus and of the temporary changes in the cells of her body (such as enlargement of uterus), but it is only a partial index of the nutritive needs of the fetus.

PROTEIN. One of the substances essential for the growth and development of the fetus and for maternal well-being is protein. Protein is a part of every living tissue. It performs a role in a diversity of body functions, including osmotic relations, blood clotting, antibody production, oxygen transport, enzyme and hormone production, muscular contraction, pigment formation and detoxicating mechanisms. The foods we eat contain many kinds of protein. Some are more valuable to the body than others. Some will maintain the body and promote growth, some will only maintain the body, some will neither maintain the body nor promote growth when they are the sole source of the protein intake. The value of a protein in maintaining the body and promoting growth is determined by its components, amino acids. Some cannot be synthesized within the body and so must be furnished through food. These are called "nutritionally essential." For man, eight have been found to be essential as determined by nitrogen balance studies* in which individual amino acids were fed to human beings.[366, 713]

Schoenheimer[725] has given valuable confirmation of the indispensable character of certain amino acids in animal experiments, in which heavy nitrogen† was used to label certain amino acids taken in the food. He found that the amino acid, lysine, when treated with heavy nitrogen and given to an animal, could be traced in his tissues, and that it had yielded its nitrogen for the formation of other amino acids but it had never been regenerated. This further confirms the findings of earlier workers and establishes the fact that some amino acids cannot be synthesized by the body and must be provided in the food. Schoenheimer's experiments with animals using isotopes as markers have contributed further to our knowledge of the rapid and continuous changes taking place in the cell when protein food is taken into the body. In his experiments with rats on feeding labeled leucine to animals who were in nitrogen equilibrium, he could ascertain how much of the leucine was lost in the urine and the feces and in what organs it had become a part of the cell protein. It had appeared in the blood, the spleen, the liver, intestinal walls, the testes, and in the nervous and muscular systems. Schoenheimer's work gives a clearer picture of the way in which the food taken into the body becomes a part of the cells and how rapidly these changes are brought about. It also demonstrates that for some (essential) amino acids there is no way the body can obtain them except through the food eaten.

The requirement for protein during pregnancy increases owing to

* Nitrogen is a component of amino acids. An individual is in nitrogen balance when the amount of the intake in foods and output of nitrogen in the urine and feces is equal. If more nitrogen is lost than is taken into the body, the body is said to be in negative nitrogen balance; when less nitrogen is lost than ingested, the balance is positive.

† Substances such as heavy hydrogen and heavy nitrogen (N^{15}), known as isotopes, are used to label or mark or identify compounds.

the growth needs of the fetus and those of the placenta, uterus and mammary glands of the mother. For this growth it is estimated[848] that 870 grams of protein are needed during pregnancy. In addition metabolism studies[171, 379] have shown that the maternal organism tends to store nitrogen in excess of these calculated growth needs. This storage serves as a reserve for the losses during delivery, the postpartum period, and lactation. A daily intake of 80 grams of protein, an increase of approximately 43 per cent over that of nonpregnant women, is the allowance recommended by the Food and Nutrition Board of the National Research Council[261] for the third trimester (last three months) of pregnancy. The increased needs during the first and second trimester are so small as to be negligible. This allowance, as well as the allowance for the other nutrients, is liberal, since it includes a margin of safety over minimum requirements. These allowances are designed to serve as a guide in planning for normal individuals who have entered pregnancy in optimum nutritional condition. Individual needs may differ according to the woman's health at the time of conception and her progress during pregnancy. Deficiency of protein in the diet of a pregnant woman may affect the condition of the infant at birth[149, 217] and has been indicated to be one of the factors leading to nutritional edema,*[848] to anemia,[109] and a lowered milk supply.[171]

FATS AND CARBOHYDRATES. Fats and carbohydrates, which supply energy, are usually supplied in sufficient quantities in the average food intake. Their importance, aside from furnishing calories, is in their absorption of vitamins by the fat and the protein-sparing action of carbohydrate. The energy requirement during the last trimester of pregnancy increases about 17 per cent above the requirement for nonpregnant young women. However, the calorie requirement varies widely with activity. When this increased energy requirement is compared with the increased needs for protein, minerals and vitamins, which in the instance of calcium is 88 per cent greater, it is obvious that the increased needs for fats and carbohydrates do not parallel those of other nutrients. Burke[146] states that a minimum of 2000 calories is needed to meet the increased needs for nutrients. On the other hand, an excess of carbohydrate or fat is likely to lead to excessive gain of weight, which is undesirable.

* The presence of abnormally large amounts of fluid in the intercellular tissue spaces of the body caused by dietary deficiency is a condition referred to as nutritional edema.

The pregnant woman usually has found the carbohydrate and fat intake suited to her body needs before she becomes pregnant. In general as pregnancy proceeds she will meet these needs while increasing the protective foods, namely, those rich in proteins, minerals, and vitamins. Most women have to guard against excessive use of rich pastries and desserts, cakes, ice cream and candy during pregnancy.

CALCIUM, PHOSPHORUS, AND VITAMIN D. Calcium is one of the most essential elements of the diet during pregnancy, not only from the standpoint of the mother but also from that of the growing fetus. The fetal needs for calcium are small in the early months but increase rapidly from the fifth month to term. In the last two months of pregnancy 65 per cent of the total body content of calcium at birth is laid down, and 64 per cent of the total phosphorus content.[823] The recommended allowance for calcium based on balance studies* is 1.5 grams during the last trimester of pregnancy. To meet this allowance inclusion in the diet of calcium-rich foods, namely, milk and cheese, is very important. Again the value of being nutritionally prepared for pregnancy should be emphasized, because recovery from mineral undernutrition is slow and good absorption may be achieved only after many months of a good diet.

Research has demonstrated that vitamin D is related to the utilization and retention of calcium and phosphorus in the body.[414] However, vitamin D cannot insure their retention unless the supplies of calcium and phosphorus are adequate. The amount of vitamin D required is not definitely known. The Food and Nutrition Board of the National Research Council recommends 400 units.[261]

The amount of calcium and vitamin D in the mother's diet may affect the calcification of the bones and teeth of the infant.[848]

The phosphorus requirement is also high in pregnancy. Allowances should be at least equal to those of calcium.[261] Phosphorus is found in most of the protein-rich and calcium-rich foods, so that if the daily food intake is adequate in protein and calcium it will in all probability contain sufficient phosphorus.

IRON. Iron is another essential nutrient since it is important for maintaining the hemoglobin level of the mother and for the growing fetus. The demands of the fetus for iron are insistent since the fetus is growing rapidly and there is need for iron to supply the hemoglobin in the expanding blood volume and in the building up of muscle. In

* See references given by Burke and Stuart.[150]

addition, the fetus must accumulate a reserve store of iron for use after birth. The proportion of iron to fetal weight is fairly constant. During the first six months the mother transfers about 0.4 mg. of iron to the fetus daily, but in the last three months, when the weight of the fetus increases rapidly, the transfer is about 4.7 mg. daily or ten times the amount transferred in early pregnancy.[895] The iron content of the infant shows a reserve of about 186 mg. which carries him through the first months before he can eat foods that are good sources of iron.[895] During pregnancy there is a so-called physiologic anemia.* An inadequate diet, including too little iron, may carry this anemia beyond the range of normality and interfere with the well-being of the mother, with the fetal synthesis of hemoglobin, and with fetal storage of iron which is so important during the early months of postnatal life.† Certain studies by Burke and her associates show a definite relationship between the amount of iron in the mother's diet during pregnancy and the hemoglobin value for the mother during and after pregnancy as well as that of her baby at birth.[147] Smith and Rosello[778] have observed cases of anemia in infants that resulted from inadequate storage of iron in utero.

A daily allowance of 15 mg. of iron, recommended for the latter half of pregnancy,[261] is considered adequate when a woman enters pregnancy with adequate stores of iron and a normal hemoglobin level. In general, a woman needs to increase her intake of iron about one fourth. Fruit, green vegetables (especially greens and legumes), potato, egg, liver, whole grains, and molasses are high in iron content.

IODINE. The thyroid gland may become overactive during pregnancy, and an increased amount of iodine is needed to provide for the secretion of this gland. Under ordinary circumstances the diet would supply sufficient quantity, since there is some reserve in the gland itself, but if the diet has been low in iodine, as may occur in the region of the Great Lakes and the Northwest, where the amount of iodine in soil, water and foodstuffs is very low, it may have to be supplemented. This should be done under medical direction. In regions where goiter is not endemic, a diet with an abundance of green vegetables, whole cereals, and some sea foods will meet the average demand for iodine.

* The hemoglobin values are lower during pregnancy: 12.5 gm. per 100 ml. in the first trimester; 10 gm. per 100 ml. in the second and third trimesters, and 12 gm. per 100 ml. by the fifth day postpartum.[315] This is believed to be because of the increase in blood volume which is a characteristic of pregnancy.

† See Toverud, Stearns and Macy.[848]

Iodized salt is a desirable way of adding iodine to a diet that may be low in this element.

VITAMINS. The role of vitamin A in reproduction is uncertain, but it is known that vitamin A is required for growth, for proper vision and for normal functioning of epithelial tissue. The importance of vitamin A in the development of the fetus is suggested by animal experiments[910, 911] in which vitamin A deficiency resulted in an increased incidence of abortions and fetal malformations, especially in the eyes, the genitourinary tract and the heart. A later experiment[912] indicates that these malformations in the offspring are due to vitamin deficiency during the period of organ formation. Extreme deficiencies as cited in such animal experiments are seldom seen in human beings. The recommended allowance for vitamin A is 6000 international units.[261]

Thiamine stimulates appetite, is necessary for normal motility of the digestive tract and also for maintenance and normal function of the nervous system. It plays an important part in the metabolism of carbohydrates. In fact, the thiamine requirement depends on the amount of carbohydrates to be oxidized.[687] In pregnancy the daily allowance is 1.5 mg. in the third trimester, an increase of 25 per cent. Ebbs, Tisdall, and Scott[236] reported the changes which took place when the intake of thiamine was doubled or tripled in women who had been on poor diets. Many of the minor aches and pains and numerous complaints disappeared. The mental attitude of many of these patients changed from one of apathy and discontent to one of interest in the outcome of their pregnancy. Toverud[847] also reported that cramps in legs, numbness of fingers and toes, and neuralgic pains in pregnant women receiving insufficient thiamine generally disappeared when adequate thiamine was added to the diet. Rich sources of thiamine are pork, liver, yeast, whole cereals and fresh green vegetables.

Riboflavin is associated with the oxidation processes of the cell. Since riboflavin is essential for growth, increased need for it in the latter months of pregnancy is self evident. The recommended daily allowance is 2.0 mg. for the last trimester.[261] Good sources of riboflavin are milk, egg white, liver and leafy vegetables.

Niacin is one of the factors necessary for the prevention of pellagra. Its principal role is that of a constituent of a group of coenzymes which are essential in biologic oxidation, especially the oxidation of carbohydrates. While no specific role in pregnancy has been ascertained for niacin, the requirement is probably increased. A specific requirement for niacin is difficult to estimate since the need for it is conditioned by the tryptophan content of the diet. A daily allowance during the last trimester of 15 mg. is recommended.[261] Good sources of niacin are meat, poultry, yeast, peanuts and cereals.

The need for B_6, a coenzyme operating in many of the enzyme systems, may be increased in pregnancy since an alteration in tryptophan metabolism which is relieved by B_6 has been demonstrated in pregnant women.[870, 871] It is too soon, however, to be able to estimate the requirement. The ordinary well balanced diet undoubtedly will meet the need for this vitamin.

At the present time there is no information regarding the requirements during pregnancy for the other essential B complex vitamins, such as pantothenic acid, folic acid, B_{12} and biotin. It can be assumed that a well balanced diet which meets the other dietary needs will satisfy the needs for these vitamins.

Ascorbic acid (vitamin C) plays an important part in all growth processes and is found abundantly in active, growing tissues, so that an increased demand is to be expected during pregnancy. Studies[520, 828] showing that the need is increased and that the level in the blood is directly affected by the amount in the diet have been reported. The daily recommended allowance is 100 mg., during the third trimester,[261] an increase of about 40 per cent. If oranges, grapefruit, tomatoes, raw cabbage, raw or properly cooked leafy vegetables and potatoes cooked in the skin are part of a pregnant woman's regular diet, this requirement will probably be met.

Vitamin E has never been proved to be essential to man and the possibility of any deficiency in the average human diet is remote. Evidence of the efficacy of vitamin E in the treatment of habitual abortion is conflicting.[848]

Vitamin K is administered to mothers before onset of labor or during labor as a preventive measure against hemorrhage in the newborn.[102] Vitamin K plays a role in the body's production of prothrombin, one of the factors associated with the clotting mechanism of the blood. Its presence in green leafy vegetables is an added reason for including some of these in the daily diet during pregnancy.

DAILY DIETARY NEEDS. Calories, and protein, vitamins, and minerals, whose needs have been discussed, can be supplied satisfactorily in their proper amounts if the daily diet of the pregnant woman is planned intelligently. The quantities recommended by the

Food and Nutrition Board of the National Research Council[261] will be provided if the daily diet includes approximately: 1 quart of whole milk; at least one liberal serving (4 ounces) of lean meat (with liver once a week); at least one egg; potato (cooked in the skin); two or more servings of cooked or raw vegetables, including dark green leafy or deep yellow vegetables, and legumes several times a week; two or more servings of fruit, including two medium oranges, a cup of orange juice or grapefruit juice or its equivalent as one of the fruits; 4 slices of whole grain or enriched bread or its equivalent in cereal (½ cup of cereal being equivalent to 1 slice of bread); 2 tablespoons of butter or margarine fortified with vitamin A; a supplement of fish liver oil or its equivalent to provide 400 units of vitamin D; and additional foods dictated by her energy needs, preferences, and tastes.

Elimination.   Bowels.   Elimination is another important aspect of the nutritional cycle. The need of a regular bowel movement cannot be too greatly emphasized. It is not a matter to be ignored until pregnancy occurs, for the establishment of a regular rhythm of elimination from early childhood is an essential health measure at any time. During pregnancy, however, regular bowel evacuation, which for most is daily, is especially important as a safeguard against constipation. If, despite a well established habit of bowel movement, constipation does occur, a woman may add certain laxative foods to her diet and increase the amount of water she drinks, taking a glass or two, preferably of warm water, on first rising in the morning, to stimulate peristalsis. Exercise becomes even more important than before, and she should keep up the usual amount unless for some reason the doctor advises against it. Laxatives should *not* be taken without the doctor's permission as these may cause trouble by irritating the bowel.

Kidneys.   The importance of the kidneys as excretory organs is increased during pregnancy. The woman knows herself whether or not her bowels are moving adequately, but she cannot tell whether or not her kidneys are functioning properly unless she reports to the doctor. He may want to know the amount of urine passed in twenty-four hours, and will also want a sample of urine at given intervals. The woman can promote satisfactory kidney function by eating a proper diet and by drinking plenty of water. Four to six glasses daily are generally enough.

Skin.   The skin, too, may be helped to do its work in a satisfactory manner. Through the action of the sweat glands, the skin serves as an important excretory organ, and during pregnancy it has more work to do. In addition to the obvious perspiration, the skin is also constantly excreting waste products of which we are not conscious. A woman who seems to perspire more freely during pregnancy need not be troubled by it or attempt to stop it, but can try to aid the activity of the skin by drinking plenty of water, breathing deeply, exercising, and dressing warmly enough. A woman who becomes thoroughly chilled because she is not adequately dressed may seriously inhibit the action of the sweat glands, reduce the efficiency of the skin as an excretory organ, and thus throw an extra burden on the kidneys. Daily warm baths, however, not only stimulate the skin and promote comfort, but also remove the accumulated waste matter. During the last six weeks daily showers or sponge baths are preferable to tub baths because by this time it becomes harder for the woman to keep her equilibrium in a slippery tub, and falling becomes a real risk. Tub baths may also increase the danger of infection at this time.

Exercise and Rest. Walking and gardening are excellent ways for a pregnant woman to get fresh air, sunshine, and exercise. These activities bring into play and strengthen some of the muscles which will be active in labor. Exercise to which the woman is accustomed may usually be taken in moderation, but the risks of bad jolts, jars, or falls must be considered, and exercise which incurs any such danger should be avoided. Housework is also an opportunity for exercise during this period, and is an excellent way to keep the muscles in good condition and to further the normal functioning of digestion and elimination. It is not, however, a substitute for exercise out-of-doors.

Special exercises in breathing, relaxation, contraction and relaxation of the pelvic floor muscles, which will help the woman later to co-operate at the time of delivery, can be practiced during pregnancy.[838, 839] For instruction in these the woman should consult her physician or the clinic she is attending.

The right balance of activity and relaxation will prevent undue fatigue, which must be avoided. This can be achieved by relaxing for a few minutes frequently while working, lying down for a rest at intervals during the day and having at least eight hours of sleep each night. Every woman must work out a regimen which meets her own particular needs. If a woman has not acquired the art of relaxation she can be helped to learn how to relax.[411, 838] The ability to relax will be an asset all during pregnancy, at the time of delivery, and throughout her life.

Clothing.   The clothing of a woman in pregnancy deserves consideration. No clothing should be worn which would in any way constrict the veins of the lower extremities. Round garters should be avoided. As size increases, a properly fitting maternity corset may be worn, which supports the uterus without binding and can be adjusted to the changes in the figure. A brassiere which supports the breasts, thereby giving relief from the discomfort of congestion, should be worn, but the breasts should not be compressed. A properly fitted brassiere also aids greatly in maintaining good posture.

As the woman increases in size and changes her mode of walking to some extent, she may feel somewhat unsteady on her feet and be conscious of the need of a firmer base on which to stand. She may, therefore, need to change her shoes to a larger size with lower heels. But she must be sure that her arches are well supported, as her increased weight might cause a flattening of the unsupported arch. High heels may be a cause of backache, as they tend to throw the pelvis out of alignment. Moreover, they do not support a woman as securely as lower, broader heels, and are therefore likely to increase the danger of her turning her ankle or falling.

Care of the Teeth.   The old wives' tale, "for every child a tooth," has been disproved by modern scientists. While the tooth is a dynamic structure and there is an exchange of calcium and phosphorus in both enamel and dentine as indicated by isotope studies,[49] this exchange is much slower than that in bone. It can be said, therefore, that the bones rather than the teeth provide the calcium for the fetus when adequate amounts of calcium are lacking in the mother's diet. Moreover, studies of the incidence of dental caries[457, 931] indicate that pregnant women have no more dental decay than other women of like age. However, some believe that mouth acidity may be increased during this period and that bacteria become correspondingly more active. It is sometimes advised, therefore, that a mild alkaline mouth wash be used frequently. It is strongly recommended also that any necessary repair work be done and regular trips to the dentist continued. The old idea that dental work causes miscarriage has no basis in fact.

Care of the Breasts.   During pregnancy nature is preparing the mother for nursing her baby. The use of a good support for the breasts has been discussed under clothing. If the colostrum, which may begin to ooze from the nipples about the fourth month, tends to be irritating, the nipples should be washed with warm water and soap, and a little cold cream, lanolin, or cocoa butter rubbed on. If the nipples seem so flat that they will be hard to grasp by the nursing infant, the doctor's advice can be sought.

Common Discomforts. Any specific treatment for any of the discomforts of pregnancy, that is, anything beyond the general hygienic measures described above, should be undertaken only on the advice of the physician. Three of the commoner discomforts of pregnancy are nausea, heartburn, and constipation. Constipation ordinarily responds to diet, exercise, and fluids; no laxative should be taken except on the advice of the physician. Successful treatment of nausea and heartburn with various vitamins of the B complex has been reported by some.[334, 883, 908]

Regular Examination. The importance of good obstetrical care and of diagnosis by the physician as soon as pregnancy is suspected has already been emphasized. Usually at the first visit the physician will make a careful examination and, if he has not previously seen the patient, will take a complete history. The examination will include all laboratory and other procedures necessary to give the physician a complete picture of the patient's physical status. He will probably want the patient to return monthly during the first seven months, at two week intervals the next month, and every week thereafter, in order to give positive direction on care during successive phases of pregnancy. He will also be alert to any adverse change in order to institute treatment at once to avoid any serious complication.

Emotional Influences. Pregnancy is an experience with psychological as well as physical components.* These two are closely intertwined. Feelings and attitudes contribute to physical well-being or distress and, on the other hand, the physiologic changes of pregnancy may act as a trigger in arousing new anxieties and fears and in reactivating dormant ones. Many women at this time have some anxieties and fears, and their feelings may vary. A woman's attitude toward pregnancy is intimately related to her emotional maturity, to her past and present experiences and to her personal adjustment.†

The feelings of women about their pregnancies and the birth of their

---

* For discussions of woman's reactions to her own female body which in turn may influence her feelings about pregnancy see Deutsch,[212, 213] Freud,[272] Horney,[369] Mead,[564, 565]

† See Deutsch,[213] Chap. 6.

babies have been investigated by Newton* in a comparison of a group of women who complained about pregnancy with a group who reported that they felt fine during pregnancy. She found differences which, in general, indicated the following:

"... women who were negative toward pregnancy were more likely to wish to be men and were apt to have fewer motherly desires. Women who were positive toward pregnancy were more apt to be motherly and were less likely to wish to be men. It was the women who were negative toward the pregnancy who were most likely to terminate their pregnancies with easy childbirths."†

She also states:

"Other research studies suggest that feelings about pregnancy may change from rejection to acceptance as pregnancy progresses, and that feelings of nausea during pregnancy may be related to undesired sexual experiences and excessive dependence on the mother."†

Newton, also, in comparing women who felt childbirth was hard with those who felt childbirth was easy, found differences which, in general, indicated the following:

"... women who felt negatively about birth were more likely to be physically less motherly women. They had fewer children, and were more likely to dislike breast feeding and rooming-in care‡ of their babies. Women who felt positively about birth, on the other hand, were more apt to want to breast feed and almost always enjoyed the rooming-in care of their babies. They had more babies."§

In discussing other research, Newton stated:

"Other research shows that the experiences of childbirth sometimes caused severe emotional trauma and, conversely, that psychological influences can affect the experiences of labor."§

Lack of knowledge of the physiology of pregnancy, of the meaning and significance of physical disturbances and of the normal progression of pregnancy, can contribute to feelings of insecurity, fear and anxiety. Self consciousness, undue attention to body functions such as breathing

---

* Two hundred and forty-six mothers of newborn babies were interviewed in the rooming-in wards of Jefferson Hospital in Philadelphia. One hundred and twenty-three interviews on the first or second postpartum days were used in the statistical analysis. Rooming-in was compulsory for all healthy ward patients. The majority of the group were married, Protestant, Negro multiparas, and some unmarried or separated mothers, mothers with first babies, white and Catholic women were included. No significant differences were found between Negro and white mothers in their expressed feelings toward their biologically determined role but significant differences were found between different age groups and socio-economic groups.[629]

† Newton[629] (p. 29).

‡ See p. 131 for discussion of rooming-in.

§ Newton[629] (p. 40).

and the beating of the heart which go on automatically, minute analyses of feelings and a tendency to introspection may lead to misinterpretation of conditions and sensations which are normal to pregnancy. An understanding physician, by listening and explaining, can help a woman in understanding herself and the vicissitudes of her pregnancy, and thus enable her to live more comfortably from day to day.

Psychological Care During Pregnancy

During the early months of pregnancy women may be self-centered, and consequently suffer from physical discomforts which are induced by poor mental health. In extreme cases, a woman may adopt a state of semi-invalidism and give way to nervousness, irritability, moodiness, and fits of introspection and self-pity as part of her "rights" attendant upon pregnancy.

It is natural for women during pregnancy to have moments of doubt and uncertainties mixed with their feelings of pleasure and happy anticipation. These ambivalent feelings need to be accepted and can be dealt with more easily by the woman if she can discuss them with an understanding person, perhaps her husband, her mother or a friend. The husband can further assist his wife in her vacillating feelings by his acceptance of her moods.

Need of Freedom from Emotional Strain. In addition to living a satisfactory life from a physical point of view, it is most important that a woman should have a life as free from emotional strain as possible. Emotional strain may be generated within the person or created by circumstances outside the person which in no way are under her control. The former need not occur if the woman is emotionally mature, is ready for pregnancy, and has a means of allaying the fears and anxieties which may arise at this time. Many of the latter can be prevented if the members of her family are understanding and do their share in creating an atmosphere in which mutual understanding, self-control, and happiness predominate. A woman can meet the unavoidable situations with less emotional disturbance if she has strength within herself and support from others. The day-to-day changes in her feelings can be kept at a minimum by living a life which meets her physical, social, and emotional needs. There is no reason why a woman at this time should not experience a normally wide range of emotionality, but the emotional life of the family should proceed as normally as possible.

Since the physical and the emotional aspects of life are subtly inter-related, a regular physical regimen which keeps a woman in good physical condition should also help to maintain her emotional balance. Fatigue can be minimized by having a well organized plan of living that provides a balance of rest and activity and includes wholesome recreation as well as work. Social activities and other interests help to prevent self-centeredness. Briefly, a pregnant woman should expect to live a normal, wholesome life, taking precautions to avoid mishaps. On the whole, she should live about as any married woman lives who lives healthfully, avoiding excesses of any sort but carrying on her ordinary work and play and living a life which is satisfying to her, emotionally and sexually.*

Preparation of Children for the New Baby

The woman ordinarily has nine months in which to make her plans for the arrival of her baby and to make the readjustments in family life which may be necessary. If there are other children, they must be prepared for the new baby in such a way that they will welcome him into their midst with pleasure. It is not always easy for the one who has been the youngest and has therefore been the baby in the family to see his position taken by another who must for many months, at least, absorb much of the mother's time.

A young child can be expected to have some feelings of jealousy toward the baby. The intensity of these feelings will depend to a large extent on the understanding of the mother and the ways in which she uses her understanding in making the older child feel comfortable. She can prepare herself for this eventuality by realizing that some jealousy is to be expected, and that the child may express it overtly in his behavior toward the baby or by reverting to infantile behavior such as wetting himself or seeking the same attention that is given to the baby.

The degree and manner of preparation of a child for the coming of a baby will depend on the degree of intellectual and emotional maturity which he has achieved.

Telling the Children. Children often long for a baby sister or brother and welcome the news of an expected arrival with pleasure, but

---

* Sexual intercourse is normally permitted by the physician throughout pregnancy except during the last two months and sometimes at the time of the second and third menstrual periods.

care must be taken that they do not get erroneous ideas. It is important to tell them the truth about the matter and to realize that their knowledge of a baby may be so limited that they may picture the advent of someone who will immediately begin to play with them. They must know that the baby will be little and helpless, will need much of mother's care, must be treated gently, and may be a brother or may be a sister. Picture books of young babies, pictures of themselves when they were babies, and visits to see very young babies will help children to learn about them.

Children need to be told the truth about reproduction in simple but correct terms. It is not well to say that the baby is growing in mother's stomach, for example, for that is not the truth. The term that some people use in the effort to tell the truth, "growing beneath mother's heart" has a sentimental flavor about it which young children do not need. They accept quite simply and naturally the statement that the baby is growing inside mother's body in a special place meant for a baby to grow called the "uterus," if one wishes to give it its name. They have a wholesome normal interest in the matter, and they should have the truth. Indeed, the truth is much more logical to children than some elaborate fiction. If the mother is to go to the hospital when the baby is born, the children should know that. If the hospital is near by it is well for them to see it or some other hospital in order that they may have a feeling of familiarity about hospitals which engenders a sense of security. They should not have the shock of wakening some morning to find that mother has disappeared in the night and gone to some strange place of which they know nothing.

Answering the Children's Questions. Fear that children will talk makes people hesitate to answer their questions correctly, and often induces them to hush the questionings as if it were not right for them to ask. But if children are going to talk, it is better that they spread the truth among their friends than the untruths and unwholesome descriptions which they obtain furtively because their parents have forbidden their quite legitimate queries. The way in which parents answer their children's first question about sex has much to do with the early attitude which the child will have toward sex. Those first patterns formed will possibly affect the individual's entire outlook on sex and all its ramifications.

The matter of answering the children's questions about birth cor-

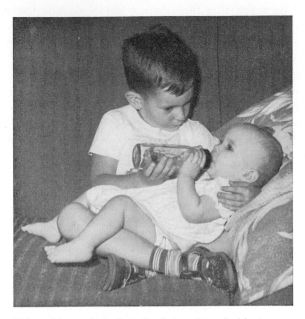

Figure 21. Being able to feel that the baby sister is his too means a great deal to this older brother.

rectly is important not only from the sex point of view but also from another aspect, that of the need consistently to tell children the truth. The questions about the birth of a baby or of animals, which are usually asked at an early age, are often the first questions which parents are tempted to answer untruthfully. This is true partly because they themselves may be embarrassed and so find it difficult to answer such questions simply and naturally without emotional color, and partly because they have not acquired sufficient scientific knowledge to give them the correct vocabulary or enough background to answer the questions in a simple but truthful way. To reduce scientific truths to simple terms which can be grasped by a child and which can be given in the amounts he is ready to receive presupposes a sense of assurance which comes from having a sound basis of scientific knowledge at one's command.

Whatever may be the cause for the untruths or half truths which parents so often give in answering these first questions about sex, the fact remains that this may be the first time when parents fail to be honest with their children. In this way the first lessons in untruthfulness may come from the parents themselves who complain a few years later of their children's tendency to falsehood. Another undesirable effect of a parent's attempt to hush a child's questioning is that a child thwarted in his normal desire for information may turn to undesirable sources, and may be less likely in the future to go freely to the parent with his questioning. To prepare the other children for the new baby by telling them the truth is therefore of prime importance. It may be wise not to do this until the later part of pregnancy, as several months of waiting will seem unduly long to a child. Then, too, since there is some possibility of a miscarriage, unnecessary disappointment to the children may result. It is well to delay the telling until obvious preparations are being made.

Children's Share in the Preparations.　In the preparations for the baby and his care after birth the children can have some share so that they may have a sense of ownership and responsibility toward the new baby which will do much toward reducing any undue feeling of resentment or jealousy engendered by the great amount of attention the new baby will receive.

If there is to be some readjustment of rooms in order that the baby may have a room to himself, the children can help in making the change. The new baby clothes or those that have served the other babies may be arranged in the baby's bureau drawers or basket and the children thus learn how tiny and helpless the baby will be, needing the mother's attention for a long time after he is born. The crib can be seen by the children, and they may delight in helping make it up with the tiny sheets and blankets. They can, indeed, join in many of the preparations for the new baby, thereby learning in a normal wholesome way something about birth and baby care.

If the children have a special desire for a brother or sister, they must know that no one knows about that before the baby is born, and be prepared to welcome either brother or sister. Parents should refrain from expressing their desires in regard to this matter too freely before the children lest the children reflect the parental attitude which so often is not as fixed an attitude as it seems to be. A child may take the parents' expressed preference more seriously and be less ready than they to make the adjustment to disappointment. If the child has been wanting a brother or sister and the new baby is of the opposite sex, often an opportunity to assist in naming the new baby will create interest and a sense of possession, and any feeling of disappointment the child may have had will disappear.

Obstetrical Period

The Advisability of Hospitalization. In preparing for the birth of the baby, one question which must always be decided is whether the baby is to be born at home or in a hospital. Doctors tend to recommend hospitals if a good hospital is available, especially if it is a first baby or if there have been any symptoms of complications. The reasons for advising the hospital are: (1) the hospital has absolutely all the equipment necessary for meeting any emergency which may arise; (2) the hospital has additional trained people to call on immediately in case they are needed; (3) at the hospital there is every facility for giving the baby any special care it may need; (4) at the hospital the woman will live a perfectly regular life during the postpartum period and will escape the consequences of any emergency which may arise in the home. One must bear in mind that there is as much need for maintaining surgical asepsis during and after delivery of a baby as in a surgical operation. The hospital is prepared to make an aseptic delivery and thus minimize the danger of complications due to infection.

In a nation-wide survey[18] on Child Health Services conducted by the Academy of Pediatrics in 1949, it was found that more babies were born in hospitals than formerly, and that the opportunity for hospitalization was greater for urban than for rural women. In 1935, 37 per cent of all babies were born in hospitals; in 1946 the figure was 82 per cent. In greater metropolitan areas only one in twenty births occurred at home; in isolated rural areas more than half the babies were born at home. In some states nearly 100 per cent were born in hospitals; in others less than 50 per cent.

Factors associated with the increase in hospitalization were: (1) the growth of prepayment plans for obstetrical care; (2) the Emergency Maternal and Infant Care program developed during the war to provide maternity care for wives of men in the lower ranks of military service; and (3) the increase in level of income.

A mother of young children sometimes feels that she cannot make satisfactory arrangements for them while she is away from home. However, the experience when the mother is away from home can be a good one for a young child if it is planned carefully so that the child feels loved and secure in his mother's absence.

Plans for Children During Mother's Hospitalization. During pregnancy parents need to make plans for the care of the children while the mother is in the hospital. The selection of the person to assume responsibility for the care of the child or children will, of course, depend on circumstances. It may be a relative, a servant under supervision of the father, or a friend. Fathers have been known to plan their vacation at this time and themselves take over full responsibility for the older children. These plans need to be made fairly early so that the children can be prepared for the time when the mother will be out of the home. The father can play an important role, making this a time for establishment of a good sense of comradeship with the young child. Before the birth of the baby the father can, if circumstances permit, take over some of the care of the child, have the child with him as he works about the house, and participate in his play more than formerly. The child can be shown the hospital and given an explanation, in terms he can understand, of the reason why the mother will be there for a time. Satisfactory plans for communication between mother and child while she is away can be made. Mothers have used various devices for keeping in touch with their children.*

Home Delivery. A home delivery may be necessary because a good obstetrical hospital or a general hospital with an obstetrical department separated from other departments is not available, or it may be the choice of the woman.

If delivery is to be at home, a list of supplies essential to a successful confinement at home should be obtained from the physician. Such equipment should be gathered together in one place about eight weeks before the baby is expected, in case of a premature birth. The services of a well-qualified nurse should be secured, if possible, both for the time of delivery and for the postpartum period. If a full-time nurse is not possible, the services of a visiting nurse may be obtained in some communities, although rural communities especially are still seriously lacking in this respect.

A home delivery has one advantage in that the mother can have her

---

* One mother, who had access to a telephone in her hospital room, called her child each day. Another mother wrote little notes to mail each day. Yet another had a series of small packages containing some little daily surprise for her child. One mother arranged for her husband to bring the children to the hospital grounds and she appeared at the window to wave to them.

baby in the room with her. This has many advantages both for the baby and for the mother. There is a growing interest in such an arrangement in hospitals also. Such an arrangement, called *rooming-in,* has been introduced in some hospitals in various parts of the country.[408] This practice is further discussed under postpartum care.

How to Compute Birth Date.   As stated earlier, the full development of the fetus requires approximately 266 days (ten lunar or nine calendar months from the date of the last menstruation). Although it is impossible to set the exact date for the expected birth, an approximate date may be reached by counting back three months from the date of the beginning of the last menstruation and adding seven days. For example, if the last menstruation began on April 19th, the birth date might be expected to be January 26th.

Beginning of Labor.   After about nine months of uterine life the baby is ready to be born, which means that the uterine muscles must begin to contract at diminishing intervals until the baby is expelled, a process which is called labor. Just what excites these muscles to begin the necessary series of contractions is not known; it is still a question for which the answer must be sought by further research. However, when the uterus begins these contractions, the woman begins to feel labor pains, and she knows that the birth process is beginning. She should notify her doctor immediately. If the woman is to be at home, she should have the nurse with her, or if she is to go to the hospital, she will be told by her physician when to go.

Duration of Labor.   Duration of labor varies from a very short time to thirty-six hours or longer. As a general rule, the first labor lasts longer than labors which follow, averaging fifteen to eighteen hours. During the course of labor, the neck of the uterus, or cervix, must first flatten and then dilate sufficiently to let the baby through into the vagina. The vagina, too, stretches from the small opening it usually is into a canal big enough for a baby to pass through; and the perineum, a triangular-shaped muscle between the vagina and the anus, must also stretch as the baby's head presses down upon it. Skillful handling on the part of the physician does much to save the perineum from tearing. Sometimes the perineum will not stretch sufficiently, and the physician may decide to cut it rather than to let it tear. In either case the perineum can be repaired immediately after the birth of the baby without causing any undue discomfort to the mother.

Stages of Labor.   Labor is divided into three stages. The first, preparatory, stage is the longest, lasting from the first sign of labor until the time when the cervix is completely dilated. The membrane or sac which contains the baby and the amniotic fluid ("bag of waters") usually ruptures at the end of the first stage. During the second stage, the baby actually leaves the uterus and passes through the birth canal into the outside world. The third stage consists of a brief period of uterine contractions which expel the placenta.

Position of the Baby. The normal position of the baby in the uterus (see Fig. 20) is such that the head will be born first. The proportions of a baby's body are very different from the proportions of an adult's body, the circumference of the head being slightly larger than the circumference of chest or abdomen. Hence, if the birth canal is large enough to let the baby's skull through, it is large enough to let the rest of the body through. One provision for facilitating the birth of the baby's head through the pelvic opening is that, unlike an adult skull which is rigid and impervious to outside pressure, the bones of the fetal skull have intervening spaces which permit a certain amount of molding of the head by the overlapping of the bones as the baby goes through the birth canal. Because of this malleability, which permits adaptation of the skull to the opening through which it must pass, the head of a newborn frequently seems to have a queer shape, which might seem alarming to one who did not understand its cause and realize that within a short time the skull would assume its normal shape.

Role of the Mother During Labor. Childbirth is called labor because it requires hard work on the part of the mother. In fact it has been called an athletic feat by one author. As an athlete prepares for a contest so a woman can prepare herself during her pregnancy for the task of giving birth to her child.

In the first stage of labor the woman cooperates by being as relaxed as possible and by consciously relaxing at the time of contractions. By so doing the pain is reduced. In the second stage she helps in the actual birth by pushing or bearing down with her abdominal muscles at the time of contractions and resting between contractions. In the last stage of labor she again bears down during uterine contractions to expel the placenta. This experience can give a woman a sense of accomplishment and great satisfaction, or it can be something fearful to anticipate and to experience.

A different approach to childbirth, called *natural childbirth,** or better, *cooperative childbirth,* enables women to find pregnancy and

* For discussions of natural or cooperative childbirth see Goodrich,[310] Jackson,[406] Miller and Flannery,[588] Read,[682, 683] Thoms and Roth,[839] Thoms and Wyatt.[840]

labor rich, satisfying, and meaningful experiences. "Reduced to its essence, natural childbirth is best described as intellectual, physical, and emotional preparation for childbirth, to the end that mothers realize their potentialities and in so doing enjoy the bringing forth of their babies."*

The preparation during pregnancy includes knowledge of the nature of pregnancy and of the birth process, the woman's role in it, and how she can expect to feel during it. She also learns about hospital procedures and the role of the doctor and nurses. Much of the anxiety or fear of childbirth can thus be eliminated. Through a series of exercises she learns how to relax and strengthens the muscles involved in parturition. These exercises, plus the elimination of fear, result in reduced pain and, therefore, less need for medication. When labor begins and throughout the procedure she is kept informed of her progress. Some one is with her throughout to give assurance and help when needed and medication when desired. It is sometimes possible for the husband to remain with his wife during the first stage of labor. Throughout the birth process she participates actively, and she can see and hold her baby while still in the delivery room.

The exact procedure at childbirth will naturally vary according to the individual and will be decided by the obstetrician in light of the circumstances.

Postpartum Care.   After childbirth it is important that the mother have a period of rest. Indeed, for the period of six to ten days of which five or six are usually spent in the hospital, most women are content to be quite lazy, and interruptions for meals and nursing their infants prove quite enough diversion. Even visitors other than husband and mother can prove very fatiguing.†

It has become the custom in many hospitals, because of the danger of infection of infants when visitors are allowed indiscriminately in the

---

* Goodrich[310] (p. 2).

† On this point Dr. Eastman has quoted from Francois Mauriceau, the Parisian obstetrician of the seventeenth century: "The Citizen's wives have a very ill Custom, which they would do well to refrain, that is, they cause their Children to be baptized on the third Day after their labour; at which time all their Relations and Friends have a Collation in the Childbed Room, with whom she is obliged to discourse, and answer the Gossips, and all Comers a whole afternoon together, with the usual Compliments of those Ceremonies, enough to distract her; and *tho' there is scarce any of the company which do not drink her Health, yet by the Noise they make in her Ear, she loses it.*" (Eastman,[235] p. 172.)

obstetric units, that visitors be limited to the husband and the two grandmothers, or sometimes just to the husband. Many women have admitted that it was a relief not to have visitors, and at least one study has shown that under such isolation (husband the only visitor), women were better able to nurse their babies. Darner and Hunter[187] found, when 100 such women and their infants were compared with a control group of 100 mothers and infants under the same routine of care but without the ban on visitors, that the initial weight loss of the infants in the rest group averaged 79.3 gm. less than the average loss of those in the other group, and the babies in the first group received on the average 56.7 cc. more breast milk daily than those in the latter group. While sixty-six mothers in the control group were able to nurse their infants without complementary feedings, eighty-four mothers in the rest group were able to do so.

Women are now encouraged soon after childbirth to get out of bed for brief periods of time at first and later walk about in order to stimulate circulation and improve muscle tone. Moving about helps to promote an early return to a woman's accustomed vitality.

It is the general practice in hospitals for babies to be cared for in a nursery and brought to the mother at regular intervals. In some hospitals plans have been made for the baby to remain with the mother in her room. This practice in which the mother and her baby are cared for together in the same room is called *rooming-in*. It is "a plan to maintain natural mother-infant relationships, to reinforce the potentialities of each mother and infant, and to encourage the family unit."* In such an arrangement a mother becomes acquainted with her baby, learns his needs and how to meet them, and actually participates in his care so that when she returns home she has confidence in her ability to care for her baby. The baby's needs can be met promptly. He can be fed when hungry, diapered when wet, comforted when he cries. Thus both mother and baby get off to a good start. The father has an opportunity to share with his wife in becoming acquainted with their newborn and in learning the essentials in taking care of the baby. Thus he develops a feeling of being a necessary, active member of the family group rather than an onlooker who may feel excluded or rejected, and can be a great help to the mother in assuming her responsibilities after returning home from the hospital. One mother has reported that other

* Jackson and Trainham[408] (p. 6).

children in the family may benefit also. She found that since she and her husband had become acquainted with the newborn in the hospital they could devote more time to the other children when she and the baby returned home. Rooming-in is a natural sequence to cooperative childbirth and provides an opportunity for the setting up of a self-regulation program for the infant without delay.*

Such an arrangement is not available to all mothers and is not necessarily desirable for all. Again, as in cooperative childbirth, its employment depends on the individual and the circumstances.

Return from the Hospital.   By the time the period of hospitalization is ended, many mothers feel rested and think themselves ready to tackle anything. However, the reproductive organs do not return to normal before six to eight weeks, and most mothers find that they fatigue very easily during this period. It is important that a mother have adequate rest and that she increase her activities gradually. Someone to perform household duties which may tax the mother's strength and who will leave her freer to spend her time and energies on the baby and other children is invaluable. The father may be able to take over some of the household tasks. The mother is much more likely to continue lactating sufficiently to nourish her baby and will regain her normal energy sooner if she can have some help during this period. Just how promptly she will pick up her usual activities will depend on the advice of her physician. He will want her to return for a postpartum examination at the end of six to eight weeks. During the interim certain exercises may be prescribed to aid in getting the abdominal muscles back to normal strength and the uterus back to normal position.

Topics for Study and Discussion

1. Have students bring to class popular beliefs and superstitions about pregnancy. Discuss them in terms of current knowledge of prenatal development and prenatal influences.

2. Have several students bring to class the actual diets, kinds and amounts of food, of pregnant women. Evaluate these in terms of the nutritional needs of the mother and fetus.

3. Have students bring to class some examples of actual anxieties and worries of pregnant women. Discuss these in relation to factors contributing to them, their effect upon the health of the women, and how they were met.

4. Have a panel discussion of how parents can prepare young children for a new baby in the family. Invite two or three mothers who have young infants and preschool children to participate in this discussion with the students.

* See Jackson.[406]

Selected Readings

Chaney, M. S.: Nutrition, ed. 5. Boston, Houghton Mifflin Co., 1954 (pp. 332-334).

Eastman, N. J.: Expectant Motherhood, ed. 3. Boston, Little, Brown & Co., 1957.

Genné, W. H.: Husbands and Pregnancy: The Handbook for Expectant Fathers. New York, Association Press, 1956.

Goodrich, F. W.: Natural Childbirth. New York, Prentice-Hall, Inc., 1950.

Mussen, P. H., and Conger, J. J.: Child Development and Personality. New York, Harper & Bros., 1956. Part I, Chaps. 2, 3.

Patten, B. M.: Human Embryology, ed. 2. Philadelphia, The Blakiston Co., 1953.

Scheinfeld, A.: The New You and Heredity. Philadelphia, J. B. Lippincott Co., 1950.

Sears, R. R., Maccoby, E. E., and Levin, H.: Patterns of Child Rearing. Evanston, Ill., Row, Peterson and Company, 1957. Chap. 2.

4

The Child's Physical Equipment
for Growth, Development
and Functioning

Development of the Individual

The child's body is his equipment for living. Through it he receives impressions from life about him. He thinks, feels, and acts; he uses this body both to express his thoughts and feelings and to manipulate his environment of things and people. It is, therefore, essential to have an understanding of the physical nature of the child in order to understand his total personality.

His body is "fearfully and wonderfully" made. Each organ or system in the body performs a specific function and by coordinating its function with those of others contributes to an integrated whole. Throughout childhood this body is changing—changing in size, in shape, and in structure and function. In fact, it has been aptly said that change is the one constant factor in a child's life. The totality of these changes, as life progresses, is called *development,* which is the emerging and expanding of the capacities of the individual to provide progressively greater facility in functioning.

Developmental Processes.   The processes involved in development are growth, maturation, and learning.

GROWTH.   Growth is increase in bodily dimensions. Children grow

134

taller and heavier. Their bones and muscles grow larger; so do their hearts, lungs, and other organs. Since the rate of growth of various parts of the body is not the same, growth involves changes in body proportions, and changes in the relative amounts of different tissues.

MATURATION. Maturation is the term used to designate qualitative changes, that is, changes in the complexity of structure which make it possible for a structure to begin functioning or to function at progressively higher levels. Maturational changes make it possible for a child to acquire voluntary control of elimination, to feed himself, to climb stairs, and to acquire all the other many skills he learns.

LEARNING. Learning, the third process, is the exercise of structures, the practice of a new function with satisfaction which brings about changes in the structures involved and in the function itself. Thus a child learns through practice to climb stairs with more and more facility. By practice he is stimulating the development of certain muscle groups.

These processes do not occur independently and unrelated to one another. In such a complex organism as man they are very closely interrelated and interdependent. As a child grows, he is also maturing and learning. The term development, therefore, becomes useful in studying children as an over-all term. Motor development, for example, involves growth of the body, maturation of sensory organs, bones, muscles, nerves, and learning to use this equipment through practice. In this book the reader will find the term development used to designate the over-all changes, and also to refer to changes in a specific area such as physical, social, or emotional development.

Frequently for the sake of brevity the term growth is used as an over-all one to mean growth, maturation, and learning. The reader will find this use of the term appearing occasionally throughout the book.

External Dimensions and Weight of Child's Body

Length. The term "body length" means length from the top of the head to the soles of the feet, measured with the child lying on his back in a horizontal position. This term is used to indicate stature throughout these early years.

At birth a baby is generally 19 to 21 inches long. Boys tend to be slightly longer than girls and the first born tends to be a little shorter than later babies in the family.[570] Babies of obese mothers tend to be larger than those of mothers of standard weight.[903] According to Stuart's norms* 80 per cent of newborn boys range from 18.9 inches to 21 inches; girls range from 18.8 inches to 20.4 inches. Length at birth however, gives little clue to ultimate height in adulthood.†

Growth in length in infancy and early childhood is characterized by a rapid but decelerating rate from birth to two years and by a slowly decelerating rate for the preschool years. By three months a baby will have gained 20 per cent of his birth length; by one year, 50 per cent; by two years, 75 per cent. At about four years he will have doubled his birth length. The slowing down of growth in length in the preschool years is dramatically indicated by the fact that a baby in the first year of life gains about an inch and a quarter more than he will gain between the ages of two and five years.‡

With this early rapid growth it is not surprising to note that a large percentage of adult height is achieved in the first few years. Half of adult height is usually attained by girls between one and one-half and two and one-half years, and by boys between two and two and one-half years. Sixty per cent is achieved by girls at three and one-half years and by boys at four and one-half years.[761] Thus girls progress toward mature height faster than boys. Figure 22, showing the same girl at 1 year, 7 months, at 5 years, and at 16 years, 3 months, illustrates the proportion of mature height attained during the early years. This girl at 1 year, 7 months had attained 49 per cent of her mature height, and at 5 years had attained 66 per cent.

Individual children vary considerably in stature. Sex differences have been mentioned above. The early superiority of boys becomes negligible for four- and five-year-olds.[761] Within the same age and sex children can be expected to show considerable variability. Figure 23 showing two healthy girls of the same age but of different size and physique illustrates individual differences in stature. According to Stuart's norms[821] 80 per cent of two-year-old boys will measure between 33.1 and 35.9 inches; 80 per cent of five-year-old boys will measure between 40.8 and 45.2 inches. Similar differences can be expected of girls.

* These norms are based on measurements of a group of healthy white children of north European ancestry living in or near Boston, for the most part of lower economic status but all under regular health supervision.[821]

† Tanner et al.[826] found a correlation between height at birth and adulthood of .25 for boys and .29 for girls.

‡ From Stuart's norms.[821]

Children of widely differing backgrounds will show even greater variability.

The pattern of growth in stature for individual children is somewhat stable, as indicated by the Berkeley Growth Study.[89] During the first year, the children's stature correlated close to .5 and .6 with their stature as adults. This correlation increased to .83 and .85 for boys and girls respectively at three years of age, and to .86 and .84 respectively at five years of age.* However the pattern of growth in stature

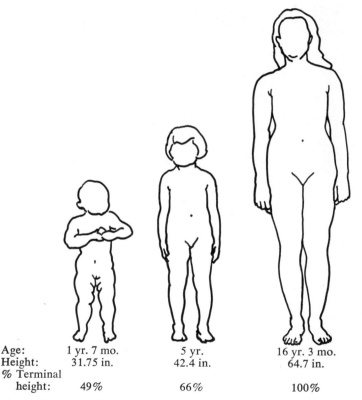

Age:	1 yr. 7 mo.	5 yr.	16 yr. 3 mo.
Height:	31.75 in.	42.4 in.	64.7 in.
% Terminal height:	49%	66%	100%

Figure 22. Proportion of mature height attained in preschool years at 1 year 7 months and 5 years.

---

* Tanner et al.,[826] also in correlating early stature with adult stature found the correlation at two years to be .79 and .74 for boys and girls respectively, and at five years to be .77 and .81 respectively.

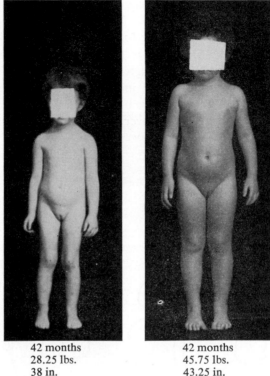

Age:	42 months	42 months
Weight:	28.25 lbs.	45.75 lbs.
Height:	38 in.	43.25 in.

Figure 23.   Two healthy girls at same age, but differing 17½ pounds in weight and 5¼ inches in height.

may vary from child to child. Some may be fast growers from the start, others may be slow growers. Yet others may change their tempo, perhaps by beginning slowly during the first few years and increasing their tempo later. Children in the early years may not resemble their parents in tallness or shortness but become similar to them as they grow older. Bayley[84] gives an example of one child who resembled his parents in stature from an early age while still in the preschool period. Another was consistently tall for his age until sixteen years of age when he stopped growing and became an adult of average height. Yet another, who was a slow grower, was unlike her parents before adolescence. Bayley[89] found that most children tended to become more like their parents in stature as they grew older. Correlations between the adult stature of the parents and that of the children increased and became significant before they had passed beyond the preschool years. Thus these studies indicate, not only are there differences in growth patterns, but also that a genetic factor is involved in determining the stature of an individual.

This family line heredity, which includes race,[279, 571] is one of the variables which contribute to differences in stature. Environment,* which can be said to encompass diet, health, living standards, family surroundings, an atmosphere of contentment or tensions, is also a factor.† Young children in a superior environment generally are taller than children of comparable age who live in less favorable circumstances.[717] Racial differences can be noted by comparison of stature of white children in the United States with Japanese and with Negro children. Japanese children are shorter than American white children.[478] Negro children also tend to be shorter than white children.[571, 580] These differences, however, cannot be attributed solely to race. A strong environmental component is present, as has been demonstrated by studies in which comparisons have been made of children of the same race living under varying circumstances. Japanese children born and reared in America have been found to be taller than those born and reared in Japan.[786] A study[729] of the growth in height and weight of Negro infants from families in the lower middle class has shown that the growth curves of Negro and white infants from comparable economic levels are similar. Growth in length of an individual child is, therefore, dependent on the interaction of his heredity and his environment. Heredity sets the potential for growth in length; health and environment determine the degree to which that potential is achieved.

Not All Parts of Body Grow at Same Rate. It is obvious that a newborn baby differs in body proportions from an adult. At birth the head comprises one fourth of the total body length, whereas in an adult the head is about one eighth of the total length. The proportion of legs to total length changes from approximately one third at birth to one half at adulthood. The differences in the rate of growth of the different segments of the body during the developmental period is illustrated in Figure 24, which shows that during the growing years the head about doubles itself, the trunk triples itself, the arms increase about four times, and the legs about five times.

* For a review of research on environment and human plasticity see Kaplan.[443]
† See[111, 165, 224, 574, 658, 717, 900]

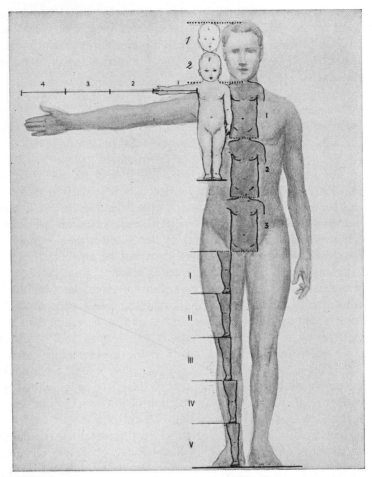

Figure 24. The proportions of a child are quite different from those of an adult. During the growth period the head doubles its size, the trunk triples its original size, while the arm grows four times as long and the leg five times as long. (Kahn, F.: Man in Structure and Function, Vol. I. Alfred A. Knopf, 1943.)

During infancy and early childhood relative differences in linear growth are evident. During the first year stem length* and total length are increasing at approximately the same rate.[91] After the first year

* Measurement from the top of the head to the buttocks taken when the child is lying in a recumbent position.

legs begin to grow more rapidly than the combined head and trunk. By two years the legs are about 34 per cent of total length, and by five years about 44 per cent.* By two years a child's legs have doubled their length; by five years they have almost tripled their length. In the first two years there is a more rapid increase than between two and five years.[575]

Stem length is less than doubled by five years of age. About half of the increase during infancy and preschool years occurs before eighteen months.[575] Thus both growth in stem length and in leg length indicate a rapid but decelerating rate in these early years, as was indicated earlier for total length. These changes are illustrated in Figure 25.

Body Weight. The weight of the newborn in the United States varies considerably but generally falls somewhere between 5½ and 9½ pounds. Boys are generally a little heavier than girls. Babies of obese mothers tend to be heavier than those of mothers of standard weight.[903] The first born is a little lighter than later babies in the family.[570] Babies under 5½ pounds are considered premature or immature. According to Stuart's norms[821] 80 per cent of the newborn males range from 6.3 to 9.1 pounds; girls range from 6.2 to 8.6 pounds.

In the first three or four days, infants generally lose weight. This loss

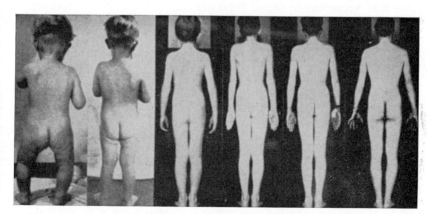

Figure 25. Changes in body proportions, with growth shown in photographs of the same boy at six ages: 15 months, 30 months, and 6, 11, 14 and 18 years. All are adjusted to the same height. (Bayley, N.: Individual patterns of development. Child Development. 27:45-74, 1956. Fig. 2 opp. p. 48.)

* Calculated from data by Meredith and Knott.[575]

may amount to as much as 10 per cent and is greater among heavy babies than among smaller ones.[821] It represents chiefly the loss of body fluid which can be attributed to the transition to extrauterine life and attendant adjustments in water metabolism.*

During early life growth in weight is characterized by a rapid but decelerating rate for the first two years, slow deceleration in rate from two to three years, followed by a gradual acceleration in rate for the remainder of the preschool period.[761] Thus an infant doubles his weight by five months, triples it in the first year, and quadruples it by the end of two and one-half years.[821] The gain in weight from two to five is less than the amount gained in the first year of life.

By two years of age a child is approximately one-fifth as heavy as he will be at eighteen; by five years he has achieved approximately one third of his weight at eighteen.† Girls are slightly advanced over boys in their progress toward attaining mature weight.

There is a wide variability in weight among small children of the same age. Children who are heavier at birth tend to remain heavier[30, 387] throughout infancy and early childhood.‡ One study[349] reports that about 25 per cent of the variability in children at three years of age can be attributed to birth weight. Boys have a slight tendency to be heavier than girls, and also there are some differences at the same age for the same sex. According to Stuart[821] 80 per cent of boys at two years weigh between 24.7 and 31.9 pounds; at five years 80 per cent weigh between 35.5 and 46.7 pounds. These wide individual differences are also true of girls. Figure 23 illustrates differences in the weight of healthy children of the same chronological age.

The factors contributing to individual differences in weight are family-line heredity,§ which includes race,[571] emotions[111, 900] and environment.[165, 224, 574, 658, 717]

The environmental factors, especially those related directly to nutri-

---

* See Meyer and Nassar.[579]

† Calculated from median weights by Stuart.[821]

‡ Tanner et al.[826] report correlations between adult weight and birth weight of .38 for boys and .42 for girls. At two years, the correlation with adult weight was .51 and .43 for boys and girls respectively, and at five years .59 and .46, respectively.

§ The resemblance in the early years between parents and children is less for weight than for height. Bayley[89] found correlations between parent and son to be rather low but with a tendency to increase with age. The father-daughter correlations indicated some relationship by five years but never reached statistical significance. However, the daughter-mother correlations showed strongly increasing similarities which were significant by six years of age.

tion, have a particularly strong influence on weight, as indicated by studies of height and weight of children in time of war. A summary[454] of studies during World War I and World War II provides evidence that during wartime with its food restrictions, weight, and height to a lesser degree, are affected, the extent of the growth deficit being related to the severity of malnutrition. Studies in Germany, France, Belgium, Holland, and Greece bear this out. However, evidence from World War I and the rehabilitation of Dutch children liberated from Java and sent to Australia in World War II[202] indicates that children can recover from periods of deprivation, if not too prolonged, and catch up in growth in weight and height. However, children who grow up under substandard living conditions, with inadequate food, will not have the opportunity of rehabilitation and will, therefore, be unable to achieve their potential for growth.

In addition to differences in weight between children, fluctuations in growth in weight occur from time to time in an individual. The curve of growth in weight is not as smooth as that for growth in height.* This can be expected since weight, which represents body bulk, including muscle, bone, the various organs, fat and water, is fairly easily affected by environment and the health vicissitudes of a child.

Evaluation of Length and Weight. The ultimate value of learning about growth in length and weight of children is the use of that knowledge in understanding the growth of an individual child. The adequacy of growth is determined by assessing both the child's status and his progress. Status is determined by comparing his growth with that of other children; progress is determined by comparing the child with himself from time to time through the accumulation of serial measurements. Population norms or standards provide the means for evaluating status. The effectiveness of the use of these standards depends to a large degree on the selection of the particular standard and the interpretation made of the comparison. Different standards represent different groups of children, that is, children of varying hereditary and environmental backgrounds. The standard chosen for use should be one compiled from a group of children with backgrounds and living circumstances similar to those of the child being studied. Because of the sex differences in growth, standards for boys and girls are separate. A satisfactory stand-

---

* The instability of the pattern of growth in weight has been indicated in the Berkeley Study[89] in which correlations with adult weight were found to be .44 for boys and .59 for girls at three years and .44 and .68 respectively at five years of age.

ard, in addition, includes not only an average but also a range, thereby indicating a zone of normality. This zone of normality is sometimes expressed in terms of an average and standard deviation and sometimes in terms of percentile rank.*

Standards are used most effectively when progress and status of a child can be observed concurrently. This can be done when standards are presented as curves which give the pattern of growth of a large group of children over a period of time. Such, for example, are the Iowa curves[410] consisting of three curves, one representing the average and the other two representing plus one and minus one standard deviations for height and percentiles for weight; the Bayley curves[83] consisting of curves representing heights and weights of children of accelerated, average and retarded physical maturity based on skeletal assessment and per cent of attained adult stature; and the percentile curves from the Division of Maternal and Child Health in the Harvard School of Public Health.[821] In all cases these series of curves are drawn on coordinate paper so that actual height or weight, as may be the case, can be plotted against chronological age. When a child's series of measurements are plotted, a comparison can be made between the individual curve and the group curve. A child will tend to maintain the same relative position with respect to his age group from time to time unless circumstances interfere with his particular pattern of growth.

Another device for evaluating height and weight is the Grid-Graph formulated and developed by Wetzel.[478, 889, 890, 891, 892] There are two Grid-Graphs, the Wetzel Grid[889] and the Baby Grid.†[892] The Baby

---

* When averages and standard deviations are used, approximately 68 per cent of the children measured might normally be expected to fall between plus and minus one standard deviation; approximately 95 per cent will fall between plus and minus two standard deviations.

In a standard based on percentiles, measurements are ranked according to magnitude from the smallest to the largest as they would be found in any typical series of 100 children. The middle point or median is represented by the fiftieth percentile. Half of the children might normally be expected to fall between the twenty-fifth and seventy-fifth percentiles, which are equidistant from the median. Eighty per cent of the children might be expected to fall between the tenth and ninetieth percentiles.

† The principles of the Grid apply throughout the span of human development, from an embryonic weight of 1 gram to maturity. In the Baby Grid there are two parts to the channel system. The left group of channels represents the "sidetracks of infancy," since infants are naturally more chubby than older children. The right group contains the channels of the "main line" of human development into which children return at about school age. The shift from the "side tracks" to the "main line" is indicated in the Baby Grid by the gradual bearing right of the course which infants take in the channel system.

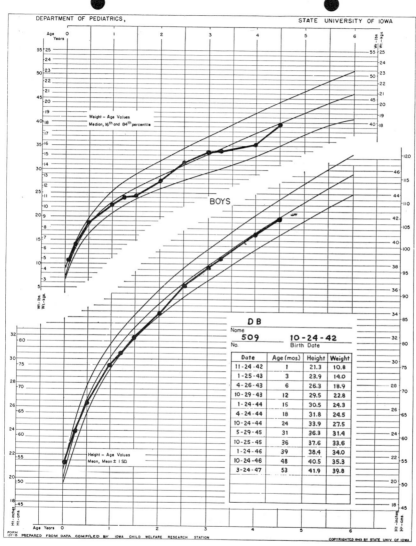

DEPARTMENT OF PEDIATRICS,   STATE UNIVERSITY OF IOWA

BOYS

Weight – Age Values
Median, 16th and 84th percentile

Height – Age Values
Mean, Mean ± 1 SD

D B

Name
509   10-24-42
No.   Birth Date

Date	Age (mos.)	Height	Weight
11-24-42	1	21.3	10.8
1-25-43	3	23.9	14.0
4-26-43	6	26.3	18.9
10-29-43	12	29.5	22.8
1-24-44	15	30.5	24.3
4-24-44	18	31.8	24.5
10-24-44	24	33.9	27.5
5-29-45	31	36.3	31.4
10-25-45	36	37.6	33.6
1-24-46	39	38.4	34.0
10-24-46	48	40.5	35.3
3-24-47	53	41.9	39.8

FORM
(37-8 PREPARED FROM DATA COMPILED BY IOWA CHILD WELFARE RESEARCH STATION
COPYRIGHTED 1943 BY STATE UNIV. OF IOWA

Figure 26. Height and weight of a boy, DB, from 1 month to 5 years of age plotted on Iowa curves.

Grid is discussed here because it covers a larger proportion of the age span covered in this text than does the Wetzel Grid. This Grid is a height-weight gauge of individual progress, and consists of two parts. The first part on the left is a channel system on which height is plotted against weight and which represents gradations of build from slender on the right, to stocky on the left. These channels are crossed at regular intervals of 10 units by horizontal "developmental level lines" which are in effect increment units. The second part, on the right, is a Grid for plotting developmental levels against chronological age with a series of curves (auxodromes) indicating the speed of development for advanced, average and premature infants. Healthy development travels channel-wise and parallels one of the auxodromes. With the provision of this series of preferential paths for individual children both in the channels and along the auxodromes it is possible to evaluate the progress of the child in light of his own unique pattern of growth, whether he be stocky or linear in physique and whether the growth rate be slow or fast. A shift in channels or lag in schedule indicates a need to examine the child and his environment in order to determine whether something is preventing the progress which is typical for him. Further study is needed to ascertain what degree of constancy in channel position can be expected of infants and young children, and how wide a deviation from a channel can be tolerated.*

In Figures 26 and 27 the height and weight of the same child are plotted on the Iowa curves for height and weight, and on the Baby Grid. In the former, the curves extend to six years of age. On the Baby Grid the boy reaches the limits of the Grid at two and one-half years. Both graphs indicate that he begins as a fairly stocky infant but

---

Figure 27. (*See pull-out opposite this page.*) Height and weight of a boy, DB, plotted on Baby Grid, showing his progress along the channel system during the first two and one-half years.

In Panel X, 1 designates the main line channel system with channels B_3 to A_4; 2, the side tracks for infants A_5 to A_{12}; 3, the level lines of development which measure size in body surface; *a* and *b*, the weight and length scales, respectively; 4, the path into which most infants fall and which begins to turn toward the main channel around the end of the first year. In Panel Y, 5, 6 and 7 identify standard schedules of development for advanced, average and premature babies, respectively, and show the drop during the newborn period with recovery in 2½ weeks. Panel Z contains the scales for energy requirements at successive developmental levels.

* Studies of the Wetzel Grid[278, 479] indicate that some degree of change in channel may be expected for many children of school age.

changes to a boy of medium build. This is shown in the Grid from a shift to the right into the middle channels, and in the Iowa curves by a comparison of the position of the height and weight curves in relation to the middle curve (mean values for height and median values for weight). He loses status in height during the first and second years but grows steadily in the following years. In weight he also loses status during the first two years, and again at four. The speed of development as indicated on the auxodrome panel of the Grid indicates a somewhat advanced schedule.

Components of Weight. Weight is a measure of mass, which, however, reveals nothing about the nature of that mass. That which is represented by weight comprises the organs and systems of the body which are engaged in the body's daily housekeeping. It is, therefore, important to know more than merely the weight of a child and his progress in weight.

The components of weight vary in their proportion of the total weight with age and between individual children of the same age. For example, at birth about 25 per cent of the total weight can be attributed to muscle, 16 per cent to the vital organs, and 15 per cent to the central nervous system, whereas at maturity muscles, viscera, and the central nervous system will represent approximately 43 per cent, 11 per cent, and 3 per cent respectively. Two individual children may weigh the same, and yet one may have relatively large muscles and bones while the other may have relatively more fatty tissue.

Studies* in the growth of muscle, bone, and subcutaneous tissue (largely fat) demonstrate differences in the pattern of growth of these tissues with age and between boys and girls. Figure 28 illustrates the differences in the pattern of growth of muscle and bone and that of subcutaneous tissue during infancy and early childhood. It has been found that muscle growth occurs at a rapidly decelerating rate during the second year and at a more slowly decelerating rate until the onset of the puberal spurt of growth.[517] The growth of muscle tissue lags behind growth of the body as a whole during infancy and childhood.

Subcutaneous tissue, largely fat, has quite a different pattern of growth. This tissue tends to increase rapidly in thickness during the

* Stuart and his co-workers at Harvard[517, 819, 820] and Reynolds at Fels Institute[691, 692] established technics to study differential tissue growth through the use of x-rays of the leg. By comparison of the shadows of skin and subcutaneous tissue, muscle and bone of the calf of the leg, relative amounts of these tissues are ascertained.

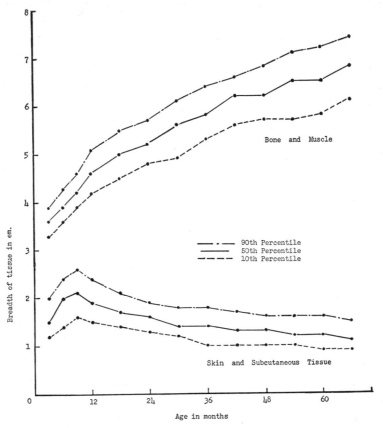

Figure 28. Graphs of breadth of bone and muscle and of skin and subcutaneous tissue, as measured on anteroposterior roentgenograms of the calf of
the leg for boys from 3 to 66 months, in terms of the tenth, fiftieth, and ninetieth
percentiles, illustrating the different patterns of growth and individual variability.
(Graphs made from data by Lombard[517] and Stuart and Sobel.[820])

first nine months of life, to decrease rapidly from then until two and
one-half years, and to decrease less rapidly until about five and one-
half years of age. At five years it is approximately half as thick as at
nine months.[821] This contributes to the appearance of chubbiness in the
infant and to subsequent loss of chubbiness and gradual emergence of
the type of physique which will be characteristic of the child.

Just as there are individual differences in the growth of height and
weight, there are individual differences in the growth of tissues. Boys
consistently have more muscle and bone than girls; girls have more fat

than boys.[517, 692] Individual variability in these studies indicates that among both boys and girls there will be those with larger bones and muscle and those with relatively large amounts of fat. We need to be aware of these differences and try to ascertain what they mean to children and their parents.

These differences in the relative growth of tissues indicate that the use of height and weight alone in evaluating the growth progress of a child is not enough. What constitutes that weight is very important in assessing the health and growth of any child and understanding the whole child.

Body Form or Physique. Body proportions, and the amounts of the three tissues and their distribution, which have been mentioned earlier, contribute to an over-all body form, build or physique which is a part of the uniqueness of the individual. In infancy and early childhood, the child changes from a slender (slender in proportion to length) newborn infant to a broader plump infant during the first year, and later to an increasingly slender child up to seven or eight years. Within this general pattern individual physiques emerge.

Most of the studies reported on physique have been done with adolescents and adults.* One study, however, found differences in build between ectomorphs (linearity delicacy) and mesomorphs (muscular solidarity) during childhood which pointed to some constancy for these types throughout childhood.† Observations of many children who have been followed throughout their growth years indicate that there are individuals who show consistency in build throughout their growth years and those who show an inconsistency. Bayley[84] offers some examples. One child is reported to have had obese periods in infancy and around the age of thirteen years. One heavy set boy had a short period in infancy of relative slenderness, while another heavy infant completed his growth as a tall, rather slender, adult. One slow grower remained slender; one fast grower remained plump. We need further studies in this area of the constancy of physique during childhood.

---

* For discussion of body build in older children and adolescents see Breckenridge and Vincent.[131] See Sheldon et al.[749] for somatotyping of adults.

† Dupertuis and Michaels[232] have studied the growth in height and weight of a group of children followed longitudinally and somatotyped at twenty-one years of age. Between the ectomorphs and mesomorphs, significant differences in weight occurred at all ages, and the index $\frac{Ht}{\sqrt[3]{Wt}}$ was greater for ectomorphs, throughout the period of two to seventeen years, than for mesomorphs.

Need for Understanding Structure and Function of Child's Body.
Rapid and significant changes of a structural and functional nature
occur within the child's body between birth and five years which are
not reflected by height and weight alone, and which influence his potential development as an individual. These changes occur in many of the
systems of the body and mark the child's progress toward his own
maturity. The child's body is delicately coordinated and dependent on
the functioning of the various systems that compose it. In order to
understand growth and development one must know the structure and
function of the different parts of the body and their interrelationship.
Since the feeding, care, and guidance of young children are based on
the knowledge of their bodies and their stage of maturity at the various
age levels, this basic information is essential to adequate understanding
of certain procedures. To make this period of dramatic physical change
real and vivid to those interested in child development, a brief review
has been made of the systems of the body and their development during
the first five years of life.*

It is to be remembered that all systems of the body are interdependent, and the stage of functional maturity of one system is in part
reflected in the stages of maturity of the others. For example, the
immaturity of the neuromuscular mechanism is reflected in the activity
of the digestive tract. It is our desire to present in this chapter and the
following one the physical potentialities with which the child starts life
when he is born and how far he has progressed toward maturity by his
fifth year.

The transition from a dependent life inside an amniotic sac within
the uterus of the mother to an independent existence in an outside
world necessitates prompt and extensive readjustments for the newborn. With almost no effort on his part he has received all that was
necessary to maintain life from his mother's blood stream and excreted
his waste products through her. When the cord is severed he leaves
quite suddenly this sheltered environment and his dependent existence
and begins to breathe for himself. The lungs must function adequately
when the first breath is taken, and the whole respiratory mechanism
must be set immediately in motion; at the same time circulation must

* Some of the systems, in their service to the body, are not completely understood; others are the subject of current research. Some are understood in their
function at the adult level but have not been explored at the early childhood level.
This review presents the facts that are pertinent to the discussion of the growth
of the child in the first five years of life.

be altered so as to pick up oxygen from the lungs and nutrients from the intestine, and the latter must be distributed to the body tissues if the child is to live. He must take his nourishment in a more complex form and digest and absorb it; he must eliminate feces and urine and accustom himself to sound and light. To him it is a strange, new, complex existence.

Skeletal System

A child comes into the world with a body consisting of a rigid framework of bone held together by muscles and tendons, which together with the enveloping skin supports, surrounds, moves and thereby protects the delicate organs essential for the maintenance of health and activity. The framework takes about twenty years to grow and develop its full potentialities. Each organ, if it functions at all, must function to full capacity, harmonious with the changing needs of the growing body. Since the skeleton is a structure which takes a long time to reach maturity, it has characteristics which afford excellent examples of stages of maturity which the individual reaches at all ages. Bone, the tissue which constitutes most of the skeleton, is a living, growing labile tissue composed of living cells which participate in the functioning of the body and contribute their part to its well-being. The bones support the structure of the body, determine its stature, and help with overlying soft parts to determine its physique. Any study of the skeleton must contemplate three aspects: bones as supporting structures and agents in locomotion; bones as a source of mineral, particularly of calcium; and bones in their role of blood-forming organs through the agency of red marrow.

Functions of Bone. As stated, one of the functions of bone is to *support structures* and serve as an *agent in locomotion*. The skull protects the delicate tissue of the brain, the ribs enclose the lungs and heart, the pelvis supports the abdominal organs. As part of an integrated activity of a group of systems the bones participate in making movement possible. The coordinated action of bones, muscles, and nerves makes possible the balance of the body, locomotion and use of the hands and arms in manipulation of one's environment.

The bones of the body not only serve as a framework to support the body but are *storehouses of minerals* from which the blood can obtain substances essential for the life and health of the body cells.

The spongy part of the bone is a network of bony trabeculae (rows of cells bridging intercellular spaces), the size of the mesh having a family pattern but being subject to modification in any individual from time to time. In health, the open spaces of the mesh are well filled with labile mineral, providing a floating store from which the mineral is obtained for blood coagulation, muscle tone, kidney function and functioning of the nervous system. When the body draws on the bone for mineral, two modifications may occur in the network of trabeculae and the enclosed labile mineral, which is best described by the metaphor, "snow-covered chicken wire," employed by Todd. "As the snow filling the interstices melts, the chicken wire mesh becomes more plainly visible and parts that have suffered corrosion stand out as breaks in the mesh. But if the melting snow freezes afresh, the trabeculae become coated with ice. They may not appear thicker but will stand out more clearly and the places where the wire strands of the mesh are intertwisted will appear as nodes in the network. Spongiosa well filled with mineral corresponds to the snow-covered net of chicken wire. Withdrawal of the labile mineral corresponds to the melting of the snow. Breaks in the trabeculae represent a heavier drain on the stored supply. Transformation of labile mineral into the more stable phase corresponds to the ice-covering with knots or nodes in the network."* These changes can be revealed by taking roentgenograms of an individual over a period of time.

The degree of mineralization, or the *density* of bone, can be revealed by the depth of the shadow in an x-ray. Studies of consecutive x-rays of children show that in some well children the density of bone varies from time to time. The cause of the fluctuation of density, undoubtedly associated in some way with calcium metabolism, has yet to be ascertained. Todd said: "So frequently do we find lightly mineralized bones in the highly strung child, who is prone to fatigue, restless, often very alert, irritable, poorly adjusted, apprehensive and fearful, with deficient powers of attention and concentration, that we have come to suspect deficiency in mineralization as the physical counterpart of this emotional maladjustment. But one should point out that one is dealing here not with cause and effect but merely with different aspects of a constitutional handicap."†

The third function, that of *manufacturing certain blood cells,* is carried on in the red marrow of the bones. The marrow cavity of bone

---

* Todd et al.[843] (pp. 28-29).
† Todd[842] (p. 157).

becomes filled with various cells that are concerned in making red blood cells, some white blood cells, and platelets. In the fetus the marrow is distributed widely throughout the bones. During the postnatal growing years the space in bones in which red marrow is found decreases and becomes localized in certain areas such as the diploe* of the skull, the ribs and sternum, vertebrae, in cancellous tissue of some of the short bones, and the ends of long bones.

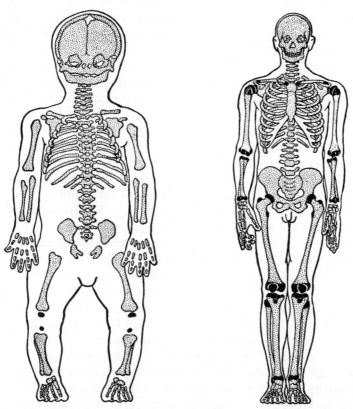

Figure 29. Diagram of skeleton of newborn and adult reconstructed to same height, illustrating stage of skeletal development at birth in contrast to that at maturity. (After Patten, B. M.: Human Embryology. The Blakiston Co., 1946.)

* Diploe is the cancellous layer between the outer and inner tables of the bones of the skull. Cancellous bone is characterized by a lattice structure, as the spongy tissue of bones.

How Bones Develop. Most bones develop from a cartilaginous model which is laid down early in utero. This cartilage is gradually replaced by bone, beginning at ossification centers from which it spreads concentrically. Through intricate cellular processes, the organic matrix of the bone is formed and minerals, predominately calcium and phosphorus, are deposited. The mineral salts give bone its hardness and rigidity; the organic material determines its tenacity. The process of replacement of cartilage by bone begins in early embryonic life and continues until the skeleton has reached full maturity. Bones grow by appositional growth rather than interstitial growth. In other words, growth takes place at the edge of existing bone, not by expansion from within. Bones grow in width by adding new bone at the outer edges underneath the periosteum, and long bones grow in length toward each end of their cartilage models. In long bones another center of ossification appears at the ends of the cartilage model and is termed an epiphysial center of ossification or epiphysis.* While a long bone is growing there remains a noncalcified area, observable in an x-ray, between the shaft or diaphysis and the epiphysis. New bone is produced by cellular activity at the edge of the diaphysis in this area. At the same time the ossification of the epiphysis continues. Growth of the long bones is terminated when the epiphysis and the diaphysis unite, as seen in the hand of the eighteen-year-old in Figure 30.

Some bones develop in a membranous area rather than a cartilaginous one, as, for example, the bones of the vault of the skull. The same cellular processes occur to produce bone, and from ossification centers bony tissue spreads concentrically to form the bones of the skull.

Bone development continues throughout the growing years and is not completed generally until the individual is in his twenties. The skeleton in the early years has many aspects of immaturity and therefore is quite different from that of an adult. Some of the differences can be observed in Figure 29, which shows the skeleton of a new-born and of an adult. In the young child all of the cartilaginous model has not been replaced by bone and larger spaces between bones exist at the joints of the body. With more space between the ends of bones at the joints, and longer and less firmly attached ligaments, the child has more flexibility in certain movements, all of which gives him the appearance of being "double jointed." Immature bones also have proportionately more

---

* In Figure 30, at age 5 years, note the middle finger of the hand. Each bone has a smaller bone at one end. This small bone is the epiphysis.

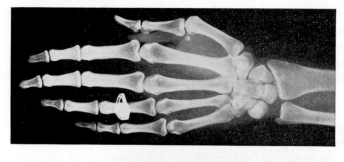

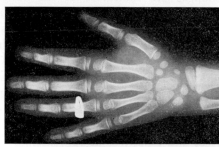

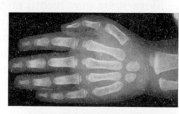

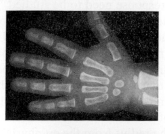

Birth   1 year   2 years   5 years   18 years

Figure 30. X-rays of hand and wrist showing skeletal maturation of girls at birth, 1 year, 2 years, 5 years, and 18 years (mature hand) according to the Greulich and Pyle standards. (Reproduced from Greulich, W. W., and Pyle, S. I.: Radiographic Atlas of Skeletal Development of the Hand and Wrist. Stanford, California, Stanford University Press, 1950.)

water and protein-like substances and less minerals. Thus young bones are less resistant to pressure and muscle pull and, therefore, are more liable to deformity. Growing bone, also, has a rich supply of blood. Being more vascular the bone not only receives a steady supply of bone building materials but also will be subjected more readily than mature bone to any infecting organism which may be carried in the blood stream.

As bones grow they pass through a regular series of changes in form that characterize their progress until they achieve their mature size and form. These changes are indicators of the maturational process.* X-rays, taken at intervals of time, reveal the maturational progress in skeletal development and the developmental patterns of individual children. Figure 30 shows the bone development of the hand and wrist that can be expected of most girls according to the Greulich and Pyle Atlas[316] at birth, 1 year, 2 years, 5 years, and maturity. Note the absence of epiphyses and carpal (wrist) bones at birth, the gradual appearance of epiphyses and carpal bones, the changing of the shape of the bones during early childhood, and finally the mature hand with complete union of epiphyses and diaphyses at 18 years.

Bone Scars.   Bone scars may record metabolic disturbances resulting from severe illness and other adverse circumstances, and may also appear in the early stages of recovery from malnutrition. Transverse lines may appear on certain long bones, indicating that normal growth has been interrupted.†[239, 316, 333, 480] Some children, after a severe illness, will show bone scars; others, of comparable age and with illness of the same severity, will show none. The reasons for the individual difference in response need to be studied. The absence of scars does not necessarily mean that a recent illness or other traumatic experience has not had an adverse effect on a child. However, the presence of such scars would indicate that it is highly probable that it had done so.

Greulich and Pyle[316] discuss scars appearing after two widely different kinds of experiences. X-rays of the hands of children in Nagasaki and Hiroshima, taken after the war, showed bone scars in a large percentage of children. These scars were located at about the same distance on the radius from the epiphysial line in children of comparable

---

* ". . . maturity indicators are those features seen in the radiograph, which because of their regular and irreversible sequence of appearance, mark the development of the bone to its mature form." Pyle and Hoerr[675] (p. 15).

† For a discussion of the processes involved in the formation of bone scars see Park.[650]

age. It is believed that these lines indicate interruption in growth caused by radiation and other injuries incurred at the time of the atomic bombing. Finer transverse lines have appeared in the radius of some children with severe malnutrition after their diet had been supplemented with milk. "It appears, therefore, that such transverse lines or scars indicate the occurrence of periods during which the equilibrium between the rate of deposition of mineral and other osseous material and the rate of growth of the bone has been disturbed, either by a rapid deceleration or an interruption of growth or by a sudden increase in the rate of deposition of these substances."*

Individual Differences in Skeletal Development. Children differ in skeletal development as they differ in height and weight, although the process of skeletal maturation is less subject to fluctuations than that of growth. Differences between skeletal development of boys and of girls are present at birth and continue as the children grow older. For example, the fifth carpal bone does not appear in boys until an average age of sixty months; it appears in girls at the average age of forty-eight months.[676] Even among children of the same sex differences can be expected. There are fast maturers and slow maturers in bone development just as there are fast growers and slow growers in height and weight. There is evidence that heredity influences the pattern of bone growth.[690] Endocrines likewise influence skeletal development.[904] Chronic malnutrition has a retarding influence on skeletal maturation.[225, 787]

Determining Skeletal Maturation. Skeletal maturation, as stated previously, can be assessed by x-ray examination of joints of the body, comparing with a standard the time of appearance of ossification centers, changes in the shape of these centers, and finally union of the epiphysis and the diaphysis. In infancy and early childhood the first two criteria are available. The growth of the bones in the hand and wrist is considered by many to be a satisfactory representative of the growth of the skeletal structure as a whole.† The changes in density of these bones, too, are considered to be quite representative of the generalized changes throughout the body. Bone development of the body, therefore, can be evaluated by inspection and comparison with a standard roentgenogram of the contours of the ends of bones of the hand, of the

---

* Greulich and Pyle[316] (p. 17).
† An x-ray picture of the infant's foot also gives evidence that is valuable in interpreting his stage of maturing.[676]

wrist bones and the epiphyses, and of the progress toward union of the epiphysis with the shaft of the bone. Standards used are Greulich and Pyle,[316] which is a revision and extension of the standards of Todd[843] and Flory.[260] The degree of maturity is expressed as skeletal age. In the atlas by Greulich and Pyle[316] each bone is given an age equivalent so that comparison of the child's separate bones with the standards makes it possible to assess the age of each bone. These separate ages can then be averaged to give the skeletal age for the hand. By assessing each individual bone it is possible to observe the degree of symmetry of the development of the bones in this area. This procedure calls attention to any imbalance in skeletal development that might be detected in the x-ray of the hand and prompts investigation of the health history of the child in an attempt to find the factors which may be contributing to this imbalance.

The range in the degree of development of the bones in this area can be observed easily by plotting the most advanced age, the least advanced age, and the skeletal age assigned to the hand as a whole. With the plotting of a series of assessments consistently balanced or unbalanced development or changes can be observed. Such a graph is termed a "Red Graph"[316] and the method is termed the "Red Graph Method" for observing symmetry or asymmetry in skeletal development.

Another method of assessment which has been suggested by Acheson,[1] is that of considering skeletal maturity in units instead of by skeletal age. These units are based on maturity indicators, or the distinct changes in the shape of the bones. The measure of maturity is the sum total of the units observed.

A child's progress toward maturity is more important, as emphasized by Todd,[843] than his status at the time of an x-ray.

If, for example, in six months his skeletal age has progressed six months, then his progress in skeletal age is keeping pace with his progress in chronological age. If, on the other hand, he has progressed only two months in skeletal age during the same period, his skeletal growth is lagging behind. If he has gained nine months in skeletal age during this six-month period his bone growth has been accelerated. The slow rate of skeletal maturing may be the normal pattern for one child, just as the accelerated rate of maturing may be the normal pattern for another.

Skeletal Status and General Bodily Maturity.   Individuals concerned with children need some understanding of how a child is maturing physically to understand his total growth and to appreciate his behavior and his needs. In order to determine general bodily maturity separate assessment of each organ system would be most satisfactory, but is not yet possible. One of the systems which can be assessed is the skeleton. Its role in determining bodily maturity is important because (1) its maturation covers the whole growth period with maturity indicators distributed throughout this period, (2) the process can be observed by the use of x-rays, and (3) its development is closely related to the development of the reproductive system, which is assumed to be a reliable indicator of general bodily maturity. This assumption is based on the fact that many changes in tissues, other than those of the reproductive organs, including skin, hair, sweat glands, distribution of subcutaneous fat and muscle growth, occur during pubescence. Thus skeletal development is used as an indicator of physical maturity.* How much reliance can be placed on this indicator depends greatly on the degree of harmony of a child's development in all its parts. Naturally the value of any tool in assessing development depends on the manner in which it is used.

Head and Skull. The head of a child at birth measures 12 to 14 inches in circumference, the circumference being slightly larger in boys than in girls.[879] By one year the head has increased about 33 per cent; by five years, when it closely approximates its adult size, it has increased 48 per cent.

The skull is the bony framework of the head, enclosing the brain and supporting the face. At birth the bones of the skull have not fully developed. Most of the bones have grown enough so that they are separated by "narrow seams" of relatively undifferentiated connective tissues. "An arrangement whereby adjacent bones are joined by connective tissue is termed a *suture*. At points where more than two bones meet, the sutures, however, are wide and such areas are termed *fontanelles*."† Growth of the vault of the skull takes place at the sutures between the individual bones. There are six fontanelles at birth, but only two can be observed in a physical examination. The largest one lies in the midline between the two parietal bones and the frontal bone. This diamond-shaped area is called the anterior, or frontal, fontanelle (commonly known as the soft spot). In the midline between the parietal bones and the occipital there is a smaller area, called the posterior, or occipital,

---

* For detailed discussion see Greulich and Pyle.[316]
† Ham[328] (p. 197).

fontanelle. The posterior fontanelle closes usually between the fourth and eighth week. The anterior fontanelle usually closes somewhere about one year of age. One study showed that 90 per cent of these closures occur between seven and nineteen months.[3] During infancy the skull grows rapidly to accommodate the brain, which is increasing steadily in size. At birth the upper, cranial, part of the skull, enclosing the brain (the brain case) has a capacity of 350 cc.; this increases to 750 cc. by one year of age and to 900 cc. by two years. The brain reaches its approximate adult size of 1500 cc. by six years, and in well grown children it may be practically adult in size by four and one-half years. Thereafter the increase in the size of the brain case is very minor in amount.

The lower part of the skull is the facial portion. Of the facial area, the upper portion is much more fully developed at birth than is the lower. The bones of the face grow steadily but relatively slowly until the late teens. This is in contrast with the cessation of growth in the brain case in earlier childhood, but is due to the increasing size of respiratory passages and jaws, and appearance of the permanent teeth. The early growth of the brain case results in its relatively large size as contrasted with the smallness of the face.

Part of the increase in the size of the face during childhood is due to development of the air sinuses. The antrum and ethmoids grow rapidly during the first two years. The average age at which either frontal sinus is definitely evident above the nose and at which it begins to increase in size has been calculated as three years, although this is a difficult evaluation to make, and the age may vary widely.[553]

Since the sinuses are not visible in x-rays at birth, their growth as revealed through roentgenograms can bc considered as one of the maturity indicators of the skull.

Examination of Figure 31 will aid in recognition of fontanelles and sutures, the relative proportions of cranial and facial parts of the skull, and the changes which occur with growth, such as obliteration of the fontanelles and the increased relative growth in the facial area.

Thorax.   The chest is barrel-shaped in infancy, and the downward slope of the ribs is less pronounced than it is in later childhood and in adult life; its circumference at birth is 12 to 14 inches, slightly less than that of the head. By the end of the first year the chest circumference is 17 to 19 inches, slightly larger than that of the head.

There is considerable individual variability in the time at which a child's chest assumes the adult shape.* Some children at five and six years of age continue to have a relatively barrel-shaped chest, whereas in others it is approaching the adult shape.[879]

Vertebral Column. The spine or vertebral column of the newborn is a flexible structure. Before the child is born his head and legs are curved toward the front of the body and his spine is, therefore, curved like a "C." When he is born he must breathe; that requires that his head be raised from his chest and the cervical spine (neck) begins to assume its individual form of curvature. As the child learns to sit up and learns to balance himself for standing and walking the normal curvatures of the spine develop. From these normal curvatures as well as the differences in contour and size of the vertebrae, we have come to recognize four spinal regions in man, the cervical, thoracic, lumbar, and sacral. The cervical and lumbar parts of the vertebral column are free, in that they are not attached to other bones; the thoracic spine articulates with the ribs, and the sacral region articulates in a more limited fashion with the pelvis. The head rests on the cervical spine.

At birth the spine is largely cartilaginous, just as the bones in the

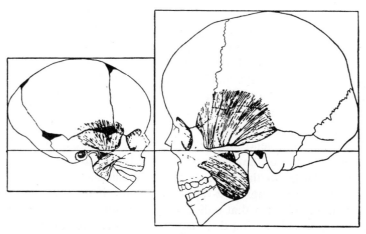

Figure 31. Skulls of newborn child and six-year-old boy drawn in their natural proportions. (Brash, J. C.: The Growth of the Jaws, Normal and Abnormal, in Health and Disease. London, The Dental Board of the United Kingdom, 1924.)

---

* In the adult the anteroposterior diameter is approximately 75 per cent of the lateral diameter.[879]

arms and legs are largely cartilaginous, but the spine becomes less flexible as the child grows older, both because the cartilage is replaced by bone and because its motility is limited by its function, namely, that of maintaining the body in an upright position.

The ribs of the fetus are important. Their ossification begins very early in fetal life but is not completed until about the twentieth year. They not only enclose the lungs but supply attachment for the accessory muscles of breathing as well as the diaphragm. These factors are important in the posture of the body (see p. 169 ff.).

Learning to sit and to walk may put a temporary strain on the muscles and the soft tissues attached to the vertebrae, and it is desirable to prevent young children from becoming exhausted in the pleasure they have in this new skill.

Pelvis.   The pelvis of the child consists of two sets of three bones (ilium, ischium, and pubis), one set on each side, which unite at twenty years to form a single hip bone. The two hip bones, bound together with the sacrum by strong ligaments, form the pelvic girdle which supports the weight of the body on the legs. This circle of bone lodges the urinary bladder, the lower end of the large intestine, the organs of reproduction of females, and the large vessels and nerves to the lower extremities, and serves as a protection to them.

The pelvic cavity of the newborn is much smaller relatively than that of the adult and is more horizontal in position. In a study of the pelvis during the first year of life and in another study of the pelvis of children between two and nine years, Reynolds[688, 689] found that the pelvis as a whole grows most rapidly during the first three months, after which the rate of growth decreases throughout infancy and prepuberal childhood. He found that boys tend to have larger pelvic measurements relating to the outer structure of the pelvis, whereas girls tend to have larger measurements relating to the inner structure, including a relatively larger outlet. From observation of x-rays of the same children taken at different ages it would seem that a distinctive individuality of shape persists as growth proceeds during these early years. Reynolds found that children who had larger pelves at birth also were longer and heavier and had larger heads. Larger pelves were associated with earlier appearance of the first tooth in both sexes and with advanced ossification of bones in boys. No significant relationship was found between pelvic size or shape and time of walking.

The change in gait evident at about the age of three results from a widening of the pelvic girdle and an increase in the relative length of the legs.

Extremities. The arms are relatively shorter in the infant than in the adult (see Figure 24). The clavicle (collar bone), the first bone in the body to ossify, is short and therefore helps to produce the narrow sloping of the shoulders of the infant. The radius and ulna of the forearm are more nearly equal in thickness than in the adult. The hands of an infant are quite different from those of an adult; the fingers are relatively shorter and stubbier. The hand changes gradually in shape and size as the child grows.

The legs of the newborn are short and flexed, and the soles of the feet are directed toward each other. As the infant grows his legs straighten. Growth of the foot* in length decreases in rate rapidly from a high in infancy, to four or five years of age when a plateau is reached. During these years there is no difference in the size of the feet of boys and girls. By five years of age, girls have attained between 70 and 75 per cent of the total growth of the foot while boys have attained between 65 and 70 per cent. When the growth of foot, stature and length of the leg bones were compared in terms of progress toward their mature size, it was found that the foot, at all times, was nearer its mature size than either stature or the bones of the leg.†

The foot of the infant is characteristic of his stage of development and is flexible, relaxed, and more mobile than that of an older child. The arches are much less rigid in infancy than at later periods of growth. In the bottom of the foot is a fat pad which gives the appearance of "flat footedness." Even after the child has started to walk, the ligaments are relaxed and the large muscles, not yet accustomed to maintaining balance, are unable perfectly to carry out their new task. The feet are therefore held widely apart in order to widen the base of support and there is a tendency to "toe out," throwing the weight on the inner side of the sole of the foot.

X-ray pictures of the foot of the newborn show two tarsal centers;

* Information from a semilongitudinal study by Anderson et al.[41]

† For example, at one year of age the feet of the girls were already half as long as they ever would be, whereas these same girls did not attain half of their mature stature until 18 months, and did not attain half of their mature leg length until three years of age. In boys, the same order was true, although the ages were somewhat later.

Figure 32. These twins of eight months illustrate the body proportions of infants—the relatively short legs and long trunk and head. They also illustrate the chubbiness of infancy and individual differences in size.

for boys at one year of age there are four tarsal centers; at three years of age there are eight epiphyses and the fifth tarsal center has developed; at five years all seven of the tarsal bones and all of the epiphyses of the metatarsals and the toes have appeared.[676] Ossification in the feet of boys lags behind that in girls. Soon after the practice of walking is established the bones in the arch take on the characteristic individuality of their relative position, i.e., low or high arch. Although much of the bone is still in the cartilaginous state the adult characteristics of the arch are forecast. Whatever modifications occur thereafter are largely due to injury or reduction in muscle tonus and the like. From the facts revealed by studies it has been concluded that as early as five years there is a strong genetic component revealed by the shape of the arch.[705]

Nervous System*

The nervous system, with its two parts, the central and peripheral, is the mechanism concerned with the correlation and integration of various bodily processes, with the reactions and adjustments of the organism to its environment, and with conscious life.

The central nervous system consists of the brain and the spinal cord, which are continuous with one another. The peripheral nervous system consists of a series of nerves by which the central nervous system is connected with the various tissues of the body. For descriptive purposes these nerves may be arranged in two groups, the cerebrospinal and the autonomic; the two groups are intimately connected and closely intermingled. It is largely through the agency of the central nervous system that all the various tissues and systems of the body are integrated into a smoothly operating unit. The functional unit in the central nervous system is the reflex. "The growth of the mind is profoundly and inseparably bound up with the growth of the nervous system. . . . Five months before the baby is born all of the nerve cells he will ever possess have already been formed and many of them are prepared to function in an orderly way. At this time the fetus makes movements of arms and legs . . . ; the eyelids can wink; the eyeballs can roll; the hands can clasp; the mouth can open and close; the throat can swallow; the chest makes rhythmic movements in preparation for the event of birth, when the breath of postnatal life will rush into the lungs."† The growth of the nervous system, like all growth, is a patterning process. It produces patterned changes in the nerve cells, which in turn produce corresponding changes in patterns of behavior. In the young child it is these changes in patterns of behavior which give us an understanding of what changes are taking place in his nervous system. It is significant that by the sixth year the child's nervous system is well developed and adequately stocked with mature cells. This development has to do with his learning processes, his activity, the maturity of his habits, and the functioning of the systems of his body.

At birth the nervous system is very immature in its functioning,

---

* For detailed discussion of the nervous system see Ranson's The Anatomy of the Nervous System; Its Development and Function, revised by S. L. Clark,[680] and Carlson and Johnson's Machinery of the Body.[154]

† Gesell and Ilg[291] (p. 18).

although the brain grows much more rapidly in fetal life and early infancy than does the rest of the body. The brain at birth has reached about 25 per cent of its mature size, whereas the body as a whole has attained only 5 per cent of its mature size. By one year it has reached approximately 67 per cent and by six years approximately 89 per cent of its mature weight.* Certain reflex activities essential to life are well developed at birth, such as sucking, swallowing, emptying the bladder, coughing. A number of other reflex activities are present at birth but are not fully developed and efficient.

According to the limited knowledge about the developing nervous system it is believed that the cerebral cortex of the newborn is too immature to function to any appreciable extent,[169, 170] and, therefore, that early infant behavior is controlled by subcortical centers. This fact is sometimes used in support of the view that the newborn baby and the infant in his first few months of life cannot be "spoiled." In infancy, stereotyped behavior is common because of this incomplete neural development. McGraw,[540] in studying neuromuscular maturation, states that as the cerebral cortex matures it appears to have an inhibiting effect upon some activities under subcortical control and to permit emergence and integration of other neuromuscular performances. When the cortex matures to the point of performing a significant role in controlling behavior, the characteristics of cortical behavior become evident, namely, a planned element in the mode of reaction, a latency of response, and a fertile variety of response. This latter characteristic replaces the earlier stereotyped kind of behavior. Growth of all parts of the cortex does not progress uniformly, and evidence[169] seems to show that the motor region is more advanced at birth and advances at a faster rate in the early months than the other regions.

Gesell[292] points out a possible structure-function relationship in that the increase in size and complexity of the cerebellum† closely parallels postural development. It grows slowly during the first few months, but grows rapidly in the last half of the first year and the first half of the second year. It attains practically full size before five years. The period of rapid gain occurs at the time when the child is gaining control of erect posture and manual and locomotive activities. Certainly neurological development is one of the several areas in which maturational readiness serves as a basis for behavior.

* Calculated from figures given by Watson and Lowrey.[881]
† The chief role of the cerebellum is the modulation of muscle movement lending refinement to movement and the maintenance of posture.

Voluntary control of body movements such as sitting, standing, control of bladder and bowel movements, and the like, involve learning and a later stage of physical and mental maturity as well as further bone and muscle development than do the earlier reflex activities. Gentry and Aldrich[284] found that certain toe reflexes disappeared when voluntary control, as indicated by the use of feet for locomotion, was established. The exception was the Babinski reflex, which disappeared gradually during the first and second years. The disappearance of these reflexes and the appearance of the early stages of locomotion might be considered a maturity indicator of the change from subcortical to cortical control. Ability to achieve these voluntary controls follows an orderly pattern of development as we shall see later, but the chronological age at which it is achieved varies among children.

The ability to register sensations is in most instances present at birth, but the impression made by the stimulus is much less acute then than it is in later life. Later, also, come the associations which give meaning to these sensations. This is discussed later under sensory development.

Muscular System

Movements of the body are produced by muscular action. Muscular activity is produced not by muscles alone but by virtue of their structure, their attachment to bones, and their innervation. Muscles are formed of bundles of a special kind of cell which is able to shorten or elongate under nervous stimulation. Muscles under the control of the will, such as those of the arms and legs, are known as voluntary; others, such as those of the stomach, are known as involuntary. They differ in the character of the cells that compose them. Muscles cover most of the skeleton and are disposed in all directions, so that a great variety of motion is possible. In most instances muscles are in pairs, so that one counteracts the pull of another.*

The growth and maturation of this system continues throughout the developmental period. At birth the muscles represent one fifth to one fourth of body weight, in contrast to one third at early adolescence and two fifths at maturity. The growth of the muscles follows a pattern similar to that of the body as a whole, but lags somewhat behind general growth during infancy and childhood. Knowledge of the growth in certain muscle groups has been extended through the study of x-ray

* For detailed discussion of the nature and function of muscles see Carlson and Johnson.[154]

Figure 33. This child at two years and four months has good muscle development.

shadows.[819] X-rays will also demonstrate the density of muscular tissue.
Krogman says: "children with 'light' muscle shadows fatigue easily,
they are prone, likewise, to mental fatigue, with overt symptoms of
restlessness, impatience, and irritability. . . ."* Maturation changes have
been observed indirectly through tests which measure motor ability and
strength. In young children many of these tests cannot be utilized.

* Krogman[481] (p. 283).

It is probable that no new muscle fibers are added after birth. Changes are due to increases in length, breadth, and thickness of the fibers, to their structure, to their attachment, and to their control through the nervous system. In the newborn the muscles of greatest development are found in the eye and in the respiratory tract. The arm muscles are better developed than those of the leg. During the course of development other muscle groups outstrip those best developed in the newborn, so that in adulthood the thickest bundles are found in the leg and in the back. In the early years the large muscles are better developed than the small, fine muscles. The young child is more skillful, therefore, in activities involving large movements than in activities involving precision. In the newborn the connective tissue is only moderately developed, and elastic fibers are absent. Both of these types of fiber increase in number with age; thus, as the child grows his muscles function more adequately. The condition of the muscles at all ages depends on the constitution of the child, his health, and his habits of eating, sleeping, and activity. In turn, one of the indicators of the health of a child is the degree of muscle tone, which is the condition of constant partial contraction. The tone of the muscles is important since it affects much of the support that various structures of the body require, such as that which the muscles of the abdomen give to the digestive organs when a person stands upright.

Body Dynamics

"Posture has long been thought of in terms of standing and sitting, and correct posture as the erect position assumed when one is under inspection, but posture should really be considered as the sum total of the positions and movements of the body throughout the day and throughout life. It should include not only the fundamental static positions in lying, sitting and standing and the variations of these positions but also the dynamic postures of the body in motion or in action, for it is here that posture becomes most important and most effective. Posture has a direct relation to the comfort, mechanical efficiency and physiologic functioning of the individual."*

"Good dynamic posture implies the use of the body or its parts in the simplest and most effective way, using muscle contraction and relaxation, balance, coordination, rhythm and timing as well as gravity,

* Howorth[372] (p. 1398).

inertia and momentum to optimum advantage. The smooth integration of these elements of good dynamic posture results in neuromusculo-skeletal performance which is easy, graceful, satisfying and effective and represents the best in the individual physical activity as well as in the physical activity of the individual.*

It is generally accepted that efficient use of the body has a beneficial effect on the general health and physical well being of an individual, and equally accepted that poor body dynamics, with its accompanying lack of muscle tone, lowered threshold of fatigue, and lessened available mechanical energy, has a bad effect on the general health. The body, like any other machine, can be mechanically efficient only when all its parts are maintained in equilibrium.

The body dynamics of a child at any time must be considered in terms of contributing to his physical and emotional well-being at the moment and his continued well-being as he grows and matures. What happens to him in this area in his early life may have significance for him later.

Five important factors must be taken into consideration in discussion of the body dynamics of a child: (1) force of gravity, (2) condition of bones and muscles, (3) stage of development, (4) individual differences, (5) environment.

Influences of Force of Gravity. A child's body is subject to the laws of gravity, and therefore maintenance of good balance with the least muscular effort demands that the body must be, as nearly as possible, arranged symmetrically about a line that passes through the center of gravity. As indicated in Figure 34, this line passes a little in front of the ankle, through the knee, hip joint, the center of the shoulder, and the ear. Figure 34 also shows that when the body is out of balance some part is likely to be pushed or pulled out of its normal place or must work under a strain.

Condition of Muscles and Bones. The condition of the muscles and bones influences balance. The muscles attached to the bones hold the body in position as well as make locomotion possible. Good muscle tone is, therefore, important. All the skeletal muscles are arranged in pairs, and in order to have good balance of parts of the body these opposing muscles must be of equal strength. When one pair of muscles is strong and the other weak, equilibrium is lost, and that part of the body is thrown out of balance. Forward shoulders illustrate this point.

* Op. cit. (pp. 1401-1402).

Influence of Stage of Development. Balance of the body is influenced by the child's stage of growth and development. His body is growing and changing in its proportions. Muscles are immature, ligaments are loose and relaxed. He has greater mobility and flexibility of joints than adults. This range of movement in joints is reduced by the gradual tightening of ligaments and fascia, and by the strengthening of muscles.

A very young child is unstable when he stands because a high center of gravity and a small base make him top heavy, and immaturity of the nervous system makes it difficult for him to readjust his balance when it is disturbed. We will see, as we discuss the changes in balance as the child develops, just how important this third factor is.

The uterine position persists in the newborn infant. With legs and arms flexed and a convex curve which includes head and body, he is practically a little ball. Much of the first year he is in a recumbent position and the force of gravity operates horizontally, tending to "unroll" the "coiling" which had been his uterine position. The activity

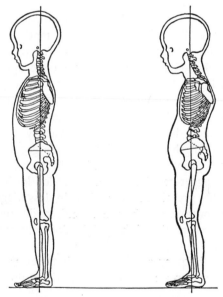

Figure 34. Good and poor posture. ("The Child from One to Six, His Care and Training." Children's Bureau Publication No. 30, U. S. Department of Labor, p. 31.)

of the infant also is a factor. When the neck muscles become sufficiently mature to hold up his head, the first of the adult spinal curves appears, the cervical curve. Later, when he begins to stand and walk, the lumbar curve at the lower part of the back appears with a compensating dorsal curve. At the same time the pelvis is tilted forward and the abdomen becomes prominent.

The legs have lost some of the natural curve that is often confused with the condition called bowlegs, which may be one of the character-istics of a rachitic child. During the period of early infancy when he kicks, stretches, and stiffens his legs and feet when he cries or anticipates being taken up, he is practicing the shortening of the external rotators of the thigh and exercising the muscles in the abdomen and buttocks. This stretching and adjustment of muscles in the hip, back, legs, shoul-der, chest, and abdomen are part of his development in preparation for crawling and walking. He should be free to use his arms and legs and encouraged to do so within the limits of his strength, but certainly not to the point of fatigue.

To maintain balance the child, when he begins to stand and walk, stands with everted (toeing-out) feet far apart and with knees flexed. This adds stability by increasing the base on which he stands and lowers his center of gravity. The weight of the body tends to fall on the inner part of the foot and pronation* occurs. The relaxed ligaments and fat pad under the arches give the pronated foot the appearance of being flat. A degree of knock-knees is also present. Gradually, as the rate of growth slows down and relative strength and coordination increase with increased activity, skillful movement becomes as important as weight bearing in the child's balance. With the variety of activity and the resulting muscle strength of the various muscle groups, by six or seven years feet and toes point straight ahead and knock-knees have become straight.[452] The exaggerated lumbar curve called lordosis, which is still present during the preschool years but in less degree than during infancy, and the prominent abdomen tend to disappear later. Adult posture, with its upward tilt of the pelvis, does not become established until adolescence.

One study[706] of the posture of children between the ages of two and twelve, which has set up a method for appraising posture, has referred

---

* "Pronation refers to a position of the foot in which the weight in standing is borne on the inner side of the foot; also eversion or valgus." Kendall, Kendall and Boynton[452] (p. 16).

to this age period from a postural point of view as the "ugly duckling stage." Most of the conditions they studied, knock-knees, pronation, lordosis, slumped back and hyperextended knees,* unless exaggerated, improved with age.

Individual Differences. Individual differences occur in the area of body dynamics as well as in other phases of child development. Some children use their bodies with ease and grace; others apparently use up more energy than most in the daily activities of life; still others, because of their unique body structure, have certain limitations in achieving all-round good body dynamics.

Because of differences in body structure children will demonstrate differences in body dynamics. The stocky child and the lean child, by nature of their physical equipment will differ in the way they balance the segments of their bodies. For example, a relatively heavy child will have more weight to balance, which may affect his leg and foot posture. Differences in relative tissue growth, discussed earlier, may contribute to postural differences in children. Thus there is no one best posture for all children. Posture for each child must be evaluated in terms of his own physical structure and functioning.

Environmental Influences. Many environmental factors contribute to posture, all of them by their direct or indirect relation to the condition of the muscles and their functioning. Good muscles cannot exist without good nutrition. Good nutrition implies not only an optimum diet but also the proper absorption and utilization of the chemical substances in that food which go to make up the tissues of the body and provide for their function. It is necessary, therefore, to consider digestion, elimination, the balance of rest and activity, and the emotional tone of the child.

A good balance of rest and activity with times for relaxation during the day and plenty of sleep at night will guard against accumulative fatigue, which contributes heavily to poor body balance. Small children require shorter periods of activity than older children, and need alternating periods of relaxation. It is difficult at times for the adult to remember that sitting erect for a little child is a serious physical undertaking, and to stand alone is an incredibly complex and delicate mechanical achievement, throwing into new tensions every one of the complicated muscle-bone levers of his body. Much energy is exerted

---

* Hyperextension is a condition in which the knees are pushed back beyond their normal position.

by the infant in these newly acquired skills and he needs time for recuperation.

Generally the young child, as his skills develop, enjoys all kinds of activity, running, climbing, digging, swinging, etc., thus strengthening all the muscles of his body. Occasionally, however a child limits himself and is very hesitant to try new activities. Some muscles of such a child lack the stimulation of vigorous exercise and do not develop as well as others, which may lead to poor body balance.

The feelings of a young child are expressed by the way he uses his body. A happy confident child carries his body in one way; an unhappy, insecure child will likewise express his feelings through his body balance. In our experience we have seen preschool children who were insecure and unhappy indicate their unhappiness by the sagging of shoulders, the tilt of the head, the gait of walking, or the lack of activity. On the other hand, we have seen children demonstrating their happiness with a buoyant, vigorous bodily approach to all activities. Children who carry a physical burden or handicap may also indicate this through posture. The child with a focus of infection will lack vigor. A child with a defect such as poor hearing or limited vision may develop a characteristic posture because of this limitation.

Certain aspects of the child's surroundings may easily affect his posture. The clothing of young children today is generally loose and light, so that their activity is not impeded. However, outdoor clothing may be so heavy and cumbersome that it limits the possibilities of activity. Shoes and socks need watching. Socks may become too short after washing and thus cramp the toes. After shrinking, the socks should be ½ to ¾ inch longer than the child's foot.[252] Shoes should fit the foot so as to give both support and flexibility. When an infant is beginning to walk a proper shoe can both protect the immature foot and aid in walking. Shoes for infants at this time should be long enough to allow at least ½ inch space beyond the limit of the big toe, for the foot is growing rapidly. A good shoe has a straight inner border, flat soles, and firm heel structures against which an infant can brace his feet in walking. Later, during the preschool years, laced shoes or oxfords with combination last are recommended because of the relatively broad toes and narrow heel of the young child. Some children wear shoes only occasionally. Going barefooted on surfaces that have some resilience, such as sand, grass, or a heavy carpet, can be a good experience for a child. However, the immaturity of the foot of the young child would indicate the value of supplying support and protection when he is walking on hard surfaces such as pavements or floors without carpet or rugs.

Beds should be flat and firm. Chairs should be low enough for feet to touch the floor, shallow enough for the child to sit with his back supported. When he sits in a chair too high and too deep the weight of his dangling feet pulls his shoulder girdle forward and thrusts his head forward.

Role of the Adult. Parents or other adults can provide the child with his needs for growth, offer him a satisfactory environment, give him the freedom to explore that environment, and be satisfactory models for him to imitate. Children tend to imitate the postural habits of adults, especially those of their parents, in activity and in repose. In addition, the adult can provide for regular health examinations by a physician, in order to assess the child's progress and detect the beginning of any difficulties. A child also needs protection against illness, as far as possible, and, when illness is inevitable, protection from fatigue

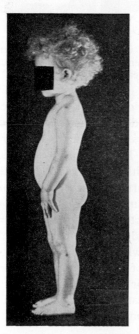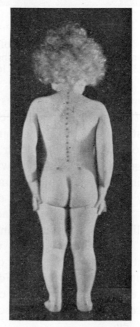

Figure 35. Good posture in a girl of nursery school age (two years, six months).

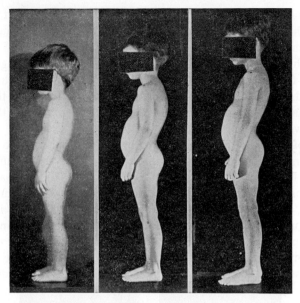

Age: 3 years, 1 mo.   4 years, 9 mo.   5 years, 10 mo.

Figure 36. Poor postural pattern of child persisting at different age levels. Note sharp angle of pelvic tilt, prominent abdomen, lordosis, round back, flat chest, forward shoulders, and forward head.

as he is convalescing. The muscles of a child who has been sick have lost some of their tone. Time is needed for their recuperation.

Poor Posture.   In the early years the beginning of poor posture, as well as of good posture, may occur. Figure 35 shows a child with good posture; Figure 36 shows a child with poor posture. Note the muscular relaxation in the latter child. Stuart and Stevenson[821] point out that functionally poor posture is not surprising in the early years, since children in these years are characterized by relative thinness, loose ligaments, limited musculature, and constant physical activity during the waking hours, characteristics which may lead to chronic fatigue.

Poor posture may be the result of an exaggeration of some phase of development or its perpetuation. For example, pronation may be severe enough to require attention at an early age, or may continue too long. Poor posture may also be due to some body asymmetry, such as shortness of one leg.

Again, it may be due to lack of vigor which is the result of some organic disturbance. It may be due to poor nutrition, chronic fatigue, or unsatisfactory environmental conditions which make it impossible for a child to maintain good balance. A review of his environment and of the gratification of his physical and psychological needs, and an evaluation of his health and developmental status should reveal the disturbing elements in his life and disclose the conditions which need prompt attention.

Habits of posture which become crystallized in later years may have begun in childhood and persisted through the years. However, this is not inevitable. Children with relaxed musculature resulting in poor balance need not carry that posture throughout life. On the basis of careful physical and emotional evaluation of the child, an adult can plan for that child so that all his individual needs will be met. When that plan is carried out he will be on his way to good body balance for

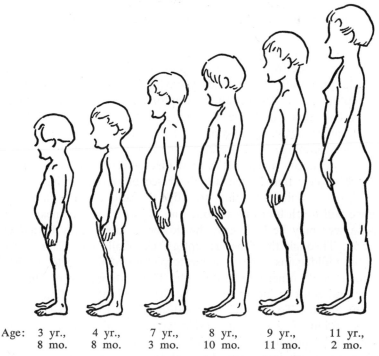

Age: 3 yr.,   4 yr.,   7 yr.,   8 yr.,   9 yr.,   11 yr.,
      8 mo.   8 mo.   3 mo.   10 mo.   11 mo.   2 mo.

Figure 37. Posture of a girl from 3 years, 8 months, to 11 years, 2 months, showing improvement after the preschool years.

him. Figure 37 shows improvement in muscle tone that resulted from adequate nutrition, a good balance of rest and activity of various kinds, and, in the preadolescent years, guidance in maintaining good balance.

Organs of Special Sense

Through the organs of special sense the child becomes acquainted with the world in which he lives, and learning for the normal child is largely dependent on the efficiency of these organs. Therefore, familiarity with the structure and functions of the organs through which his brain receives stimuli from the outside world is essential to understanding of the learning processes.

The organs of special sense may be divided into (1) those of the special senses of taste, smell, sight, and hearing, and (2) those associated with the general sensations of heat, cold, pain, pressure, etc. What we commonly think of as sense organs are those which have receptors that are stimulated by or directly acted upon by some energy change. The sense of touch can only be stimulated if the source of the energy comes into actual contact with the surface of the body or at least only a short distance from it. The receptors of the eye and ear, on the other hand, can be affected by energy having its source at a distance. Their receptors are called distance receptors. For example, the light emitted by the stars can be seen although the source of the light is millions of miles away. Light waves, though they come from great distances, must impinge on the retina of the eye to stimulate it.

So far as we know the infant cannot distinguish the distance from his body of objects that he can touch or see or smell. By individual learning he can acquire the ability to judge the source of the stimulus. Experience will teach him that to touch an object it must be near him; the sun he sees may be far away; the flower he smells may be a few yards away. Through the sense receptors, especially the distance receptors, the child gains a more accurate picture of the world outside himself than would otherwise be possible. The development of sensory awareness and sensory judgment will be discussed later in Chapter 9.

Sense of Sight.   To appreciate the discussion of the development of the perception of size, shape and distance in children, knowledge of the physical equipment with which the child is endowed to make perception possible is important. Through the sense of vision the child detects light, senses form, recognizes color and perceives depth and distance in space.

The eye, as an organ, is equipped in its internal structure with the retina, which has specialized kinds of sensory cells called rods and cones. Although the retina is not structurally complete until the child is about sixteen weeks old, the rods which detect the intensity of light and make vision possible function immediately after birth. The cone cells insure the recognition of color and contribute to the recognition of form. Certain color discrimination is possible as early as the third or fourth month, for by this age the cones may be developed. However, accurate perception of both color and form depends on learning and comes at a later stage of development. The accurate perception of distance and depth is made possible by focusing both eyes on the object at the same time, and the two images are perceived in consciousness as one. The ability to fuse two images into one, known as single binocular vision, is an important aid in judging distance. This acquired ability depends both on coordinated eye-muscle activity and on learning and is achieved slowly, being achieved by most children at the age of six or eight years. The perception of size, shape and distance is discussed further in Chapter 9.

Sense of Hearing. The auditory apparatus consists of the ears, two auditory nerves to convey stimuli to the centers of hearing in the brain. The ear is divided into three portions: the outer, middle and inner ear. The outer and middle ear are conducting mechanisms which convey sound waves to the cochlea of the inner ear, containing the sound receptors. Sound waves enter the external auditory canal, setting the ear drum in vibration, are transmitted across the cavity of the middle ear by the three little ear bones, bridging the space from the ear drum to the membrane separating the middle ear from the inner ear. The inner ear contains two mechanisms anatomically in close relation but physiologically quite separate: the cochlea and the vestibule. The cochlea belongs to the auditory organ; the vestibule, a series of organs, is concerned with equilibrium and has no connection with hearing.

The cavity of the middle ear has almost reached its final size at birth; in fact, the ossicles of the middle ear have reached their mature size in the middle of fetal life. The tympanic membrane has practically completed its growth by the time of birth. The bony labryinth of the inner ear has attained its adult size and proportion at the time of birth.

Hearing in the newborn is probably established within a few days. In the infant the eustachian tube, the channel connecting the middle ear with the throat, is short, straight and comparatively wide. This may account for the greater incidence of middle ear infections in infancy, bacteria from the throat having easy access to the ear.

Senses of Taste and Smell. The sense organs of taste and smell, called chemoreceptors, are normally stimulated directly by chemicals in solution, initiating an impulse in the nerve fibers responsible for taste and smell. The chemicals must be in solution in the saliva or in the secretions of the nasal cavity. A perfectly dry tongue does not taste, and the dry nasal cavity cannot be stimulated by aromatic substances. These receptors have very low thresholds and can be stimulated by solutions of great dilution (one part in two million).

TASTE. The receptor structures for taste, known as taste buds, occur chiefly on the tongue, but a few are found also in areas in the throat and in the posterior part of the mouth. The sensations of salt and sweet are recognized at the tip of the tongue, bitter at the base of the tongue posteriorly, and acid along the borders. Taste buds seem to be fairly well developed at birth, and newborn infants are able to differentiate pleasant and unpleasant sensations. By 2 or 3 months taste is so acute that the infant will notice changes in the amount of carbohydrate in his formula and indicate displeasure at substances which are disagreeable to his sense of taste.[881] The taste buds increase considerably in number during the first year. In the early years they are distributed abundantly on the inside of the cheeks and in the throat, in addition to those on the tongue. Later, during adolescence, they decrease in number and chiefly those of the tongue remain.[486] Thus with the same food, the taste sensations of infants and young children may differ from those of older children and adults.

SMELL. Each nasal cavity has small areas of ciliated cells, known as olfactory epithelium. Each is bathed in liquid, and substances to be detected must be soluble in this liquid. The moist receptors lie in the upper portion of the nasal cavity, so that in ordinary respiration the stream of air does not come in contact with them.

No satisfactory classification of smells has been made. The olfactory sense is easily fatigued, but even if it is so fatigued as to be insensitive for one kind of smell it is still normally excitable for other smells. Our knowledge of the sense of smell is still incomplete and unsatisfactory at the present time.

Cutaneous System

The cutaneous system consists of the skin and its appendages or accessory parts: the nails, hair, sweat glands and sebaceous or oil glands. The skin performs important functions: it protects the underlying parts from injury, from invasion by foreign organisms, and also from drying. It serves as a sense organ, in that it is richly supplied with sensory nerves. It plays an important part in the regulation of body temperature, since the loss of heat from the body occurs almost entirely through its surface. It also has limited excretory and absorbing powers. Absorption of ultraviolet rays by the skin and their action on a chemical substance in the skin produces vitamin D. Exposure to sunlight, therefore, is one way children can receive this necessary vitamin. There is a continuous output of carbon dioxide through the skin, although the amount leaving the body in this way is negligible, compared with the amount exhaled through the lungs. The skin reflects the general well-being of the body, and observation of its texture and color is important in children.

The skin of nearly every part of the body, except the palms of the hands and soles of the feet, is supplied with hair follicles. The cuticle layer of the skin is kept supple and preserved from the drying effect of the atmosphere by being constantly impregnated with sebum. This fatty material is secreted by the sebaceous or oil glands which are distributed all over the surface of the body wherever hair follicles are found, the duct of the gland opening into the hair follicle. The secretion of sebum begins when the child is about a month old and continues through life.

The tissue just beneath the skin has the capacity to store various materials either provisionally or permanently. Of these materials the best known is fat, which is laid down in fat cells. "The other type of storage which takes place in the skin is what was called by Cannon *storage by inundation,* and which may be compared with the storage of water in a bog. . . . When the blood is flooded with soluble substances, these may likewise find temporary storage, accompanied by water or not, in the subcutaneous tissues. The most noteworthy instances are of glucose and salts."[*] The amount of subcutaneous fat under the skin of babies and the firmness of the flesh show great variation. The

* Evans[249] (p. 1041).

changes in the amount of subcutaneous tissue with age have been discussed on pages 147 and 148.

The Hair. At birth the hair is very fine and black and varies in amount. Some babies have almost none; some have a heavy growth. This hair, however, is not indicative of the color, amount or texture of later hair. It is believed to be lost during the first year and replaced by other fine hair which, in turn, is replaced by hair of a coarser texture. This change to coarser hair tends to occur at a rapid rate during the first three years, and somewhat less rapidly and less uniformly thereafter.[852] A certain amount of the fine hair persists.

During the first two years of age, hair tends also to change in shape from a nearly round to a more oval type. The significance of the shape of the hair is not entirely understood.* The color may also change. There is a tendency among whites for hair to darken with age, except in some black haired strains.[182] It also tends to become less curly.

As the child grows his hair varies much in length, thickness and color on different parts of the body and in different races of mankind. There is no doubt that growth and distribution of hair follicles are affected by hormones but exact knowledge of the effect is not yet available. The thyroid hormone is essential to the proper growth and normality of the hair. Hair does not grow indefinitely, but after a period of growth the length remains stationary and sooner or later the hair may fall out, and a fresh cycle begin. Each hair follicle has its own characteristic growth rate and cycle. The hair, like the skin, reflects the health of the child, and when healthy it is glossy, smooth and elastic.

The Sweat Glands. The sweat glands are fully formed at birth, are distributed over almost the whole surface of the skin, begin to function when the child is one month old, and serve a minor role in excretion. Their chief function is the secretion of sweat, whose evaporation cools the surface of the body. The most plentiful constituent of sweat is sodium chloride. The secretion is under the control of the central nervous system, and except for the palms of the hands and soles of the feet has been shown to be almost entirely adapted to the regulation of the body temperature.

Sense of Touch, of Pain, of Temperature. "We are accustomed to distinguish several qualities of sensation among those having their

---

* It is true only in a general way that this characteristic is indicative of its behavior (straight, wavy, curly, frizzly).[852]

origin in the skin, . . . the sense of touch, including that of discrimination, the sense of pain and the sense of temperature. The very different qualities of sensation included under these three classes suggest that there may be a special mechanism, or class of mechanism, for each sense, and a careful investigation of the sensory qualities of the skin surface bears out this idea. Isolated stimulation of minute areas on the skin does not excite all the sensations together, but only a sense of touch or of pain, or a sense of cold or warmth."*

By means of the sense of touch the child arrives at a conclusion as to shape, texture, hardness and similar characteristics of bodies with which the skin comes into contact. This is important in the learning process. Certain areas are more sensitive to stimulation than other areas; for example, the fingertips are more sensitive to touch than the back of the hand; the lips are more sensitive to heat than the hands. Not all areas of the skin are sensitive to all kinds of stimuli; an object warmer than the temperature of the skin will stimulate only heat spots; a moderately cold object activates only cold spots. Each of the senses undoubtedly has its own special receptor structure which is adapted to stimulation by the definite kind of environmental change with which it is associated. These structures possess the same degree of specificity in their relation to the effective stimulating agent as do the rods or cones for light.[154]

The senses of touch and pain are present at birth but not well differentiated. A pain stimulus must be strong to elicit response. Later the response is immediate and diffuse, with general body movement, crying and possible reflex withdrawal. At one or two months the response is more delayed. Gradually, localization of the point of irritation develops. By twelve to sixteen months the child's hand moves directly to the point, rubs or pushes the stimulus away and will fix his eyes on the area if this is possible. This activity indicates the beginning of cortical participation in this type of behavior.[540] Proprioceptive receptors are active at birth, and they also gradually come under cortical control.†

A keen awareness of temperature is shown in the infant's response to changes in temperature of milk when artificially fed. He is likely to protest if the temperature of his feeding is not constant at all times.

---

* Evans[249] (p. 480).

† Conel states that special sensory areas of the cortex mature later than the motor areas.[169]

Glands of Internal Secretion

Growth is greatly influenced by the glands of internal secretion, small glands in various parts of the body that secrete and pour into the blood and lymph complicated chemical substances, called hormones, which are essential to life and to the growth and health of the body. These glands vary widely in their structure and in the nature of their secretions, and have the special functions of initiating, regulating, and controlling some of the activities of organs and tissues. Even before birth, if a child's thyroid gland is not functioning properly, he may be born in the abnormal condition known as cretinism. After the child is born his own glands must supply all his hormonal needs, changing as they do from time to time. Growth and development are influenced by at least three types of hormones, namely, the pituitary growth hormone, the thyroid hormone and androgen derived from either the adrenal gland or the testis. All these hormones stimulate protein anabolism, which means the use of protein in tissue building, and increase nitrogen retention. Much has yet to be learned about the details of their effect on growth and development. Probably each of these hormones manifests its effects at a different period of life and in a different way.[904] The thyroid probably exerts its most important influence on growth and development during the first few years of life, when development is most rapid. The adrenal androgens probably are responsible for the growth spurt of both sexes at adolescence. The period of life when the pituitary growth hormone is effective is not known. It is believed by some that it may be of little importance in the first few years, since the cessation of growth in pituitary dwarfism is not often observed until the third or fourth year.[904] Since dwarfism can be recognized during early childhood the pituitary is probably important then. Other glands indirectly affect growth through their part in metabolic processes, thus providing for a healthy body and materials for growth.

Although the amount of the secretions of these glands may be almost inconceivably small, they have incredible potency. Entire separation of the specific actions of the glands of internal secretion is impossible, since they are so intricately interrelated and affect each other as well as the various organs of the body. Judgment of the efficiency of their activity is based on the physiologic or metabolic functions which are influenced specifically by certain hormones and on the evaluation of the growth and development of the child.

Thyroid Gland. The thyroid gland is probably the best known of the endocrine glands because of the pathological effects produced when its functioning is abnormal, i.e., either overactive or underactive. The thyroid gland, located in the front of the neck, consists of large lobes on either side joined by a narrow isthmus. Its development begins early in fetal life and it probably becomes functional long before birth. After birth it continues to grow in size until puberty. Its secretion acts chiefly to aid in regulating the metabolic processes of the body. Underactivity of the gland lowers the activity of the body tissues, and, if the condition is present from birth, both mental and physical growth are retarded, and the child is known as a cretin. However, if thyroid is given early enough and continued uninterruptedly, the chances for approximately normal physical development are good. Mental development usually will remain somewhat retarded because of possible damage done to the brain during embryonic life and early infancy.

Overactivity of the thyroid is accompanied by a rapid pulse, restlessness, nervous irritability, tremor of the hands, increased perspiration, and loss of weight. Hyperthyroidism occurs infrequently in the early years.

Iodine has come to be recognized as essential for the normal activity of the thyroid gland. The use of iodized salt in endemic goiter regions, where insufficient iodine is found in drinking water or foods, is advisable for children as well as for adults.

Parathyroid Glands. These four tiny glands lie adjacent to the thyroid gland. They attain their maximum growth and their mature structure at puberty. Their secretion is essential for maintaining levels of calcium and phosphorus in the blood which are necessary for regular tissue activity.[825] Indirectly, through its effect on calcium metabolism, this hormone plays a role in maintaining the integrity of bone structure, in regulating neuromuscular activity, in the conduction of heart impulses, in the coagulation of blood and in the permeation of cellular membranes. Through its regulatory effect upon the availability of phosphorus, it can influence body tissues, many enzyme systems and the regulation of acid-base balances in the body. The parathyroid secretion varies according to physiologic need. When the hormonal secretion is not in accordance with physiologic needs, which rarely occurs in children, characteristic symptoms are noticed. Underactivity will result in a reduction in calcium in the blood which limits the amount available for bone formation; if severe enough, this may produce tetany, an abnormally increased reactivity of the nervous system to external stimuli which results in painful muscle spasms. Overactivity leads to decreased neuromuscular irritability so that the muscles of the body are less responsive to stimuli. Demineralization of bone may occur resulting in spontaneous fractures because of bone fragility.

Adrenal Glands.   The adrenal glands are two very small bodies lying in front of the upper end of each kidney. Each gland consists of an external cortical portion and an internal medullary portion. The cortex apparently develops first, being recognized at about the fourth week of embryonic life.

The adrenal medulla secretion, consisting of epinephrine and norepinephrine,* plays a role in aiding the body to adapt to sudden stress. It causes the release of ACTH from the pituitary gland which, in turn, stimulates the secretion of hormones of the cortex.†[904] It also produces similar effects to those produced by stimulation of the sympathetic nervous system. Under normal circumstances, the secretion is too small in quantity to be of *observable* physiologic significance, but under emergency conditions of emotional stress or danger‡ the secretion is enough to cause constriction of the blood vessels, acceleration of heart rate, some delay of fatigue, rise in blood sugar and increased coagulability of the blood. Commercially produced epinephrine, when injected as a stimulant, produces some of the same effects for an hour or two.§

Hormones of the adrenal cortex are essential to the maintenance of

---

* While the two hormones combine to produce the characteristic effect of the adrenal medulla secretion, they function differently. Both raise blood pressure but the mechanisms by which this is done are different. Epinephrine has a greater metabolic effect, as, for example, in increasing oxygen consumption and in raising blood sugar levels, than has norepinephrine.[264] Another difference appears to be in their response to emotions. Evidence seems to show that anger elicits the secretion of norepinephrine while fear and anxiety elicit the secretion of epinephrine. See Funkenstein.[277]

† This action is due chiefly to epinephrine.[300]

‡ The adrenal medulla secretion is stimulated by the sympathetic nervous system which, in turn, has been stimulated by the hypothalamus.

§ These effects seem to be due to a mixture of epinephrine and norepinephrine.[854]

life. They influence (1) metabolism of sodium, potassium and water, (2) carbohydrate, fat and protein metabolism, and (3) the production and maintenance of sex differences. An excessive production of androgens, which are responsible for protein anabolism, produces rapid growth, marked muscular development and accelerated skeletal development and deviations from the regular pattern of sexual development.* These hormones, therefore, affect development, play an essential role in the body's homeostatic mechanisms and in muscle fatigue, and also aid in the body's adaptation to stress and strain.†

Pituitary Gland. The pituitary gland is a small gland, about the size of a pea, lying in a depression of bone, called the sella turcica, in one of the most protected parts of the head. It consists of two parts, a glandular anterior portion, and a posterior neural portion. The anterior lobe elaborates hormones which profoundly affect almost every organ in the body, either directly or indirectly through influence on the activity of other glands. One hormone influences the growth of bone and soft tissues. An excess of this hormone in the growing years may cause excessive growth in stature. If the excess comes after the growing years (about twenty-five years), the bones become coarser and heavier. If there is a deficiency of this hormone during the growing period, infantile characteristics persist.‡

Another hormone secreted at the end of pregnancy initiates and provides for the continuation of lactation. Other hormones stimulate the growth and function of many other endocrine glands such as those affecting the thyroid (thyrotrophic), adrenal cortex (adrenocorticotrophic, ACTH), and sex glands or gonads (gonadotrophic).

The pituitary is responsible for maintaining equilibrium among the different endocrine glands. Ham[328] calls the pituitary gland the "chairman of the endocrine society." All the different members report to it regularly about their activity and the pituitary, in turn, by a series of hormones has a controlling influence on the structure and function of the various members. The pituitary, it appears, is in turn controlled by the hypothalamus of the central nervous system[825] and is affected by hormones of the other glands.

---

* See Talbot et al.[825] and Wilkins[904] for details regarding the effects of adrenal androgens upon development.

† See Selye.[743, 744]

‡ For discussion of dwarfism of various origins, including both endocrine and hereditary, see Wilkins,[904] Chap. IX.

The posterior neural portion regulates water metabolism, causes contraction of all involuntary muscles, especially of the uterus and breasts, and raises blood pressure. An extract of the posterior pituitary is sometimes used during delivery to stimulate contractions of the uterus.

Thymus Gland. The thymus gland is found a little below the lower border of the thyroid gland, lying partly in the neck and partly in the thorax behind the sternum. In structure it consists of small nodules or follicles somewhat fused together. Each follicle consists of a medullary and a cortical portion. The cortical part consists of lymphoid cells, while in the medullary part peculiar nestlike bodies are found and fewer lymphoid cells. The thymus, therefore, is essentially a lymphoid organ and its classification as an endocrine gland is questionable.* It attains its maximum growth during childhood. After puberty it gradually dwindles in size. The involution of different parts of the thymus begins at different ages: that of the lymphoid tissue begins at four years and that of the medulla at puberty. The connective tissue and fat continue to increase until old age.[125]

Sex Glands. The testes and ovaries are part of the reproductive system and produce internal secretions which lead to their classification as glands of internal secretion. The testes produce not only sperm cells but also hormones, called *androgens,* that are responsible for bringing about many of the physiological and psychological changes incident to maturity. Failure of the testes to produce this secretion at puberty causes a continuation of growth typical of childhood, thus producing overgrowth with an accompanying failure of sex development.

The ovaries produce ova and internal secretions containing the hormones, *estrogen* and *progesterone.* Estrogen acts as a general stimulant to sex differentiation. Progesterone adds a secondary stimulation that prepares the uterus for reception of the fertilized ovum and regulates various processes of pregnancy. The cyclic changes in the secretion of estrogen and progesterone result in the menstrual cycle.†

The ovaries and testes remain relatively quiescent during early childhood. It is not definitely known when the secretions of the male hormones begin—probably not until middle childhood. One type of

* There is considerable confusion as to the function of the thymus, and further investigation is needed before its functions can be definitely stated.

† See Talbot et al.[825] or Smith.[772]

ovarian hormone, estrogen, is secreted in the early years, but only in small amounts. If the sex glands fail to produce these hormones, sex development is delayed and the infantile characteristics continue. An excessive secretion in early childhood will produce precocious puberty.

The sex glands are related functionally to the other glands of internal secretion, and are influenced in turn by the activity of these glands.

Reproductive System

The primary reproductive structures in the human body are the ovaries in the female and the testes in the male. They produce the reproductive units, the ova and the sperm cells. A number of accessory structures, especially in the female, facilitate fertilization and provide more adequately for the development of the embryo. Other structures in the male sexual system serve as an accessory function in reproduction. From the third or fourth month of life until the eighth to the eleventh year, the beginning of the adolescent spurt, reproductive development is largely in abeyance. The testes are in the abdominal cavity during the greater part of fetal life and usually only reach their permanent scrotal position shortly before birth.

Topics for Study and Discussion

1. Select three five-year-olds who are relatively short, relatively tall, and "average" for their age, for whom there are a series of measurements from early infancy. Plot the height and weight and draw curves for these children on the Iowa curves and on the Baby Grid. Discuss the children's progress in relation to the standard curves and their positions on the grid. Relate their growth patterns to their physical needs.

2. Observe the body balance of a two-year-old and that of a four-year-old in activity and standing. Discuss the way each child balances his body and how his developmental stage and his environment contribute to it.

3. Discuss the significance of knowledge of bone maturation for students in child development. If possible, have x-rays of a boy and girl of the same chronological age and two children of the same chronological age but with different skeletal ages for observation in class.

4. Observe the behavior of a young infant and a preschool child and discuss how the behavior of each reflects changes in the developing nervous system.

5. Discuss the physical and physiological basis of the developmental task of learning to walk.

Selected Readings

Carlson, A. J., and Johnson, V.: The Machinery of the Body. ed. 4. Chicago, University of Chicago Press, 1953.

Greulich, W. W., and Pyle, S. I.: Radiographic Atlas of Skeletal Development of the Hand and Wrist. Stanford, Cal., Stanford University Press, 1950.

Krogman, W. M.: Handbook of Measurement and Interpretation of Height and Weight in the Growing Child. Monograph XIII (3). Evanston, Ill., Society for Research in Child Development, 1950.

Lerrigo, M. O.: "Is My Child Normal, Doctor?" Today's Health 30:32-33, 64, April, 1952.

Lerrigo, M. O.: Stories in Bone, Today's Health 30:36-38, June, 1952.

Phelps, W. M., Kiphuth, R. J. H., and Goff, C. W.: The Diagnosis and Treatment of Postural Defects. ed. 2. Springfield, Ill., Charles C Thomas, 1956. Chaps. 1, 2.

Washburn, A. H.: Appraisal of Healthy Growth and Development from Birth to Adolescence, in Brennemann's Practice of Pediatrics, Vol. I, Chap. 8. Hagerstown, Md., W. F. Prior Co., Inc., 1957.

Watson, E. H., and Lowrey, G. H.: Growth and Development of Children. ed. 2. Chicago, Year Book Publishers, Inc., 1954.

5

The Child's Physical Equipment for Growth, Development and Functioning (Continued)

Nutriture, defined as the condition of nourishment or sometimes as nutritional status,* is significant in the lives of children since nourishment plays a most important part in providing for optimum body functioning, a feeling of well-being, and growth. Nutriture depends upon metabolism, the series of related body processes which coordinate to build up cells, tissues, and organs, and provide for their proper functioning. Seven processes are connected with metabolism: (1) ingestion (the intake of food), (2) digestion (the breakdown of food), (3) absorption (the pick-up of digested nutrients), (4) excretion (the disposal of waste products), (5) circulation (the distribution of materials to the body cells), (6) respiration (the supplying of oxygen and elimination of carbon dioxide), (7) oxidation (the process by which the nutrients are used to build tissue, and to create heat and muscular and mental energy). The systems concerned with these processes are discussed in this chapter.

Maturation of the Nutriture and Its Indicators

During fetal life the food supply to which the child has access is elemental, such as calcium, iron, phosphorus, protein—not peas,

* See Dann and Darby.[184]

carrots, or spinach. The portal of entry is through the child's blood stream, and all nutriment must be in a form in which it can be transferred from the mother's blood stream to that of the fetus across a living tissue barrier.

At the moment of birth, as soon as respiration is established, filling the child's lungs with air, and the necessary process of oxidation of tissue-building material begins, the way in which the infant's body obtains its food suddenly becomes entirely different. The mouth becomes the portal of entry for nourishment. The whole digestive system is immature at birth, and still demands a highly simplified form of food. This food, however, is still supplied through the products of the mother's body, namely, mother's milk or its substitute. During the first few days of transition from a fetal existence to that of an independent organism the newborn receives colostrum, the first secretion of mother's milk, which is a highly specialized product adapted to his needs.

As the child grows he needs essential substances to build his own body which the products of his mother's body do not furnish in adequate quantities. This is the first transition from complete dependence on food from the maternal body to utilization of other food material. Vitamin D is administered in some form to insure the laying down of calcium and phosphorus in the skeleton, and vitamin C intake is supplemented generally by giving orange juice. Orange juice can usually be given at an early age because it contains easily digested food elements, and does not contain any large complex molecules as are typical of foods such as meat. This is as real a stage in nutritive maturation as is walking in motor development. While reliable indicators of nutritive maturity are still unknown, we believe that digestive response to increasingly complex foods is one of the soundest indicators of nutritive maturation.

The next stage in maturation of the nutriture is administration of semisolid foods, such as cereals, and puréed vegetables and fruits, added to supply the increasingly complex food elements the body demands. Puréeing of food reduces its complexity, some simplication still being demanded at this stage of the child's nutritive maturity.

Toleration of well chopped foods might be designated the "premature" nutritive stage. This slight simplification of adult food is necessary because the child has not learned to chew and has an inadequate number of teeth to masticate his food satisfactorily. It would seem highly probable that his digestive tract is in a corresponding state of maturity.

The child moves into the mature stage when he can eat solid, nonsimplified adult foods. He selects and combines them from their intact, natural form, and they are prepared for digestion and reduced to their simple form entirely within his body.

It may be said that there are six stages of the maturation of the nutriture: the fetal stage, newborn, infant stage I, infant stage II, "premature," and mature, as shown in Table 2.

Table 2.   Stages of Maturation of the Nutriture

Fetal Stage . . . . .Nourished from maternal blood stream.

Newborn Stage . . . . .Simplified and highly specialized food (colostrum) still supplied through products of his mother's body and adapted to needs of the newborn.

Infant: Stage I . . . . .Infant dependent on mother's milk, a product of her body (or a substitute for it), essential substances added which are not supplied sufficiently by mother's milk. Begins to be independent of his mother.

Stage II . . . . .Infant diet has semisolid, puréed food added.

"Pre-mature" Stage . . . . .The diet is increased in complexity by adding well-chopped food.

Mature Stage . . . . .Solid, nonsimplified adult foods, prepared for digestion and reduced to simple form within child's own body.

These six stages of maturation of the nutriture, it is believed, can be detected by observing the concurrent maturational changes of oral activities which are related to the ingestion of food.* The *rooting and sucking reflexes,* present at birth, are the infant's mechanism for finding and taking fluids into the mouth. Some time later, a *biting reflex and salivation* appear. The infant bites and begins drooling. This behavior is an indicator for introducing puréed food. The next oral indicator includes two kinds of behavior which appear close together: *the ability to swallow small lumps* and *destructive biting.* Now the infant can manage chopped foods. The final oral indicator is *chewing,* by which the infant is able to reduce food to a consistency which can be swallowed. This requires at least the first molars. By this time the child can eat solid, nonsimplified adult foods. With this concept one

* Personal communication with Dr. C. G. Jennings.

can apply these and any other nutritive indicators to a better understanding of the reasons underlying individual differences which are not
explained by age alone. It seems quite possible that a child can be
three years old chronologically and yet immature nutritively.

Lags in nutritive maturing seem most commonly due to environmental factors such as illness, accompanied by poor appetite, and
therefore are correctable under ordinary circumstances. Also, children
may be physiologically ready for the later stages but psychologically
unready.

Digestive System

The digestive tract is the child's equipment for utilizing food.
Through its activities of motility, secretion, digestion, absorption and
excretion, food is changed to substances which the body can use; these
substances are made available to the body tissues, and that which the
body does not need is excreted. These activities are made possible
through finely regulated mechanisms in which nervous and chemical
elements participate and cooperate.

The digestive tract consists of a tube, which varies in size at different
levels, and functionally consists of two parts, (1) the alimentary canal,
through which food passes and within which digestion takes place, and
(2) accessory glands (salivary glands, pancreas, and liver), which
produce juices vital to digestion and absorption of food.

The alimentary canal is a musculomembranous structure which,
like the heart and lungs, is largely under the control of the involuntary
nervous mechanism of the body. It is well named a canal, for it is
richly supplied with fluids which soften the dry foods, and at vital
points the movement of the food through the canal is regulated by
circular bands of muscle, called sphincters, which resemble the locks
of a canal. The muscular walls are well supplied with blood vessels,
and the membranous lining contains specialized types of vessels, called
lacteals, through which digested food is absorbed into the blood
stream without being poured into the large blood vessels directly.
They also contain glands which secrete substances, enzymes and
hormones, which are necessary to the digestive processes. The muscular
walls have layers of circular and longitudinal smooth muscles which
make possible a churning movement, for mixing food with digestive
enzymes, and the movement of the contents along the tract. These

muscles are covered with tough, elastic, flexible connective tissue.

The accessory organs of digestion are of two types—those which are purely mechanical in function and those which secrete fluids necessary to digestion itself and are connected directly with the alimentary canal by ducts. The teeth (see pp. 211–216) and tongue are the mechanical accessory organs, and the salivary glands, pancreas and liver are the functional accessory glands. The secretions of the accessory glands are added to the food at two points, in the mouth and in the first portion of the intestine.

Three pairs of salivary glands empty into the mouth by their excretory ducts. Their secretion softens the solid food and acts chemically on the starches, changing them into simpler compounds. The pancreas secretes pancreatic juice which contains enzymes capable of splitting carbohydrates, fats and protein and changing them from their natural state to one in which they can be absorbed into the blood stream. The pancreas is also in part an endocrine gland; special cells secrete, directly into the blood stream, insulin, which is vital to the metabolism of sugar.

The liver, the largest gland in the body, secretes bile which acts upon fats so that they are broken up into fat droplets, thus converting them into a fine emulsion, like the fine droplets in cream, and prepares them for chemical conversion into fatty acids that can be absorbed. The bile, which is secreted continually, is accumulated in the gallbladder until it is needed. Release of bile from the gallbladder is controlled by hormonal action.

The secretions in the stomach provide for partial digestion of protein and for digestion of fats which are in a finely divided form. Enzymes are available in the intestine to complete the digestion of all aliments, namely, protein, carbohydrates and fat. The intestine also contains certain bacteria which are responsible for synthesis of vitamin K and some of the B-complex vitamins.

All secretions along the digestive tract are regulated either reflexly or chemically, or by a combination of both. The secretion of saliva is a good example of one that operates under reflex control and can be conditioned. Sight, smell or taste of food will stimulate the flow of saliva. Even the thought of food or of a particularly favorite food can start salivation. The act of chewing will also increase the flow of saliva. On the other hand, the secretion of the pancreas is wholly chemically controlled. Gastric secretion, however, has both elements of control.

The reflex aspect of control has significance to students of child development. When a healthy person puts food into his mouth, reflexes initiate secretion of gastric juice. Also sight and smell of food which has earlier become associated with taste will also set up the pouring out of gastric juice. Thus pleasant associations with food aid in the digestion of food.*

Stage of Maturation of Digestive Tract of Young Child. MOUTH. The mouth of the infant and young child is an area which is very sensitive to stimuli. Because of this sensitivity infants react strongly to the temperature, consistency, and taste of their food, and especially to changes in these qualities. The newborn is well equipped to ingest fluids by sucking, with a relatively short lower jaw, fat pads in the cheeks, adequate muscles, and a strong sucking reflex. Later teeth appear and chewing is possible.

SALIVARY GLANDS. The salivary glands are said to increase in weight about three times during the first three months and five times during the first two years. By the end of the second year the salivary glands assume the appearance of those of an adult.[404] The salivary glands are ready to function at birth and may be stimulated by the presence of milk in the mouth, or by a nipple. The content of ptyalin (the enzyme acting on carbohydrates) in the saliva increases during the first year, and at the end of that year the concentration is equal to that of an adult, which is five times that of a newborn.[404] The amount of salivary secretion is scanty at birth, but in the next two to three months it increases, until at the age of two and one-half to three months drooling may appear. It has been estimated that the infant secretes 50 to 150 cc. of saliva per day; the adult secretes about one to one and one-half quarts.[403]

In the nursing infant, saliva acts physically by reducing the firmness of the milk clot, thereby aiding gastric digestion and evacuation. Although ptyalin is found in the saliva of the newborn in sufficient quantities to be significant, it cannot be considered important in his digestion. Drooling of the teething infant probably can be attributed in part to the increased secretion of saliva caused by irritation of the gums and to the infant's inability to manage to swallow it.

STOMACH. The capacity of the infant's stomach varies widely with the size and age of the infant and is not fixed except by its maximum limit to distend. On occasion it can stretch to several times its usual

* For a full discussion of the digestive tract, see Carlson and Johnson.[154]

size and can also adjust its content by emptying some into the intestine.[769] The infant's stomach can adjust, within limits, of course, to varying amounts of food. The capacity approximates 30 to 90 cc. at birth, 90 to 150 cc. at one year, 500 cc. at two years, and between 750 and 900 cc. in later childhood.[881]

At birth the mechanisms for secretion of gastric and intestinal juices are ready to function. The appetite mechanism, which stimulates gastric secretion and involves association of food with past experiences, generally begins to appear in the latter part of the first year. Hunger contractions, which register need for food, are present at birth and in newborns generally begin from two to four hours after feeding.[769] In infants from one to six months old the average time for onset of hunger contractions is about three hours after the meal.[408] In young adults the time is four to six hours after a meal.[404] Thus young children tend to become hungry somewhat sooner after meals than do adults.

Enzymes and hydrochloric acid, necessary for digestion, are present at birth but in small amounts. The amounts increase during infancy. Pepsin, the protein-splitting enzyme, increases so that by four months it has reached a level which remains constant.[881] Hydrochloric acid also increases in amount and continues to increase throughout the early years. One study[462] indicates that the adult range of free acidity in the stomach is not approached until after four years of age.

PANCREAS. The pancreas doubles its birth weight in six months and quadruples it by one year.[722] It assumes adult cellular appearance by one year[881] but continues to grow. By three years it has attained about 33 per cent of its adult weight.[722] Like the stomach, the pancreas at birth secretes all of its enzymes, but in smaller amounts. However, even in the first few weeks of life, the pancreatic secretions appear to be adequate for the infant's needs. In the early months of infancy the starch-splitting enzyme is absent or present in only very small amounts. During this time the protein-splitting and fat-splitting enzymes are only slightly lower than in later childhood.[408]

LIVER. The liver in the newborn is proportionately large, occupying nearly two fifths of the abdominal cavity and forming 4 per cent of body weight, although physiologically immature.[881] In the first year it more than doubles its weight. In the third year the weight has increased threefold. The relative size of the liver of the infant, compared with that of the adult, indicates its special importance in early life. The bile, secreted by it, plays the same part in the metabolism of food as in the adult.

INTESTINES.   At birth the length of the small intestine of the infant is quite variable, and the variation seems to have no association with variations in body length or weight. The length of the small intestine at birth averages 338 cm. In the first year its length has increased about 50 per cent. At six years the small intestine is 60 per cent of the adult length.

The most marked difference between the intestine of the infant and of the adult is that in the infant the mucous membrane is more developed in proportion to the muscular layers than in the adult. Because the supportive structures are relatively immature, distention may occur in the young infant and some irregularities in peristalsis may be expected.

Scammon has given the length of the large intestine at birth to be 66 cm.; during the first year it increases about 26 per cent, and when the child is six years old his large intestine has attained 60 per cent of the adult length. The rectum is relatively longer at birth and in early life, than in the adult. Because of the relatively greater length of the intestines and because the digestive and absorptive surfaces of the small intestine are completely developed, even the newborn infant should be able structurally to absorb appropriate food quickly and easily.[769]

Child's Ability to Digest Food.   The food, by the time it reaches the stomach, must be in a well divided form so that the digestive processes can act upon it. Therefore, it must be given to an infant first as liquid, then finely divided, and finally as whole foods according to the degree of maturity of muscles, nerves, and teeth. When foods are reduced to a simpler form, as in the case of puréed meat,[502] they may be introduced at an early age. Healthy infants and young children should be able to digest a variety of foods provided in reasonable amounts. At birth an infant is equipped with the ability to digest protein, fat and simple carbohydrates when fed to him in an appropriate form. The ability to digest these aliments is one of degree. With an increase in the amount of enzymes and hormones of the digestive tract the process of digestion becomes physiologically more efficient.

The healthy infant can absorb almost all (90 to 98 per cent) of the fat in milk in about three hours. Ability to digest double sugars, such as lactose and maltose, is well developed in the infant. The supply of amylopsin in the intestine during the first few months of the child's life is reported to be small. However, the research of Simchen,[760] who fed healthy infants (one to twelve months of age) on a mixture of milk and cooked flour, testing their stools for starch, indicated there was sufficient amylase to digest relatively large quantities of cooked starch. According to Ivy, "The breast-fed baby absorbs approximately 80 per cent of the ash of the milk and retains in his body between 40 and 50 per cent of it. The baby receiving cow's milk absorbs less of the ash, but retains almost the same amount as the breast-fed infant. The retention of sodium, potassium and phosphorus is appreciably higher when the infant is on breast milk."*

Transportation of Food Along Digestive Tube of the Child. The food to be digested is accepted into the body through the mouth, which is provided with the mechanical means for preparing it to be swallowed. The teeth function in grinding the food, the tongue in mixing it with the saliva and in keeping it pressed between the grinding surfaces of the teeth. After the mass of food has been moistened and lubricated by saliva, it is rolled by the tongue and hard palate into a bolus (rounded mass) and the tongue forces it back into the pharynx.

The swallowing movements of the infant show no important differences from those of the adult. Swallowing of food consists of three phases, localized in the mouth, in the pharynx, and in the esophagus. The initial phase of swallowing is involuntary in the early months of life and does not become voluntary until several months after birth.[655] Until swallowing becomes voluntary the infant does not swallow food or liquids put on the anterior part of the tongue but pushes them out. Therefore, in feeding him with a spoon, the food or liquid should be placed in the back of the mouth. The pharyngeal phase of swallowing is very complex and is accomplished by one of the most delicately coordinated reflex mechanisms found in the body. Studies have shown peristaltic waves sweeping downward from the upper end of the esophagus to the stomach in a continuous progressive movement. In general, there is one esophageal peristaltic wave for each swallowing movement initiated in the mouth. Water or semi-liquid foods immediately pass rapidly down to the lower end of the esophagus by the action of gravity. The peristaltic waves coming down a few seconds later merely sweep the fluid past the sphincter guarding the entrance into the stomach.[154]

* Ivy[403] (p. 13).

In the first few months of life the child ingests his food by sucking, accomplished by depressing the jaws, which tends to produce negative pressure in the mouth cavity. This cavity in the newborn is very shallow; the hard palate is flat, not having acquired the concavity characteristic of the adult palate. In the act of sucking the infant uses the tongue, hard and soft palates, the cheeks, the uvula, the gums, and the lips. The act is greatly facilitated by the sucking pads, a small mass of fatty tissue in each cheek.

MOVEMENTS OF STOMACH OF INFANT. The food is carried through the stomach by waves of contractions of the walls, called peristalsis. Peristaltic activity of the stomach is not as marked in the infant as in the child and the adult. This lesser peristaltic activity is due either to incomplete development of the neuromuscular mechanism responsible for peristalsis or to low tone of the sphincter. During the early months food is propelled chiefly by means of a general contraction of the stomach as a whole, somewhat like that of the urinary bladder, rather than through a peristaltic mechanism.[403]

As the child grows older and the peristaltic mechanism becomes more mature, the peristaltic activity becomes stronger and assumes mature characteristics.

The time that food remains in the stomach of a child varies widely, being influenced by a number of factors, including the condition of the musculature, the character and consistency of food, and hunger and appetite. Food eaten with pleasure in a calm atmosphere passes through the stomach faster than food eaten under conditions of anxiety or excitement.

INTESTINAL PERISTALSIS. In the intestine the food is moved by two types of activity, one of a churning nature, which aids in digestion and absorption, and the other of a wavelike nature, which propels the contents forward. Slowly and interruptedly the food moves finally into the large intestine. Usually by the time the large intestine is reached digestion has been completed, and nearly all absorption of the digested food has taken place. The motility of each segment of the digestive tract is intimately related to that of the other parts.

The time required for passage of food through the gastrointestinal tract varies markedly in different individuals. For breast-fed infants the average time is fifteen hours, with a range from four to twenty-eight hours; for the bottle-fed baby it is slightly longer.[403] As the infant and child grows and develops the passage time increases so that at five years the average time is eighteen hours, with a range of eight to twenty-eight hours.[543] For most adults the time ranges between twenty and seventy-two hours. In the infant food moves at a steady rate through the stomach, small intestine, and colon. There are no pauses in the stomach, which acts as a reservoir, but there are brief periods of quiescence, which may be prolonged when the child is disturbed significantly during feeding. In the adult, food passes through the stomach and small intestine at the same pace as it does in the infant and young child, but in the colon it may take twenty-four to forty-eight hours longer than in the infant. Slowing up of the passage of food through the colon begins soon after infancy, and in a few years the rate may approximate that in the adult. As the child grows the sphincters become more vigorous in action. It is evident that the slower rate of evacuation of the adult colon is due to more powerful sphincter control and differently coordinated reflexes.[921]

Absorption of Products of Digestion. By the chemical changes brought about by digestive juices and by the physical changes induced by peristaltic movements of the digestive tract, most of the insoluble constituents of the food are converted into soluble substances of smaller molecular size which can pass into the blood. The products of digestion in the alimentary tract are in a closed tube, and the blood and lymph are in other closed tubes. The material must pass across the boundary between two biological membranes if the products of digestion, the salts, the water, and the vitamins are to become available for use by cells of the body. This transfer of dissolved material from the intestines to the body fluids, known as absorption, is never accomplished by open ducts, but is effected by other processes.

Absorption is a process of osmosis and diffusion plus some other, as yet unexplained, dynamic action of the cells by which some materials are permitted to penetrate the walls of the intestine and others are withheld.[329] For example, sodium chloride is promptly absorbed, and magnesium sulfate is not. This activity involves cellular activity with the expenditure of energy. By absorption the products of the digestion of protein and carbohydrates pass through the absorptive cells to blood capillaries; fat is absorbed chiefly through the lacteals, a part of the lymph system. Thus these products ultimately find their way into the tissues, where they are either metabolized and used, or stored or excreted.

Many of the inorganic substances in the food are absorbed, although to a varying extent. Those which may form insoluble salts are not always well absorbed. Examples of such insoluble substances are the insoluble calcium soaps formed when a calcium compound combines chemically with a fatty acid, and insoluble calcium oxalate formed when a calcium compound combines chemically with oxalic acid (found in some foods).

Evacuation. The residue of undigested food and a considerable quantity of water which has been taken with the food or derived from the digestive juices passes into the large intestine, where the feces are formed.

Through the absorption of water the residue is changed to a soft, semi-liquid mass, the feces. A few times a day, particularly after meals, "mass movements" carry material to the rectum. The tendency of these movements to take place after the first meal of the day[17] constitutes one of the reasons why children are frequently encouraged to go to the toilet after breakfast.

The digestive tract is one of the paths for the excretion of minerals from the body. Among the inorganic substances claiming special attention are calcium and phosphorus. Undue loss of these substances is very significant in children.

The centers for control of colon activity are located in the central nervous system, indicating that its activity may be affected not only by local reflexes but also by habit formation and nervous states. The sigmoid and rectum are very sensitive to distention or irritation, and the passage of fecal matter into the rectum gives rise to the sensation that Ivy[403] designates the "call to stool." This sensation sets in motion the comparatively complex reflex mechanism of defecation. In the infant this mechanism is not under cerebral control. When it does come under cerebral inhibitory control the mechanism of defecation may be conditioned, and the "stool habit" formed. The entire colon is quite active during defecation, but the portion of colon content that is evacuated varies considerably.

Feces. The feces consist in large part of intestinal secretions and excretions, of cellular material from the intestinal walls, and of bacteria and food residues, which in turn depend on (1) composition of the food eaten, (2) capacity for digestion and digestive activity of the stomach and intestine, (3) irritability of the digestive tract, and (4) capacity for absorption.

The meconium, which is the first discharge of the colon of the new-born, is composed of bile, mucus, cellular waste, intestinal secretions, fat, hair, and vernix caseosa swallowed with the amniotic fluid. Some of it is generally passed within the first ten to twelve hours,[751, 769] all of it generally being evacuated by the fourth day.[769] For the next three days the stools are thin, sour, slimy, and brown to green, and may carry some remnants of meconium, after which the characteristic infant stool appears, the exact nature depending on the kind of feeding. As the diet becomes more varied and the relative amount of milk decreases, feces become more formed and darker; they tend to assume the characteristics of the adult stool by two years.

FREQUENCY OF BOWEL MOVEMENTS. The frequency of defecation varies with individual children. Bowel movements decrease in frequency during the early months and become more regular. By around six months an infant generally has one or two movements a day. In a study of two-and-one-half-year-olds[704] most of the children had one or two movements a day; however, an occasional child had a rhythm of one movement every other day. About half the children had their bowel movements at approximately the same time each day, and the other half had them at an unpredictable time. Boys were significantly more "regular" than girls. The frequency found for these children is probably that for children throughout the preschool period. Constipation is not indicated by the infrequency of stool, but by its consistency. A constipated child has hard stools.

Excretory System

There is a constant flow of materials through the human body which, in the process of metabolism, either yield up their energy or are subject to more or less complex chemical transformation. When these processes have been completed, the useless or injurious end-products are eliminated from the body. The mechanism for eliminating some of these wastes has been discussed in the section on the digestive system. Since elimination and excretion may be confused, it may be well to state the way in which these terms are used in this text. Elimination means evacuation of those hollow organs in which waste material has accumulated, and it depends essentially on mechanical changes (such as pressure), which force waste into the outside world: the voiding of urine from the bladder, for example. Excretion deals with extraction of wastes from the internal environment, from circulating body fluids, and their passage into temporary waste depositories, into lungs, bladder, and gastrointestinal tract. Excretion is, "in large part, carried out by cellular activity, involving cellular work and the expenditure of energy by the cell. . . . This cellular activity may be modified by physical forces such as osmosis, filtration and diffusion but cannot be accounted for entirely by them. Activity of the living cells contributes largely to the phenomena."*

The excretory system consists of the lungs, the kidneys, the liver and the colon. The work of the kidney is discussed in this section. The other organs of excretion are treated under other systems of the body.

Kidneys.   The kidneys lie back of the abdominal cavity, one on each side of the vertebral column. They function as excretory organs in removing from the body useless and injurious end-products of metabolism. They also aid in maintaining in the internal environment the conditions necessary for life, by playing a part in regulating the composition of the blood. The urine, which is constantly excreted by the kidneys, is stored in the bladder until eliminated.

Before birth the kidneys excrete urine and some is collected in the bladder. This is relatively little in contrast to the amounts excreted after birth. The kidneys at birth are sufficiently mature to respond remarkably well to the sudden load thrown upon them. In structure the kidney of the newborn appears to be complete, but its functions apparently require further maturation, up to perhaps twenty to twenty-four months, in order to acquire the efficiency of the adult kidney.[769] In weight they are about one-twelfth that of the adult kidney. In the first six months their weight has doubled; by one year it has tripled, and by five years it has increased fivefold. The physiologic growth seems to lag slightly behind the anatomic growth.† It is evident that as the kidneys increase in size the bladder must make corresponding growth.

Chemical analysis of the urine excreted by the adult kidney shows that normally it contains salts, urea (product of protein metabolism), uric acid (the end-product of nucleoprotein, abundant in cell nuclei), creatinine (from protein and muscle metabolism) and several other

---

* Carlson and Johnson[154] (p. 356).
† See Watson and Lowrey.[881]

materials. Urine is derived from blood; everything in the urine has first been present in the blood, from which the kidneys "separate" it.*

Quantity of Urine Excreted. During the first few days of life the urine is scanty and concentrated, tallying with the small amount of fluid taken and the large water output from the lungs. In contrast to the adult, who excretes approximately 1500 cc. daily, the baby one or two days old excretes 15 to 50 cc. The one- to three-year-old excretes 500 to 600 cc., and the three- to five-year-old 600 to 750 cc.[881] The amount excreted varies considerably, since it is influenced by many factors such as liquid ingested, the environmental temperature, and the state of the digestion or the nervous system.

Urination. The process of urination is first under involuntary control and later under voluntary control. The newborn urinates through reflex activity, presumably under the dominance of subcortical centers. As stated in discussion of the nervous system, the cerebral cortex is very immature at birth. Even at six months the part of the cortex which governs urination is not functioning, according to the evidence offered by McLellan.[542] McGraw,[538] in a study of two sets of twins, indicated the sequential changes in behavior which accompany and denote the development of voluntary control in urination. At the time the child begins to pay attention to the act of urinating and its result, he shows a sharp rise in his response to training. This time may correspond with the maturation of cerebral sensory centers which mark bladder sensibility. There is also probably some development of the cortical centers of the motor areas governing sphincter control. A drop in achievement follows, which seems to correspond to a period of rapid advancement in associational behavior and the beginning of discriminative and generalizing powers. The subsequent rise in achievement indicates that these powers have become integrated with the act of urination. There is probably another regression phase when the child begins to engage in fantasy and becomes interested in things beyond the immediate situation. The newly developed cortical centers are still not well integrated. When these centers become well integrated the child can integrate his many interests with his responsibility for controlling urination.

Some children achieve this control earlier than others. The speed with which this maturation process occurs influences the time when he develops full responsibility and the ease with which he achieves it (see

* For exact chemical analysis see a textbook on biochemistry, or Carlson and Johnson[154] (p. 357).

discussion of toilet training, in Chapter 7). If the child is very slow in maturing he may not have reliable control until a rather late age. Such a child should not be confused with a child who has gained control and then regressed because of some physical or more likely psychological cause. Such a child lacks control not because of immaturity but because of some impact of the environment upon him.

In the first and second days of life the infant voids urine from two or three up to six times. After this, urination is frequent throughout infancy, varying from four to six or even thirty to forty times in twenty-four hours. After bladder control has been established the frequency usually varies from six to eight times in twenty-four hours. At two and one-half years one study[704] found that approximately four fifths of the children had a two or three hour interval for urination in the daytime. Urination is never as regular as bowel evacuation because of many influencing factors. A child will tend to urinate more often when he drinks more fluids, when it is cold, or when he is excited or under some other strong emotional tension.

Blood-Vascular System

The blood-vascular system consists of the heart, the arteries, the veins, the capillaries, and the blood. The functions of the system are: to transport to the remotest parts of the body nutriment, oxygen, hormones, disease-resisting substances; to collect wastes, liquids and gases; to preserve the conditions essential for normal cell activity. It is also involved in preservation of life through its coagulation mechanism and in maintenance of the acid-base balance of the body.

Before birth very little blood flows through the lungs, since there is no oxygen in them, but the blood in both sides of the heart flows through the general circulation and out through the arteries in the umbilical cord to the placenta. This is made possible by an opening between the right and left chambers of the fetal heart. In the placenta the fetal blood is aerated. When the umbilical cord is cut, this circulation must cease; the blood is forced into the lungs where oxygen can be obtained as soon as respiration is established. After pulmonary circulation is well established the opening between the sides of the heart closes.

At birth and throughout infancy the blood pressure is low and the pulse weak. However, they both increase gradually as the child grows older. At birth the heart is slightly large in proportion to body weight. It doubles its weight in two years, and by five years has increased four fold. During the first four years it grows more rapidly than at any time prior to adolescence. Changes in structure are also taking place which are reflected in the functional changes. The heart rate during rest decreases from between 100 and 150 beats per minute during the first year to 90 to 125 at the end of the second year, and to approximately 85 to 105 at five years.[879] The adult rate is approximately 70 per minute.

Throughout childhood the pulse rate varies considerably. A rapid increase can be expected in response to muscular activity or emotional stimulus. During the preschool years the heart sounds begin to assume the quality which is found in the older child and the adult.[879]

The red cell count drops from between 5,000,000 to 7,000,000 per cu. mm. at birth to 3,000,000 to 4,500,000 at six to ten weeks. A rise follows so that at six months the count is 4,000,000 to 5,000,000; this remains constant throughout the rest of infancy and preschool years. The hemoglobin changes from a range of 17 to 25 gm. per 100 cc. blood at birth to 11 to 15 gm. at six to ten weeks, to 12.7 to 16.1 gm. at six months, and continues the same throughout infancy. During the preschool years the hemoglobin is 12 to 15 gm. per 100 cc.[879]

The white count is quite variable in infancy, fluctuating from day to day. These fluctuations decrease during the second year. At birth the count is 15,000 to 30,000 cells per cu. mm. It soon settles down to 5,000 to 20,000 and during the preschool years 6,000 to 15,000 (adult range, 6,000 to 10,000).[879]

Lymphatic System

A physician examining a young child feels the glands in the neck, under the arms, and in other parts of the body. In these areas the lymph glands come close to the surface of the body, and if they are enlarged the condition can be felt. Lymph is important to the body in manufacturing lymphocytes, a type of white blood cell which destroys bacteria, and in removing worn out blood cells and other kinds of debris from the fluids of the body. Antibodies probably are formed in part or completely in this system.[881] It is readily seen that its main function is one of protecting the body. The fact that the lymphatic system increases relatively rapidly in infancy and childhood, that lymphoid tissue is very abundant at birth, that the lymph ducts are more numerous and the lymph glands larger and more prominent in childhood than in later life, would seem to indicate the importance of the lymphatic system to normal development.[722] Tonsils and adenoids, which are lymphoid tissue, follow this pattern of increase and decrease in size. Kaiser[442] found that tonsils of infants were usually small. In the second and third years they increased in size, reaching maximum size at four or five years of age, and then decreasing so that between eight and ten years of age they assumed an insignificant appearance. Their maximum development at the time when acute infections of the respiratory and alimentary tracts are most common would seem to indicate that they are part of a natural defense mechanism. Lymph tissue during infancy and childhood responds to infection by rapid and excessive swelling and increase in size. With advancing age, this response to infection becomes less dramatic.

The lymphatic system consists of: (1) complex capillary networks which collect the lymph in the various organs and tissues; (2) an elaborate system of collecting vessels which conduct the lymph from the capillaries to the large veins of the neck, where it is poured into the blood stream; (3) lymph nodes which are interspaced in the pathways of the collecting vessels, filtering the lymph as it passes through them and contributing lymphocytes to it. Lymph, in general, originates as tissue fluid, the fluid surrounding all cells, which, in turn, has reached the cells from the capillaries of the blood-circulation system. Lymph closely resembles blood plasma in composition, consisting of the blood constituents which are able to pass through the capillary walls, plus elements added to it by the tissues. It contains no red blood cells and has much less protein than blood plasma.

Respiratory System

One of the first acts of the newborn is to breathe. Nature has provided a respiratory apparatus consisting of a nose, larynx, trachea, bronchi and lungs, together with the diaphragm and the large and small muscles attached to the ribs which aid in the mechanics of breathing. It is now believed that respiratory movements begin late in fetal life, in the absence of actual respiration, and at birth lung tissue is sufficiently inflated to enable the infant to sustain life. The remainder of the lung tissue expands gradually during the next several weeks.

The breathing of the newborn differs from that of the adult.[769] Newborn infants breathe faster (about 45 per minute, in contrast to 16 per minute), less deeply, and more irregularly. Restlessness produces irregularity, and crying tends to slow and deepen breathing. In the early days of life different patterns of breathing have been observed among normal resting infants.[204] No one type seemed to be more efficient than another in providing air from which oxygen can be secured, and no one single rhythm was consistently exhibited by an individual infant. Thus healthy infants can be expected to vary their rhythm and speed of breathing from time to time. With increasing age respiration grows deeper and the mechanism works more economically and shows greater elasticity. According to Watson and Lowrey,[881] the rate for quiet respiration decreases from approximately 30 to 80 per minute for the newborn, to 20 to 40 per minute at one year, and 20 to 35 per minute at two to seven years. The rate varies considerably among children of the same age and size, and in the same child from time to time.

Respiration is important because it is the means of supplying to the body the oxygen which is necessary for its metabolic activities, and of removing from the body some of the waste products of metabolism, namely, carbon dioxide, volatile nitrogenous products, and the like. Therefore, the respiratory mechanism at all ages must meet the immediate needs of the body for oxygen. The healthy newborn is physiologically so constituted that he is able to obtain the oxygen he needs even though his respiratory mechanism is immature. In the first place, nature has endowed the newborn with an unusual ability to withstand degrees of oxygen lack which are intolerable or much less tolerable to the adult.[769] This does not mean that some newborn infants still may not have sufficient oxygen for maintaining satisfactory metabolism of the body tissues. It does mean that it is wise to be aware at all times of the structural and functional differences of individuals as they develop. Secondly, breathing of the normal infant, though extremely variable in rate and depth, moves more air in and out of the lungs in proportion to body weight than does that of an adult. Compared on the basis of surface area of the body, the amount of air inspired and expired per minute is approximately the same in newborn infants and in adults. This is achieved by the more rapid and slightly more shallow breathing of the infant, implying a greater respiratory effort.

The amount of air entering and leaving the lungs with each inspiration increases with age. At one year the amount is 48 cc.; between three and seven years it is 125 to 200 cc., or somewhat less than half the amount in adults.[881] The smaller intake is compensated for by the more frequent breathing.

The type of respiration changes as development proceeds. At birth and during the first few months respiration is essentially abdominal. Changes toward the adult type of thoracic breathing begin when the infant sits up, and should be normally well under way by two years. Somewhere between three and seven years, the combined abdominal and thoracic type of respiration is established.

Basal Metabolism.   Oxygen, obtained solely through the respiratory system, is essential for the life and activity of body tissues. Oxygen is necessary for the chemical changes involved in provision of energy to maintain body temperature, in the functional activities of the several organs, and in electrical exchanges occurring in the body. These chemical changes are included in the term "metabolism." These reactions are, in the last analysis, the result of oxidation and their sum total is expressed accurately by the amounts of oxygen taken up by the lungs and of carbon dioxide liberated by them. This is measured by a calorimeter and the energy exchange is expressed in heat units, i.e., calories produced per hour. When the body is completely at rest, comfortably warm, and without stimulating influence of food, it is considered that all the heat generated by the body is due to the activities of the internal organs (heart, blood vessels, lungs, glands, etc.) and to the "resting metabolism" of the cells. This so-called "basal metabolism" registers the energy expended for internal housekeeping when the body is resting and relaxed. Measurements for neonatal infants are not made under "basal" conditions since infants are not "normal" when food has been withheld long enough to eliminate the digestion factor. Heat production for them is determined when all disturbing factors except digestion are removed, and the result is termed minimal or standard metabolism.[769] Some physiologic factors which affect energy metabolism are age, size, growth, under-feeding or over-feeding and subnormal temperature or fever. The role of "basal metabolism" in the calculation of calorie needs of a child is of special significance in these early years.

The periods of rapid growth, of which the first year is one, are associated with a greater increase in heat production than other times. Weight for weight the infant at birth is somewhat more active metabolically than the adult, although less than the child of one or three years whose heat production is well over two calories per kilogram of weight.[106] Heat production increases with age as long as growth continues. Individual differences and deviations from the average are greater in children than in adults. The younger the child the greater the normal variation from the average tends to be.[450] Knowledge of basal metabolic requirements has provided reliable, scientific information which has been useful in establishing recommended calorie allowances for young children and in understanding individual differences in calorie needs.

Temporary Teeth

Teeth, which are mechanical accessory organs of digestion, begin to form in the seventh week of fetal life and by the time a child is born all twenty of the temporary, or deciduous, teeth and the first permanent teeth (six-year molars) are developing. Their development is influenced by heredity, prenatal conditions, nutrition, illness and certain endocrine factors.

The teeth are essential for the mastication of food and its preparation for swallowing and for digestion. The order of appearance of teeth in the mouth seems to fit in with the increasing ability of the child's body to use more complex foods, although the analogy is not too close. Observation of the timing of the stages of maturation of nutriture and of the eruption of the teeth reveals that the gradual change from foods requiring no mastication to those requiring biting and cutting and finally chewing parallels to some degree the sequence of eruption of incisors, cuspids and molars. Liquids and semisolid foods which require no mastication are taken during the first half year of life, before the eruption of teeth. Chopped foods can be managed when the incisors, which are used for biting and cutting, are erupting. Solid foods, which demand vigorous chewing before swallowing, can be managed after the eruption of molars, which provide grinding surfaces. During the latter part of the first year the incisor teeth are generally present in the mouth. In the second year almost all the remainder of the deciduous teeth are erupted, including the molars. Between two and three years, the child has twenty teeth and is able to eat adult food. This marks maturity for the eruption of his temporary teeth. The sequence of ages for the completion of the enamel, completion of the roots, and eruption of the deciduous teeth are shown in Table 3.

Table 3.   *Enamel Formation and Eruption of Deciduous Teeth**

	First Enamel Formation Month (Prenatal)	Enamel Completed Month	Eruption Month	Root Completed Year
Upper teeth				
Central incisor	4	1½	7½	1½
Lateral incisor	4½	2½	9	2
Cuspid	5	9	18	3¼
First molar	5	6	14	2½
Second molar	6	11	24	3
Lower teeth				
Central incisor	4½	2½	6	1½
Lateral incisor	4½	3	7	1½
Cuspid	5	9	16	3¼
First molar	5	5½	12	2½
Second molar	6	10	20	3

* From Drenckhahn, V. C., and Taylor, C. R.: Your Child's Teeth. Chicago, American Dental Association, 1940, p. 36.

The tooth has a central canal containing nerve fibers and blood vessels which bring nourishment to it. Dentine, which forms the largest part of the tooth, encloses the canal and is covered in the exposed part with enamel. The enamel is fully formed before the tooth erupts; the dentine continues to form until the roots are completed, some time after the tooth has erupted. The enamel and the dentine of the crowns of the temporary teeth begin to form in about the sixteenth week of fetal life; those of the first permanent molars begin to form at birth.

The crowns and roots of the teeth are completed during the early years. Formation of the crown of these teeth requires seven to fourteen months; the time required for the same process in permanent teeth is three to six years. The growth of the roots requires one and one-half to two and one-half years for the deciduous teeth, and five to seven years for the permanent teeth.

The permanent teeth continue to develop throughout these early years, so that by five years of age the crowns of the six-year molars and the incisors† have been completed.

Deviations in Time and Order of Appearance of Temporary Teeth. There are deviations among children in the order of appearance of the teeth and in the age at which the teeth erupt. Although most children

† Data on crown and root formation taken from Schour and Massler.[726]

have their first tooth before they are eight months old some children may have none until they are a year old. Rarely do teeth erupt before the age of four months, and sometimes they do not appear until early in the second year. At six months one out of three infants has some teeth. At one year, in rare cases, an infant may have less than two or more than ten. Some children acquire all their teeth in less than one year; for others it takes almost three years.[572, 573] Thus in dentition, as in other aspects of growth, some children are fast and some are slow in moving along the path to maturity. For some even the path may differ, for there is more than one road to maturity. The general pattern of eruption is the same, but minor deviations do occur. The order is generally lower central incisor as the first tooth, followed by the upper central incisor; then the lateral incisors, first molars, cuspids, and, last, the second molars. The teeth tend to erupt in pairs, with intervening periods of quiescence. One study indicated that the most frequent change in order was variability in eruption of the lateral incisors.[707]

Studies in dentition have indicated that there is no significant difference between boys and girls, although boys are slightly ahead of girls in their first dentition, and that size as measured by weight, height or facial measurements has no relation to time of eruption.[718] Since siblings often show a resemblance in their dentition, it is possible that heredity may affect the eruption pattern. There is need for further investigation of the factors influencing the age at which teeth erupt.

Occlusion. Occlusion is the regular arrangement of the teeth and the resultant contact of the two jaws. The pattern of its development varies from individual to individual. Occlusion changes constantly throughout development, and follows no pathway common to all children. Each type of occlusion is the resultant of the growth of the face and, especially, that of the jaws and teeth.

During the first three years, the pattern of the face is being established. Following this period, the changes in the face are characterized, not by marked changes in proportion, but rather by more or less proportionate increases in size.[139] Jaws grow in height, depth and width.

At birth the upper jaw is further developed than the lower jaw. Thus the upper jaw protrudes, as is apparent in Fig. 38 which demonstrates good occlusion from birth to twelve years. The relative position of the jaws of the infant aids in sucking, and the growth or forward movement of the lower jaw during the preschool years makes good occlusion possible. Thus we see the efficient, functional performance of the teeth.

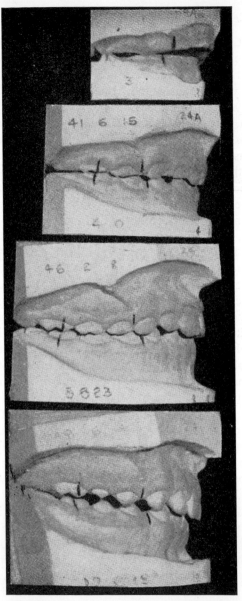

Figure 38. Casts of side view of jaws and teeth of a boy with good occlusion from birth through 12 years of age. Note posterior relationship at three days; good relationship at 4 years, 1 month; 8 years, 8 months, 23 days, and 12 years, 19 days. (From Sillman, J. H.: Serial study of good occlusion from birth to twelve years of age, American Journal of Orthodontics 37:481-507, 1951, C. V. Mosby Company.)

214

In the young child, a period of more rapid increase in the growth of the jaw generally occurs about the time of the eruption of the deciduous teeth. If growth of the jaw is normal, during eruption the teeth will come into normal occlusion; if growth is inadequate, the teeth will be crowded and may remain crowded.

When there are irregularities in the position of teeth and the teeth of the two jaws do not fit together properly the condition is called "malocclusion."* This can be due to the fact that one jaw grows more rapidly than the other, or it may result from disharmonious growth of jaws and teeth. Malocclusion does not appear frequently in first dentition but is found more often in mixed and permanent dentitions. When it interferes with the chewing of food malocclusion becomes a serious problem.

Irregularities in the development of the teeth and dental arches may be of the type that corrects itself during development, it may be within the range of normal variation, or again it may be a type beyond the range of normality which becomes a permanent condition with possible increasing severity. The interplay of heredity and environment is believed to produce malocclusion. In this interaction the heredity is considered a very strong component.[130, 757, 758, 804]

It is advisable that the growth and development of the teeth and jaws be watched carefully; that the child be examined by a dentist who understands the development of teeth and their occlusion, and that growth appraisals be made, a history kept, and changes noted and interpreted. It is considered a good practice to watch the development of the jaws beginning when the child is about three years old so that the beginnings of difficulties can be noted and appropriate action taken.

Thumbsucking is *one* of the causes of protrusion of the upper front teeth.[512, 758] A serial study[758] of a group of children from birth to fourteen years reveals that some thumbsuckers have malocclusion and some do not. The former tend to be those with poor bites; the latter those with good bites. Thumbsucking can displace teeth but does not seem to affect the relationship of the molars. Spontaneous correction tends to occur when thumbsucking is stopped, even after the preschool years.[512, 758] Sometimes during the period of tooth eruption, biting, which is part of the oral development of the child and should not be interfered with, may be mistaken for thumbsucking. Parental inter-

* For a discussion of the causes of irregularity and malocclusion of teeth see Brash, McKeag and Scott.[130]

ference in thumbsucking tends to entrench it and thus may increase both the length of time it continues and also the intensity or force of sucking, both of which increase the effect on the dental structure.

The premature loss of teeth, either through accident or decay, may affect the alignment of the permanent teeth. Since such premature loss may prove a hazard to good alignment of the permanent teeth, the care and preservation of the deciduous teeth are important.

Exercise of the jaws and teeth in chewing develops the jaw muscles, which in turn stimulate the growth of the jaw bones and the circulation of blood in the gums. These factors contribute to the presence of "healthier" teeth.

The early introduction of such foods as toast or zwieback, which exercise the jaws and teeth, is, therefore, important. The young child must learn to chew. He learns most easily if he has opportunity for chewing when he is physically ready. Opportunities should be given to him when he demonstrates the physiological urge for biting at the time teeth are beginning to erupt and all during the tooth eruption period. The mistake is often made of giving sieved and mashed food for too long a period after the child's teeth have erupted, when he should be learning to chew. Helping the child learn to chew requires patience and close supervision on the part of the parents, and allowing food to be swallowed in large unmasticated pieces is undesirable.

For a discussion of dental caries see the section on health protection in Chapter 7.

Homeostasis

The individual organs and systems have already been discussed and the importance of the interrelationships among them to physiological functioning has been indicated. At the beginning of the discussion of the child's physical equipment the functioning of the body as an integrated whole was mentioned. This integration of the systems of the body and the effectiveness with which they can maintain stability of the cellular environment throughout the body are of utmost importance to the life of the individual. This maintenance of a steady state in the environment of the body cells has been termed "homeostasis" by Cannon.[153] The body must maintain its equilibrium within certain prescribed limits with respect to temperature, acidity, amount of available oxygen, water, salts, etc., even in the presence of changes in the external environment or changes in the activity of parts of the body.* Thus the ability of the body to adapt physiologically to changing conditions depends on this mechanism. The preservation of homeostasis is largely due to the integrative and correlative abilities of the neuroendocrine system.†

The body is more variable in its physiologic state at birth than in adulthood. Most of the mechanisms which keep the body stable are immature. "Such things as the salt and sugar content of the blood, the water content of the body, the basal metabolic rate and the heart rate are changed by relatively small changes in diet and in external conditions. It takes as many as five years for the child's body to settle down to something like the physiologic stability of the adult."‡ This, in part, justifies the protection given to infants and young children against too great and too sudden environmental changes. As the physiologic adaptive mechanism becomes more mature, a child is able to cope with change in the environment with increasing ease.

As stated previously, equilibrium within certain limits must be maintained for body temperature. The *regulation of body temperature* will now be discussed in some detail.

One of the first precautions taken when a baby is born is prevention of undue loss of body heat by exposure of the body surface to cold air or cold surroundings, since a newborn's ability to regulate body temperature is immature. In fact, for the first few months of life special care is taken to keep an infant warm. "The demands of relatively great surface area, the immaturity of sweating and shivering mechanisms, the probable disadvantages of delicate skin and meager subcutaneous fat, all are very apparent handicaps to controlling both rate and amount of heat loss."§ Body temperature is regulated by a combination of chemical and physical processes. Temperature is maintained when the oxidative processes in the tissues liberate more energy as heat than the body loses by contact with surrounding air, by evaporation of the perspiration, by warming cool air taken into the lungs, and by warming cool liquids and foods taken into the stomach. Oxidation is constantly taking place in all the tissues of the body. However, the skeletal muscles, constituting more than half the weight of the soft tissues, are responsible

* For discussion of homeostasis see Cannon[153] or Shock.[755]
† See Friedgood.[273]
‡ Havighurst[343] (p. 14).
§ Smith[769] (p. 167).

for a considerable share in the function of maintaining body temperature, since 75 per cent of the energy used by the muscles is set free as heat. Movement of the child's body, then, has a significant relation to body temperature. Heat production can be increased by voluntary exercise or by increased food consumption, and heat loss can be modified by the amount and kind of clothing worn or by wetting the surface of the body, as in bathing.

Since the loss of heat depends on the difference of temperature between the surface of the body and the surrounding air or immediate environment, it will be largely affected by the surface temperature and therefore by the amount of blood flowing through the skin. The blood flow is under control of the central nervous system, and when the skin is cooled the central nervous system can regulate heat loss by altering the size of the blood vessels in the skin.

Children do not maintain the same temperature every hour of the day and night. Each individual has a characteristic curve of temperature which is slowly acquired after birth, is related to the child's routine, and is fully established around two years, when the child is walking and very active.[460]

In infants and very young children the temperature of their bodies is usually taken through the rectum. The study of Bayley and Stolz[95] on well, healthy children between one month and three years of age indicated that rectal temperatures tend to increase during the first seven months, remain constant until twenty-four months, and then drop. A temperature below 99.0° F. they found to be rare between six months and twenty-one months; readings of 100° F. or slightly higher were comparatively frequent during these ages. Even at six years of age the average temperature taken by mouth was 99.2° F. To expect all children to have a constant temperature at the so-called normal, 98.6° F., is unreasonable. Even a temperature of 100° F. need not necessarily indicate illness.

One child may have a consistent tendency toward a high temperature, another toward a low temperature. One child may pass through this maturational change at an early age, another may be slower. One child may react more vigorously to his environment because of a more poorly developed temperature-regulating mechanism, another child may be more stable because of a better developed stabilizing mechanism. All children acquire more stability as they grow older. The instability in young children is intensified by a larger surface area and capillaries nearer the surface, which permit considerable loss of heat in the early years. Temperature in a well child may vary because of changes in external temperature, exercise or emotional disturbances.

Topics for Study and Discussion

1. List the facts given in this chapter about the digestive tract and relate them to the feeding of infants and young children.
2. Discuss the significance of homeostatic immaturity in caring for infants and young children.
3. Invite a dentist to class to discuss dental problems of the young child.
4. Observe the respiration of a very young baby and a four-year-old while relatively quiet. Discuss observations in class.
5. Invite a pediatrician to demonstrate a health examination before the class. Provide for a discussion period following when students will have an opportunity to ask questions.

Selected Readings

Carlson, A. J., and Johnson, V.: Machinery of the Body, ed. 4. Chicago, University of Chicago Press, 1953.

Schour, I., and Massler, M.: Development of the human dentition, J. Am. Dent. A. 28:1153-1160, 1941.

Shock, N.: Ageing of Homeostatic Mechanisms, Cowdry's Problems of Ageing, ed. 3, A. I. Lansing, editor. Baltimore, Williams and Wilkins, 1952.

Washburn, A. H.: Appraisal of Healthy Growth and Development from Birth to Adolescence, in Brennemann's Practice of Pediatrics. Vol. I, Chap. 8. Hagerstown, Md., W. F. Prior Co., Inc., 1957.

Watson, E. H., and Lowrey, G. H.: Growth and Development of Children, ed. 2. Chicago, Year Book Publishers, Inc., 1954.

6

Meeting the Physical Needs of the Growing Child

Now that physical development and functioning of the young child have been presented, this chapter and the following one will discuss the child's physical needs which will provide for that growth, give a sense of comfort and well-being, and lay the foundation for a sound, positive attitude toward the rules of health, so that he is neither neglectful of nor overconcerned about them. The needs for warmth, nutrition, sleep, elimination and protection against health hazards will be discussed here. The need for activity is discussed in Chapter 8. These needs are present at all ages but differ from time to time in the quantity and in the manner in which each is met. Ability to provide for these needs with confidence, flexibility, and ease comes with an understanding of each, plus an ever present awareness that the child is a growing, changing organism living in a specific environment.

An adult, in order to provide appropriately for a child's physical needs, should be aware of the maturational level of the child. The timing of introducing new foods, the beginning of toilet training, etc., need to be synchronized with the child's readiness for each experience. This means an understanding of the sequences of maturation and the awareness of clues by which the infant or child reveals his readiness. Secondly, it is to be remembered that each child is an individual with his own physiological rhythms and his own speed of development. As

220

stated in Chapter 1, children are not standardized products; they are inherently different and respond differently to their environment. Some grow fast; some grow slowly. Some have few respiratory infections; some catch colds easily. Some have a small capacity for food; some can eat large amounts at one time. Some have unbounded energy; some tire easily. Such differences indicate a need for individualizing of a child's day-to-day living. Thirdly, no one physical need can be met satisfactorily without, at the same time, meeting other physical and psychological needs. To be well nourished a child needs not only food but also adequate activity, sleep, elimination and a feeling of security and of being loved. Physical needs can be provided for in an environment in a manner which permits the young child to acquire a sense of trust, then autonomy, and later initiative at the appropriate times. Finally, each child lives in a family which has its characteristic mode of life, habits and attitudes. How his physical needs will be met will depend on the family and the circumstances in which the family lives. Just as there are many paths or patterns by which children develop, so there are also many ways in which their physical needs can be met.

Warmth

Since the newborn has been accustomed to the constant temperature of the uterine environment and his mechanism for maintaining a constant body temperature is immature, it is necessary to protect him from chilling by keeping a warm, even temperature around him. If he is born in a hospital, he will be kept in a warm nursery or, if he stays in the room with his mother, the temperature of the room will be carefully regulated. During infancy, a temperature of 68° to 72° F. will be satisfactory until he is running about. By that time, because of his almost constant activity, he can thrive well in an environment of 65° to 68° F. Some homes are equipped with heating facilities which provide a steady, even temperature; some homes are not. Babies can be kept comfortably warm by the kind and amount of bedding and clothing that is used and the regulation of its use according to temperature changes.

The first bed may be a bassinet or straight-sided clothes basket, or a full-size crib which will serve all through infancy. Whatever is used, it needs to be large enough to give the infant ample room to move his head and wave his arms and legs freely. Because he will move a great deal and may bump the sides, and also to protect him from drafts, some kind of soft lining, such as a quilted pad, is useful around the inside of the basket or crib.

Clothing is planned according to the climate. In a constantly warm climate, the baby may need no clothing except his diaper, and the toddler and young child may need only a sunsuit. When warmth is needed, a child can be kept warm enough without becoming so warm that he will perspire and later become chilled. Clothing can provide warmth and still be light enough to permit freedom of movement. Even outdoor winter clothing can be warm and light in weight. The qualities of lightness and protection from cold are important at all ages. Each mother needs to choose her child's clothing according to the circumstances.* Other aspects of clothing are discussed in Chapter 7, under the subject of dressing.

Nutrition

The nutritional needs of an individual are the same in kind for all ages, but they differ in amount and in the form in which they are met. Nutrition of the body involves four categories of substances or nutriments: aliments, nutrients, oxygen and water. Aliments are nonspecific chemical compounds used by the body to produce energy which keeps the machinery running and provides for activity. These aliments may also be used for growth and cellular repair. They include carbohydrates, fats and proteins. Nutrients are specific chemical substances which are essential for the processes of body metabolism as well as for growth and repair of cells. They include such substances as minerals, i.e., calcium, phosphorus, iron, etc., essential amino acids (from protein), essential fatty acids (from fat), and vitamins. Meeting the needs for these are discussed in relation to the steps of the maturing nutriture (see Chapter 5), and with consideration of maturing of motor abilities, the child's growing desire for independence, and the gratification of his emotional needs.

Oxygen. In utero the fetus obtains oxygen through the placenta. After birth, oxygen is obtained through the activity of the respiratory system (see Chapter 5), which functions adequately to meet the infant's need of oxygen. The natural source of oxygen, of course, is fresh air. An abundance of fresh air is, therefore, desirable at all ages. In early

* For detailed information see Infant Care[859] and Thompson and Rea.[837]

infancy, especially, care must be exercised that provision of fresh air does not also involve exposure to cold.

Water. Because of the higher metabolic rate and the greater excretion and evaporation from the proportionately larger skin surface, the infant or child requires much more fluid in proportion to his weight than does the adult. In fact, the daily requirement for an infant is 150 cc. per kilogram of body weight (2.25 ounces per pound) with at least a 10 per cent variation*[329] or about three times as much per kilogram as for the adult. While the infant who is breast fed and getting enough milk to satisfy his nutritional needs ordinarily gets enough fluid in the milk to satisfy his fluid needs, it is still well to offer water two or three times a day at some time between feedings when he is awake, so that he learns early to drink it. For the artificially fed baby the doctor will plan the formula to include enough fluid, or will expect the baby to drink enough between feedings to make up the difference. In any case, it is well to offer water between feedings. If the baby drinks a great deal of water, when the weather is not warm enough for excessive skin loss, the mother may suspect that the baby is not getting enough food. The child who has been offered water during infancy can usually be trusted later to drink enough water to meet his needs. The mechanism of thirst apparently operates efficiently in young children.

Infant's First Food. Food, like oxygen, is provided for the unborn fetus by the placental blood, but after birth it must be ingested by the infant by way of the oral cavity. During the first few days of life the digestive tract of the newborn must begin to digest and absorb food so that his body may have adequate nourishment. Nature provided for such a transition period in the secretion of colostrum, the initial secretion of the mammary glands, adapted to the ability of the digestive tract of the newborn.† It contains less fat and more protein, ash and vitamin A than does the milk when lactation is completely established. The colostrum period varies with individual women from one to five days. During the next five days, the composition changes gradually to that of mature milk according to Macy,[544] although some investigators believe that mature milk does not flow for four to six weeks after delivery.

When the infant can digest and absorb the mother's milk, he begins

---

* This is for an infant living in a temperate climate. In warmer climates more water will be needed.

† For discussion of the digestive tract, see Chapter 5.

the third stage in his progress toward maturation of the nutriture (see p. 193). The mother's milk is nature's food for the infant, supplying all the nutritional essentials for the early months with the exception of vitamin D and, if the supply is adequate, providing the necessary calories. It is easily digested and is suited to meet the infant's physical needs. The amount of breast milk which the infant receives depends on ability of the maternal body to synthesize milk and the demands he makes in sucking. The usual amount is about one pint after the first week or two and increases to about one quart a day in the fifth month.[848] The amount which the infant needs at a feeding can be determined by him if he is fed when he is hungry, as indicated by rooting, sucking, or crying, and permitted to nurse until he is satisfied. He cannot be expected to take the same amount at each feeding. He may take a little at one time, and a large amount at another time. During the first few days the time at the breast may be limited to five or ten minutes in order to allow the mother time to become adjusted to the pulling on her nipples and to help prevent sore nipples. A short nursing time seems to satisfy the infant during the first few days.

If the mother is unable to nurse her baby, artificial feeding will be prescribed by the physician. An infant from birth should be under the regular care of a physician who will watch his progress and prescribe accordingly. Under such guidance, a vast number of infants are reared successfully on cow's milk mixtures.* The same self-regulation type of feeding program as mentioned above can be followed with bottle-fed babies.†

The differences in composition of human and cow's milk[545] mean

---

* While breast-fed infants tend to show a smoother course in the early months[359] their growth patterns in height and weight have been shown to be similar to those of bottle-fed infants of similar socioeconomic groups.[648] Millis,[590] and Stewart and Westropp[809] also found no superiority in weight of breast-fed infants in higher income families at the end of the first year. In lower income groups, Millis found the superiority of breast-fed infants at 24 weeks to be lost by 52 weeks.

† One mother, whose young baby was bottle-fed and varied his intake at different feedings, met the problem by dividing the milk unevenly among the bottles for the day. This particular baby was taking 35 ounces. She distributed this in two bottles of six ounces, three of five ounces, and two of four ounces. She found that the baby, after having been asleep, wanted to eat several times at one and one-half to two hour intervals and so took less at those times. When she anticipated that he would sleep four or five hours after a feeding, she gave him six ounces. Thus she was able to satisfy the baby without waste of formula or keeping the baby waiting in the middle of a feeding in order to warm another bottle.

that infants receive, ounce for ounce, different amounts of certain constituents and different proportions of these constituents. The actual differences in the amounts of each of the nutrients depend on the formula used in artificial feeding. Cow's milk contains about three times as much protein, almost four times as much calcium, and about six times as much phosphorus as human milk. These constituents, and others not mentioned, when absorbed in excess of bodily needs must be excreted. This greater load of soluble materials, which must be excreted by the kidneys when cow's milk is fed, puts a heavier load on kidney function and is, therefore, more of a drain on the water reserves of the body. The breast-fed infant, therefore, has an advantage over the bottle-fed infant in respect to his water reserves.[359]

The protein of cow's milk forms a heavy curd in the stomach, whereas human milk, having less casein and more lactalbumin, forms a finely divided, flocculent mass which is easily digested by the infant. However, in present day feeding mixtures the casein (one of the milk proteins) is so changed that it forms soft, small, digestible curds. The superiority formerly attributed to the fat of human milk over that of cow's milk is now being questioned.[359] Human milk has more vitamins A and C, more niacin, less thiamine and riboflavin, and more iron than cow's milk.[545]

Lactation. FACTORS AFFECTING LACTATION. The ability to produce adequate milk depends on a number of factors, namely, the size and anatomical structure of the mammary glands, the amount and kind of food intake, heredity, environmental conditions, such as rest and activity, the amount and intensity of work, the emotional makeup of the individual, and the emotional climate. The potentiality for both the quantity of milk and the length of time that lactation continues under normal conditions is inherent in a woman.[547] Various conditions will determine how much of that potential will be utilized, one of these conditions being the demand made by the baby.[547] A hungry baby who nurses vigorously does much to stimulate the flow of milk. Thus, nursing the baby when he indicates hunger, as is done on a self regulating rather than a rigid schedule, is an aid to lactation.*

Diet is another factor. The dietary preparation for lactation begins

---

* Illingworth and Stone[388] found that 80.3 per cent of babies on self-demand feeding in Jessup Hospital for Women in Sheffield, England, were fully breast fed at one month, against 64.5 per cent of those on schedule. This difference was significant.

before the birth of the baby.* Diet after the birth of the infant is similar to that in pregnancy, but is increased somewhat in order to supply the required nutrients for the elaboration of milk. According to the Recommended Allowances of the Food and Nutrition Board,[261] diet during lactation should be increased over that of pregnancy about one-fifth in calories, about one-fourth in protein, about one-third in calcium and vitamin A, about one-fourth in riboflavin, and about one-half in vitamin C. With these amounts added to an adequate diet during pregnancy, there will be sufficient energy and nutrients (1) to maintain a mother's own body and to meet her energy needs, (2) to provide the essentials for her milk, and (3) to provide the added energy involved in the activity of the mammary glands. The nursing mother will probably find that she can eat with zest the additional food needed. The need for extra calcium and phosphorus, riboflavin, vitamin A and protein indicate a liberal intake of milk. At least one quart a day is advisable. Liberal amounts of fruits and vegetables, including citrus fruits, are also indicated. Other foods providing calories can be chosen according to the individual's needs and preferences. There is no evidence to prove that overeating by the mother will increase the supply of milk. If, however, the necessary ingredients for the synthesis of milk are lacking in the daily food, the milk flow may be decreased or may become deficient in some constituents or the needed elements may be drawn from her body tissues. A marked deficiency in protein and calories is usually associated with a decrease in the flow of milk.[280] An inadequate intake of vitamins may result in a milk deficient in vitamins,[42] while an insufficient intake of minerals may cause a drain on the maternal reserve.[223, 378] The drain on the reserves of the mother can be reduced in the case of nitrogen by ample storage during pregnancy[379, 380] and in the case of calcium by adding calcium and vitamin D to the diet.[849] Additional amounts of nutrients are most satisfactorily supplied by eating more of the natural foods rich in the specific nutrients because of the importance of the proper balance of the various food factors in metabolism. Vitamin D can be supplied by cod liver oil or vitamin D concentrates.

A mother who is rested and relaxed is more likely to be successful

---

* A study in Australia[923] indicates a consistent correlation between the duration of lactation and the level of maternal diet previous to and during pregnancy. See Chapter 3 for discussion of preparation for lactation during pregnancy.

in nursing her baby than one who is tired, or tense from concern about the care of the baby or from something else that is disturbing her emotionally. The flow of milk from the breast is the result of a very complex psychosomatic mechanism.* Stimuli to this reflex[631] include sucking of the infant and associations with the nursing situation (sight of the baby, time for feeding, breast preparations for feeding). Pain and distraction inhibit it. Newton and Newton[631] make the following suggestions for helping this reflex to function: (1) feeding the baby when he is hungry to afford more vigorous nursing, (2) no supplementary bottle if possible, (3) avoiding pain, emotional conflict, and embarrassment, (4) conditioning this reflex by the use of pleasant stimuli—for example, favorite food or music preceding nursing, nursing in the same quiet place, stroking breast with clean tissue or the use of manual expression of a little milk.

To be rested, relaxed and confident about nursing the baby, a woman needs guidance while lactation is being established. She needs help in the technique of nursing. She needs someone who will answer her questions and with whom she can discuss her concerns. Her physician, who during her pregnancy has helped her to prepare for lactation, can be of considerable assistance, as can the nurses in the hospital.† Mothers sometimes become concerned because milk is slow to come after delivery. The doctor and the nurse can reassure the mother that this is natural. The child may receive almost no milk for the first few days. At this time his needs are small and he is learning to suck. Later after returning home the mother may lose some of her relaxation and confidence as she assumes the responsibility of the baby along with her housekeeping duties. At this time she may discard a regular schedule of rest and diet and become tired and anxious over her new responsibilities. As a result her milk supply may decrease. Her confidence in her ability to care for her infant will be increased by knowing what to expect in the behavior of the infant and having had some opportunity to care for babies prior to this time. Becoming acquainted with her

---

* The presently accepted explanation of milk flow is as follows: Stimulation of the nipples excites nerves of an afferent arc to the midbrain which results in the release of required amounts of prolactin, thyrotrophin, ACTH and oxytocin.[772] For the mechanism of milk secretion see p. 91, also.[772, 854]

† The techniques necessary for successful management have been demonstrated by Sedgewick,[738] Waller,[875] Barnes et al.[75]

baby in the hospital is an asset* so that he is not a stranger when they arrive home. The husband at this time can assist by giving support to the mother and seeing that she is relieved of some of the household responsibilities.

The woman's attitude toward nursing her baby is also a factor in her success. One study[632] found that more mothers who had the desire and determination to breast feed their babies were successful than those who either did not have the desire, disliked the idea, were indifferent or had mixed feelings about it.

While most women are able to breast feed their babies, some cannot. From a study of 900 consecutive patients of which 776 attempted nursing, Stewart and Pratt[810] concluded that approximately 87 out of 100 mothers who attempt breast nursing will have adequate milk supply on the fifth day and the chances for full breast nursing are 65 to 74 per cent. Women over 30 years of age at the birth of their first child have less chance of an adequate supply of milk that younger mothers.[637] For those who cannot breast feed their babies, there is ample evidence that babies can thrive well on bottle feedings. Also these mothers can give their babies the essential "mothering" during feeding time and at other times of the day. No mother should feel inadequate or have a sense of self-reproach because of inability to nurse her child.

VARIATION IN QUANTITY OF MILK SECRETED. While milk flow usually rises from about one pint after the first week or two of lactation to about one quart in the fifth month,[848] the quantity of milk secreted from day to day, and the output from week to week may vary considerably.[548] The gradual increase in milk flow is evidently peculiar not only to the individual but also to each particular lactation period. The average daily output of milk, studied by Macy and co-workers[548] in three women from the sixth week through the fourteenth month of lactation, was 2602 cc. in one lactation period and 3134 cc. in another lactation period in the same subject, 2366 cc. for one period in another subject, and 1419 cc. for the third subject.† They demonstrated also that the total quantity of breast milk produced during a lactation period depends not only on the individual's immediate capacity to produce but also on the demands placed on the mammary glands and on the dura-

---

* Jackson et al.[407] found a significantly longer period of breast feeding (up to seven months) among mothers who had rooming-in and thus had their babies with them, than among mothers whose babies were kept in the nursery.

† These women produced especially large quantities of milk.

tion of the lactation period. Their results showed that, if augmented milk production is to be secured, the milk should be removed from the breast at regular intervals and as completely as possible. Their observations confirm the belief that excessive exercise and heavy work tend to depress maximum output of milk and also that nervous factors such as excitement, fear and anxiety lessen the flow, and severe shock may cause complete cessation.

Nutritional Advantages of Breast Feeding. As Jeans says, "Despite all our modern knowledge of infant nutrition and all the current refinements of artificial feeding, feeding at the breast of the mother remains an ideal procedure. This is true despite the fact that human milk contains only a bare minimum of most of the nutritional essentials and the fact that the body composition of the breast-fed infant departs widely from that which preceded and that which follows, in contrast to the body composition of the artificially fed baby, which maintains more closely a smooth continuance of the fetal and post-infancy curve."*

NITROGEN RETENTION IN BREAST-FED AND ARTIFICIALLY FED INFANTS. Stearns[800] compares the nitrogen content of infants given larger amounts of undiluted cow's milk, treated so that it forms a fine curd in the stomach, and that of infants fed human milk. After birth the percentage of nitrogen content of infants fed cow's milk increases in a curve continuous with the curve of prenatal content; in contrast, when mother's milk is given, a sharp change in direction of the percentage composition occurs after birth, and for a time the proportion of nitrogen in the body stays at the birth level or decreases slightly (see Figure 39). Greater retention of nitrogen in artificially fed infants is thought to represent larger amounts of tissue protein, since nitrogen is not stored in any other way. The larger part of the increase in tissue protein is represented in muscle. Infants who receive cow's milk in the larger of the customary amounts have approximately 25 per cent more muscle mass than infants receiving mother's milk. The muscle masses of breast-fed and artificially fed infants increase in a parallel manner but with larger values for those receiving cow's milk. There seems to be no disadvantage to the breast-fed baby because of lesser amounts of muscle.[413] Artificially fed babies, in order to have as good tissue turgor and motor development as breast-fed babies, apparently need to have higher retention of nitrogen and thus higher protein intake than the babies breast-fed.[413]

* Jeans[413] (p. 297).

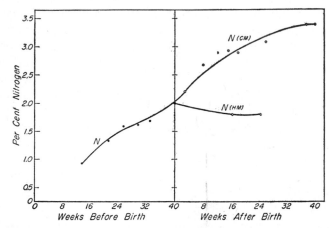

Figure 39. Changes in relative nitrogen content of fetus and infant. The regression line of nitrogen content of the fetus is drawn from data in the literature. (*CM*), infants fed cow's milk; (*HM*), infants fed human milk. (Redrawn from Stearns: Mineral Metabolism of Normal Infants, in Jeans, P. C.: The Feeding of Healthy Infants and Children, in Handbook of Nutrition; A Symposium. Chicago, American Medical Association, 1943, p. 342.)

CALCIUM AND PHOSPHORUS RETENTION. The percentage of calcium in the body of an infant fed cow's milk differs from that of one fed human milk. A decrease occurs in both types of feeding for several weeks after birth, after which period the body content of calcium in the infant receiving cow's milk starts to rise. On the other hand, the body content of the infant receiving human milk continues to fall for several weeks more and probably does not reach the birth value until the infant is one year old. The calcium of human milk is used by the growing infant more efficiently than that of cow's milk, but the amount retained from cow's milk is much greater because of the larger quantity. The significance of these differences in body composition of the infant is not clear.

The growth in length of infants fed a standardized cow's milk formula is related to the amount of calcium retained,[802] which in turn is affected by the vitamin D intake. Stearns[802] reports differing retentions of calcium with varying vitamin D intake in an otherwise constant standardized diet. Infants with poor calcium retention grow at average to below average rates; infants with higher calcium retention grow at a greater than average rate. Thus a higher retention of calcium by artificially fed infants would appear to be advantageous to them. However, the breast-fed baby makes excellent growth in length, even with much lower calcium retention, and grows at a definitely greater rate than the infant receiving cow's milk with the same calcium retention.[413] Because breast-fed infants grow and develop well with less retention of calcium, it is suggested that the extra calcium acquired by bottle-fed babies may not necessarily be needed.[413] It has been shown that calcium is stored in the bones of newborns.[240] This stored calcium may possibly be utilized in early infancy to permit rapid growth with a low ingestion of calcium and phosphorus.[799]

The phosphorus content of the body and the phosphorus requirement depend on the amount of calcium and nitrogen retained. Infants on breast milk receive sufficient phosphorus to meet their needs in relation to the amounts of calcium and nitrogen retained.

IRON. Human milk is twice as rich in iron as cow's milk.[545] This extra amount and its utilization are important in the early months when the baby receives no other iron and is using up its iron reserves. The iron stored in the body of the infant at birth is adequate to maintain the hemoglobin at a normal level for the early months, after which time additional iron is necessary. After three months of age, iron retention on the customary formula of cow's milk approximates zero; in the breast-fed infant the average retention approximates 0.11 mg. A retention of 0.7 mg. is required after six months to maintain the normal hemoglobin level.[803]

VITAMINS. Colostrum is especially high in vitamin A, and mature human milk generally contains more A than cow's milk[545] so the breast-fed baby receives more vitamin A in his milk than does the artificially fed one.

The vitamin C content of human milk varies directly with the diet of the mother, but is generally large in comparison with that of cow's milk formula. Human milk in this country will normally contain 48 mg. of ascorbic acid (vitamin C) to the quart[497]; a cow's milk formula prepared by boiling and diluting may contain almost none.[808] Human milk, if the mother's diet is adequate in vitamin C, meets the recommended allowance, but the cow's milk formula falls far short of it. This deficiency is made good by giving some good source of vitamin C such as orange juice. Although human milk seems to contain adequate amounts, it is safer to provide additional vitamin C for the breast-fed infant also.

Thiamine content of human milk varies widely, depending on the diet of the mother.[596] Cow's milk, although subjected to heat, contains more thiamine than human milk. While the breast-fed baby has no thiamine to spare, he seems to do very well nutritionally. The thiamine requirement is more equally met by the two types of feeding than seems apparent, because of the higher proportion of calories from fat in human milk and the fact that thiamine is not concerned with fat metabolism. The allowance of 0.3 mg. at one to three months to 0.5 mg. at ten to twelve months of thiamine for infants recommended by the Food and Nutrition Board of the National Research Council can hardly be attained by use of the average human milk or the average cow's milk formula. Using either of the milks, it is highly desirable to supplement the infant's diet with foods high in thiamine at an early age.[413]

The riboflavin content of human milk varies widely; that of cow's milk varies less; both are affected by the intake. The average riboflavin content of cow's milk is more than three times[545] that of human milk. The recommended allowance for infants, from 0.4 mg. at one to three months to 0.9 mg. at ten to twelve months, is met both by human and cow's milk in the first few months but later supplemental foods are needed.[359]

Both cow's milk and human milk are poor sources of niacin, but human milk has about twice as much as cow's milk.[545] However, milk is a good source of the amino acid, tryptophan, which can substitute for some of the requirement of niacin. B_6 and B_{12}, which are also of concern in the nutrition of infants, are apparently supplied in adequate amounts in both human and cow's milk.* Neither human nor cow's milk contains significant amounts of vitamin D, thus the requirement of the infant must be met by some supplement, since vitamin D is essential in the efficient utilization of calcium and phosphorus.

Other Advantages of Breast Feeding.   When the mother's diet is really adequate, and her milk correspondingly so, breast feeding has a number of other distinct advantages over artificial feeding. Breast milk is, to an appreciable extent, a prophylactic food. Breast-fed babies have significantly less respiratory infections during the second half of the first year than the artificially fed, as indicated by several studies reported by Stevenson.[808] He suggests that the greater intake of vitamins A and C and the fact that they seem to utilize them better, or to have less need of them, may be contributing factors to the resistance of breast-

---

* Symptoms due to vitamin B_6 deficiency have been noted in infants fed a commercially prepared modification of cow's milk.[173, 563, 780]

fed babies even though they are breast-fed for only three or four months. Stevenson found that in a series of carefully supervised infants* who were given complements of vitamins currently considered adequate there was no significant increase in the incidence of gastrointestinal and other infections in the artificially fed group. The prophylactic effect in gastrointestinal disturbances is more noticeable among children in the less favored economic classes,[4] where lack of knowledge and facilities militates against carrying out adequate health measures, or where the careful supervision of the infant's feeding by doctors and nurses is not available.

Another advantage, if the mother herself is caring for her baby, is that breast feeding is distinctly easier. No time is spent in preparing the formula, sterilizing bottles, nipples, and other utensils, warming the formula to correct temperature, and cleaning bottles and nipples after feeding. In some households the refrigeration of the formula may be a real problem. Breast milk is automatically prepared, is the right temperature for the baby, and the only time spent is that in actual nursing, which must be spent in any case.

Psychologically both the infant and mother gain something in the nursing situation. The young infant gains comfort in his close physical contact with another individual. Anyone who has ever held a young baby knows how responsive he is to cuddling, how he snuggles against the person holding him with obviously pleasurable reactions. The infant also profits indirectly by the effect of nursing upon the mother. Breast feeding is a physiologic maturation process for mothers. "It is maintained that women benefit physiologically and psychologically by the accomplishment of this part of the normal development of maternity. In this intimate situation, as in no other, a mother obtains a demonstration of her real importance to the infant. She not only feels her importance but acts it. This is just as necessary to her mental health as it is to the baby's, and in addition the physical pleasure which a well adjusted mother receives from nursing must contribute to her feeling of closeness to the infant."†

Spock[793] quotes mothers as saying, "It's wonderful to be giving him something that no one else can give." "It's pleasurable both physically

---

* Subjects were infants who were followed in a longitudinal study of child health and development, which is still in progress in the Department of Maternal and Child Health of the Harvard School of Public Health.

† Aldrich[4] (p. 915).

and emotionally." "It makes me feel closer to him." A woman has confidence in herself as a mother and thus is relaxed, confident and consequently more effective in her other relations with and care of her child.

Bottle Feeding. It has already been said than an intelligent, capable mother under the guidance of a physician can meet her infant's needs both nutritionally and emotionally by bottle feeding.* Sometimes women are unable to nurse their babies because they are unable to produce enough milk to satisfy the infants' needs. Others cannot because they must work. Still others may have strong feelings against breast feeding.† In this event, even if the mother could nurse her baby, the experience would satisfy neither mother nor child. In any case, the mother should have no sense of inadequacy or self-reproach.[506]

Meeting Additional Requirements in Infant Stages I and II. NEED FOR VITAMIN D. Neither human nor cow's milk is adequate in the vitamin essential for the laying down of the minerals calcium and phosphorus, contained in the milk, as bone. Vitamin D may be obtained (1) by ultraviolet rays of the sun activating a substance, cholesterol, in the skin; (2) by milk fortified with vitamin D; (3) by fish liver oil, such as cod liver oil; or (4) by a vitamin D concentrate. Milk fortified with vitamin D is sometimes used in artificial feeding. It is obvious that for the young infant the source from sunshine is not appropriate. He will generally receive his vitamin D in the form of fish liver oils, such as cod liver oil, or some vitamin D concentrate as prescribed by the physician. Jeans[413] states that fish liver oils in appropriate amounts may be expected to produce no digestive difficulties at one or two weeks of age. The recommended allowance of the Food and Nutrition Board[261] for vitamin D is 400 units. Evidence exists that amounts greater than 1500 units taken daily will be followed

---

* A study based on standardized interviews with mothers of five-year-old children[733] showed that the early feeding experience, whether breast or bottle fed, had no consistent effect upon later behavior such as aggression in the home, "considerable" or "high" conscience, dependency, severe feeding problems, bed-wetting at age five, or strong emotional reaction to toilet training. The authors point out that feeding experiences as well as other experiences affect the individual child, but the evidence presented in this study suggests that the way in which feeding experiences affect the child is specific to each child and that the technique of feeding does not have any constant effect for all children. See also Newton[630] and Orlansky.[643]

† For some reasons given by mothers for not breast feeding their infants see Sears et al.[733]

after several months by a decrease in appetite with consequent decrease in calcium retention and in rate of growth.[415] The dosage of vitamin D should always be considered in terms of units, not quantity.

NEED FOR VITAMIN C (ASCORBIC ACID). Next to the need for vitamin D comes that of vitamin C, because shortly after birth the blood level of ascorbic acid in infants begins to fall. The breast-fed baby may be receiving appreciable amounts by the fifth day, provided the mother's diet is adequate in this constituent. If the infant's diet of milk does not supply a sufficient quantity of vitamin C, as is true in the case of those artificially fed and may be true in some instances of those breast-fed, additional C needs to be added to furnish the recommended allowance of 30 mg.*[261] Orange juice† is most generally used as a source of vitamin C beginning with small amounts and gradually increasing the quantity until the full amount is being taken. Tomato juice, cabbage juice and ascorbic acid tablets are also used as sources of vitamin C.

NEED FOR INCREASED AMOUNTS OF VITAMINS, MINERALS AND CALORIES. The infant thrives on this diet of milk supplemented with vitamins D and C until about three months of age.

The present tendency to give solid foods to many infants as early as the second or third week of life, and to many more at the beginning or middle of the second month, appears to be based more upon social pressures than upon nutritional needs.‡ While the infant's digestive tract apparently can tolerate these additions, Hill[359] cautions that an infant's water reserve under certain conditions might be jeopardized by too early addition of minerals and protein which might place too heavy a load upon the kidneys.

By three months, the infant's reserve supply of iron normally present at birth is becoming insufficient to meet his needs.§ His need for the B complex vitamins has also increased. He has grown and become much more active, which means that more food is needed to supply the increased demand for energy. To meet these increasing needs, additional foods are introduced. For the recommended allowances see

---

* Hill[359] recommends that 30 to 50 mg. be given to artificially fed infants, beginning shortly after birth.

† Two ounces of orange juice supply approximately 30 mg. of vitamin C.

‡ Deisher and Goers[203] found no differences between two groups of infants, one fed solids during the first three months and the other fed solids at three months or later.

§ Iron reserves are usually adequate for the first three to four months.[359]

Table 4, page 244. As the needs mentioned above have increased, the infant has been maturing so that he can manage more complex foods. He begins to drool at about this age, an indication that his salivary glands, which secrete a starch-splitting enzyme, are maturing. His digestive tract, because of the presence of starch-splitting enzymes, can handle carbohydrates of a more complex composition than that of simple sugars. His digestive tract has further developed so that he can use semi-solid foods in a finely divided form. Thus a variety of foods may be introduced. Those included are cereals, either whole grain or enriched or the specially prepared, fortified proprietary cereal foods, egg yolk, meats, vegetables and fruits. The order in which they are introduced makes little difference, and is generally dependent upon the preferences of the pediatrician.

When whole grain cereal is given it is strained, since the digestive tract of the infant is not mature enough to utilize the more complex food.* The food is introduced in small amounts, ¼ to ½ teaspoonful, diluted with boiled milk or the formula. Beginning with a very thin consistency and gradually making it thicker after the infant becomes accustomed to the flavor may make acceptance of it easier, since he has to become acquainted with both a new flavor and a new consistency. The cereal is fed from the tip of a spoon and put well back on the tongue because the mechanism for swallowing is immature. As the infant learns to like and to take the cereal eagerly, giving it thicker helps prepare him for the consistency of the next food to be introduced into the diet.

Egg yolk free from the white of the egg is generally cooked. The vegetables and fruits are sieved or puréed. Sieved meat is available and can be fed at an early age. Studies[502, 503] have indicated that meat fed to infants beginning at six to eight weeks promoted the formation of hemoglobin and red blood cells. These infants had fewer colds, slept better and appeared more satisfied than a group of infants who had no meat. These new foods are offered to the infant one at a time in one-half teaspoonful amounts or perhaps only a taste at first, with the amount gradually increased as he learns to like them. He will take an increased amount according to his appetite, which can be the mother's guide of quantity. These foods not only supply the needed food elements, but help to accustom the infant to variety in the flavor and texture of foods. We believe that this is the basis of good eating habits.

* See Maturation of the Nutriture and Digestive System, in Chapter 5.

The sieving of fruits, vegetables and meat makes it easier for the digestive tract to utilize their contents. The infant as yet has no teeth with which to chew them.

Needs of Child Reaching "Pre-mature" Nutritive Stage. The infant's teeth usually begin to erupt some time between six and nine months of age. This is the period when he puts everything in his mouth, and many think that this is the time when he is ready to learn to chew. By this time also the pediatrician has advised introduction of chopped foods into the daily menu. He is given a piece of well toasted white bread, a dry crust of bread, or a piece of zwieback. It is important that he be given the opportunity to learn how to chew, because young children who have had only liquid and sieved foods throughout the first year frequently refuse coarser foods when they are offered. During this period mashed vegetables, and chopped vegetables, baked potato, meat including liver and fruits are offered.

By the age of nine months, many infants will be taking their food in three meals a day, with perhaps fruit juice or milk between meals. Some children are ready for this routine at an earlier age; with some it is delayed until later.

IMPORTANCE OF EARLY EXPERIENCE WITH FOODS. When the child is a year old, if wisely fed, he will have become acquainted with and learned to eat almost all of the foods that form the basis of an adequate diet throughout his lifetime. The time to pay attention to food habits is while they are being formed, and during this first year the child is learning to eat. The attitudes established are, therefore, of importance in determining whether the future feeding of the child will be easy or difficult, and they will contribute in a real way to the maintenance of health as he develops. (The establishment of eating habits is discussed on pp. 247–263).

IMPORTANCE OF BALANCE IN DAILY FOOD INTAKE. All food substances needed by the body, although required in widely differing amounts, are equally important. The 7 mg. of iron required daily is just as essential to sound health in the young child as the 40 gm. (5700 times as much) of protein. The importance of maintaining balance among the nutrients is one of the more recent contributions to our knowledge of the nutrition of human beings. It takes a variety of foods to maintain this balance even in the diet of the young child. Overemphasis on any one food, such as milk, eggs, liver, cereals or the vitamins, may destroy the nutritional balance of the diet. Even milk, as excellent as it is as a source of calcium, proteins, and fats, should not be used to the exclusion of other essential foods.

Meeting Requirements of Maturing Child. The child is maturing rapidly during his first year; he crawls, stands, and moves his hands and feet almost constantly when he is awake. He uses more energy, he needs larger amounts of food, and he is becoming increasingly independent. His body structure is maturing; the digestive system that formerly required puréed food can now utilize chopped food. This readiness of his body to use food in a more complex form is indicative of the rapidity of the maturation of his nutriture. His willingness to change from puréed foods to chopped foods and to accept new foods is a sign that he is reaching nutritive maturity and will soon be ready for solid food.

Children vary widely in the time required to learn that they can eat solid food. Usually by the time a child has twelve to sixteen teeth he is beginning to masticate his food quite satisfactorily and he can feed himself (not too successfully from the adult standpoint, but very well considering his stage of maturity). At this stage he may be having some of his meals with the family and can share the family diet. This is, in a certain sense, a transition period from feeding himself part of his meal and being fed the rest by his mother, to participation in a group and becoming independent in taking on the job himself.

As soon as a child has learned to masticate his food, he can have foods such as adults eat and as they are prepared for the family. Root vegetables, such as carrots, beets and potatoes, are rich in their starch content and valuable in their minerals and vitamins. Potatoes are a fairly good source of vitamin C and iron.

Green vegetables, such as spinach, chard, turnip greens and green string beans, are low in starch content but valuable in vitamin A content and in minerals. Fruits are valuable for their vitamin and mineral content and also contain appreciable amounts of cellulose, which occurs in the pulp and is a desirable source of roughage. Leafy vegetables and fruits are especially important. A green vegetable is valuable as a regular part of every child's daily food intake. Sugar is best used in the child's diet in small quantities to improve the flavor of food. All fruits contain some sugar, and there is reason to believe that they contain an amount adequate for body needs.

Additional sugar beyond the need to improve the flavor of some food is not needed. Those experienced in feeding children well chosen diets know that such children do not necessarily crave sweets.[543] Desire for sweet foods may be the result of being conditioned to sweetness earlier, as for example, by use of an oversweet formula or by frequent experiences with sweet foods in a family that likes and eats sweets often.

AMOUNTS OF FOOD CHILD CAN BE EXPECTED TO EAT AT THIS PERIOD. Adults often misjudge the amount of food a child should be expected to eat. They may regard two to three level tablespoonfuls as a totally inadequate serving, and yet for the young child it may be all he can consume at one time. Some children will eat more than others. Large children and those who are growing fast will probably eat more than small, slow growing children. The progress of the child, as assessed by a physician, will indicate whether his food intake is adequate for him. Children also vary in their appetite and thus in their food intake from time to time. Toward the end of the first year, the infant's appetite begins to slacken. This is not surprising when it is realized that he is now growing more slowly and thus needs less food for growth. At the same time his motor and social growths are accelerating. He is showing a strong desire for independence in his activities, including feeding. This is a period of growing independence in self feeding, expression of choice, replacement of soft foods and especially prepared infant foods with those of coarser texture, and changes in the acceptance of specific foods. Now begins the period of change in appetite and food acceptance which continues into the preschool years. A longitudinal study of food intake* revealed that all children changed in appetite and food intake between one and three years of age. For some, intake was gradually lowered (most markedly in milk and certain vegetables); for others it dropped abruptly. This change appeared anywhere from one year of age to three years. The low plateau lasted for a few months or persisted for two years or more. Apparently, all children can be expected to go through this stage; for some it will be a matter of months, and for others a matter of most of the preschool years. If a generalization may be made for most children from the Denver study, children will not suffer nutritionally from this drop in appetite, as will be seen later. Parents, therefore, can

---

* Nutritional studies are a part of the study of the growth and development of a group of healthy Denver children of the upper middle class carried on by the Child Research Council. Analysis of the dietary histories to five years of age have been made.[97, 98, 99]

anticipate this and accept it without concern. Parents who are unaware of this may push food on their children, and in so doing create an appetite problem.

The Child Reaches Nutritive Maturity.   When the child can eat solid foods such as adults take, and they are prepared for digestion and reduced to their simple form (ready for absorption) entirely within his own body, he is nutritively mature and his body is physiologically capable of utilizing the foods served to the family.

Many children have reached this stage of maturity by their second birthday, although there is no chronological level to be fixed for the individual child. The mother now can plan one meal for all.* Each family will plan the family food according to its own food pattern. Family food patterns differ since families differ in their cultural patterns, in their food habits, in their food preferences and in their incomes. Children's nutritional needs (see Table 4) can be met within these differing food patterns by including the following in the daily dietary of each child:

1½-2 pints of milk
1 egg
1 serving† of meat, fish, or cheese
1 serving of raw green leafy or yellow vegetable
1 serving of cooked green or yellow vegetable
2 fruits—one a citrus fruit
1 serving of whole grain or enriched cereal
1-3 slices of whole wheat or enriched bread
1-2 tablespoonfuls of butter or margarine fortified with vitamin A
Cod liver oil or vitamin D concentrate as prescribed by the physician
Iodized salt for seasoning in endemic goiter regions

This framework provides plenty of opportunity for respecting individual differences in amounts and in preferences.

The foods listed herein are natural foods and foods which, in most cases, furnish a number of nutrients. Processed foods can give satiety easily without meeting other needs. The use of sugar has been men-

---

* It is not hard to adapt the family diet to the young child. He can have the lean portions of meat. He can have the fruit out of the fruit pie and perhaps a small amount of crust. Rich gravies and sauces or highly spiced foods can be omitted. Food can be salted mildly and the adults can add more salt and pepper to their food if desired.

† Nutritionists sometimes estimate an average serving at this age as about one level tablespoonful of meat or vegetable per year of age.

tioned earlier. For the preschool child the time for sweets, candy and ice cream cones, etc., is at the end of the meal. They are to be considered as food and not as treats. Cookies containing dried fruits or peanut butter supply not only calories but nutrients as well. The following family menus illustrate how a mother can plan one meal for all.

FAMILY MENUS

I	II
Breakfast	**Breakfast**
Orange juice	Grapefruit
Soft boiled egg	Oatmeal, with milk
Toast, butter	Toast, butter
Milk, coffee	Milk, coffee
Lunch	**Lunch**
Chicken soup	Scrambled eggs
Open-faced sandwich of	Buttered green beans
cheese, tomato, bacon (1)	Muffins, butter
Rice pudding	Fruit jello
Milk	Milk
Dinner	**Dinner**
Meat patties	Baked liver
Baked potato	Parsley potatoes
Buttered broccoli	Buttered carrots
Tomato aspic salad (2)	Tossed salad (4)
Bread, butter	Bread, butter
Lemon chiffon pie (3)	Peaches, custard sauce
Milk, coffee	Milk, coffee

Modifications for the young child:
1. Wedge of cheese, wedge of tomato, bacon served as "finger foods," bread and butter.
2. Piece of lettuce.
3. Filling of pie with a small amount of crust.
4. Ingredients of salad served as finger foods.
Coffee for adults.
Fortified margarine may be substituted for butter.

As stated earlier, the lessened appetite of later infancy extends into this period. In the Denver study, with the drop in appetite between one and three years of age, the calories, carbohydrate and fat intake increased slightly, protein intake remained stationary and the calcium, phosphorus and iron intake dropped. Of the vitamins studied, the thiamine intake maintained a plateau from fifteen months until just after three years. Riboflavin, like calcium, decreased, and niacin tended to increase although the children with the high intakes during the second year generally showed a decrease during the third year. Intakes of all the nutrients increased approximately after three years of age. Calcium and riboflavin values reflected the decrease in milk consumption, which was lowest (16 ounces) between two and one half and three years of age. Niacin intakes reflected meat intake. The changes in iron intake reflected the change from prepared baby foods, to which iron had been added, to foods prepared at home. Even with these decreases, when compared with the National Research Council recommended allowances, the intakes showed that the median calories were close to the recommended allowances, the protein median was above for the first two years, and similar thereafter, and iron was low for most children after two and one half years.* Calcium† also was low, the median thiamine was slightly higher, riboflavin tended to be greater and niacin to be lower than the recommended allowances. The high protein intake probably compensated for the low niacin, for no niacin deficiencies were evident. Individual patterns of nutrient intakes varied considerably. Some were consistently high, some consistently low and some varied from time to time. This variability in the food intake of healthy children indicates a need for more information regarding individual variability in metabolism.

During this period, a quart of milk is still considered ideal by many,[416] although a well child receiving vitamin D and a nutritionally adequate diet may retain sufficient calcium from a pint of milk.[183, 646] During this period the rate of growth slows and the relative proportion of body weight due to skeletal muscle increases.[799] The need of minerals for bone, therefore, is less than at any other time of growth and that of nutrients for soft tissue is proportionately high. One might expect that the calcium intake could be reduced. However, with the addition of other foods, the increase in undigestible material and a decreased ratio of calcium to phosphorus in the diet tend to decrease absorption of calcium. Also, as the child increases his contacts with

---

* Since the hemoglobin level and the red cell count were satisfactory, the amount of iron for these children can be assumed to be adequate. Perhaps the requirement for iron needs reevaluation.

† The changes in the level of intake of calcium paralleled a theoretical calcium retention curve formulated by Stearns[801] for calcium needs for childhood growth. The recommended allowances of the National Research Council are maintained at the same level of 1.0 gm. from ten months through nine years of age.

other children and adults the number of illnesses with fever tend to rise. Such illnesses are accompanied with decrease in calcium absorption.[799] For these reasons it seems advisable for preschool children to have a quart of milk if possible. Many children do not have the capacity for such an amount at this age. In this event the milk the child cannot drink can be used in cooking, such as cereal cooked with milk, creamed foods and puddings, or the calcium can be provided by using more cheese. By no means should a child be urged to drink milk. It is better for a child to have less milk for a relatively short time in his life than to set up an aversion to it which will operate perhaps for many years. It is better, not only with milk, but with all foods, to serve too little rather than too much. The child will indicate if he desires more.

Sometimes a child tires of a food and refuses to eat it. This happens occasionally with cereals. This is not surprising since it is one of the foods introduced early, given daily for many months, and frequently not varied in kind. Some children will eat the same food, day after day, year after year, but others like variety. Breakfast cereal is not necessary as a part of the daily food intake of the child. It is a convenient way of serving the cereal grains and the child may consume more than he would if it were prepared in some other way. However, toast made from whole wheat or enriched bread, muffins made with whole cereals, and mush made from cornmeal (made of whole grain or enriched) are excellent substitutes. A food which is refused may be omitted from the diet for a time and later reintroduced. Refusals are generally a temporary matter if the adult accepts them in a matter-of-fact manner.

Many children need a snack between meals, because they become hungry before mealtime. It has been found that more outbursts of anger occur late in the morning and late in the afternoon.[302] Children become tired and probably hungry at this time. It is believed that some easily digested food taken in the midmorning and midafternoon will help to alleviate this situation. One study[447] of the behavior of nursery school children demonstrated that a midmorning feeding of fruit juice (unsweetened pineapple juice) was beneficial in relieving fatigue, in reducing irritability and tension, and in promoting a feeling of satisfaction and well-being between that time and lunch, and also did not interfere with eating at lunch time. Another study of convalescent children in a rest home[920] indicated that milk between meals did not interfere with appetite at mealtime. Yet another study of nursery school children[607] suggested that snacks when offered early enough in the morning need not interfere with the noon meal. It is advised that eating between meals be a regular procedure at a regular time. Fruit juices and cracker, fruit or milk are good foods to use at this time. Giving food between meals is an individual matter. For some it is advisable; for others it is not because it may interfere with their appetite at mealtime.

RECOMMENDED ALLOWANCES. Just as there are standards against which the growth of a child is checked, so there are tables of recommended allowances for checking the intake of nutrients. Table 4 gives

*Table 4.   Recommended Daily Allowances for Infants and Young Children**

	1-3 mo.†‡	4-9 mo.‡	10-12 mo.‡	1-3 yrs.‡	4-6 yrs.‡
Calories	120/2.2 lb.	110/2.2 lb.	100/2.2 lb.	1200	1600
Protein (gm.)	3.5/2.2 lb.	3.5/2.2 lb.	3.5/2.2 lb.	40	50
Calcium (gm.)	0.6	0.8	1.0	1.0	1.0
Iron (mg.)	6	6	6	7	8
Vitamin A (I.U.)	1500	1500	1500	2000	2500
Thiamine (mg.)	0.3	0.4	0.5	0.6	0.8
Riboflavin (mg.)	0.4	0.7	0.9	1.0	1.2
Niacin (mg.)	3	4	5	6	8
Ascorbic Acid (mg.)	30	30	30	35	50
Vitamin D (I.U.)	400	400	400	400	400

* Taken from Food and Nutrition Board, National Research Council: Recommended Dietary Allowances. Revised 1953. National Academy of Sciences—National Research Council Publication 302, 1953.

† During the first month, desirable allowances for many nutrients are dependent upon maturation of excretory and endocrine functions. Therefore no specific recommendations are given.

Dietary requirements for some of the nutrients, as for example protein, are less if derived from human milk.

‡1. Iodine—The need is met by the regular use of iodized salt.

2. Phosphorus—In general it is safe to assume that if the calcium and protein needs are met through common foods the phosphorus requirement will also be met.

3. Other members of the B complex (in addition to thiamine, riboflavin and niacin), B_6, B_{12}, folacin, pantothenic acid and biotin, are also required although no values can be given.

the allowances in terms of nutrients needed during infancy and early childhood. These quantities are allowances and not requirements, and allow for a margin of safety in meeting the needs of children. They are based on metabolism studies, plus the experience of individuals well versed in child nutrition. They are revised from time to time in order that the latest scientific knowledge may be utilized.*

Facts to Remember When Feeding a Young Child. Nutritional allowance tables are to be used in a flexible manner as a check-up on the individual child's intake in relation to children in general. The results are to be interpreted in terms of the individual child, his size, activity and his growth.

The child has needs for the present but is also building for the future in terms of body structure and food habits. "One year of good feeding at the beginning of life is more important than ten after forty, and a baby's needs are not to be judged by an adult's inclinations. Feeding must be a matter of principle and not of impulse; the reward will be partly in the present—much more in the future."†

This period is so important in establishing a normal appetite, good attitudes toward food and good food habits, that undue emphasis cannot be placed upon it. The adult assumes great responsibility in the choice of food placed before the child and the way in which it is prepared.

The child's needs for nutrients are higher in relation to his size than those of an adult and his digestive capacity is smaller. Therefore, foods rich in the needed nutrients are musts in a child's diet.

The child's digestive tract is still immature. Therefore, foods which can be digested easily are selected. The child needs to be protected against foods that will irritate the lining of the tract, such as foods high in roughage and highly seasoned foods.

Consider the whole child. He needs "psychological vitamins," a term Frank[267] applies to love, affection, tenderness, patience and understanding, as well as chemical vitamins. He needs these for appetite, digestion and absorption of food, since emotions influence the activity of the digestive tract.

Young children go on food jags. A child may eat large quantities of a food for a time, then taper off or stop eating it entirely for a while. Later he will return to it. Children have been known to eat as many as five eggs or four bananas at one sitting.[190]

* Students are advised to watch for the latest revision of the Recommended Dietary Allowances.

† Rose[712] (p. 184). By permission of Macmillan Company, New York.

For discussion of long-time effect of diet as demonstrated in animals, see Sherman and Lanford[750] (pp. 5-6, 148-154, 239-240, 289-290, 364).

A child's appetite varies from day to day and from meal to meal. One day he may eat like a bear, another day like a bird. Some children eat better at one meal of the day than another.

The young child is often slow in eating and dawdles. He may become tired in the process of feeding himself, for he is still not adept at this process of self feeding. A helping hand with the last bites may be advisable. Dawdling may be reduced by making the eating process as simple as possible. Utensils can be selected that will facilitate eating. Foods such as soup or custard can be drunk from a cup more easily than spooned out of a dish.

Young children tend to make a ritual of eating as they do of other routines. Perhaps foods are eaten in a specific order. Perhaps a particular spoon or dish must be used, or the table must be set just so. When these rituals are respected, mealtime tends to go smoothly; when disregarded, the meal may be disturbed and little or no food eaten.

Young children have preferences. They like simple, unmixed foods. A meat pattie is preferred to meat in a stew. They are aware of textures. They like a variety of crisp, chewy and soft foods in a meal. Mashed potatoes may be acceptable when soft and fluffy, yet be rejected when sticky and gummy. Young children have difficulty in swallowing anything dry. They also prefer mild flavors. Therefore, the preparation of such vegetables as broccoli, cauliflower, cabbage, etc., is important. They prefer food to be lukewarm. If food is too hot they may not have the patience to wait for it to cool. They like foods that are easy to eat. "Finger foods," or foods which can be picked up by their fingers, are popular. Carrot and celery sticks, pieces of lettuce, cabbage, etc., are popular and furnish an excellent way to introduce the foods which they will meet later in salads. Some young children in the second year will eat vegetables more readily if they can pick them up with their fingers. A whole string bean may be acceptable, but beans may be rejected when cut up and served with a spoon.

Each child has his own particular preferences. These preferences may refer to specific foods or to ways of preparing them. Children vary in the number of foods they like and the intensity in their feeling about individual foods. Most children like what they are accustomed to having. Therefore, as said before, early experience with a variety of foods is very important. It is wise to respect children's preferences. No child need be expected to like all foods. His nutritional needs can be met with various combinations. A healthy, happy child will eat a wide enough variety of foods to meet his nutritional requirements.*

Eating Habits

The foundation for good eating habits is laid when the newborn infant has his hunger promptly satisfied. He is thus conditioned to the natural sequence of hunger, ingestion of food, satisfaction, physical well-being. As indicated earlier, in hunger a series of contractions of the stomach occurs, causing hunger pangs which are announced by the infant by crying. These hunger pangs are not under the control of the higher brain centers but rather under subcortical control. However, appetite, or the desire for food, which depends in large measure on pleasant experiences with food, is related to the higher brain centers. Thus it can be completely suppressed through a series of unpleasant associations with or memories of food. It becomes the task of the adult to nurture appetite by building up pleasant associations with food.

From birth it is important, therefore, to time the feeding of a baby according to his own physiological rhythm. Thus self-regulation or feeding the infant when he expresses a need for food is a sound procedure. The normal full term newborn has a well developed reflex capacity to suckle and to swallow. It is known that he has hunger contractions when his stomach is empty, and that these contractions cause him discomfort. When the contractions occur, he wakes from sleep suddenly and cries lustily. As soon as some liquid reaches his stomach, he ceases to cry and begins to relax as if relieved. Thus through gratification of his need, pleasant conditioning toward food and the process of eating is set up. This is a preparation for the time when eating becomes a more complex, voluntary act, under conscious control. "It is back here in the comparatively simple performance of the earliest days of life, that the child begins to develop the positive conditioning and the sense of competency which we recognize as so important for the later success of the individual."†

On a self-regulating schedule the newborn is fed each time he gives evidence, by rooting, sucking or crying, that he is hungry, and he is

---

* See Davis[190] for a discussion of feeding children after the first year.
† Aldrich[5] (p. 579).

permitted to nurse as long as he pleases, except for breast-fed babies during the first few days when feeding time may be limited to allow the mother's nipples to become accustomed to the pull of the sucking infant.

Since the infant operates largely on a reflex basis for about the first three months of life, and since his reflex cry registers protest against many other discomforts besides hunger, it becomes important to use a good deal of judgment and common sense in determining when the cry does indicate hunger. The mother must be given some guides. It is known that the stomach ordinarily takes two or more hours to empty itself of food. Thus when the baby has just recently been fed, it seems reasonable to suspect that some other cause than hunger is operative. One investigates in any case, but particularly in this circumstance, to see whether the baby is wet, soiled, cold, too warm, in need of fondling, and so forth. In an investigation conducted by Dr. Aldrich and others[9] of causes of crying in a newborn infants' nursery, crying was ascribed to hunger when it occurred near feeding time and was accompanied by sucking movements. When the baby was wet or soiled or had just vomited, crying, when it occurred, was ascribed to these causes.* Dr. Aldrich and his co-workers suggested that a complete list of causes of crying should include the need for fondling and rhythmic motion.

The hunger cry is usually quite insistent and is not assuaged by other means than by food. The cry of colic, which occurs quite frequently in babies under three months of age, is also an insistent cry, but is more apt to occur soon after feeding than near feeding time. Dr. Eugene Roseman[19] points out that the baby who cries with his head thrown back does not have the colic but is hungry, while the child with colic cries with head pulled forward, knees drawn up, and arms across the chest.

Mothers who have successfully fed their babies on a self-regulation schedule, in which the baby decides when he is to be fed, declare that it is relatively easy to learn to understand when the infant is in need of food and when he is in need of some other attention. The frequency

---

* For fifty babies observed for twenty-four hours over an eight-day period, crying was ascribed to hunger in 2760 incidences or in 35.5 per cent of the total crying time. An even larger number of incidences, 3295 was ascribed to unknown causes.

of feeding on a self-regulation schedule has been observed in infants in the first week of life in a hospital,[639] in individual infants fed by mothers,[762, 851] and in a group of breast- and bottle-fed infants throughout their first year.[7]

In 100 breast-fed newborn infants on a self-regulation procedure,[639] the total number of breast feedings rose to a maximum on the fourth day and averaged 8.6 feedings. The maximum number for one baby in one day was seventeen. The records of one mother and her pediatrician[762] on two infants show that both babies nursed frequently during the first two weeks, sometimes as often as eleven times in twenty-four hours. By the third week they averaged eight and six times in twenty-four hours, and by the tenth week both were well stabilized on five feedings daily. Figures 40 and 41 show graphically how rapidly two babies, fraternal twins, put themselves on a quite regular schedule and reduced the total number of feedings when they were fed according to their own needs. The female twin took only four feedings on four of seven days as early as the third week. By the eighth week she was quite well stabilized on the four-feeding day and by the ninth week began occasionally to take only three feedings daily. Her twin brother in the ninth week took only three feedings four days out of seven. Aldrich and Hewitt[7] studied 100 breast- and bottle-fed babies on a self-regulating schedule for the first year and found, as illustrated in Figure 42, that babies chose to lengthen their feeding intervals gradually. At one month 10 per cent chose a two hour interval, 61 per cent a three hour interval, and 26 per cent a four hour interval. The peak for the four hour schedule came at three months, and that for four meals a day at seven to nine months. The schedule of three feedings a day was adopted by some at four months, with the number increasing until at 12 months 91 per cent selected this adult feeding schedule. Thus infants tend to adopt a regular schedule early and reduce their periods to three times a day some time during the first year. With established regularity of demands for food even by three months, the infant's feeding schedule can be adjusted to fit the mother's conveniences.

This procedure is satisfying to the infant, and fosters "a confidence in the lawfulness of the universe,"* thus providing a good basis for later socialization. During the early months of reflex control there is no

* Gesell and Ilg[291] (p. 56).

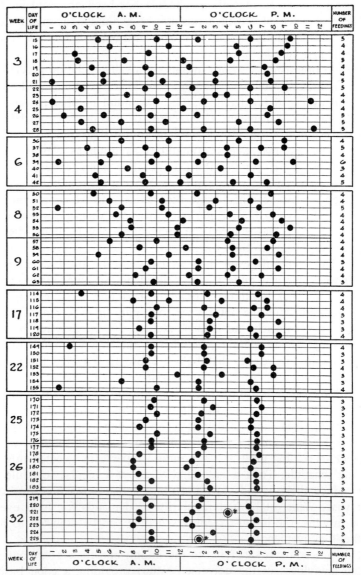

Figure 40. Chart showing feeding schedule of female twin. Cup feeding, on 221st day, given not in response to demand for food but as educational device to accustom infant to drink milk from a cup. (Trainham, G., Pilafian, G. J., and Kraft, R. M.: Case history of twins breast fed on self-demand regime, Journal of Pediatrics 27:97-108, 1945, C. V. Mosby Company.)

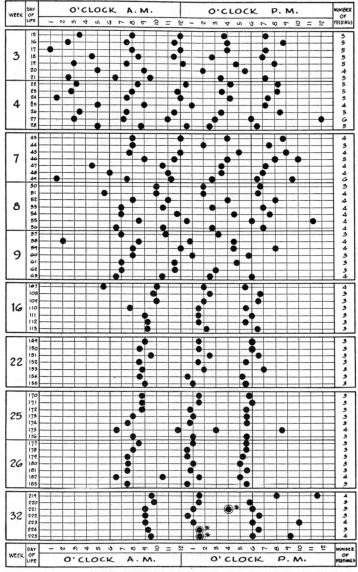

Figure 41. Chart showing feeding schedule of male twin. Cup feeding, on 221st day, given not in response to demand for food but as educational device to accustom infant to drink milk from a cup. (Trainham, G., Pilafian, G. J., and Kraft, R. M.: Case history of twins breast fed on self-demand regime, Journal of Pediatrics 27:97-108, 1945, C. V. Mosby Company.)

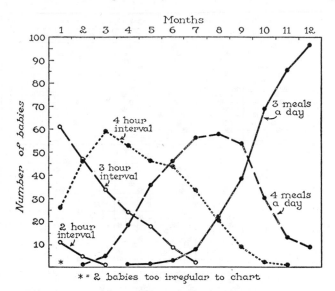

Figure 42.   Graph showing increase or decrease, as age advanced, in number of infants on self-regulating schedule who adopted each feeding interval. (Aldrich, C. A., and Hewitt, E. S.: A self-regulating feeding program for infants, Journal of American Medical Association 135:340-342, 1947.)

danger of spoiling the baby by too frequent and too prompt gratification of basic needs, the result of which is a conditioning to pleasurable associations with persons, with food and with other things.

For the mother such procedure in the early months and years of the child's life requires intelligence, common sense and self confidence in her ability to manage herself and her baby on such a flexible schedule. Her role is one of "anticipatory guidance," that is, watching for signs of her child's needs and his increasing maturity, and guiding him in his environment according to his needs, his maturity, and the family situation. At times there is some misunderstanding and consequently misuse of the permissive attitude toward children's feeding programs as in other aspects of their lives, with parents playing no positive role in their development. A mother will need some guidance herself in preparing for this task and in carrying it out. This guidance she can receive from her physician and the one she selects for her baby, if she has a pediatrician. The type of feeding regimen appropriate for mother and child can be determined by the physician after talking it over with the mother. Many believe that a middle course is most satisfactory for the majority of mothers and babies, that is, a plan whereby the baby is not put on a rigid schedule but is guided into reasonable feeding habits.*

At the beginning the mother's role is relatively simple. When the child is well established in his feeding regimen, if breast-fed, he can be given an occasional bottle which not only gives the infant experience with another form of feeding but also permits the mother some wider freedom. Later as more functions come under conscious control and wants and interests are added to needs, the wise parent or other adult must seek a judicious balance which allows prompt gratification of real needs and reasonable desires and at the same time, with equal firmness and promptness, denies unreasonable and dangerous wants. Thus there is begun the balance between love and discipline. The child is beginning to fit into the life of the family. Expectations of him in eating will rest upon his degree of maturity and the situation. The adults provide him with his food, they provide the environment in which that food is eaten, serve as examples in behavior and attitudes, and by the quality of their guidance lead the child into more and more mature eating behavior, according to his ability, or relegate him to a kind of "infantile autocracy" which prevents him from becoming a full participating member of the family.

When foods, other than milk, begin to be introduced, a new element enters the feeding picture—that of choosing not only the amount of food to be taken but also the kind. At this time the adults play an extremely important role in determining what kinds of foods will be made available to their children. They will determine whether the child will have natural foods containing a variety of nutrients in generous quantities, or many highly refined foods, a preponderance of sweet foods and other foods inappropriate for young children. The food

---

* In a study in a university community based on interviews with mothers during the first and second years of their child's life,[374] it was found that 12.5 per cent had a regular feeding schedule, 28.6 per cent had a semi-demand schedule and 58.5 per cent fed on demand. There was a tendency for those mothers who did not have a very definite schedule for household tasks to feed their babies on demand. In another study of mothers in two suburbs of a large metropolitan area of New England of middle class and working-class families,[733] 12 per cent followed complete self demand, 8 per cent a rigid feeding schedule. The others ranged between these extremes, with varying degree of scheduling. There was a positive correlation between the use of scheduling and the measure of the mother's anxiety in the area of child rearing.

habits of the family will now strongly affect the developing food habits and attitudes of the young child.

Self Selection of Foods.   It would seem from animal experiments[728] and the experiment of Davis[192] with newly weaned infants that learning through trial and error is the process involved in the self selection of food.* Thus all the factors involved in learning would seem to apply to the eating situation. Dr. Davis' experiment greatly influenced the practice of feeding infants and young children. She experimented with a group of newly weaned babies who were allowed to select their own food from a variety of natural foodstuffs. Nothing was done to influence the choice of the child, and all pressure and inhibition were removed. The food was natural, unmixed and unseasoned, and suitable for children. Each child ate alone and had a tray with all the food before him. A nurse helped him to get the food he could not reach. No food was offered either directly or by suggestion. The children ate their food eagerly, in a matter-of-fact way, ate astonishingly large quantities, and stopped with an air of finality. From the standpoint of appetite and digestion, optimal results were shown, the children's general physical condition indicating that their nutrition did not suffer but was well above average. It should be noted here that all the foods offered to the children were good for them; they were not exposed to undesirable foods. This experiment demonstrated that under *certain conditions* the complete removal of pressure and the granting of freedom in the choice of suitable foods would help children to develop normal food habits and would avoid many problems faced by the average parent. Sometimes people, not well informed about the experiment, have used it as justification for a laissez-faire type of feeding, believing that it demonstrates that children can select a well balanced diet in a home situation, regardless of the kind of food made available.

The question of how far the average home can adopt Dr. Davis' method and insure the child an adequate diet and preserve the ideal psychological setting is a problem. Dr. Davis herself has demonstrated that an adaptation of this method can be used successfully in a private home, as well as in routine feeding of children in a hospital.[191]

One family has reported a modified self-selection method of feeding for two young children, one from birth to four years, the other

---

* For a discussion of experiments on self selection of nutrients by rats see Nutrition Reviews,[716, 740] and for another on experiments of salt selection by adrenalectomized rats, see Nutrition Reviews 14:123-124, 1956.

from 18 months to six years.[321] Three meals were prepared at regular times unless the children asked to eat earlier and it was convenient. Usually they ate at an attractively set table in the kitchen before the adult meal; small portions were served. The mother remained nearby to give help when sought. The children were allowed almost complete freedom in what they ate and how they ate it, in being able to eat as long as they wished, and in eating as much as they wished with the exception of limitations on sweets.* Ready-to-eat and non-messy foods were available at any time of day. Certain restrictions were imposed, such as no sweets between meals, only certain places used for eating, food was not to be thrown about and wantonly made unfit to eat, children were not to annoy their parents while eating. The mother reported that the children had good appetites, their food intake met requirements and they fussed very little about the limitation of sweets. The variety of selected foods increased. They liked all fruits, almost all kinds of meat, fish, fowl and cereal, and about fifteen vegetables. At five years they showed an interest in adult table manners and had pride in eating what was given to them away from home and in being polite. Table behavior at home was unconventional but not objectionable and became more "civilized" with age.

About one-half or more meals were well balanced. Rarely were milk and citrus fruits omitted. About one third of their food was taken between meals, and generally consisted of fruit, vegetable, or milk. The children generally ate two or three foods at one meal. The author states that such a program presupposes a happy home without emotional tensions and success depends on the attitude of parents and on the children eating by themselves.

For a great many families, for various reasons, such a program would not be feasible. The average family need not adopt such a procedure to give their children good eating experiences from both a nutritional and a psychological point of view. The principles followed in these studies can be utilized to provide good experiences at mealtime in various types of home situations.

Introduction of New Foods. A few adventurous infants and young children accept new foods with joy the first time they are offered, even foods with such definite flavors as asparagus and cabbage. More often, however, the child learns through repeated experimentation to accept

---

* At lunch and supper sweets were limited to one cookie, a small piece of candy or ice cream.

the new food. Thus, for most children it is wise to consider the introduction of each new food as a learning experience at first rather than as a means of meeting nutritional need. One method is to offer a very small amount of the new food in the same meal with some food which the child already likes. With some children the new food is best accepted early in the meal while appetite is keen. With many others it is advisable to allow the child first to satisfy hunger and at least part of his appetite with some food he likes before he is expected to sample the new food. In either case, if the food is offered with the attitude that it will be eaten, the chances are good that it will be.

The esthetic appeal of the food itself has a marked effect on the appetite of the child just as it does on that of the adult. The sight, taste and smell of the food served make a direct appeal to the senses. Meals planned to offer contrast of color, flavor, and texture attract children as they do adults. Important at any time, careful preparation becomes especially important when some new food is being offered. Each pleasant experience with a new food goes far toward building right attitudes toward the acceptance of other new foods. On the other hand, one serving of food that is burned or undercooked or too hot gives an unpleasant sensation that may occasion a food prejudice requiring months of re-education to overcome. It may also make the child fearful of trying other new foods.

Foods with new consistencies or textures may be accepted readily by some children, whereas other children require a period of slow education. Thus, when the infant is transferred from puréed foods to chopped foods, it may be necessary to introduce only a small amount of the chopped food, together with a normal serving of the purée to which the baby is accustomed. Occasionally an infant who completely refuses chopped foods may readily accept whole carrots, beans or other vegetables which he can hold in his hand and feed to himself.

As mentioned earlier, it is essential that the child be accustomed to different types of food so that he can learn to chew properly and can exercise his teeth and gums. Tough foods are not advisable, but vegetables, cooked and raw, certain raw fruits, bread crusts, toast and other foods which offer some resistance to the teeth, are useful aids in learning mastication.

Learnings in Eating Behavior. The steps in learning to feed one's self begin with the early signs of neuromuscular development and include (1) putting hand or thumb in mouth; (2) cooperation in feeding, i.e., holding the bottle; (3) ability in a sitting position to reach for and convey an object to mouth with either hand; (4) finger feeding with food that has to be chewed; (5) ability to drink from a cup held upright; (6) mastery of use of spoon; (7) mastery of use of fork; (8) mastery of use of knife.

The use of each new eating utensil must be learned. If this fact is ignored, refusal of the utensil with which the food is offered may sometimes be taken for food refusal. This learning can begin before the infant shows any readiness to use a spoon or cup. Opportunities for the infant to hold and investigate these feeding utensils while his mother is feeding him provide the infant with experiences which will familiarize him with handling the spoon and cup before he begins to feed himself. See Figure 43.

Before solid foods are offered to the baby—usually sometime between two and four months—it is well to accustom him to the spoon by using it several times to feed him his orange juice. In this way, when he is given the food he has only one rather than two things to learn at the same time. He is already accustomed to the spoon, and now has only to learn to eat the new food. The same principle works when he is asked to drink milk from a cup. Water and orange juice can be given from a cup for some weeks in advance. Also, a small quantity of milk offered from a cup between meals once a day for several days makes it easier for the baby to accept a whole milk feeding in this way when the cup is first substituted for the bottle or breast at the feeding hour. Even with these preliminary steps it is too much to expect the baby to give up the breast or bottle at all three feedings at the same time. He should be allowed ample time to become thoroughly accustomed to drinking his milk from a cup at one meal before he is asked to do so at a second and finally at a third.

The time of weaning from breast or bottle to cup varies greatly with the rate of development of the child. For most children some time during the last quarter of the first year is an appropriate time, although some are ready earlier and some are not ready until later. Sometimes babies actually wean themselves. Between eight and eleven months a number of them have bitten the mother's nipple or artificial rubber nipple and pushed the breast or bottle aside. When a mother, having already educated the baby to drink from a cup, has recognized this signal and offered milk from a cup at this feeding, the infant generally accepts it readily. At a further signal from him, the mother offers a cup of milk at another, and finally at the third feeding. Thus weaning can be accomplished gradually at the baby's own pace without any emotional strain on either the infant or the mother. According to Sears et al.[733] if the goal of weaning is to have as little emotional disturbance as possible it appears wisest to begin weaning before the end of the first year or wait until the end of the second year, to prepare the infant for the new mode of feeding and to make the transition as expeditiously as possible.

It should be pointed out, however, that not all infants wean themselves as definitely and as readily as this. "Fussy" babies who have cried a great deal from birth may be more disturbed during weaning than other babies, in spite of gentle weaning procedures.[733] Biting the nipple may not necessarily mean that the infant is ready to discontinue sucking from his mother's breast or the bottle. However, by the time the baby is seven or eight months old, or even earlier, it is usually wise to try his orange juice and water from a cup as suggested above. When he becomes proficient in this he can occasionally be offered small amounts of milk from a cup. If his mother regards the whole procedure as a gradual learning process and accepts what the baby does successfully but, at the same time, shows no impatience because of what he does not do, weaning is usually accomplished quite easily. If weaning from the breast is necessary for any reason before the eighth or ninth month, it is usually better to wean from breast to bottle and later from bottle to cup.

The age at which the baby can skillfully handle his own cup varies widely, too. Before he achieves this, he will go through a period of contentedly allowing someone else to hold the cup. A little later he will put his hands on the cup to assist. Before he acquires the skill to lift, to tilt correctly and to replace the cup, there will usually be a phase in which he insists upon holding the cup for himself but tilts it too far and spills the contents. There are apt to be times, too, when he awkwardly sets the cup down on his spoon or the rim of his tray and spills milk into the tray, or, even more trying to his mother, when he drops or throws the cup to the floor. If such accidents create too much commotion, they may sometimes be deliberately repeated to gain attention. However, if the mother sets the high chair on the kitchen linoleum before the feeding is begun, such accidents can be cheerfully ignored, for the floor is easy to clean when the baby's feeding is finished.

Learning to use a spoon, a fork and a knife are gradual processes too. For a long time the infant is quite content to have the spoon manipulated for him. It is months, however, after the baby shows an interest in the spoon before he is able to load the spoon and carry it to his mouth without dumping the food. Usually by two years he can do so with a reasonable degree of skill.* Even at eighteen months, however, he can take over a great deal of the task of feeding himself. At eighteen months he spills a great deal and at three years he will probably still spill some. Spilling is unimportant. Opportunity for the maturing child to practice growing skills without criticism from adults is of paramount importance. Some children can use a fork at two years, but a spoon or fingers are usually preferred at this stage. Often the child tires of manipulation before the meal is completed and welcomes some adult help to finish. The use of a knife and fork together to cut food requires a very complex skill, which begins to appear in the late preschool years. Some five-year-olds can cut food if it is very tender.

This whole period of learning to manipulate various eating utensils is a difficult one for the child. He often wants complete independence in feeding before he is fully capable of assuming it. It is wise to allow him a great deal of freedom, even though his messiness may be very trying to adults. He will get the food, or at least an adequate portion of it, to his mouth if nothing is done to interfere with his appetite. Acceptable table manners will be acquired later when the mechanics of eating have been so mastered that they no longer require all of the child's attention. Whether the child begins to eat at the family table as soon as he can feed himself part of his meal or whether he eats alone until he is three or four years old is a matter for each family to decide.† Whether the child comes to the family table in the second year or at four years, he will gradually acquire table manners which conform to

* The amount of help given to children by mothers varies considerably. In one study[374] during the first year's interview, 53.6 per cent of mothers reported their infants required little help in feeding, 28.6 per cent required some help and 14.3 per cent required much help. In the second year's interview, it was found that the mothers who restricted physical activity in the house tended to have given their infants more help at mealtime.

† It has been reported in one study in a university town[374] during the interview when the child was in his first year, that 53.6 per cent of the infants were being fed with the family, 23.2 per cent sometimes were fed with the family and 23.2 per cent were fed alone. During the second year's interview it was found that children tended to be fed at the family table when they required little help in feeding. Also, only children tended to be fed alone or only occasionally with the family. Infants with older siblings were more likely to be fed with the family.

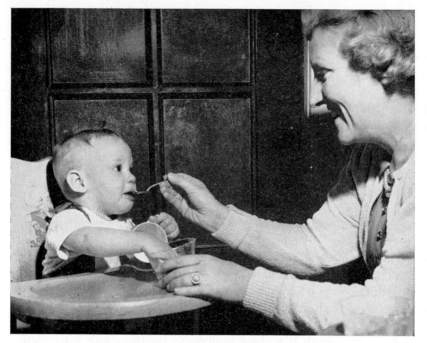

Figure 43. An infant having experiences with cup and food preliminary to learning to feed himself.

those of his family through imitation of the example set by the adults at the table. Occasional suggestion as he is able to understand it may be helpful, but nagging should be carefully avoided. It is said that, "If at the end of his fifth year a child has made progress in eating quietly, using knife, fork and spoon habitually and resorting to fingers only rarely, very seldom upsetting his milk, using napkin or bib properly, and sometimes saying 'please' and 'thank you' spontaneously, his parents should be content."*

It is not unusual for the child when he first joins the family for meals to indulge in behavior which may be very trying to the other members of the family. For many months, because of his physical dependence, he has had to be fed and waited upon; when he comes to participate in the family meals he may still desire to be the center of attention. A gradual induction into eating with the family may be a helpful procedure. At

* Strang[818] (p. 190).

first he may sit in his chair at the table after he has had his meal. Later he may have part of his meal with the family. Finally he may eat all of his meal at the family table. Since small children cannot sit still as long as adults, and their attention span is shorter, they cannot be expected to sit through the whole meal. Families can provide opportunities for movement, thus reducing restlessness. Children like to serve themselves and wait on others. Opportunities for this can be provided, such as pouring milk or fruit juice (Fig. 44), serving themselves, or carrying something to the table.

Interest in Food Stimulated by Participation in Its Preparation. Opportunity for the child to spend some time in the kitchen can be planned. The infant sitting and playing in his chair, and later the toddler spending long hours in the kitchen playing with pans, pots and spoons, grows accustomed to numerous food odors, and the good time he has in the kitchen with his mother while these odors are assailing his nostrils must certainly help to condition him pleasantly toward these foods. The preschool child who is allowed to participate actively in the preparation

Figure 44. A child in his fourth year who, like most preschool children, likes to serve himself.

Figure 45. Participation in its preparation stimulates children's interest in food. (Sweeny, M. E., and Buck, D. C.: How To Feed Young Children in the Home. Detroit, Merrill-Palmer School, 1937.)

of some of his food will acquire a sense of pride in accomplishment which will make him keenly interested in eating the foods he has helped prepare. Figure 45 shows two children intent upon preparing eggs for their nursery school lunch. Their enthusiasm at the lunch table is sure to be contagious and to help other children to enjoy this food too.

Importance of Environment. As we have suggested, the physical environment at mealtime is important. A good environment includes a comfortable position in a chair of suitable height, and appropriate and attractive dishes and eating utensils, as well as attractive and palatable food.

As important as the physical environment is, however, the psychological environment is of even greater importance. A happy, relaxed atmosphere free from emotional tensions both at mealtime and during the child's preparation for the meal, and a sense of being one of the group make for enjoyment of food, a solid basis for good habits and attitudes. The mother who encourages but does not urge, who expects success but is not anxious or concerned if the child refuses, and who does not use some foods as a reward for eating others is helping her child to develop wholesome attitudes toward food.

Environment other than that at mealtime will also affect a child's food habits and attitudes. Behavior around food may be symptomatic of conditions in a child's life not necessarily closely allied to mealtime. Thus the quality of the relationships with parents, siblings, peers and other adults, as well as emotional well-being or tensions, may be reflected in food behavior and attitudes.* To understand the food habits of a child, therefore, one must understand the whole child. Food habits are inextricably bound up with the emotional and social phases of life as well as with its physical side.

Topics for Study and Discussion

1. Discuss the development of eating habits. Ask two mothers of preschool children who are good eaters to participate in the group discussion by relating the eating history of their children. The students should be prepared to ask questions and contribute knowledge based on the study of this chapter.

2. Observe an infant around six months, another around fifteen months, and a three-year-old at mealtime. Record what the child eats, the quantities, and his behavior. Write a report of these experiences making comparisons between the children and discussing the adequacy of the food eaten in terms of food requirements for each age.

3. Have each student learn how one mother plans her preschool child's food in relation to the food for the whole family. Use this information for a class discussion of one meal for all in families. What are the assets of such a program? Are there any liabilities?

4. Select from the self-selection experiments the principles which can be used by an average family and observe them as followed in a real family situation. Use this material for a class discussion.

Selected Readings

Aldrich, C. A., and Aldrich, M. M.: Babies Are Human Beings, ed. 2. New York, Macmillan Company, 1954.

Bain, K.: Personality growth and nutrition, J. Am. Dietet. A. 28:520-523, 1952.

Chaney, M. S.: Nutrition, ed. 5. New York, Houghton Mifflin Co., 1954. Chaps. 14, 15.

Gesell, A., and Ilg, F. L.: Infant and Child in the Culture of Today. New York, Harper & Brothers, 1943.

* Sears et al.[733] found that severe training practices during the ages of three to five years were associated with increased feeding problems at that time and shortly thereafter.

Handbook of Nutrition; a Symposium, ed. 2. American Medical Association. Philadelphia, Blakiston Company, 1951.

Illingworth, R. S.: The Normal Child. Boston, Little, Brown & Co., 1953. Chaps. 1 through 6.

Sears, R. R., Maccoby, E. E., and Levin, H.: Patterns of Child Rearing. Evanston, Ill., Row, Peterson & Co., 1957. Chap. 3.

Spock, B.: The Common Sense Book of Baby and Child Care, ed. 2. New York, Duell, Sloan & Pearce, Inc., 1957.

7

Meeting the Physical Needs
of the Growing Child (Continued)

Development of Control Over Elimination

The processes of evacuation of the bowel and of urination have been discussed in Chapter 5. Our concern here is with training in cleanliness as a phase of the child's enculturation.

In voluntary control of both defecation and urination, the vegetative nervous system and the higher brain centers are coordinated to bring about control of bowel and bladder sphincter release. Both processes are equally complex, but bowel control is usually achieved before bladder control, probably because the need to defecate usually occurs more regularly and less frequently than the need to urinate. Since these functions cannot be controlled until the structures involved are sufficiently mature, achievement of control is dependent in part upon the child's readiness. As in the area of eating, the mother's role is one of "anticipatory guidance," that is, watching for clues to the child's readiness for each step with tolerance for the child's speed of progress, providing facilities, and creating an atmosphere that will create in the child a wholesome attitude toward elimination. Within this basic framework the actual plan adopted by a mother will be governed by herself, her child, and the circumstances under which they live.

Bowel Control. As previously stated, learning bowel control generally precedes learning bladder control. The child is ready to learn when (1) he is old enough to understand what the toilet is, (2) when defecation comes at a fairly regular time, (3) when a parent has learned the little signals of the child such as being very quiet for a minute or two or pushing or straining, and (4) when the child consents willingly to sit on the toilet. Toilet training can begin, therefore, when an infant can sit alone easily and often has bowel movements regularly at about the same time each day. This usually will not be until toward the end of the first year, and with many infants it will be later. One study of child rearing practices,[733] based on mothers' reports, states that either of two periods can be chosen with an expectation of reasonable comfort: the second six months of life and after twenty months.*

The child learns to associate the toilet with defecation by seeing others in the family use it and by being placed on the toilet at the time of day when he has his bowel movement and experiencing success. Time for defecation is likely to come after a meal when peristalsis is more likely to produce an evacuation. Some infants with regular defecation and willingness to sit on the toilet at an early age may have bowel movements on the toilet regularly before they have really gained control because the mother has been able to synchronize placing them on the toilet with defecation time. This earlier conditioning to pass stool or urine is not synonymous with later voluntary control.†

There are wide individual differences among children in their response to the procedure and the age at which they gain control. Girls tend to gain control before boys. One study[733] reports that gaining of control took longer when begun earlier and came more quickly when begun later. For some children in this group the task was completed in a few weeks; others took as long as one and one-half years. Another study[704] reported that 92.2 per cent of the girls and 77.5 per cent of the boys at two and one-half years were taking the responsibility for going to the toilet for bowel movements. The difference between boys and girls was statistically significant. For children who resist being placed on the toilet it is best to discontinue all attempts for the moment and wait a while before trying again.

The feeling of the child toward the routine and the mother's attitude

---

* The authors offer some reasons why a mother may begin toilet training early: advice from her doctor, suggestions from a neighbor, traditional custom in her family, tired of washing diapers, pregnant, strictness of her attitude toward sex.

† For examples of mothers' procedures see Sears et al.[733]

are important in determining the smoothness with which this learning is achieved. In one of the studies,[733] it was found that a child's tolerance for training had no simple relationship to the age he began this training. It did, however, have some relationship to the severity used in the training process. More emotional upsets were found in children who were trained in a severe manner.* Such disturbances in response to severe training were more frequent among children whose mothers were relatively cold and undemonstrative than among those children with warm mothers.† Thus the personality of the mother is an important factor.

The mother who is warm, who is content to let the clues which her child gives guide her, who is free from concern and who shows pleasure at success but ignores or minimizes failure can be an effective help to her child in establishing control of elimination.

Bladder Control. As stated previously, bladder control generally follows bowel control. The transition from involuntary to voluntary control of urination is gradual. From being unaware of urinating, the child becomes aware of the need to urinate, but extreme urgency makes it impossible to wait until taken to the toilet. Later he acquires the ability to hold urine after the desire for urination has been registered. The child indicates these steps to maturity by (1) showing awareness of having passed urine, (2) telling just before he urinates but not in time to get him to the toilet, (3) telling mother in sufficient time to place him on the toilet, and (4) going to the toilet himself. Daytime control generally comes first, followed by naptime control and finally by control throughout the night.

Very few children are ready to learn this control at one year of age. The time to begin can be governed not by chronological age but by the child's capacity to make appreciable response.‡ McGraw's study[538] of

* Fifty-five per cent of the children who experienced severity in toilet training showed emotional disturbance, in contrast to 17 per cent of those whose training was not at all severe, 11 per cent under light pressure, and 26 per cent under moderate pressure.[733]

† The percentage of children who showed emotional upsets over toilet training when training was severe: 23 per cent when mothers were warm, 48 per cent when mothers were relatively cool. The percentage when training was mild: 21 per cent when mothers were warm, 11 per cent when mothers were relatively cold.[733]

‡ In one study of the attitudes and practices of mothers,[374] it was found that most mothers began toilet training later than the first year. Of these mothers 14.3 per cent began training during the first year, 23.2 per cent around a year, 62.5 per cent later than a year. Only 7.1 per cent reported that the child was nearly trained in the second year. Mothers of only children tended to have begun

(Footnote continued on page 268)

the training of two sets of twins in bladder control (see the discussion of urination on page 205) indicates that this stage is reached some months after the development of the cortical centers governing sphincter control. It comes only after the child has also developed powers of discrimination and generalization and is able to integrate these powers with the act of urination. In the case of Hugh Putney in the McGraw Study, this period began at about the age of twenty months. His success curve rose sharply at this time, and was stabilized in the ninetieth percentile by the time he was two years old.

The mother is usually forewarned of the approach of this period by the child's frequent reporting of "accidents." If the child can be given opportunity to observe other children on the toilet, and if he is occasionally placed there himself after a meal or when he awakes dry following his nap, it is usually not long before he begins to report before rather than after an accident. When this happens he is well along the road toward self control of this function. At this time a little judicious praise for successes will do much to increase the frequency of control. However, praise can be overdone and result in too much concentration upon a normal physiologic function.

Bladder control, like walking, must be learned and, just as the toddler has many falls before he finally learns to walk skillfully, so also there will be a series of progressions and regressions before he is completely master of the toilet situation. "Even after the child has become proficient in verbalizing his needs before voiding there may occur another regressive phase as his horizon of interests and imagination come into play. At this time the child is too occupied with new experiences to take notice of the old familiar bladder sensation. Subsequently the child will be able to respond to physiological urges and to attend to play interests at the same time. When he is observed squirming holding his legs tightly together, but at the same time absorbed in play, one can know that he is on the verge of a new level of control. The time is

---

(Footnote continued from page 267)

toilet training earlier than one year and claimed that their children had learned a little by that time. Mothers of second or third children tended to delay training and to offer no claim that the child had learned anything in this area. The authors state—"These data suggest that the experience of the first child brought to the mothers a belief that success in toilet training can be achieved only when the child is older, perhaps these mothers of more than one child were also busier and unable or unwilling to devote themselves to this teaching before they knew the child was really ready. They probably were less anxious than mothers of only children. Greater satisfaction was expressed by these mothers with their training methods as compared with that of the mothers of only children" (p. 217).

approaching when he will be able to manage both functions satisfactorily. Soon he will be able to drop the play, relieve the bladder pressure, and return to pick up the play activity where he left it."*

As in bowel control, there are wide individual differences both in the manner in which it is achieved and in the age at which it is attained. Girls tend to assume responsibility for urinary control earlier than boys.[704] Accidents may be expected, but with decreasing frequency, throughout the preschool years.

The case history of E. R., given here, illustrates how the wise management of a mother promoted success and a wholesome attitude toward elimination in a child who resisted toilet training for some time. The case history of N. L. illustrates how a working mother carried out a program of toilet training, which began in the middle of the second year and proceeded rapidly.

When E. R. was sitting alone with confidence at thirty-eight weeks, her mother tried putting her on a nursery chair at the doctor's suggestion. E. R. rebelled, however, and after a few trials her mother wisely gave up the attempt at training. A second attempt several weeks later and another at thirteen months were resisted. At seventeen months she accepted the toilet for bowel evacuation but again rebelled against the frequency with which her mother took her to the toilet for urination. Again the mother abandoned the effort except for bowel movements. By eighteen months E. R. was saying "toi-toi" long enough before a bowel movement to enable her mother to place her on the toilet seat in time for this procedure. Although she was having two or three bowel movements a day at this time, E. R. rarely had an accident. At about twenty months she began to be aware of her wet pants and came to her mother to be changed. Within a very short time she began with increasing frequency to say "toi-toi" in advance of this function also. By twenty-two months E. R. consistently asked to go to the toilet, even calling her parents during the night when she needed to go. When she was two years of age, her mother was occasionally wakened during the night by E. R. in the bathroom in the dark alone, rattling the toilet seat. Such independence is unusual for a child of two, of course, but it does illustrate how rapidly an intelligent child may assume personal responsibility for eliminative behavior when adult guidance follows the maturity cues which the child herself gives. At twenty-six months E. R. went with her family to a cottage on the water. There the many new and fascinating experiences were sometimes so absorbing that toilet needs were forgotten, and there were wet pants occasionally. When this happened E. R. would say, "Oh! accident, I sorry." After a few weeks in the new environment, however, she was able to stop her play in time to reach the toilet to relieve the bladder pressure. Before thirty months she was entirely reliable in her ability to control this function. E. R. would probably have achieved bowel control somewhat earlier had her mother attempted this phase of her education singly. Possibly thus the resistance created by the frequent interruption of play necessitated by the more frequent placement might have been avoided. E. R. did, however, achieve consistent bowel control several months before she acquired bladder control.

* McGraw[540] (p. 127).

In the case of N. L. this order was reversed, possibly because his mother had no time to observe and take advantage of his natural rhythm in bowel evacuation. Forced to support herself and her son, the mother was teaching in a nursery school which N. L., although under age, was permitted to attend. By the time he was sixteen months old he showed some evidence of discomfort when wet. His mother had a week of freedom from her teaching duties and decided to take advantage of the child's possible readiness for training. The first day she put him on the toilet every hour. This was obviously unnecessary. On the second day she extended the interval to two hours with almost 100 per cent success. By the end of the week she was taking him to the toilet six or seven times during the day at convenient intervals. This was continued when mother and child returned to the nursery school. N. L. readily accepted the procedure and was usually dry during the day, but his mother assumed responsibility. By nineteen months he quite regularly gave advance notice of his need by pulling an adult toward the toilet. At about this time, while sitting on the toilet after breakfast, he began to evacuate his bowels after he had urinated. Soon he refused to get off the toilet after urination if he felt the need to defecate, answering attempts to lift him from the toilet by grunting. At twenty-one months he used the term "toitet" to express the need either to urinate or to defecate. At this time he usually slept through the night— eleven to twelve hours—without urinating, or, if he needed to do so, he wakened and called "toitet." In a nursery school with older boys he had opportunity to observe that they urinated while standing. Before N. L. was twenty-four months old he had adopted this posture on his own initiative. At this time his mother reported that he had had no toilet accidents either during the day or night for two months.

Sleep*

Sleep is part of the balance of activity (see Chapter 8) and rest which is so essential for the well-being of a child. Rest varies in degree from rest of certain muscle groups by changing activity, to quiet play which requires less energy, to relaxation of the whole body while lying in a relaxed position, to sleep wherein the functioning of the body is paced more slowly.

Sleep is a positive function. It is not a cessation of bodily activity but a readjustment of the whole machinery of the body, including the central nervous system, to protect the total welfare of the organism. The mechanism of sleep is still poorly understood but it is agreed that a center in the hypothalamus plays a role in the regulation of sleep, although there is no complete agreement as to the manner of its operation.[550]

* Most of the studies quoted in this section on sleep are not recent, since research on the sleep of young children has been very limited in recent years. Studies of the various aspects of sleep are needed as is the patterning of sleep habits of children reared according to a permissive philosophy.

Sleep is a part of a sleep-wakefulness cycle which according to Kleitman[459] is an inborn pattern of alteration of rest and activity. These two phases are related as are the crest and trough of a wave. The duration and shape of the wave are modified by experience and training.

Gesell and Ilg[291] discuss three distinct phases of sleep: going to sleep, staying asleep, and wakening. The first depends on a higher cortical control which enables the child to fall asleep; the third on an active wakefulness nerve center. As these brain centers mature, association becomes more and more involved and the integration of sleep with the rest of the child's active life becomes more and more apparent.

Maturing of Sleep Behavior. The maturing of sleep behavior is manifested in the shift of dominance from the sleeping phase to the wakefulness phase until in adulthood the former takes up one third of the time, or about eight hours. Thus the amount of sleep decreases with age. By the time the child is approaching the end of the preschool period he is sleeping, according to Despert[211] eleven and one-fourth hours of the twenty-four. With the lengthening of the wakefulness phase, the cycle becomes synchronized with the periodicity of night and day and is thus transformed into a rhythm which becomes firmly established. The rhythm is influenced by physical variations of light and temperature accompanying the succession of night and day, and the "social time-table" of living routines, with its factors of activity, noise, etc. "A further manifestation of diurnal synchronization of the sleep-wakefulness cycle is the gradual establishment of a twenty-four hour body temperature curve which usually attains its adult characteristics between the ages of twelve and eighteen months."* When this diurnal body temperature curve is fully established physiologic readiness for sleep is associated with a rather sharp drop in temperature at a particular time.[458]

As the child matures a series of changes occur in the pattern of sleep behavior. At first sleep is shallow and the demarcation between sleeping and waking is not sharply defined. The child awakes because of internal proddings, especially that of hunger. He is fed, sleeps, wakes when he is hungry, is fed and goes back to sleep. Thus the early association between feeding and sleeping is extremely close. Kleitman[459] has shown that this wakening pattern of the newborn requires no special mechanism other than stimulation of the subcortical center. Environmental

* Kleitman[458] (p. 64).

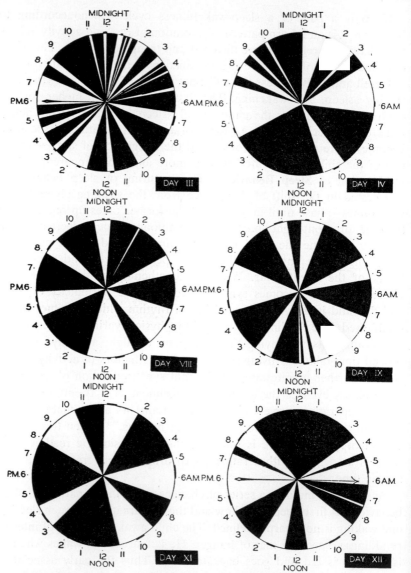

Figure 46. Diurnal cycle of behavior of an infant for days 3, 4, 8, 9, 11, and 12. Sleep, awakeness, and feeding shown on 24-hour clock dial. Black segments indicate sleep; white segments indicate awakeness. Feedings are shown at margin. (Reproduced from Gesell, A., in collaboration with C. S. Amatruda: The Embryology of Behavior. New York, Harper & Brothers, 1945.)

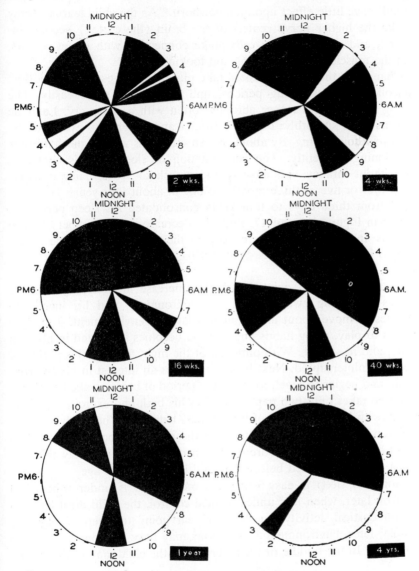

Figure 47. Diurnal cycle of behavior of same child at 2, 4, 16, and 40 weeks, 1 year, and 4 years. Sleep, awakeness, and feeding shown on 24-hour clock dial. Black segments indicate sleep; white segments indicate awakeness. Feedings are shown at margin. (Reproduced from Gesell, A., in collaboration with C. S. Amatruda: The Embryology of Behavior. New York, Harper & Brothers, 1945.)

stimuli have little effect upon the newborn.* As the child learns to stay awake the higher nerve centers of the brain (the cortex) become involved, and cortical nerve cells make connection with his eyes, ears, and the muscles used in staring and looking.

Changes in the phases of sleep take place. He wakes more smoothly, consolidates his sleeping periods, and falls asleep more easily. The young infant wakes rather abruptly, often with a sharp cry. Later he wakens more smoothly; his cry is briefer and softer, and even later he wakes without crying. By about sixteen weeks his waking mechanism is functioning efficiently. The consolidation of sleep periods continues throughout infancy and most of the preschool years. They decrease from four or five at three months to one at about four years. How one child from three days to four years consolidated his sleep periods is shown in Figures 46 and 47. Both the decrease in the number of sleep periods and the shift to more sleep in the night hours can be noted. It is to be noticed that this child still has one nap a day at four years of age.

Paralleling and associated with this increase in wakefulness is the child's increasing awareness of his environment, and his increasing abilities to move about and to manipulate his environment. The child begins to play, using hands and feet; he becomes interested in his own body, and in sounds. With omission of the night feeding, this period of sleep is uninterrupted. Next he sits up, takes an interest in his environment, and begins to reach for toys; the period of being awake lengthens. Then he takes only two naps, one after his bath and exercise, and one other, with longer periods of wakefulness between. When only one nap is taken, the child is awake most of the day. This occurs before two years of age in many children; later in others. In our society this nap tends to be abandoned before the child is five years of age.

Going to sleep is easy while this mechanism is under subcortical control; later, when it is under cortical control, the child must learn to inhibit cortical activity. In the first year going to sleep is relatively simple; later, environmental conditions may have a stronger deterring influence. In the middle of the second year the child may begin to take

---

* There is evidence[458] of the beginning of enculturation even at this early age by the greater incidence of longer intervals between awakenings during the night when infants are on a self-regulating schedule[556] and by the somewhat higher percentage of time spent in sleep at night than during the daytime hours.[287]

something to bed—some toy, woolly animal, or blanket. He may use some presleep device to help him to go to sleep.* Routines at bedtime become important. In one study of a group of two-and-one-half-year-olds[704] 90 per cent of the children had definite enough routines that their mothers could describe them. About two-thirds of the routines were simple, such as asking for a drink, a kiss, a special toy or blanket. The other one-third of the routines were elaborate and ritualistic. Most of the children used some comfort device as part of their routine. For some it was a toy, for others a bottle, for still others a special blanket. About half of the children used some form of self-comfort such as thumbsucking, hair-twisting, ear-pulling, or rocking. Young children often have a period of calling the mother back perhaps for a drink, another kiss, or a trip to the toilet. This behavior for the healthy, happy child is often part of growing up; it will disappear as he continues to mature, if his parents are understanding and use common sense in their management of him.

Activity in Sleep. Children do not sleep "like logs"; they move from time to time. Some of this movement, undoubtedly, is the result of discomfort that comes from lying too long in one position. Garvey,[281] studying motility in sleep, found that children from two to five moved on the average once every seven or seven and one-half minutes. This activity he found was rhythmic or periodic. Of the two-, three-, and four-year-old groups, the three-year-olds were most active; the four-year-olds the most quiet. Boynton and Goodenough,[126] observing children at naptime, found in a group of fifty-six nursery school children, which included those studied by Garvey, an average of one change in posture in twenty-five minutes.

Motility in sleep has been found to increase under certain conditions. Activity just before retiring and listening to fairy tales disturbed the sleep of some children.[444] Putting a child who has been accustomed to sleeping alone in a room with another child increased activity during sleep.[444] Eating a large amount of food[297] or a heavy meal[487] markedly

---

* Figures for presleep time for preschool children vary from study to study. Most children studied by Despert[211] took less than one-half to slightly more than one-half hour to go to sleep. Average presleep time, according to Garvey,[281] was thirty to thirty-five minutes; according to Reynolds[693] it was one hour. Studies of naptime in nursery schools have given the average presleep time as 26 to 38 minutes,[693] 24.4 to 34.8,[178] 14 to 48.9 minutes.[796] Dales and Reynolds found that presleep time in nursery school increased with age.

increased motility. Fear, worry, disappointment or pleasant anticipation interfered with quiet sleep.* [296]

Individual Differences.   Some children apparently need more sleep than others; some need less. Some vary in amount of sleep from day to day; others are consistent in their hours of sleep.[211] Spacing of sleep varies[211]; some children sleep less at night and take longer naps, and some have a reverse pattern. Sleep may vary greatly in depth and integratedness among children. Some children are good sleepers; some are poor sleepers. Conditions which tend to disturb children's sleep, such as changes in the digestive tract in the early months, later wetness or some other bodily discomforts, and still later changes in the environment, fear or undue excitement, may affect one child more easily than another.

Reynolds[693] found that the amount of sleep taken by a preschool child varied considerably from day to day, but there was a fairly constant average over several weeks' time. There was no consistency in the variations of different children, and at no time did her group of seventy-seven children between the ages of one and one-half and six years behave like a unit in the periodic changes in the duration of sleep.

It can readily be seen that no general rule about the total amount of sleep can be made since children vary so greatly in their needs and their rate of maturing. However, it is necessary for a child to have adequate sleep if he is to have optimum health and growth, and a nap or a quiet rest period during the day generally is a valuable part of a young child's daily living.

Adults can tell by the appearance and behavior of children whether or not they are having adequate sleep. Unusual irritability, hyperactivity, crying easily, and taking longer to go to sleep are some of the indicators that point to the possibility of need for more sleep.

Sleep Regimen.   Since control of sleep, like the control of eating, involves a complex process dependent on cortical control, it is essential that the child be given opportunity to learn to manage this function which is so basic to his well-being. An infant can develop his own sleep

* Despert[211] gives examples of children who, after some disturbing experience, took longer to go to sleep and were more restless during sleep. For example, a three-year-old boy became restless when his parents left abruptly on a trip. One four-and-one-half-year-old became restless and awoke crying after the birth of a sibling. A two-and-one-half-year-old girl became restless and sleepless after the divorce of her parents and the loss of her nurse.

habits if given the chance to do so. The baby is fed when he wakens. His bath and play periods are scheduled according to his schedule of waking time. Natural fatigue from activity, the satisfaction of relieving hunger, and the contentment that comes from affectionate and loving care help to reinforce the natural rhythm of sleep and wakefulness. Here, as in eating, the adult guides the child and sets reasonable limits according to the child's ever increasing maturity. The adult guidance can determine whether the child progresses in his sleep habits so that he fits into the family pattern of living or fails to progress and becomes the autocrat of the family. Consistent but not rigid regularity, with a definite routine in getting ready for bed and association of bed with sleep by putting the infant and young child to bed when he is sleepy, will help the parents to guide him into good sleeping habits.

Two studies of child rearing practices have been reported recently which included some observations on children's sleep. In one study[733] which used interviews with mothers, it was found that putting children to bed at a certain time, whether the children were sleepy or not, was a common practice. Some mothers reported that their children were ready to go to sleep; others reported that the children remained awake for some time, in some instances for as much as two hours each evening after the lights were out. Children were put to bed either for their own welfare or to relieve the parents from the pressures engendered by their presence and to give them some privacy.

In the other study,[374] in which mothers were interviewed during the first and second years of the child's life, it was found that during the second year the majority (60.7 per cent) of the children were expected to remain in bed at bedtime. There appeared to be a relationship between leniency on the mother's part and her feelings about her child's earlier reactions to the introduction of new foods. Mothers who were pleased with their children's reaction to new foods in the first year tended to be lenient with their children at bedtime, allowing them to get up fairly often rather than to stay in bed.

In most families, the father is away from home most of the day when the infant and young child is awake. Since it is important for the father and child to have time together, plans often have to be made to provide for it. Perhaps with slight readjustment of the child's schedule, the mother can see that there are spaces of time when father and child can be together without disrupting the child's sleep habits. Participation of the father in putting the child to bed is one kind of father-child contact.

Nap. The number of daily naps taken by infants and young children has already been mentioned. In our culture the adult sleep pattern, that of one long period of sleep and one of wakefulness, is usually acquired by the child before he is five years old.

Information about naps of young children has been provided through observations in nursery schools and through reports of mothers. From a number of studies it has been found that during the preschool years there is (1) a decrease in the duration of afternoon nap,[211, 178] (2) an increase in time taken to go to sleep,[178] (3) wide individual differences in the duration of the afternoon sleep and presleep time,[211, 178] (4) no significant seasonal differences in naps,[178] (5) a dropping out of the nap on an all-or-none principle as age increases,[178, 161] * (6) no interference by nap with night sleep in the early preschool years[161, 211] or in the later preschool years according to Despert[211] but some interference in the later preschool years according to Chant and Blatz,[161] (7) no interference with the nap when sleeping in a room with other children.[211, 178] Foster[265] showed that the decrease in total sleep from one to five years is due mainly to the decrease in daytime sleep.

In one study,[374] many mothers in their interviews during the second year appeared to consider the naptime important to the point of being strict about it. Only a small proportion of the mothers (8.9 per cent) allowed their children to omit naps. Half of the mothers kept their children in bed to sleep while 35.7 per cent insisted on some rest if not sleep. Differences in attitude were noted between mothers of one child and mothers of more than one. Mothers of only children seemed contented if their children only rested or played quietly. Mothers of second or third children were more strict about their children sleeping at naptime.

Importance of Physical Environment. The sleep of the newborn infant seems little affected by sound in his environment. Indeed, in a study of crying in a newborn infant's nursery Aldrich et al.[8] found that crying did not seem to be contagious from one baby to another in spite of the fact that hearing in newborns is acute.

Later the vulnerability of sleep to external factors becomes evident, and elements in the external environment may need greater scrutiny. A cool, quiet, dark room, and a comfortable bed with light-weight covers are helpful factors in promoting sound sleep at any time. Al-

---

* Children tend to take less naps as age increases, but when they do nap the nap tends to be as long as formerly.

though ordinarily usual household noises need not be curtailed, it is well to eliminate loud, penetrating noises from the child's sleep environment.

Importance of Psychological Environment. The emotional climate of the home is as important in promoting good sleep habits as it is in establishing good eating habits. It is said that the child takes his day to bed with him. In other words, the child who goes to bed after a happy day, secure in the affection of his parents, is much more likely to sleep well than the child who approaches sleep with some emotional disturbance. It is wise to avoid conflicts just before bedtime, as well as just before and during meals. Similarly, too active and, therefore, too stimulating play just before bedtime is unwise. If this is the time of day when the father and child are together, activities of a quiet kind rather than a general roughhouse can be planned. The vigorous type of play can be reserved for daytime hours.

Parents can do much in promoting good sleep habits in their children by the attitude they assume toward their children's sleep, especially by accepting the child's particular pattern and needs. One child may thrive better on a long afternoon nap and a later bed hour; another may sleep little during the day and have a longer sleep at night. As in other areas of child care, the guidance of children's sleep habits is based on a good understanding of a child's needs and growth and keen observation of them at all times. Also, the attitudes which the parents and other children in the family have toward sleeping will easily be reflected in the young child's attitude toward going to bed and sleeping.

Health Protection

The physical hazards of illness, defects and accidents may interfere with optimum health and growth. Therefore, it is desirable to prevent these as far as possible by providing a safe environment for children and supervising their health and their progress in growth.

Parents can be guided in their care of the child by the physician whom they choose to supervise their child's progress and to care for the child when such care is needed. This physician should be one who has knowledge of the growth of well children as well as of disease, namely, a well-informed general practitioner or a pediatrician. Since one of his obligations will be the establishment of a good relationship with the child, he needs to be one who likes children, understands their psychological development and needs, and has ability to apply this knowledge in dealing with the child. This physician will observe the child regularly to check both his health and growth progress, guide the parents in their care of the child and carry out an immunization program so that the child will develop an active immunity to as many of the acute communicable diseases as possible. In many communities there are clinics for well babies and children where families who cannot afford a physician may obtain such care for their young children.

Illness is both a physical and a psychological hazard for the infant and young child. It interferes with the regular processes of the body and produces stresses and strains in the parent-child relationship. Diseases which leave permanent handicaps make it difficult for the child to lead a normal and happy life, although the latter can be achieved under the guidance of wise parents and physician.

Much can be done to insure a sound, healthy body with good general resistance to disease by attending to the bodily needs which have been discussed. In addition, parents can help to keep young children well by keeping them away from those who are ill and protecting them from other possible sources of infection. Safe water and food, including pasteurized milk, are the responsibilities of the community, as well as health education facilities. Protection against certain communicable diseases, such as whooping cough, diphtheria, tetanus, and smallpox, can be provided by an *immunization program* which is begun as soon as the infant is mature enough to produce antibodies against the specific organisms.

The infant is born with a passive immunity to some diseases since antibodies from the mother's blood pass through the placenta to the fetal blood. Thus, if his mother is immune to these diseases, the newborn infant is also immune to some degree for a brief duration of time to measles, diphtheria, tetanus, mumps, smallpox and probably poliomyelitis and the common cold. Premature infants have less protection than full term infants.[768] This passive immunity, plus careful protection of young infants from contact with infection, must serve as protection until the infant is capable of manufacturing antibodies. This ability is still immature in the young infant. Newborns have some ability to manufacture antibodies[220, 645] and this ability improves rapidly during the first two months. Osborn et al.[645] from their experimentation with diphtheria and tetanus toxoids have stated that it is quite possible that an individual has reached physiologic maturity of forming antitoxins of diphtheria and tetanus by about three to six months.

While newborns have some degree of immunity to several diseases as stated above, they are usually not immune to whooping cough, which is especially serious for infants. Deaths from this disease are largely concentrated in the first year.[471] Early protection, therefore, is important. Protection is important in the case of diphtheria, also, for fewer babies may have passive immunity to diphtheria than formerly because of a lower incidence of diphtheria. The result is that less adult immunity is passed on to newborns.[220] Where programs of immunization are in effect, the drop in the incidence of these diseases is very striking. Garvin[282] compared the tables of incidence of whooping cough per 100,000 population among children under five years of age in two Ohio cities. In Cleveland where no whooping cough vaccination was offered by the department of health it was estimated that in that city, with a population of 1,000,000, only 10 per cent of the susceptible children were being immunized. In Shaker Heights, with a population of 25,000, it was estimated that 75 per cent of infants were immunized during a five-year period. In Cleveland during this period there was no drop in the rate of incidence of the disease. In Shaker Heights the rate dropped from 365 in 1934, to 182 in 1935, 54 in 1936, 74 in 1937, 21 in 1938, and 45 in 1939. In 1921 Michigan had the highest diphtheria death rate (954 deaths) in the world. In 1922 the state began a free distribution of biologic products, aimed chiefly at first toward preventing diphtheria. In 1953 only 2 deaths in the state were attributed to diphtheria.[581] By such a radical reduction in the number of cases through immunization a department of health not only protects the children immunized but also does much to protect the very young infant, who cannot be immunized, from exposure to a disease which might easily be fatal to him.

Active immunization against diphtheria, whooping cough and tetanus can begin at one to two months of age with a vaccine that protects against the three diseases. Two additional doses of the triple vaccine at intervals of one month will complete the infant's first protection against these diseases. A booster shot to keep the level of immunity from dropping is recommended at twelve months after the third injection, and again at four years of age. One month after the third injection of the triple vaccine, a smallpox vaccination may be given. This is repeated at five to six years. Six months later, or soon after that age, the first polio-myelitis injection may be given; following later at two to eight weeks is a second injection. A poliomyelitis booster injection is then given seven months later.*

The early *recognition of physical defects* of eyes, ears, posture, etc., is important since it permits correction or prevention of their progress to a point of serious impairment. One of the big health problems in this country is *dental caries*. Those caring for young children need to be cognizant of this problem not only because of the caries in the decidu-ous teeth, but also because the permanent teeth are forming during these years.

While there is a scarcity of surveys on the incidence of dental caries in these early years the available information indicates that caries of the deciduous teeth frequently begin soon after eruption of the teeth and increase dramatically thereafter.†

The cause of dental caries is not simple. Many factors are involved, and among these are undoubtedly body metabolism and oral environ-ment.‡ There is full agreement that dental decay begins at the surface of the enamel and progresses inward. There is also agreement that bacteria in the mouth are necessary for the production of dental caries. There is some controversy, however, as to whether the primary agents produce acid which etches the enamel or whether they act upon the protein-like substance of the tooth and thereby cause disintegration. Probably both actions are involved.[498] The importance of carbohy-drates, especially sugars, as they are acted upon by bacteria to produce the acid which etches the teeth is generally accepted. It is also gen-erally agreed that there are degrees of tooth resistance or susceptibility to dental caries which develop primarily during the formation and maturation of the teeth.§

Various methods of preventing and controlling caries substantiated by experimental evidence are advocated. These include a well balanced

---

* This plan for immunization of the young child is suggested by the Children's Bureau.[862]

† See Finn.[256] In a study of preschool children in Newburgh and Kingston, New York, 10.4 per cent of the two-year-olds, 30.7 per cent of the three-year-olds, 54.4 per cent of the four-year-olds and 75.7 per cent of the five-year-olds had carious teeth.[257]

‡ See Mitchell[592] for discussion of the mechanism of dental caries, Cox[175] for oral environment, Shaw[747] and Phillips[659] for nutrition.

§ See Shaw[747] and Phillips.[659]

diet with emphasis on the protective foods during the years when teeth are developing,* limitations of carbohydrates, especially sugars,[412] limitation of carbohydrates in forms that adhere to the teeth,[110] limitation of the length of time the teeth are exposed to sugar,†[412] and small amounts of fluorides in drinking water.‡ Many communities with "fluoride free" water are adding fluorides, one part per million parts of water, as a public health measure. In addition, cleansing of the teeth by regular brushing and regular visits to the dentist to detect caries in an early stage are valuable. Thus, providing a well balanced diet, reducing the intake of candy, ice cream and other sweets especially between meals, providing adequate amounts of fluorides in the drinking water and teaching children to brush their teeth should all contribute to the prevention of tooth decay.

Accidents are the cause of many injuries and deaths of young children. In fact, they constitute the most frequent cause of death in children beyond infancy. They are responsible for the deaths of over one third of the children between one and fourteen years of age who die each year in the United States. This amounts to approximately 12,000 juvenile accidents each year.§ Over one half of all fatal accidents in children occur before the age of five years.‖ The peak of these accidental deaths occurs in the one to two year group.[218] In addition to the fatalities, many children are injured in various degrees of severity. These

* See Leicester.[499] This applies to prenatal life, infancy and the preschool period.

† For example, a piece of hard candy, such as an all day sucker, will take a relatively long time to dissolve in the mouth, whereas sugar in liquid form will remain in the mouth for a brief period. When sweets are eaten between meals as well as at mealtime, the teeth have a longer exposure to sugar than when food is eaten less frequently. Differences in the form of carbohydrates or in the time and duration of the teeth's exposure to sugars may account for some of the differences in the results of studies on the relationship between sugar and dental caries.

‡ See Cox[174] and Dean[197] for reviews; also Hilleboe.[362] After ten years of an experiment which added fluorides to the water of Newburgh, New York, while a neighboring city, Kingston, served as a control where fluorides were not added, the six to nine year old children of Newburgh who had been drinking water containing fluorides during their whole lives had 57 to 58 per cent less caries in erupted permanent teeth than did the children of corresponding ages in Kingston. Six times more children of these ages in Newburgh had all their deciduous cuspids and molars present and free from caries than those in Kingston.[56] Physical examinations revealed no deleterious effects of the fluorides upon the health of the children.[724]

§ In 1952 as many children were killed by accidents as those who died from a combination of the next five most common causes of death.[218]

‖ See Dennis and Kaiser[205] and Dietrich.[218]

injuries, frequently preventable, often inflict physical, emotional and economic discomforts for the children and their families.

A variety of accidents occur in the preschool years. In 1954 some of the principal causes of accidents in the United States in order of their frequency were motor vehicles, burns, drowning, falls, poisons and firearms.[218] Many of these occur in the homes, and in many cases the adults are at fault. For example, more than 50 per cent of preschool motor deaths occur when a child is a passenger in an adult-driven car. In one study of home accidents[205] the largest personal factor was a faulty adult.* This study also found a higher incidence of accidents in the afternoon and evening, indicating a possibility that lack of parental control and fatigue at these times may be contributing factors.

Poisons in the home which are available to children have been called one of the leading causes of accidents. About one third of the cases of poisoning in the United States in 1949-1950 were due to drugs.[61] A little over half of these were attributed to aspirin and other salicylates and barbiturates. The clever disguising of a drug to make it look and taste like candy, as in the case of aspirin for children, can lead to an overdose of such a drug. Poisoning may result from normal curiosity, from the desire and habit of testing the world with the mouth, or from past experiences of receiving praise for eating or drinking a variety of substances.

Some individuals seem to have more accidents than others† and can be called accident prone. The accident prone child has not yet been clearly identified. Probably hyperactivity, lack of disciplinary control, fatigue and emotional problems are causative factors.

Prevention of accidents involves protection and education.‡ During the first year of the child's life it is entirely protection. Between one and five the child is learning to protect himself. He learns by parental example, supervised experiences, and in being taught by rote if the two other conditions have been adhered to. Thus the preschool years are ones of gradually diminishing protection with an increasing effort to teach safe behavior. The parents' role requires time, ingenuity, and discipline.

The ease with which the child is protected and later educated depends

* Other personal factors were hurry, lack of knowledge, emotional causes and fatigue.
† See Langford,[495] Bakwin and Bakwin,[64] Fuller,[276] Dunbar.[229]
‡ See Dietrich.[218, 219]

to a large degree on the kind of relationship present between the parent and child. The parent assumes the responsibility of providing a safe environment and guarding the child from accidents on the street. A safe environment is one free from the hazards of fire, burns, poisons, including medicines and cleaning materials, small objects which can be swallowed and cause choking, "stumble-traps" such as toys on stairs or scattered about, knives and other sharp objects. A safe environment also means protected stairways, and a safe fenced-in space for outdoor play or supervised outdoor playtime. The mother's busiest time is that period when the infant is beginning to walk and is investigating everything around the house. One study[714] in England found, by questioning mothers of children under two years of age, that accidents were associated with the period when the children began to walk and before they had developed "heat sense." Stumbling and falling, with accompanying injuries, generally occur less frequently with children who are skillful in the use of their bodies. Happy, self-reliant, self-confident children, free from worry, tend to have fewer accidents than dependent, disturbed, unhappy ones. Therefore, a happy child with opportunities to develop motor skills has good insurance against accidents.

Helping a child to learn to protect himself from accidents is paced in accordance with his speed of maturation, and with his ability to comprehend, to respond, and to assume responsibility. Safety can be taught the positive way. "We put toys back in the play box when we are through with them." "We stand a foot back from the curb until we see the light turn green."

During the early years the child is learning much about the world about him which will help him in protecting his health. With guidance he learns that hot objects are to be avoided, that matches and stoves are to be manipulated by adults, that father's tools are to be used under his supervision. He learns how to cross a street, provided he has had good examples, but cannot always be trusted not to run out to catch a ball that has rolled into the street. He still needs an adult along when crossing a busy thoroughfare. He has learned that cuts and scratches heal faster when treated with antiseptic and bandaged, and will sometimes voluntarily take time out from play to run in with a request for a hurried application of antiseptic and bandage. He is able to accept routine visits to the doctor or dentist as a matter of course. He has acquired good motor skills, provided he has been given the opportunity to learn them, so that he uses his body skillfully and thus falls less. Even with all this growing ability to look out for himself, the health protection of the child as he reaches the time of going to school still lies chiefly in the hands of his parents and the community.

Other Routines Associated with Physical Care

In addition to routines of eating, eliminating and sleeping, two other routines are associated with physical care: dressing and washing, which also are discussed here.

Dressing. One of the factors to be observed in the selection of clothing, namely, provision of warmth or coolness, was mentioned earlier in this chapter. Other factors are: (1) *Safety:* Drawstrings or unnecessary tapes and ribbons may be dangerous. Rough seams in shoes or other clothes may hurt. Clothes for the toddler and preschool child can be planned so that he will not trip or fall. For example, he may trip over a cuff in overalls. (2) *Ease in laundering:* Clothes which can be washed are important. Materials which do not need ironing will save laundry time. (3) *Ease in putting on and taking off:* Again the time-saving factor is important, but even more important is the comfort of the baby and young child who does not like having things pulled on and off over his head. It is better that any routine as frequent and as permanent as dressing or undressing be a pleasant one from the very beginning. Gowns for infants which open down the back not only are easier to put on and take off but offer the additional advantage of requiring less frequent laundering, since the flaps can be folded back at the bottom and do not need to be wet each time the diaper is. Sleeping pajamas, later, with two pants and one top, make it possible to change only the pants when the child is wet, thus making this procedure easier for mother and child. (4) *Ease in self-manipulation:* Clothing can be planned which the toddler and young child can manipulate himself, so that as he comes to the "me do" stage and grows in independence he can gradually, step by step, take over dressing himself. This means providing clothes that can be put on and taken off with ease, i.e., those with few and large buttons, opening down the front, belts fastened on and equipped with easy buckles. If the child, when he becomes absorbed in learning to dress himself, has the facilities for learning, the learning process will likely proceed well. However, if he is deprived of the opportunity either because of the type of clothing or because of too much adult interference when he is eager to do this, his enthusiasm will disappear and what earlier would have been fascinating is now boring. (5) *Provision for freedom of movement:* At all ages clothing can be light in weight and so designed that it will not hamper freedom of movement in any way. (6) *Comfort and fit:* Clothing can be comfortable and well fitting. Infants and young children grow rapidly and may quickly outgrow their clothes, especially shoes. Hand-me-downs or second-hand clothing is often used in a family, and rightfully so. It is well to be sure that such clothes fit well and that the design and weight are satisfactory. It is well to be especially sure that second-hand shoes fit properly, for ill-fitting shoes can easily affect foot posture. Sometimes also new clothes, bought with the realization of the child's rapid growth, are too large and cumbersome for the child. (7) *Attractiveness and appropriateness:* Even small children can be aware of their clothes and react to them. A child in a group as in nursery school has been known to remain on the fringe of activities because of the inappropriateness of her clothes. A girl dressed in a party type of dress is not prepared for the vigorous activity of a group as is one dressed in overalls.

Gesell and Ilg[290] give the developmental sequence of dressing to five years as follows:

Interest in taking off hat, shoes, pants.
Removes mittens, hat, socks; unzips zipper.
Removes shoes, stockings, pants. Likes to undress.
Can take off all clothes. Better at undressing than at dressing.
Undresses himself rapidly and well.
Dresses and undresses with little assistance, especially if clothes are laid out.
Can dress himself completely, lacing shoes, buttoning front buttons. Cannot tie shoe laces.

Girls tend to dress themselves earlier than do boys.[292]

Washing and Bathing.   Bathing the baby is done for his comfort. Most babies are given a daily bath. In hot weather, baths twice a day may add to the baby's comfort. However, many hospitals now eliminate both the initial and daily bath of the newborn, because babies whose skin surface is not rubbed or handled as much as is necessary during either an oil or a soap and water bath have been found to develop fewer infections.[20, 719, 774] The danger of heat loss from evaporation of moisture from the infant's relatively large surface area is given as another reason for omitting the bath. Many physicians now claim that until the infant is creeping and actually getting dirty, bathing only three times a week is better, both because it is less drying and irritating to the infant's skin, and because this regimen gives his mother more time for adequate rest herself.

Whatever the bath schedule, a warm room is desirable so that the baby can have perfect freedom from blankets and clothes and can kick and exercise, and so that the person giving the bath will feel no need to hurry. The baby is more apt to be perfectly relaxed and to enjoy the procedure if the hands handling him are skilled and at the same time unhurried. As soon as the infant learns to reach out and grasp things he will want the wash cloth and later the soap. It is well to recognize his urge as the beginning of self-help and have an extra cloth that he may hold. Later he will want to have the soap, and still later he will dab at his own knees with the cloth. When he becomes aware of the stopper he will want to pull it out and to put it in; thus, gradually, he learns to take over the bath procedure for himself.

Bathtime can be a time of fun for child and parent, either father or mother. Like preparation for going to sleep, routines develop, and to many young children the conditions surrounding the bath and the order of procedure are extremely important. Bathtime may be a happy time if the routine is followed: it may become a struggle if the routine is changed.

For young children the washing of hands after going to the toilet and before meals is a good practice. With facilities accessible to them, they can soon learn to do this for themselves. For a time they will need to be reminded. Later they will do it without a reminder. They will learn to use their own towel and wash cloth if these are accessible to them.

Topics for Study and Discussion

1. For a discussion of toilet training, invite two mothers who successfully trained their children, one who began training during the first year and the other who waited until the child was able to indicate his need, to participate. The students should be prepared to ask questions and contribute information based on the section in this chapter.

2. Observe preschool children with adults at street crossings and children in the nursery school. How are these children learning to protect themselves from accidents?

3. Invite a doctor, a pediatrician or general practitioner who cares for a large number of children, to discuss with the class the topic of health protection. Before the discussion have each student hand in two pertinent questions.

4. Have the class make out a brief questionnaire on sleep for the mothers of the nursery school children. The students will summarize the findings and discuss them.

Selected Readings

A Family Handbook on Accident Prevention, Parents' Magazine 27 (No. 10):51-56, 1952.

Aldrich, C. A., and Aldrich, M. M.: Babies Are Human Beings, ed. 2. New York, Macmillan Company, 1954.

Gesell, A., and Ilg, F. L.: Infant and Child in the Culture of Today. New York, Harper & Brothers, 1943.

Sears, R. R., Maccoby, E. E., and Levin, H.: Patterns of Child Rearing. Evanston, Ill. Row, Peterson and Company, 1957. Chap. 4 (pp. 102-137); Chap. 8 (pp. 292-297).

Social Security Administration: Infant Care. Children's Bureau Publication No. 8. Washington, D. C., U. S. Department of Health, Education and Welfare, 1955.

Social Security Administration: Your Child from One to Six. Children's Bureau Publication No. 30—Revised. Washington, D. C., U. S. Department of Health, Education and Welfare, 1956.

Spock, B.: The Common Sense Book of Baby and Child Care, ed. 2. New York, Duell, Sloan & Pearce, Inc., 1957.

8

Aspects of Behavior and Their Development: Motor Development

Interrelationships of Physical Aspects and Various Aspects of Behavior

As the structure of the child's body matures, it acquires the ability to function in increasingly complex ways. Thus, along with physical growth, motor, intellectual, emotional and social maturings are achieved which change the child from an uncoordinated, helpless infant into a more smoothly integrated and independent member of his world at the age of five. This change involves varied and complex developments, learnings in control of body, and learnings about himself, the things and people in his world—what they are and what they are for, what people expect of him and what he does to get along with them. He learns to understand and speak the language of these people in order to find his way about their world. And he learns to temper his own feelings and desires to recognize theirs if conflict is to be decreased and harmony to be found. This is a good deal to achieve in five years; it involves a lot of growing as well as a lot of conscious and unconscious learning.

The sequence of functional development, usually achieved readily from conception through the first five postnatal years, has been presented in the form of related gradients by Gesell and Ilg.[291] Developmental sequence (with ages not to be overemphasized) is presented in Figure 48 and in the following summary:

"In the *first quarter* of the *first year,* the infant, having weathered the hazards of the neonatal period, gains control of his twelve oculomotor muscles." [*oculomotor,* pertaining to the movements of the eye.]

"In the *second quarter* (16-28 weeks) he gains command of the muscles which support his head and move his arms. He reaches out for things.

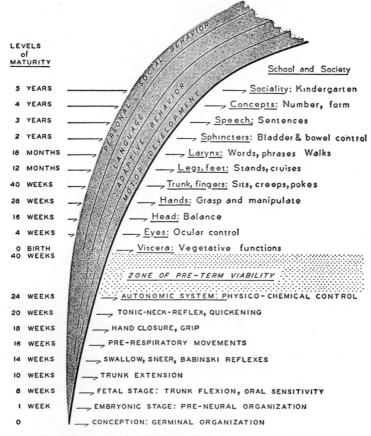

Figure 48. Diagrammatic representation of trends and fields of behavior growth from embryonic period through five years of age. (Gesell, A., and Ilg, F.: Infant and Child in the Culture of Today. Harper & Brothers, 1943, also in Gesell, A., and Amatruda, C. S.: Developmental Diagnosis. Paul B. Hoeber, 1947.)

"In the *third quarter* (28-40 weeks) he gains command of his trunk and hands. He sits. He grasps, transfers and manipulates objects.

"In the *fourth quarter* (40-52 weeks) he extends command to his legs and feet; to his forefingers and thumbs. He pokes and plucks.

"By the end of the *second year* he walks and runs; articulates words and phrases; acquires bowel and bladder control; attains a rudimentary sense of personal identity and of personal possession.

"At *three years* he speaks in sentences, using words as tools of thought; he shows a positive propensity to understand his environment and to comply with cultural demands. He is no longer a mere infant.

"At *four years* he asks innumerable questions, perceives analogies, displays an active tendency to conceptualize and generalize. He is nearly self-dependent in routines of home life.

"At *five* he is well matured in motor control. He hops and skips. He talks without infantile articulation. He can narrate a long tale. He prefers associative play. He feels socialized pride in clothes and accomplishment."*

This summary is presented to suggest the variety of competences which appear in the early years and their hierarchical quality. No individual child is expected to achieve these steps of growth at exactly the ages indicated here. Some children will move at a pace faster than this in most areas of growth, others at a slower pace in most areas. Most children will be ahead of schedule in some areas while being behind schedule in other areas. As said in Chapter 1, this is the way children grow, and we have less concern with the general speed of a child's schedule and more concern about unobtrusively "setting the stage" to enable him to move smoothly along the various growth stages at his own pace.

Having discussed physical growth and development of the body by stages, we shall now, for convenience, discuss stages of growth and development of various aspects of behavior according to additional general categories: motor, intellectual, emotional, social and spiritual. As indicated previously, these aspects of behavior and the processes through which they develop have both biological and psychological sides. Organization of material about them in this and the following chapters is as follows: First, the broad concept, theory or idea is stated, in the light of which the present-day knowledge of a particular aspect of behavior and its development is considered. Second, description of the particular aspect of behavior and its development is given. This is followed by reference to the relationship of one aspect with other aspects of the child. All of this is in accordance with a developmental-

* Gesell and Ilg[291] (pp. 62ff.). By permission of Harper & Brothers.

dynamic concept. Lastly, the significance of current thought and knowledge for those associated with children is stated.

In the consideration of motor behavior and its development, the first part of this chapter refers to control over the body in general and pertains chiefly to locomotion; the other part of the chapter refers to hand skills.

Control Over Body in General

A broad concept of use when thinking of motor development follows: *The control the child achieves over his body grows out of the structural and functional readiness of his body for learning.* The most elementary type of response is found in the noncortical capacity of the nerves and muscles (the neuromuscular mechanisms) for reflex and general activity. The more complicated type of response is found in the cortical capacity for learned control of the muscles.*

Simplest Mechanisms of Control. One of the most interesting facts about a newborn baby is that he is a fairly efficient living machine.† Until he is born, the child's breathing, eating and eliminating have been done for him by his mother's blood stream. At birth he suddenly comes into the need of doing these things for himself. The birth cry is usually given credit for inflating his lungs and introducing them to the task of respiration. A touch on the infant's lips sets up a sucking movement, a motor response which upon presentation of the mother's breast furnishes the infant with his food. Even though he does these organic things for himself, however, he is still entirely dependent upon others for his food supply and for his physical needs.

What he can do or can feel, of course, depends on the development and efficient functioning of his central nervous system. Studies‡ give

* See Spector[785] for statements of theory concerning the physical properties and mechanical characteristics of muscle, and for an abridged listing of muscles in man (pp. 295-299).

† For descriptions of the newborn (at birth and during the first month) and bibliographies, see Smith[767] (pp. 237-244, 295-296) and Pratt.[670]

‡ For summaries of these see: Dewey,[216] McGraw,[537, 540] and Pratt.[670] In McGraw,[537] a review of neural maturation of the central nervous system of the human being appears on pages 353-356. See Spector[785] for information on morphology and physiology of the brain (pp. 300-304), and of the autonomic nervous system (pp. 305-311).

In Chapter 4 the nervous system is discussed on pages 165-167.

evidence that the lower (noncortical) centers of the brain which make possible certain forms of behavior are quite well developed at birth, but that the higher (cortical) centers do not function well for several months after birth. The noncortical stage is followed by a transitional stage characterized by the onset of cortical function. The final stage is one of cortical dominance (McGraw,[540] Pratt[670]).

A NUMBER OF REFLEXES PRESENT AT BIRTH.   The newborn is well equipped with many of the neurological reflex movements common to human beings at any age. He can hiccup, sneeze, cough, blink, yawn and stretch, and he swallows imperfectly (Pratt[670, 671]). He needs a little longer time before he swallows his saliva routinely. The sucking mechanism is perfected enough to enable him to obtain fluid from his mother's breast, but a little patience is required during the first few weeks for first sucking is usually slow. Many mothers do not know this, and unless they are under the care of experienced people may become panic stricken because the baby does not nurse vigorously at once. He regurgitates, urinates, and defecates, but he has no control over his sphincters. He has hunger contractions which are sometimes vigorous. The pupillary reflex is also present.

At least three reflex patterns which disappear later are present in most babies at birth (Pratt[670]). One of these is the *grasping* (or Darwinian) reflex by which the hand closes strongly upon stimulation of the palm. This reflex is distinctly weakened (a sign of maturing) at the end of a month, and in most children it is gone by the fourth month—at about the time when hand skills are beginning to be learned (see pp. 309-313). The *Moro* reflex is named after the man who described it in 1918. In this reaction, elicited by tapping on the abdomen, by insecurity of support, and the like, the infant spreads his arms apart and then brings them together again in a bow, while the legs make a similar movement (see Fig. 49). This reflex disappears at about three months of age. A third reflex, present at birth and gradually disappearing later, is the *Babinski reflex,* an extension of the toes when the sole of the foot is stimulated. This gives place to the *plantar reflex* (contraction of the toes when the sole of the foot is stimulated) which appears as the nerve centers mature (Richards and Irwin[697]). The plantar reflex appears in the fourth month after birth in some children, and is present in nearly all children by the eighteenth month. The fourth month is the month in which, for most children, the nerves involved become myelinated (develop their myelin sheaths).

GENERAL BODILY ACTIVITY IN THE NEWBORN.   Much of the general activity of the newborn is in response to internal stimuli. For example, the amount of activity is related to events in the alimentary canal (Pratt, Nelson, Sun,[671] Irwin,[393] Richards[696]) and is greatest just before nursing. Some reaction to external stimuli is suggested by study in visual and auditory situations. General bodily activity decreases as the intensity of the visual stimulus increases within certain intensity ranges of illumination (Irwin and Weiss[400]). Decrease in activity also follows initial overt responses when auditory stimuli persist (Pratt, Nelson, Sun[671]).

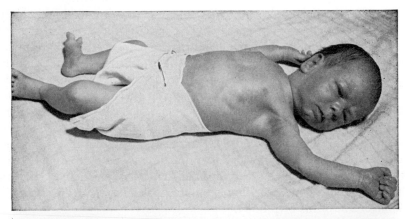

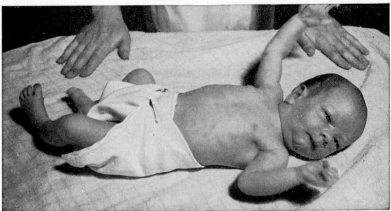

Figure 49. Newborn infant: rest and activity (Moro reflex). (Photographs are from the Newborn Infant by C. A. Smith, p. 254 in Textbook of Pediatrics, ed. 6, W. E. Nelson, editor. Philadelphia, W. B. Saunders Co., 1954.)

Pratt's description of the neonate's behavioral development ontogenetically is as follows:

"The neonate is considered to be a generalized organism because few of its responses are called forth by just one type of stimuli, few are limited to stimulation of just one sense organ or receptor area, and the responses are not sharply localized in a limited number of effector segments. . . . The infant for the most part develops in the direction of increasing specificity of response: stimuli, unless conditioning occurs to effect a generalization, become more 'adequate'; the reflexogenous zones for a given response shrink; and there is progressively less involvement of the organism in the response."*

Learning through Success and Failure.   Motor accomplishments grow from the simplest beginnings in random and uncoordinated movement. The newborn infant promises little of the motor skill and bodily grace of the five-year-old child. During the first three months a good deal of general body movement takes place, with stretching and waving of arms and legs. At this time, as well as later, freedom for such activity seems important. If there are certain periods (many mothers provide these at bathtime) when the infant may stretch and kick entirely free of clothing, practice is facilitated through which he achieves strength and coordination. If we watch a tiny infant, we can see him experimenting with his body, gradually learning to isolate out of his random activity those movements which give him results. So by trial and error, with the right movements accompanied by the satisfaction of success, the wrong movements resulting in failure, the child gradually learns the management of his own body.

Control Proceeds, from Head to Foot and from Center of Body Outward.   Within the framework of wide individual differences of maturity rates, development in control of the body proceeds, moving, in most instances, from control of the head through the torso (or trunk) to the legs, and from control of the torso, at the center of the body, outward through the arms and legs (Griffiths,[317] Irwin,[393] Shirley[753]).†

---

* Reprinted with permission from K. C. Pratt, The Neonate, Manual of Child Psychology, ed. 2, 1954 (L. Carmichael, editor), John Wiley & Sons, Inc. (p. 277).

† Reviews of research on motor growth and development are in Dewey,[216] McGraw,[537] Review of Educational Research 1941[92] and 1944.[93] Espenschade,[248] in the Review of Educational Research 1947 (p. 354) says "The past three years have produced nothing of importance in the investigation of motor development in infancy or early childhood." Bayley and Espenschade in 1950,[94] (p. 367) in referring to studies of infancy and early childhood during the years 1947 to 1950, say "very little new research on motor coordinations, as such, has been reported in this country. However, several studies of age changes in postural orientations and in the development of handedness were published." Among these studies were those of Ames,[22] Gesell and Ames,[289] and Hildreth.[355, 356, 357]

Even at the end of a month the baby begins to have rudimentary and uncertain control over his *head and neck*. By four to six months most children can hold the head up strongly and hence no longer need the support of the mother's hand as they are held. Placed on a hard table most children of four to six months can lift the upper part of their bodies and, by pulling their elbows under them, can stay up for several seconds at a time. This response is evident in Figure 50. Practically all children can do this by nine months of age. If not hampered by clothing the child growing at a usual rate can *roll* himself over from stomach to back by five to seven months. Sometimes, while lying on the floor on a blanket he may discover at six or seven months that he can propel himself by wriggling or hitching. There are wide individual differences in all of these rates of motor development, however.*

Sitting up for short intervals if sufficiently supported by pillows is done by many children at four or five months. The baby shown in Figure 51 has adult help in sitting up. Gesell[292] found that 20 per cent of the infants he studied were able to sit with slight support of pillows or blanket at four months; at six months over half sat in this way, and about 20 per cent sat alone for some seconds. According to Gesell's norms, practically all children of nine months were able to sit alone. Other studies[317, 753] have corroborated these findings so that, in general, maturational stages of a baby at six to eight months are such that he sits with slight support, falling over only when he becomes tired or when his wrigglings or a desire to reach something upset him (see Figure 52).

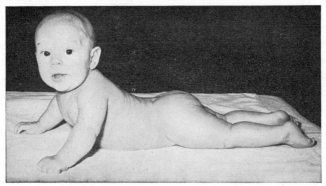

Figure 50. Four to six months: holds up head and forward torso.

* Motor items are included in infant test series, such as those of Bayley,[80] Gesell,[285] Griffiths.[317]

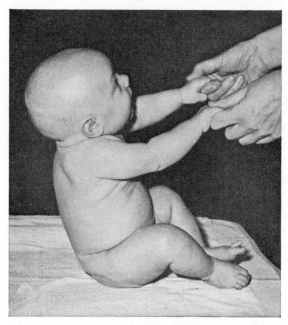

Figure 51.   Four months: can pull up with help, but cannot sit up.

Stepping movements are usually made at approximately six or seven months if the baby is held under the arms.[317, 540] At eight or nine months he has usually learned some technique or other which serves to get him from one place to another with ease. He may travel on all fours, sit and hitch himself along with his heels or scoot along on one hip, using two hands and the opposite foot for propellers. Probably the creeping methods he adopts are determined by the way he first happens to establish locomotion in his wrigglings.

Standing with support appears in most children at eight to ten months and is often fully developed by 12 months (Bayley[82]). Standing without support is almost universal by eighteen months. However, in one study around 10 per cent of children stood with help at six months (Linfert and others[513]) and around 40 per cent stood without help at nine months.

Vigorous and Coordinated Bodily Activity Characteristic of One-Year-Old Children.   The period from nine to eighteen months is one of rapidly increasing facility in locomotion. All investigators agree that this is a time in which the child learns to creep, to pull himself up by chairs, to climb, to walk and to control his body as a whole. Rapidly developing children are constantly on the move and may even climb stairs in the creeping position by twelve to fifteen months. Occasionally a few children of fifteen months climb stairs with the aid of a banister, one step at a time and on all fours much as puppies do. They come down stairs, again with the aid of a banister, by dropping to a sitting posture on each stair, wriggling to the edge, standing on the next stair below, dropping down and so on. If given opportunity for practice on stairs that do not offer too great hazard, many children of eighteen or twenty months can ascend and descend stairs in an upright position with the aid of a banister.[82, 317]

Dropping from a standing to a sitting position at this age as well as pulling up from a sitting to a standing position may require a practice period for learning to control balance and muscle action. Most children have achieved both skills by the time they are a year old. The proportion of the body, the short legs and longer trunk, demands a period of experimentation until the child can adjust the center of gravity of his

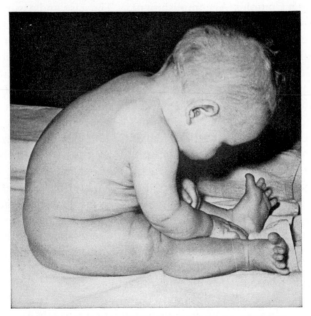

Figure 52.   Six to eight months: sitting is still wobbly.

Figure 53.   Ten to twelve months: creeping is now easy.

body so that he can sit, stand and move with the assurance of not falling.

Walking a Complex Accomplishment.   The ease and assurance with which most children learn to walk gives the casual observer no indication of the relation of structure and function, the complex learning that it represents. "Guiding parts of the body through ordinary movements of everyday life is one of the most intricate accomplishments of the human organism. With every change in position or velocity of any part of the body, forces acting on the system change and must be matched with changing muscle tensions if the desired movement is to eventuate. Analysis of locomotion must consequently deal not only with changes in position of the parts of the body, but also with changes in the forces, both external and muscular which accompany them."*

These controls and adjustments require maturing of skeletal and muscular systems and of the neuromuscular mechanism. Maturing of the functions of seeing and hearing and of bodily balance help the child in steering his course to his cherished possessions. All three skills are needed since the child not only must learn to place one foot after another; he must also see where he is going and learn to steer around or go directly to objects in his environment.†

* Elftman[238] (p. 1427).
† References on children with physical disabilities are in Jensen.[420]

Walking is a final step in bodily coordination developed over a considerable number of months of chronological age. The coordination begins when the child first tries to lift his head, and proceeds when he splashes in his bath with his mother supporting him, around three to five months of age. Bodily coordination proceeds to the final stages when he accomplishes the sitting posture by himself, then stands up and walks off. By the time he has learned to sit up he can see tiny white particles on a dark background very easily, and his hearing is acute (see Chapter 9).

Many authorities classify the initial step in locomotion according to an average birthday age. This they do at any time from eight or nine to eighteen months. The "average age" of walking is cited by many writers (Shirley,[753] Bayley,[82] Griffiths[317]) at somewhere around thirteen or fourteen months, although many children walk before then, and many others do not walk until fifteen or sixteen months. Most children have taken independent steps by eighteen months of age.[291]

The initial stages of locomotion actually begin in the prenatal stage when the fetus moves about rather freely in its fluid environment. For the first few months after he is born the infant is "grounded" while his sight and hearing are acquiring their range. His skill to move at will is built up again outside the uterus by means of a different kind of coordination, and he begins, in most instances, to creep and crawl. Bodily coordination which was achieved when he stood up and took a step now blends in with locomotion (McGraw[540]). Locomotion continues to develop through stages of awkward toddle, flatfooted paddling about, stumbling running, labored stair climbing, timid balancing along low inclined boards and other increasingly complicated adjustments of the body in locomotion. The mature accomplishment of the walking skill is arrived at when the child walks and runs with grace and ease, and when he unconsciously adjusts to and swings around obstacles in his path.

In quick *summary* the maturity stages of bodily coordination preceding and including walking may be viewed as follows:

1. Raises head.
2. Turns over.
3. Sits up with support; without support.
4. Stands with support; without support.
5. Takes steps or walks with support.
6. Walks without support; the first independent steps. At this stage movement is awkward, and the child cannot steer around objects in his path.

Figure 54. Fourteen to eighteen months: taking independent steps and beginning to "explore."

Figure 55. Around two years: tests of balance are fun.

Figure 56. Two and one-half years: walking skills and body balance are becoming unconscious enough to permit concentration on an activity.

Figure 57. Three to four years: large muscle skills are now unconscious enough to permit many variations in play.

7. Walks well enough to clear obstacles, but is still consciously aware of adjusting to them. Unless he attends to what he is doing, he bumps or falls.
8. Can move in any direction and adapt unconsciously to obstacles of varying height. Shows no hesitation or need of special attention in skirting objects or climbing over them.

Figures 53 through 57 show increasing bodily coordination as the child grows older.

Crawling and creeping are accessory to the main pattern of development. Most children go through them as a stage on the way to the walking maturity; some children do not. They do not seem to be necessary stages along the way.

Step 8 of the above series of maturity stages is the 100 per cent maturity stage of the walking skill. A few children have achieved this by two and one-half years of chronological age; many children have it by three to four years; most children have it by five years of age. There are wide ranges of individual difference at every stage. Some children adopt one channel of development, some another (Fig. 58).

Other Bodily Skills.   As the walking skill becomes smoother and as grace develops, interest in other forms of locomotion is evident. A number of variations are tried out, such as standing on one foot, jumping and hopping (Bayley,[82] Griffiths[317]). These, along with learning to ride a tricycle, a two-wheeled scooter and finally a bicycle, all follow as refinements of upright locomotion and general body balance.* Hopping, jumping over low obstacles and standing on one leg are all accomplished by most children before five or six years of age, if normal opportunity for practice is allowed. In one study, galloping was not seen in three-year-olds,[324] but many four-year-olds practiced it and many five-year-olds could do it. Skipping is still later in development for most children.

Developmental-Dynamic Aspects of Bodily Control and Hand Skills. Descriptions of the stages of development demand explanations of them. In Chapter 1, various concepts and theories were stated which can be used in connection with questions on explanations of motor development. They can be used in thinking of the bodily controls which have just been described, and in thinking of hand skills which are to be described later. In both forms of motor behavior, stages of maturity

---

* Gutteridge[323, 324] gives an excellent summary of the development of these skills. Common motor achievements at the preschool age are reported by McCaskill and Wellman.[530]

and approximate chronological ages at which they appear seem similar from one child or group of children studied to another (Bayley,[82] Gesell,[286] Griffiths,[317] McGraw,[540]Shirley[753]). This similarity of stages through which the various children studied proceed, gives support to the emphasis on the process of *maturation*. Some suggestion of a variation in pace in a racial group comes from comparison of Negro groups to norms of white children; acceleration in pace of motor development of the Negro group was reported.[254]

Relation of maturation and learning, as well as the strong influences of maturation at early age levels, are indicated in studies of twins; stair climbing and cube manipulation at a particular level of competence were accomplished more easily by the twin who was faced with the situation at a later age (but not very late) (Gesell and Thomp-

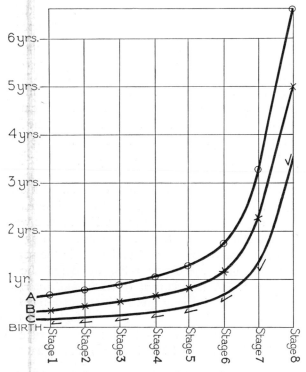

Figure 58. Possible channels of development of walking stages. Curves show ages at which three different children attained different stages of bodily coordination summarized in text.

son,[293] McGraw[536]). General practice as distinguished from specific or experimental practice is considered pertinent at early ages; the child's own activities (frequently initiated by him) are involved in the acquisition of skills when he is mature enough for them (Dennis,[207] Hicks,[350] Hilgard,[358] Munn[606]). Developmental changes in attitude seem to be one factor determining energy output in motor performance (Dammon[181]). Research evidence pertains not only to timing, in the sense of being mature enough to respond easily, but also to opportunity for practice, in the sense of having a chance to use the ability before too much time has elapsed. Certain deprivations, such as lack of opportunity to practice, can retard the beginning of walking (Dennis[207]).

On the subject of *learning* motor responses, as something different from having them emerge through maturation, whether or not the response is a universal one for human beings and its complexity, are pertinent aspects. At the later preschool ages when the skill is complex, such as rolling a marble according to a maze pattern, specific practice of it (as contrasted to general practice referred to in the previous paragraph) assists its development (McGraw,[536] Mattson[562]). Studies of sensorimotor learning have not disclosed clear-cut differences in learning according to sex or intelligence.* In studies of incentives, types of training procedure and transfer of skill, the influence of emotional tone, sequence in the individual over a period of time, and the interrelationships of aspects within the individual have not had the consideration which seems especially important from a developmental-dynamic point of view.

Anyone who has watched closely two children or more at a particular stage of motor development in some of such human universals as the ability to sit alone, the ability to walk in a mature way or to run, or in some of the skills of this civilization such as cutting with scissors or riding a tricycle, has been aware of variations in the performance of each individual. Perhaps the observer has wondered about the bases for these variations. On this subject of *individual interrelationships,* constitutional differences in body build have already been referred to (see Chapter 4). Variations from one individual to another in the amount of bodily activity, even before birth, have been reported. Studies of fetal life (Carmichael[156] and Newberry[628]) show that babies differ

---

* Research on conditioning and learning of sensorimotor skills is reviewed in Munn[606] (pp. 374-407). A number of references pertain to the prenatal period, infancy and preschool ages.

in the rate of achieving motor developmental patterns even before birth.* There are clear individual differences in general impetus to motor activity as we shall see later, but it is interesting to note that these differences appear in the developmental picture even before birth. It has been found[699] that the more active fetus is likely to be more advanced in behavior development as an infant.

Variations in general activity in the newborn have been connected with the functioning of the alimentary canal (Irwin[393] and Richards[696]). According to what we know about learning processes, we can consider that the strength of these primary drives toward activity and the satisfaction of hunger might later be connected with the amount of practice on motor responses and the satisfactions derived from it. Investigations of the sources of variation in motor responses would be of interest not only because they would provide a more thorough consideration of motor development, but also because there are possible connections between motor behavior and personality components. A number of the personality components of the early years include reference to motor performance. (For example, the child's use of his body in grasping objects is connected with his sense of trust)(see pp. 391-392).

Motor abilities in the infant do not predict later intelligence, according to follow up studies concerning infant tests. Scores on items predominantly motor in infancy do not correlate significantly with scores on intelligence tests at later ages (Bayley[87]).

(Details of information slowly being provided through research fit into the general concept that the child's control over his body grows out of the readiness of his body for learning. These details carry a connotation for the adult thinking of the motor development of children with whom he is associated. This connotation concerns *enabling the child to feel free instead of hampered in his use of his body*. Implicit in this is a concept of self discipline which is considered elsewhere. Furthermore, it assumes that the young child who feels free, will seek activity which involves the use of his emerging abilities. The following specific factors to be considered when thinking of a child's motor responses are ramifications of this connotation.)

FACTORS OTHER THAN MATURATION INVOLVED IN LEARNING BODILY CONTROL.   Walking, as we have said, is complex. It is dependent on many inner maturational factors, and its perfection takes many

---

* See page 103 for discussion of fetal activity.

months. However, parents have come to look upon the child's first independent steps as the important test of a child's motor development, and often worry about whether or not they can do anything to help their children achieve this skill. One thing they can do is to offer the child plenty of free opportunity to be as active in general bodily movement as he wishes to be. Training in muscular coordination comes to young children through climbing up and down steps and over large boxes, and pushing loaded wagons.

A case in point is that of Edward. When Edward came into a play group at twenty-five months of age, he had lived all his life in the second floor of a duplex apartment. There had been no yard or outdoor play space, and he had been carried up and down the steps into the apartment. When out on the street he was either wheeled by his mother in his "go-cart" or led by the hand for a few blocks. Upon entering the group he had had no experience in the coordination of his body in climbing stairs, mounting the jungle gym or climbing on and off a tricycle. All these movements had to be learned. It was several months before he could mount without apparent concern the small ladder by which children climbed to the measuring board in the physical growth laboratory and which most children mounted easily and eagerly. So far as one could judge this inability to climb when most children climb easily and eagerly was not due to a fear of falling. That his environment was responsible for this condition was suggested by his prompt response to opportunity to use play equipment and the subsequent disappearance of his awkwardness, lack of balance, and sense of physical inadequacy.

Parents not only can see that the child has *opportunity to practice the motor skills;* they can also see whether his muscles lack tone or whether he suffers from malnutrition, since, if he has either of these defects he cannot be expected to support himself in an upright position as soon as a normal child would. If he has been or is ill, he probably lacks the necessary muscular strength for walking which, being a new and unaccustomed activity, demands great strength and energy. *Illness* handicaps him also because it curbs his interest in activity and thus deprives him of even the amount of practice his small physical strength might endure. Parents can see that the child has plenty of *space* which is not too slippery or too drafty or too dirty to permit freedom for practice. *Clothing* and *shoes* are important, too, since the child could be hampered by garments which upset him when he tries to stand, or by shoes that are too restricting.

Certain emotional factors are also important. Severe accidents may produce fear and timidity. Too great anxiety on the part of adults over casual bumps may convince a timid child that he takes too great a risk. Too great enthusiasm over his first attempts may inhibit a self-conscious child, or too ready laughter at the "cuteness" of his gait may take on an aspect of ridicule. If the parents become overanxious because he does not have a particular skill, the feeling of anxiety may be conveyed to the child, attaching excessive importance to his learning and making him too afraid of failure.

Again, some children have less *motive* for walking or locomotion of any kind or for active motor play. They may have had less satisfaction from the thrill of movement for its own sake. It is a good idea to let the six- or eight-month-old baby struggle a bit when he has let his rattle drop only a few inches from him. The thrill of recovery will attach satisfaction to his efforts and encourage him to make the effort the next time. When a nine- to twelve-month-old baby has a ball to play with, the urge to pursue it will provide him with a motive for practice in locomotion. In fact, balls of varying sizes and weights illustrate a type of "teaching toy," from a few months of age through the entire period of childhood.

Development of Courage or Timidity a By-Product of Motor Learnings. If we regard the degree of satisfaction which every child gets from learning to walk as evidence of the innate character of that act, we can scarcely dispute the innateness of the urge toward locomotion. The thrill of accomplishment which accompanies each new bit of learning seems genuine, as the child throws back his head to crow his delight or abandons himself to an orgy of practicing his new achievement. The number and severity of bumps that some children take without complaint or discouragement in the process of learning upright locomotion seem proof of intense absorption. We miss an excellent opportunity to encourage physical courage if we curb his freedom or seem too concerned over his bumps during this absorbing learning period. If he is genuinely hurt in a fall, however, he needs sympathy and care. Terror can be averted very simply by a calm and yet alert parent. Great enthusiasm for active motor play is a part of the early years.

Development of Hand Skills

Learning To Use Thumb and Fingers. Growth in the use of the thumb and fingers is extremely significant during the baby's first months. At birth the hand, though strong enough in the reflex grip to maintain the body weight, is useless as a vehicle of the will. The

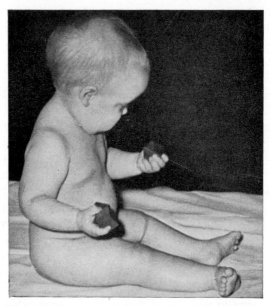

Figure 59. Sitting with ease at nine months, this baby has secured three cubes (a superior performance in grasping) and holds them with clear thumb finger or pincer grasp.

thumb lies flaccid and helpless in the palm, or fans out uselessly. However, the hand, especially the fingers, soon becomes useful as an aid to producing sensations. The fingers of the two hands come together, touching, exploring each other as early as one month after birth. Picking up an inch cube with the "palmar scoop" (an awkward scoop with the whole hand) is the characteristic approach at four to five months. The same technique was used on a small sugar pellet by 50 per cent of the babies studied by Gesell at six months.[292] By eight to nine months, however, the fingers and thumb work in opposition to each other to make the pincer technique of picking up and holding objects effective (Fig. 59). By one year, looking at a small object and picking it up skillfully with the fingers and thumb have become one smooth, coordinated activity (Gesell,[292] Halverson[327]). The greatly increased efficiency of the hand as an organ for grasping when the thumb is in opposition can be seen if the reader will try closing the thumb into the palm of his hand before grasping an object, and will then release the thumb so that it can oppose the fingers as is normal in adult grasping or in the picking up of objects.

Hand-Eye Coordination. Castner,[157] as early as 1932, called attention to the coordination of visual and neuromuscular components in the development of fine prehension (the act of seizing or grasping) in infants. McGraw,[539] in a study of seventy-three children ranging in ages from birth to four years, concludes that reaching-prehensile (seizing or grasping) behavior from the onset of its development represents a function which requires an interconnection between visual and neuromuscular mechanisms. This would mean that reaching and grasping at all stages are dependent upon connections between the hand's ability to grasp and the eye's ability to see.

*Maturity indicators of hand-eye coordination** may be viewed as follows:

1. Pre-coordination: random waving of hands and reflex grasping.
2. Initial coordination: the child begins to fix his eyes upon objects which are within near visual range. Cannot grasp the object.
3. Dependent hand-eye coordination: the child can reach effectively for the object as long as his gaze remains on the object.
4. Integrated hand-eye coordination: child is able to direct his movement for the object by one brief glance.
5. Mature coordination: both the visual and neuromuscular aspects of the performance are reduced to the minimum requirements.

Figure 60 shows the ages in days at which each of six phases of reaching-prehensile behavior described by McGraw[539] appears. Stages resemble those listed above, except that McGraw includes two phases, B and C, with regard to initial coordination. The phases listed by McGraw include the following:

Phase A. In the newborn or passive phase, there is random waving of hands and reflex grasping but no connection between the visual and neuromuscular movements educed.

Phase B. In the object-vision phase, the child begins to fix his eyes upon objects within near visual range and shows neuromuscular tension or diffuse activity.

Phase C. In the visual-motor phase, the eyes fix on the object and neuromuscular activity occurs, but the movements are purposeless and seem in no way connected with a desire on the part of the child to possess or manipulate the object.

Phase D. In the manipulative and deliberative phase, the child shows sustained attention to the object and can reach effectively for it as long as he gives

* This sequence was suggested by Idell Pyle.

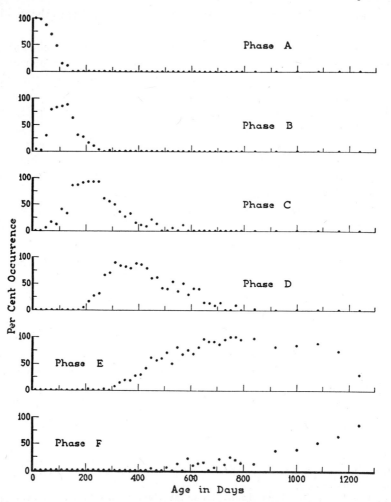

Figure 60. Curves showing percentage of occurrence of each phase of reaching-prehensile behavior as manifested by the group. (McGraw, M. B.: Neural maturation as exemplified in the reaching-prehensile behavior of the human infant, Journal of Psychology 11:127-141, 1941. The Journal Press.)

undivided attention to it, but reaching movements are interrupted if he takes his gaze from the object.

Phase E. In the visual-release phase, sustained attention is no longer necessary in order to carry out effective reaching; by one brief look the child is able to direct the movements of his hands for effective grasping, although he still may show some unnecessary movements in the process.

Phase F. Mature phase, both the visual and neuromuscular aspects of the performance are reduced to the minimum requirements.

McGraw indicates 130 days (four months) as the age at which the first phase neared completion in her group. The mature phase began for a few children as early as 450 days (about fifteen months), but was not completed for 100 per cent of the group until around 1250 days (about three and one-half years). This gives us some idea of the wide range of maturity levels present in this, as in the development of most abilities. McGraw points out in this study the relation between function of an organism and its structural maturing. She says, "There is no structural evidence that the cortex of the newborn infant is functioning to any appreciable degree."* When more mature behavior appears, we can know that the structural maturing is occurring or has occurred. When purposeful, directed reaching and grasping occur, we know that both visual and neuromuscular brain centers are reaching functional maturity.

Another maturational series for reaching and grasping has been described by Shirley[753] as follows: reaching and missing; reaching and touching; reaching, grasping, and not holding; and finally reaching, grasping, and manipulating. Shirley found that most of this learning takes place between three and nine months, the process being complete for normal children at nine months. It is difficult to compare these stages with those of McGraw, since the approach to the analysis in each instance was made from a different point of view.

Gesell[288] has an interesting test to show the child's adaptation to materials which interest him. If we present a child of less than six months with a small wooden cube and then with a second, he is more than likely to drop the first in order to take the second. At four months he usually reaches incipiently with both hands, his whole body as well as both hands participating in his eagerness. Such reaching is not as a rule effective; but soon the reaching becomes more nearly narrowed to the use of the two hands and becomes more efficient. At six to nine months the greater efficacy of reaching for objects with one hand has been learned, and as is characteristic of new learnings the child seems unaware for the moment of other possibilities; so he uses only one hand, dropping one prized object for another. He learns quickly, however. By nine months he uses each hand with enough independence from the other that he can retain the first cube while he reaches for the

* McGraw[539] (p. 139).

second (Fig. 59). Three cubes, though, are often too much; he drops one or both of the first two to gain a third. At twelve months he is equal to three, occasionally reaching for the third with his mouth, and at eighteen months he can accept a fourth or even a fifth without losing those he already possesses.

Learning To Let Go of Objects. It is interesting to note in connection with use of the hands that learning to let go of objects is almost as difficult as learning to take hold of them. Two developmental steps in this learning are: simple release and release including bodily balance. An infant's responses at different ages as he drops a cube illustrate these stages in use of his hands. Early in the "letting go" series of developmental stages is the dropping of objects because the infant has not yet learned voluntary control of the taking-hold and letting-go muscles. He drops the object because his attention and his muscular energy go elsewhere. By six or eight months, however, the letting go is purposeful to the extent that it often becomes a favorite game to throw a rattle or other object on the floor for the sheer fun of seeing someone pick it up and hand it back.

Hand-Mouth Coordination. Learning to put the hand into the mouth is often one of the earliest coordinations accomplished. As sucking gives way to more mature ways of eating food, we see the development of the hand-mouth coordination for purposes of getting food by the hand method rather than by the sucking method.

Before hand-mouth coordination develops for this purpose, however, we often see the infant's fist getting into his mouth to be used as a sucking object. This is a reflex-like pattern.

There appears to be one other form of hand-mouth coordination besides food-getting that may be relevant to growth. This is the use of the mouth as an exploratory organ. The tongue and lips are acutely sensitive touch organs, and children of six to nine months are likely to use them in order to explore everything that they can get in their hands. The baby's impulse to explore objects with his mouth provides a way of increasing his knowledge of the many objects that come within his reach. Because of this tendency to put everything into his mouth, he needs some place to play which offers him freedom, yet protection. A play pen, large enough to permit real freedom of movement but capable of restricting the territory of this young gourmand, offers the opportunity for unsupervised but safe play which is essential even in the first year of life. Of course there are also times when he seeks to travel at large and exercise his body to its full capacity.

The baby not only learns to carry his hand to his mouth but a little later he also learns to keep his hand (and objects that come into his hand) out of his mouth. This learning not to put everything into his mouth is called hand-mouth inhibition. Hand-mouth inhibition may be regarded as a part of mature hand-mouth coordination; it is present when a child can select the food which he wishes and distinguish edible from non-edible substances. In most children hand-mouth coordination is judged to have begun at around four months, to be dominant at six months, on the wane at nine months, and inhibited at twelve months. However, this is the exploratory type of hand-mouth coordination and the pattern of waning of the immature pattern. Purposeful, food-getting hand-mouth coordination does not begin until around a year (the time when the immature pattern has waned) and continues in development until nearly three years, the age at which most children have arrived at smoother hand-mouth food-getting. It is at about one year that thumb and finger coordination enables the child to be fairly skillful in manipulation of objects. He reaches for the spoon during feeding time and thus begins the process of learning to feed himself.

Increasing Skill with Hands Important to Growth of Intellect. Increasing skill with hands permits the child a greatly enlarged capacity for getting into contact with the world. He is able to provide his mind with a manifold of sensations which he gains from his new world through exploration and manipulation with his hands.

Hand Preference. The question of preference in use of hands arises here. Theories concerning handedness differ in the extent to which emphasis is placed on hand dominance or lateral dominance as inherent in the structure of the nervous system, and on the extent to which direct and indirect training influence it. Studies are being reported which provide information on ages at which preference appears.

Studies of Gesell and Ames[289] and Ames[22] reveal a tendency for alternating preferences in laterality during growth and several periods of bilaterality alternating with unilateral reaching and manipulation. Ames says, "The two hands at the earliest ages work very closely together as though they had not separated off from each other functionally. From 36 weeks through one year a separation and differentiation into an active and a passive hand seems to be working itself out. By 18 months the two hands again move together, but now in a voluntary simultaneous bilateral grasp by the two hands which are nevertheless capable of working quite independently. After two years of age, the passive hand seems to become more passive and to take on more the subordinate role in unilateral behavior. . . ."* Hildreth[355, 356, 357] emphasizes the gradual settling down to a preference of one or the other hand and the gradual increase of right handedness with age. A rapid increase in percentage of right handedness up to three or four years is followed by a gradual increase up to seven or eight years. She found differences according to activities studied. For example, more children of preschool age ate with the right hand than used the right hand to shovel or to run a toy car.

The exact time to decide whether any given child is right- or left-handed is not clear. A child may have a brief or long period when he seems to use either hand with equal frequency and ease (the ambi-dextrous period). Some children show definite preference as early as six months, but most children are twelve to fifteen months old before preference is clearly evident. If the child is not markedly left-handed, but seems as late as fifteen or eighteen months to use either hand with equal or nearly equal ease, some parents may encourage the use of the right hand by giving him things toward his right hand. However, insist-ence upon the use of the right hand, if the child seems persistently more awkward with the right and more skillful with the left, adds tension, especially if encouragement of the use of the right hand meets with emotional resistance from the child. The matter of handedness is referred to again in Chapter 9 in connection with the development of language.

Activities Change as Hand Skills Increase.   Skill in manipulation of objects develops rapidly from one to two years of age (see Figure 61). Combined with the rapid development of upright locomotion, especially of climbing and running, and associated with a rapidly growing curiosity about things, it produces behavior disconcerting in many families. The insistent getting into things, the constant handling of everything in the environment, sometimes cause sharp conflict between parent and child. However, the development of hand skill offers something of a "balanc-ing" interest. It permits certain "busy work" with blocks, clay, sand and water. Most children do not spend long periods of time seated at this sort of activity, but it does absorb some of their energy.

* Ames[22] (p. 50).

At two years most children have skills which enable them to scribble, cut gashes in paper with scissors and pile four or five blocks into a tower.[822] They can string spools on a shoe lace and use a fork and spoon, although with a good deal of spilling. A few children at two become interested in helping to dress themselves. However, Armstrong and Wagoner,[48] who studied the "functional readiness progress" of children in terms of their ability to dress themselves, report that at two years of age their children were largely disinterested and indifferent to the activity of buttoning up jackets and seemed not to have the motor control required to manipulate the buttons. Less than half of Gesell's children could put on their own shoes at twenty-four months.

At three years abilities, such as the following, differ in degree of difficulty. At this age, if they have been given opportunity to learn, most children can do many "self-care" and other motor activities. They can, for example, copy a circle with a pencil, close the fist and wiggle the thumb (so great has control of the thumb become), build a high tower with blocks, build simple block houses.[822] They are able to set a low table if told what to put on it, carry a plate or bowl, feed themselves with a fork, wipe up spilled things without aid, dust, help care for a pet

Figure 61. This child, clearly left-handed, is very skillful in use of his hands at two years. Note "duck squat" peculiar to two-year-old children. Note, also, the purposeless, accompanying activity of the unused hand. This is characteristic of one stage of hand control. Water has many possibilities as a play material.

Figure 62. This two-and-one-half-year-old likes taking off her own shoes and socks. Having time to do things for herself and having help when she needs it are both important to her.

animal and wipe a number of dishes. They also can wash themselves, turning the water into the bowl, soaping backs and palms of hands, use a wash cloth for the face, and wring it out and hang it up on their own hook. They can manage the front buttons of clothing and can undress themselves with the exception of difficult buttons and fastenings, can hang up their own clothing, and can place shoes under the bed or in the closet.

These skills by which the child cares for himself depend, of course, on the character of his clothing, the nature of the house in which he lives and the attitude of surrounding adults, as well as his intelligence and his general physical development. Figure 62 shows the interest of a two-and-one-half-year-old in using motor skills in an environment which encourages their use. The child who is faced with tiny buttons and small or concealed buttonholes finds he cannot unbutton them. He cannot hang up his own coat or suit unless there are proper loop tapes by which to hang them, and hooks in the closet low enough for him to reach. He cannot care for himself in the bathroom unless he has a box or stool light enough for him to move about, steady enough so that it will not tip over when he stands on it and high enough so that he can reach the toilet or the faucets of the basin. He will not learn respect for other people's towels and wash cloths until he has his own and a place within reach to hang them. It is true, too, that independence and the skills necessary to it are learned only gradually, and that they have only begun at the age of three. Care seems important in not forcing these learnings. "Independence of adults" is an advanced stage of development for a child. This final indicator of functional readiness to manage personal hygiene is usually attained by children by the age of five years, although the degree of personal hygiene which they consider to be adequate seldom coincides with adults' ideas. If the adult does everything for the child, he is not having opportunities to practice his independence in personal hygiene and performance of daily functions as he is capable of assuming it step by step.

Playthings and Materials to Encourage Motor Development.* Reference to the developmental-dynamic aspects of motor behavior and development at the close of the section on bodily activity serves also as an introduction to this section on hand skills. The meaning of current concepts and information was stated there (page 307). Its emphasis was on enabling the child to feel free instead of hampered in the use of his body and in the use of his hands. This has an implication concerning play activity. It suggests the importance of the availability of materials and experiences appropriate to stages of motor development. Equipment and playthings offer opportunity for motor practice when the child is ready for various steps of growth. We cannot and should not attempt to provide self-consciously chosen equipment which anticipates every step of growth. If we did so we would create an atmosphere of expectancy and resultant tension which would be unwholesome. No amount of equipment can encourage growth for which inner readiness is not yet mature. Too much equipment also tends to rob children of initiative, especially at the age when imagination is developing and when self-resourcefulness can be stifled by an overelaborate set of playthings. Even if we could bring forth the most mature behavior possible for each child for his every stage of readiness at each chronological age, we

---

* Research on play interests of a motor type is reported by Gutteridge[323, 324] and by Jones.[439]

would not try to do so, since this in itself takes on the aspect of forcing. We would not coax him into experiences, in other words; we would let him dictate a comfortable pace for himself by letting him seek each experience when he wants to. Simple toys, a space to use them in and to keep things in, and freedom to use them according to the child's own ideas are pertinent factors in the choice and use of toys and equipment.

Variation in use of toys and equipment according to stage of development is illustrated in play with blocks. In the use of a small set of blocks, for example, the child at one stage of development simply dumps them out of the box, or picks them up one or two at a time and bangs them back into the box to hear the noise they make. Considerably later in development he piles one on top of another, at first being able to achieve a tower of not more than two. About this stage he enjoys putting two or three back into the box with his mother's help, as a beginning in learning how to "put them away." Later still he can pile several into a tower before it falls over, and he may begin simple bridge structures such as two blocks set a little distance apart with one on top to bridge the gap.[822] Still later, placements of blocks are more complex.

In general toys and equipment fall into two classes: those which encourage vigorous motion of the whole body, and those which require the more difficult task of manipulating an object with the hand or hands while holding the rest of the body motionless. This is sometimes called "fine motor coordination" in contrast to "gross motor coordination." Actually it involves primarily a difference in distance range of muscular involvement. "Gross motor" and "fine motor" coordination are somewhat ambiguous terms.

The paralleling of developmental stage and use of related equipment can be illustrated as follows: For the young infant *three to four months old,* a soft, fluffy ball or a rattle hung by a cord over the cradle will give practice in reaching and grasping, in directing his hand to strike an object, and in coordinating the eye muscles to follow a moving object. The plaything, if left there all the time, may cause overstimulation or overfatigue. If very close to his eyes convergence will involve fixating at too close a range and hence tend to turn the eyes inward. From *three to seven months* control of grasping and holding develops sufficiently to make a string of large wooden beads or spools a desirable plaything. Inflated rubber animals (not too large ones) are light in weight, easy to hold and easy to wash. A piece of crumpled tissue paper makes an intriguing noise when pounded or squeezed, and along with a rattle to jingle when waved, adds other opportunities for use of the ears, as well as the eyes, the connection between movements of the hand and the results obtained. Improvised and casual playthings such as discarded containers, clothespins, ashtrays, clean short pieces of rope or firm cloth are often more interesting to the child than more elaborate commercial toys. Care is necessary to see that there are no loose pieces or rough, sharp edges which could injure the child's eyes, ears or nose, or articles which could be swallowed.

By *nine or ten months* the use of a rubber ball can provide an incentive for wriggling and pursuit and can teach much eye-hand coordination. A spoon and unbreakable cup may also lay the foundation for later food-getting hand-mouth skills. Many are acquainted with the baby, who, when first creeping, finds his way to the kitchen cupboard where he likes to pull out the pots and pans and manipulate covers, parts of double boilers and other equipment.

At *twelve to eighteen months* a box of blocks of one-inch-cube size offers practice in handling smaller objects. Larger three- to four-inch blocks are also favorites at this age. Simple boxes to open and shut, cloth books with heavy bindings showing familiar objects in bright colors, a sand box with spoons or small shovel and a sieve and pail all

Figure 63. At eighteen months this child has body balance and hand control enough to build this tower. It is even more fun, however, to knock it down.

offer opportunities for practice in hand coordination at this age. Figure 63 suggests interests of the child of this age. A small cart or push-and-pull toy will also encourage general bodily coordination.

Around *two years* of age a ten- to twelve-inch board several feet long can be set up, at first on a low block, and later on increasingly higher blocks for the child to practice balance and develop surety in use of his own body. Climbing up and down steps and slides, over packing boxes or on the jungle gym or some substitute all offers practice in use and development of the muscles of the legs, arms, and back and develops a surprising agility at an early age. Small cars and trucks, interlocking trains and twelve- to fifteen-inch light, hollow blocks all encourage activity. Dolls and cuddly animals begin to be popular with both boys and girls at this age. Peg boards with large pegs, simple two- or three-piece jigsaw puzzles and other toys of this kind offer opportunity for practice in hand skill as well as in sense perception.

At *three years* most children are ready for a tricycle, although some children can use one to advantage earlier. Transportation toys like wagons, a train, and a dump truck are popular. A place to climb and space for running are important. Blunt scissors, colored paper, crayons, clay, a soap-bubble pipe, and simple puzzles are also related to stages of motor and sensory development.

Climbing opportunities, like those for balancing the body and "stunting" or "I-bet-you're-afraid-to-do-this" activities, are increasingly sought from the age of *four years* throughout the childhood period. A trapeze and rings can now be added, as can a turning pole placed just beyond the child's reach so that he can take hold by means of a little jump. Families of dolls or play animals, a costume box, a wide variety of nature specimens, a blackboard with chalk, Tinker Toys, or simple construction sets are often sought. All of these materials become gradually larger, higher, more complex, or more challenging as the child grows into each successive stage of greater competence.

In general, equipment appropriate for children from *two to five years* of age is simple. Plenty of space, particularly out-of-door space, with a place to run, climb, and dig are in accordance with what the child seeks. The equipment might include a shovel and pail or an old pan and spoon from the kitchen, a sand pile or an open patch of dirt, a tricycle to ride, some simple and durable blocks (fairly large ones at this age) or odd bits of board, empty spools, empty oatmeal cartons, a doll (a corn stalk, dressed up will do), a carriage (a box on wheels can substitute for this), a few bits of cloth for covers, clay or a bit of mother's dough from the baking, paints and crayons, paper (wrapping paper serves), and others.* The main principle to be followed is that the material should not be useless, mechanical toys, but materials which challenge him to resourceful activity and encourage either general bodily activity or skill with the hands.'They can also provide for growth, such as the development of perceptions and judgments discussed in Chapter 9 and can teach techniques of expression. The child's success in motor control can also have a part in personality growth. Opportunity to care for his own physical needs, helping about the house or the yard, playing with other children, plus simple "do-with" equipment, provide, even as early as two years of age, a sound background for physical, intellectual, emotional, social and spiritual growth.

Topics for Study and Discussion

1. If you are studying an individual child, make a record of his motor responses in terms of (1) bodily controls and (2) hand skills. For an infant, consider aspects in bold face type discussed between pages 293 and 301 and pages 309 and 315. For a child who is walking, consider forms of behavior described between pages 298 and 309 and pages 315 and 319. Attempt to relate what is observed to maturity indicators included in these pages.

2. Consider different pieces of play equipment of the two types referred to on page 320, that which encourages vigorous motion of the whole body and that which encourages use of the hands. Indicate order in which you would provide, purchase or make them and state the reasons why.

Selected Readings

Barker, R. G., Kounin, J. S., and Wright, J. F.: Child Behavior and Development. New York, McGraw-Hill, 1943. Chaps. 2 through 5.

Garrison, C., and Sheehy, E.: At Home with Children; the Guide to Preschool Play and Training. New York, Henry Holt & Co., 1943.

Gutteridge, M.: The Child's Experiences in Bodily Activity. Chap. 7, pp. 208-222, Forty-sixth Yearbook, Part II, National Society for Study of Education. Chicago, University of Chicago Press, 1947.

Hartley, R. E., and Goldenson, R. M.: The Complete Book of Children's Play. New York, Thomas Y. Crowell, 1957, pp. 1-38.

Jersild, A. T.: Child Psychology, ed. 4. New York, Prentice-Hall, 1954. Chap. 5.

Kawin, F.: Wise Choice of Toys, ed. 2. Chicago, University of Chicago Press, 1938.

Wellman, B.: Motor Achievements of Preschool Children, Childhood Education 13:311-316, 1937.

* References on equipment that can be made are: Home Play and Play Equipment for the Preschool Child, Children's Bureau Publication No. 238, Superintendent of Documents, Washington, D. C., 1946, and Sunderlin, E.: About Toys; Make Them at Home, HE 16, Agricultural Extension Service, Iowa State College, Ames, Iowa, 1950.

9

Aspects of Behavior and Their Development: Intellectual Development

Development of Sensory Judgment

Chapter divisions, such as motor, intellectual, emotional, social and spiritual development and their subdivisions, are for convenience in dealing more thoroughly, one aspect at a time, with that which has many aspects, i.e., the young child's behavior and its development. To imply clear-cut divisions is not intended. In fact, the opposite is true, as suggested in Chapter 1 where the growing person was referred to as a "manifold." On the intellectual side of this ongoing manifold, motor behavior and the use of sense organs provide a base for other aspects which appear later. Resources within the child pertaining to his intellect, such as sensory judgment, language, reasoning, imagination and creative activities, and intelligence, hinge to a great extent upon the enrichment provided for the child through motor and sensory experiences. As the infant or young child begins to expand his world, much of his activity is in these motor and sensory forms.

How fundamental and "ongoing" sensory perception* is, is suggested

---

* References to research and bibliographies on sensation and perception are listed by Goodenough[303] and by Murphy and Hochberg.[609] Research on sensory development, before and after birth, is reviewed in Zubek and Solberg[932] (pp. 157-227). Reactions of the neonate (from birth to the end of the first month) are summarized by Pratt.[670]

324

in the following broad concept. Murphy and Hochberg[609] say that *the whole living individual participates in every perceptual act, and in coping with his environment progressively alters his modes of perception and develops more complex ones which serve him better.*

It is generally agreed that newborn infants are not very sensitive to things which happen in the world around them. They do not hear, see, taste or smell as adults do (Pratt,[671] Smith[768]). Although the sense organs (as described in Chapter 4) are structurally well developed at birth, the child comes to use them with efficiency and meaning only as he develops. At first the response to stimulation of the sense organs is one of simple awareness. Later, perception of the properties of the external world becomes more objective; the child becomes more discriminating in responding to important cues.* Also, with increasing experience the child adds to his understanding of what he sees, hears, tastes, smells or touches. Increased competence of this kind is one important part of the child's cognition, of his knowing what the world is like. The process of learning the meaning of various sensations is called the process of developing sense perceptions and judgments. At first, the newborn and the young infant have sensory reactions in response to the present situation only. Later, a similar present situation has many more meanings based on previous experience. The process of developing sensory perceptions has a connection with learning that his mother's face above his crib means comfort to him, that a cup is to drink from, and a piece of cracker is to eat, whereas a rattle is not to be eaten. This association of meaning with the things seen, heard, tasted, smelled or touched requires use of the higher brain centers. The cortical or higher centers are immature and nonfunctional at birth (McGraw[540]), although they mature rapidly within the first few months of life. The terms "onset age" and "modal age" are sometimes used to designate the age at which skill is beginning to develop and that at which function is perfected.

Use of the Sense of Touch. Although the senses of touch and pain are probably the most nearly perfect of any of the senses at birth, authors generally agree that newborn infants are not very sensitive to externally applied touch or pain stimuli (Pratt,[671] Smith[768]). There is

---

* Discussion of the attainment of objectivity, technically described as achievement of independence from field organization, is in Baldwin[65] (pp. 36-68). Influence of values on perceptions is considered in Blake and Ramsey,[114] Blum[118] and Witkin.[914]

disagreement concerning the relative sensitivity of different areas of the body.[670] Even severe scratches or blisters do not seem to cause most babies much discomfort, although there is a definite reaction to needle pricks in most infants. Even though infants seem thus fairly insensitive to surface abrasions of the skin, they are quite sensitive to varying temperatures in their bath water or in the room in which they are (see page 217). Infants are probably more sensitive to colder than to warmer temperatures (Pratt and others[671]).

The newborn infant of course begins to use the sense of touch in feeding himself a short time after he is born. His tongue and lips are sensitive to touch at a very early age; later they are used as a means of investigating things in his world. Before the third month fingers are used to produce touch sensations.[144, 753] Babies can often be seen at this age lying in the crib carefully touching one hand against the other for the sheer experience of the sensation produced. Throughout the pre-school years touch remains one of the most pleasurable of the child's sensations. He uses it for purposes of exploration of almost everything within his reach. Combined with the ability to run around the house, this may provide disturbing situations, unless some provision is made for the child to use these capacities constructively.

The sense of touch is particularly productive of education to the mind at eighteen to thirty-six months of age, when exploration of the sensations of hardness and softness, roughness and smoothness, warmth and cold is at a peak. Children of this age are usually alert for opportunities to touch fur, a raincoat, figured goods, starched cloth, silks, the woven pattern of a wicker chair and anything else that offers information about the way things feel. This running of the fingers over every available surface is really more than the mere seeking of sensations. It is also an exploration of objects as such, an endeavor to learn just what "feel" is to be associated with what "look" and what "use." The child's reaction to printed silk or to the pattern on linoleum is an example of this. He may have learned in the past to associate change of level with change of line; for example, he knows that the edge of a table means a drop to the floor line. Now he is interested to discover that in some instances change of line means no change of level; so he runs his fingers over and over the pattern printed on dress or drapery materials and sometimes expresses his discovery by saying, "This looks rough—it's smooth—why?"

Use of the Sense of Smell.   Earlier writers believed that the sense of smell was well developed at birth. The consensus of more recent work is that it is not. "It seems to be well established that newborn infants react vigorously to such stimuli as ammonia and acetic acid, but whether these rather general reactions of the body musculature are to be ascribed to the sense of smell or of pain is uncertain."*

Thorough research on changes in olfactory sensitivity beyond the first few months has not been conducted. Illustrations from observations of individual children show change as the child develops. For some months the smells that are agreeable to infants are not always considered so by adults. For example, Dearborn[199] reported that at eleven and one-half months his baby showed no dislike for the bad odor of rancid fish oil emitted by some small fish vertebrae she was playing with, but smelled of them repeatedly. He also said, however, that at one year the odor of a fresh marigold was distasteful and caused the child to turn her head away. As late as the seventeenth month Preyer[674] reported his baby as unable to separate the sense of smell from that of taste, since the infant opened his mouth upon presentation of a fragrant flower. This mistake was not made by this baby after eighteen months of age. Animals and man alike use the sense of smell to distinguish between dangerous and harmless food, objects, and living creatures. The child does not use his sense of smell for this purpose in a cognitive way until he begins to make some judgment about what is harmless and what is dangerous.

Use of the Sense of Taste. Pratt, in a summary of gustatory reactions of the neonate, says, "It is uncertain whether the neonate differentiates all four taste qualities. It appears, however, that in terms of the sucking response salt solutions tend to break up the response, whereas sugar solutions elicit and maintain it. Acid solutions to a lesser extent evoke sucking; quinine solutions seldom do."† Individual observations lead us to believe that the sense of taste is fairly discriminating after a few months. (Recall that the taste buds are structurally mature soon after birth.) Preyer[674] reports an accurate discrimination between salt and sweet during the first month. Dearborn's child refused the sourness of a fairly sour orange on her two hundredth day. Shinn[752] reports that the taste of new foods became a source of pleasure to her niece during the first half of the eighth month. The baby's pleasure in taste, like that in smell, does not always correspond with adult judgment. Dearborn says that his baby seemed to enjoy a bitter taste on her two hundred and

* Pratt[670] (page 241).
† Pratt[670] (page 243).

seventy-ninth day (about nine months) and did not object to castor oil until the three hundred and eighty-fifth day (about thirteen months). Children frequently accept without objection foods which have high nutritional value but which many adults consider distasteful. Acceptance of a variety of tastes can occur early. Learning that tastes as well as textures vary occurs through a variety of experience as new foods are introduced in accordance with the physician's recommendation.

Use of the Sense of Hearing.* The reaction of the fetus to vibratory stimuli has been reported. Auditory sensitivity in the newborn has been confirmed by a number of investigators (Pratt[670]). Whether the sound leads to certain reflex reactions or to general bodily activity has a connection with its intensity and duration. Nearly every writer agrees that sharp or quick sounds cause responsive blinking, starting, circulatory and respiratory changes, and sometimes crying during the first few days of life. Some children listen to voice sounds before the tenth day (Bryan,[142] Koffka[470]). (Recall the fact of early maturing of the tympanic membrane and other structures in the ear, p. 179.) Conditioned responses to auditory stimuli in the first few weeks have been reported (Marquis[555] and Wenger[887]). Several writers mention instances of response to piano notes, bells, and the human voice between the second and fourth months.

Gesell[285] says that an adaptive motor response to the sound of a voice or ringing of a bell which is out of visual range began in most children whom he studied by four months and was present in the form of definite and prompt turning of the head in 75 per cent of the infants at least by six months. Cooing or laughing on hearing music began to develop for many at six months and was present in 75 per cent of the children at twelve months. Several writers report turning of the head to the sound of the voice from two to four weeks before turning to the sound of a bell. The "modal age" for turning the head at the sound of a bell is five months according to Bayley[80] and "onset age" is two months according to Bühler.[144] Bayley[80] gives credit in her scale for turning the head at the sound of a bell at five months. Bühler[144] gives credit at two months if the child turns his head when a rattle is shaken a foot and a half away and out of sight. When the sound is made, eyes remain ahead at this age, but at three months credit is given if "the eyes are directed searchingly to all sides."

---

* References concerning the deaf and hard of hearing child are Templin[831] and Fiedler.[255]

Use of the Sense of Sight.* The sense of sight is so imperfect at birth that reactions to light seem to be the only sight reaction observed by any of the writers on the subject (Pratt[670]). Clear sensations of sight depend not only on adequate development of the nerve endings and nerve centers for vision (p. 179), but also on two sets of muscular adjustments. One set is necessary to turn the eyeballs (convergence); the other set controls the lens within the eyeballs (accommodation). Sight perception, or learning to associate meaning with things seen, depends on the development of motor skills prerequisite to accurate use of the eyes.

These skills of accommodation and convergence have been fairly well mastered in most infants by three months of age. Ling[514] studied the development of sustained visual (eye) fixation in infants varying in age from seven minutes to twenty-four weeks, and found that the ability to fixate the eyes for brief, unsustained periods was present a few hours after birth. This is, however, the involuntary, almost phototropic reaction of the eye to light and cannot be said to be fixation in the voluntary, or controlled, sense. This early, immature stage of fixation, Ling found, reached its peak around four or five weeks of age. "Onset age" of fixation of this kind is probably very near birth, when the eye is first introduced to light, whereas "modal age" of fixation is near the end of the first postnatal month.

Voluntary fixation is a later stage of development. The Morgans[597] have given us one of the most careful studies of this type of fixation. They found the primitive, immature type of fixation in 75 per cent of babies at five to ten days of age, and in 100 per cent of babies at fifty days. The next stage of fixation described by them is that of following an object which moves horizontally from side to side. In their study most infants could do this at fifty days and could follow a vertically moving object at fifty-five days. Following an object in a circle was accomplished by most babies only at seventy-five days or about two and one-half months. This is shown in Figure 3 in Chapter 1. The perfection of the use of the eyes in sight moves forward rapidly from this time and becomes almost as perfect as the adult level of seeing at about two years of age (Shirley[753]). Despite this very good ability to control the eyes at three months, the learning remains unstable for some time. It is not at all unusual to see children of several months of age

* References concerning the blind child are in Jensen[420] and in Norris, Spaulding, and Brodie.[635]

momentarily lose control of the eyes so that they appear for an instant to be cross-eyed. Persistent crossing of the eyes should, however, be reported to the doctor.

Shirley[753] analyzed the over-all development of vision in four maturity stages. At first vague reactions to a moving light or bright object lead to focusing on persons and objects. For three months the baby's attention is largely confined to the faces and hands of those about him, to such toys as are dangled before him or put into his crib, and to his own fingers. The second stage begins when the baby commences to sit up, when his visual range widens to include the whole room. The third stage includes fixation of attention on the remote and the minute. In the fourth stage the baby can see the shadowy, the obscure, the transparent and pictured images.

Bühler[144] places at five months the ability to look searchingly in the direction in which the child has dropped a toy. Gesell,[285] however, found that less than half of his babies did this at six months, but that at nine months all of them did so. Bayley[80] places turning the head to look for a fallen spoon at seven months and definite looking for it at nine months.

Use of Kinesthetic Sensitivity. Knowledge of the development of the "muscle sense" which provides information on the position and movement of the body parts is slight. Evidence is available which indicates its prenatal presence (Carmichael[156]). In the newborn, certain head and postural responses are elicited by the movement of the body as a whole or in part (McGraw,[537] Shirley[753]). Pratt,[670] in considering static and kinesthetic stimuli, refers to the beginnings of responses in the newborn which will lead to upright postures and walking.

Application of Sensory Judgment

Much human behavior is made up of reactions to objects in the environment and is dependent for efficiency upon accurate judgment of the size of these objects, their shape, location with reference to the observer, their rate and direction of motion, and so on. Contrary to common belief, these judgments are not innate; they are learned in every detail as is evident when the pattern of that learning is followed.

Having ability to use his eyes and ears and other sense organs, the baby learns to interpret the things he sees and hears; he learns the meaning of tastes and touches and pressures. He does this by blending experience of things seen, heard, tasted, touched and smelled. Thus, repeated sights and sounds and other sensory experiences become associated with familiar objects. Furthermore, as he proceeds from one stage of development to another, the child's cognition is a result of not only immediate reactions to cues but also of associations previously perceived, although not part of the present external situation. This suggests the importance of perceptions in the child's thinking as he grows older. Piaget's discussion of sensorimotor or practical intelligence in the first two years of development refers to the young infant's "assimilating the external environment to his own activity."* In the second phase the "increasing coherence of the schemata thus parallels the formation of a world of objects and spatial relationships; in short, the elaboration of a solid and permanent universe."† "When sensorimotor intelligence has sufficiently elaborated understanding to make language and reflective thought possible, the universe is . . . formed into a structure at once substantial and spatial, causal and temporal."‡ The child is then less self centered. This connection of the development of sensory perception and judgment with a change in the concept of self is emphasized today in connection with a number of theories of development (Piaget,[660] Jersild,[421] Escalona,[247] Russell[715]).§

At four months the child is seeing many things, is listening and is grasping and touching objects that come within reach. He looks, touches and listens, associating all the results of stimulation to his senses. It is these learnings in sense perceptions and judgments, along with the achievement of control over his own body, mastery of language, expression and control of emotion and reactions to people, which occupy the waking time of children from the time they are born.

Much Learning Takes Place by Associating One Sensory Experience with Another.   Once the child has learned to use his eyes, his ears, his tongue, his nose and his fingers, he is placed in possession of the means of exploring everything that comes within his immediate environment. An infant several weeks old will occasionally stop all his other activity to listen intently for some sound that has caught his attention. At three months he will lie in his cradle exploring the surrounding scene with

* Piaget[660] (p. xi).
† Piaget[660] (p. xii).
‡ Piaget[660] (p. xiii).
§ For additional descriptions of the young child, or "toddler," as he begins to walk and to perceive more accurately, thus broadening his horizons, see Bühler,[143] Piaget,[660] and Woodcock.[922]

his eyes, listening with absorption to chance sounds, and turning his head to "see" as well as to hear the sound.

Development of meanings through use of his sense organs is illustrated in response of an infant, about six months old, to a rattle. He seizes a rattle and waves it about, following it with his eyes, and turning to listen; he smells it; he puts it in his mouth, tasting and touching it; he explores it with every sense at his command. And from this he learns about rattles, how big they are, their shape, how hard, how heavy, how near, and what kind of noise they make. More than that, he is associating all of these things together, so that eventually the sound of the rattle reminds him of the proper size, shape, weight and use of that object. In this way, the various experiences obtained through one sense are identified with the proper equivalents in other sense realms. Each object thus acquires for the baby a variety of meanings, in terms of which he learns to recognize what to expect from it and what he can do with it.

Important beginnings in sense perceptions and judgments are achieved in infancy. The fullness and speed with which the sense perceptions and judgments are developed and the skill and efficiency with which the infant comes to understand, use and control his environment depends not only on inner maturation, but also on the richness of his environment and the freedom he is allowed in exploring it. He cannot learn what he has not experienced.

Learning Names for Sensations and Perceptions. The development of associations and meanings proceeds rapidly as the child leaves infancy, especially as he acquires the ability to walk, run and climb, and thus widen his horizon. In the course of his growth in language the child is achieving names for the various qualities of objects now being experienced by the senses. As stated in the discussion of language growth, the period from eighteen to thirty-six months is one of rapid increase in vocabulary. This association of name with sense quality is only part of the general interest in associating the proper name with every object and experience. We must not, however, conclude that the ability to sense the quality (hardness, roughness, heaviness and the like) depends on ability to apply the right language name. Children usually learn to detect and differentiate such qualities accurately before they can name them, and, conversely, they often learn the names "big," "hard," "red" and "heavy," before they can apply them accurately to the proper sense experience.

Acquaintance with His Own Body. Perception of the extent and contour of his own body has occupied the child for some months before he is a year old and seems to be fairly clear to him by the time he is three years old. He lies in his cradle when he is four or five months old, touching the fingers of one hand against those of the other, enjoying the sensation he gets. By seven or eight months he has learned to get his toes into his mouth, but he still has to learn that when he bites those toes he gives himself a sensation because the feet belong to him. Sometimes he bites a finger or a toe, then bites a rattle, learning that toes and fingers are part of himself whereas rattles are not. Before he is a year old he has begun conscious exploration of his own body, studying its extent and exploring its contour. He pats his own head, fingers his own ears, and rubs his own stomach. Not infrequently he discovers that some parts of his body give one type of sensation, some parts another. He may discover at a year or at eighteen months, sometimes at two or even at three years, that patting or rubbing the genital organs produces a particularly pleasing sensation, and he will return to the exploration of this part of his body even more often than to his play with ears or toes.

Our attitude toward this activity may determine in a large measure how often he returns and to what extent his passing interest will become fixed as a habit. If we become anxious, conveying to him that he has discovered a particularly significant type of behavior, he will reflect our own attitude of importance toward it, will return to it more often and give it more attention than he otherwise would. If, on the other hand, we regard the behavior as part of the general exploratory behavior characteristic of the ages from six months to five years, he will more than likely so regard it and will soon forget it as his interest shifts to the next natural activity. We may, of course, treat the behavior like other persistent behavior such as pulling at his ears constantly or playing with the ink bottle persistently, and we may shift his attention by giving the hands more entertaining things to do. Anything we do, however, to fix his attention on the behavior or to attach vivid significance to it serves only to deepen the impression and to defeat the end we have in view of enabling him to proceed easily to other activities.

Learning to Understand Sounds. The development of perceptions of sound is rapid from eighteen months to three years of age. The child during this period learns to identify countless sounds that have not heretofore held meaning for him. He indicates his ability to identify by sound the difference between bird calls and squirrel noises, between Daddy's voice and Mr. Smith's voice, the special tone which identifies Daddy's automobile horn and so on. Doubtless his growth in the language field makes learning of this kind seem more sudden than it really is. His vocabulary increases rapidly at this time, so that he may appear to be learning for the first time meanings which he has learned before but can only now express. In any case, he seems to be acquiring understanding of the sound world about him at a spectacular rate.

The extent of the child's sound discrimination is illustrated by an example from Templin's study of speech development. "In the preschool test, pairs of pictures which were familiar to the children and which were similar in pronunciation except for single sound elements were presented. An example of an item is a picture of a 'box' and some 'blocks' presented on a single card and the child is then asked to point to whichever one the experimenter says. . . . While both motor and perceptual skills are involved in the production of most sounds, the importance of the perceptual skill probably is increased when the sound is uttered in the proper position in a standard word."*

The child's interest in and ability with music also increase rapidly at this age. Although individual children differ tremendously in capacity to enjoy and to respond to music, most children of three years have learned to recognize a few simple tunes, can beat a simple rhythm, can detect the difference between high notes and low ones, between slow and rapid rhythms, and between loud and soft intensities in music.†

Learning to Judge Size of Objects.‡   The extent of the child's size discrimination is illustrated by measures used in some of the studies of learning of preschool children. For example, in one study of problem solving (Kuenne[483]) most of the children with a mental age of three years learned to select the smaller of a pair of squares, whose areas were 37.8 and 68.0 square inches and 21.0 and 37.8 square inches, in order to find a toy underneath. (The influence of the verbalization of the discrimination needed to solve the problem will be considered in the section on reasoning ability.)

Perception of size is becoming much more accurate from eighteen

* Templin[830] (p. 281).
† Response to music is discussed further on pages 381-383.
‡ Detail concerning chronological ages at which particular perceptions of size, shape, color and numbers usually develop, is available in the standardization data of intelligence tests (Stutsman,[822] Terman[833]).

months to three years of age, but is still inaccurate enough to prove difficult to the child. For children from one to five years old Madame Montessori,[595] as early as 1912, appreciated the interest of young children in sense perceptions and designed many types of equipment especially adapted for this purpose. She found them responsive to equipment for training perception of size: sets of cylinders varying in diameter but not in depth, or in depth but not in diameter, and one set which varies in both dimensions; a set of blocks which, arranged in graded size, builds a broad stair; and another set which, piled in order of size, builds a pyramid. Nests of hollow cubes, varying in size so that each may be fitted inside the next larger one, appeal to two-year-old children. Modifications of these toys can now be found in toy departments in most department stores. The child may learn through formal teaching with such equipment, but children were learning judgment of size, shape, weight, and the like centuries before it occurred to anyone to teach them formally. We must be careful to avoid the error of concluding that these fundamental learnings would not take place without formal teaching. Our object is to give the child opportunities to handle many objects in order to increase his familiarity with the properties of size, shape, weight, texture, and so on.

This process of self teaching also occurs in the play yard. While riding his tricycle, the two-year-old child learns to judge the width and length of the vehicle in proportion to the width of an opening through which he wishes to take it. Given sufficient practice he can, before he is three years old, become expert enough to avoid scratching the vehicle. Some months after he has learned fairly accurate judgments of the size of most objects the child may be seen trying to sit on a tiny doll's chair and looking surprised when it fails to support him. Since he sees himself least and has less opportunity to judge his own size in relation to other things, he can still be seen making mistakes in judgment of his own size even when he is well past his fourth birthday. One very intelligent child of five looked surprised when he failed to step over a three-foot chicken wire fence with the easy gesture that had carried his father over it.

Perceptions of Shape. Judgments of shape are progressing rapidly during the ages from two to five. An eighteen-month-old child can discriminate between pictures of familiar animals, and he will say "bow-wow" when he sees the picture of a dog or crow on seeing the picture of a rooster. He recognizes these pictures almost as readily up side down as right side up. The two-year-old child is just beginning to appreciate the difference between a triangular, a circular and a square block if all are about the same size. If allowed to play with pans in the kitchen, he may try to make a triangular cover fit a round pan, or a square pan fit inside a round one.

In this connection we must remember once more not to confuse the child's ability to name "square," "round" or "oblong" with his ability actually to see and appreciate the differences in contour which these terms represent. To perceive shape is one thing; to name it is quite a different thing. We are concerned now with the perceiving, with providing numerous "shape" experiences so that the child may learn to recognize everyday objects by their shapes as well as by their sizes, colors, weights, and so on.

Learning about Colors.   Color perception occupies an important place in the child's interest at an early age. Staples,[797] in a careful study of color recognition, was sure that colors are experienced as different from grays by fifteen months. Most authors agree that colors as well as brightness are recognized at about thirty months of age. This does not mean that children name colors at this age without a great deal of coaching; it means, rather, that they have learned to discriminate between colors so that they can match saturated colors accurately. The naming of the primary colors (red, yellow, blue and green) is just beginning at two years. Most children can name them accurately at around four years of age. Experiments on learned response, such as that to hue and brightness, suggest discrimination of slight cue difference (Spiker[788, 789]).

There have been several studies of the color preferences of infants and of school-age children. Staples found red the most effective color stimulus with preschool children, yellow being next, then blue and last, green. Munroe[608] studied 1612 paintings obtained from 138 children ranging in age from two years to four years eleven months. She found that the two-year-old children showed a marked preference for yellow. The three- and four-year-old children preferred red, the four-year-olds preferring it less markedly than the three-year-olds. These studies make it appear that infants prefer red or yellow, and that the preference shifts with increasing age to blue. Recent studies attempt to relate color preference to feelings of the individual child (Alschuler and Hattwick[16]).

Color naming, as we have said, seems a different matter from color discrimination and color preference. Munroe found that preschool children named blue with the highest percentage of accuracy, red is a close second, and green and yellow follow in order. The most frequently used color name, regardless of correct application, was blue.

Learning to Judge Weight. Accurate perception of weight depends on judgment of size and knowledge of the weight of various materials. Young children often find confusion because weight varies with the material of which the object is composed as well as with the size of the object. For example, at Hallowe'en time one group of three- and four-year-old children, having played for a day with a papier-mâché pumpkin which closely resembled a real one, were presented with a real pumpkin. One of the children reached out his hands to accept the gift, but made a muscular adjustment sufficient to hold only the paper pumpkin with which he had played the day before. This was, of course, insufficient to sustain the weight of the real pumpkin, which he dropped. All of the children seemed as surprised as he when they came to lift the real pumpkin, and asked many questions about the reasons for the difference in weight between that and the one they had played with the day before. Even at four years of age they had not yet learned enough about judgment of weight to avoid such an incident.

Two-year-old children are faced many times a day with situations as puzzling as this. They reach to pick up a pail with the same free gesture they have seen an adult use, and are astonished that they cannot lift it. They learn about how much muscular pull is necessary to lift a pail of sand and make the same sort of muscular adjustment to lift a rubber ball of the same size. It is not at all unusual to see a two-year-old child upset himself because he has prepared to lift a heavy object, only to find himself lifting a light one. Often he attempts to lift things he cannot move at all. One day he seems to have discovered that big things are the heavy ones and little things are light, only to find that some big thing upsets him because it is light and some little thing cannot be moved, no matter how hard he tugs at it.

Learning To Judge Distance. Some of the more complex perceptions are being built during the three- to five-year-old period, including particularly the perception of distance for which the visual acuity is present (Updegraff[864]). Reviewing the criteria by which distance is judged helps our understanding of the child's problem. An object is judged to be near or far depending on apparent size, clearness of outline, vividness of color, number of intervening objects, accommodatory and convergent strains on the eyes. A three-month-old baby reaches for a proffered toy, but his arm movements and his judgment of distance are not yet coordinated so he misses it. He has to make several attempts before his hand closes over the coveted object. An infant, however, soon learns accurate judgment of shorter distances, but at a year he still reaches eagerly for the moon, and seems unable to understand why it cannot be obtained. At three years he sometimes forgets that distance diminishes apparent size, so that he comments on "the baby automobile" which he sees at some distance. But from three to five years he makes such mistakes less and less frequently.

Concepts of distance and of space seem to be related. Language responses concerning space have been studied by Ames and Learned.[26] They describe the one-year-old as using gestures or wriggles for *up* and *down,* and the two-year-old as using such words as *up stairs, up high.* At thirty months more exactness of location is indicated by *way up, in here, in there, far,* and *far away. Next to, under,* and *between* are reported for the forty-two-month-old child. Again, distinction between the perception and the use of words to describe it must be made. Appearance of words such as these reveals interest in the perceptions.

Learning about Numbers.   Interest in numbers, although evident before three years of age, does not occupy the time and attention that it does after three. Even at nine months the baby has an awareness of "two-ness" in contrast to "one-ness," since he can put two objects together in relation to each other and prefers two clothespins to one as playthings (Gesell[291]). Children of eighteen months often lay blocks or beads out in rows of two or three. We cannot be sure whether this ability is appreciation of similarity of size and shape of groups of two or three units to other like groups, or whether it is ability to appreciate that each group is made up of one and one or of one and one and one. Children of two can often be heard counting "one and another," or "one and one" or, sometimes, "one, two." After two years interest in language is at a peak so that one can readily teach a two-year-old child to recite the cardinal numbers up to eight or ten, or, with sufficient coaching, up to nineteen or twenty. This sort of recitation, however, belongs to the category of "parlor tricks," since children of two or even of three years usually have little understanding of the meaning of number beyond "one," "two," possibly "three," and "lots." Although they can be taught to recite numbers "parrot fashion" they do not usually, without excessive coaching, actually count a series of more than four objects until they are nearly four years old mentally, or of thirteen objects until they are nearly six mentally.[833]

Learning To Judge Time Intervals. Perception of time develops very slowly and is expressed almost invariably through language, so that its actual progress is difficult to measure. Sources of confusion for the child come from situations such as the following: A mother takes her child to call on one of her friends for "half an hour." She is interested and time flies; he is bored and time drags. On another day, the child goes out to play for "half an hour," and is called to come inside after what seems almost no time at all. "Half an hour" is indeed a variable quantity to a young child who has not yet learned to judge it with the objective aid of a clock. By the time he is four, however, he has learned that "a few minutes" means less than "an hour" or "several hours," although he still seems unreasonable when he is told that "we won't be going to town for a long time—not for several hours," but returns every half hour or so to ask, "Isn't it time to go yet?" When he is two there seems no other way of explaining "when Daddy will be home" than to tell him that it will be "after you've had your lunch and have had your nap and have played a long time"; but at four years "afternoon" means after lunch, and "late this afternoon" means a long time after lunch, in fact, just before dinner. At four he will understand when we tell him that "Daddy will be home late this afternoon." Questions like "When is noon?" "How long is half an hour?" "When is tomorrow?" are familiar on the lips of four-year-old children. "Yesterday," "tomorrow," "next week" still puzzle the four-year-old. It seems probable that such complex time concepts as "last spring," "day before yesterday," "a month ago" and especially "New Year's Eve" are quite unintelligible even to six-year-old children.

Spontaneous verbalizations as well as responses to questions were considered by Ames[23] in studying the young child's development of the sense of time. In spontaneous verbalizations she found words dealing with the present appearing first, then those indicating the future, and later those indicating the past. Expression of temporal order occurred as early as thirty months, but words implying duration did not appear as a rule until thirty-six months.

DALLYING DUE LARGELY TO INABILITY TO APPRECIATE TIME INTERVALS. Inability to appreciate time units produces the characteristic problem during preschool years of dallying. Sitting indefinitely before distasteful foods and occupying endless periods of time at dressing or picking up toys, or continuing to play instead of getting ready for the next event, are responses that may cause a great deal of annoyance. The particular need of the dallying child is an appreciation that time passes, that the longer he spends in the performance of routine duties the less time he has for play or that when it is time to depart he may not be ready. Sand in an hour glass or the hands of the clock may provide interest and make clear the fact that dallying lengthens the time spent on routine and thus automatically shortens the time for uninterrupted play. Sometimes the sequence of events may clarify the fact that time passes. For example, the child who plays out of doors for a long time after being reminded that dinner will be ready soon, may discover there is no time for his father to read to him before the evening meal begins. In other situations, study of what the child goes to (the next event of his day) may provide reasons for his being especially slow. With regard to dressing and putting away toys, interest in companionship or sociability may be a key to his slowness in a situation for which he has the motor skill.

Sensory Experience Important Foundation for Other Aspects of Intellectual Growth.   Details in the preceding pages describing the child's development of sensory judgment, and the later section on the developmental-dynamic aspects of various phases of intellectual development have implications for adults in their associations with children. One implication concerns *recognition of the importance of free play.* The boy in Figure 64 is learning about a number of realities. Feeling free to manipulate materials, to experiment with them, unhurried, and with a minimum of guidance, the child adds meanings which make his perceptions more complete. He is learning through his play, as he mixes sand and water, completes a puzzle without assistance, or fits together two blocks to make their length equal to that of one longer block. Furthermore, these sensory experiences and perceptions provide facts to be used in reasoning, ideas to be expressed in language.

Realization of the extent to which the child learns through his senses leads the adult to recognize the importance of *providing a variety of experiences which are real instead of vicarious* (see Figure 64). Seeing and hearing a steam shovel at work, touching a fluffy chicken, tasting carrots for which the seeds were planted, smelling vanilla that is put into a pudding, are experiences which stories and pictures may supplement but for which they are not a substitute. Values in experience with "the real thing" are suggested by the following quotations. A city child of school age and his teacher were getting materials ready to take to school for use in the third grade. A younger brother and sister and neighborhood children of preschool age looked at the "exhibit" of kernels of wheat, wheat plants that were growing, and flour.

Unwrapping the jar of wheat kernels,
    Peter asked, "What is that?"
    Miss O'Dell: "That's wheat."
    Peter: "Kinda like corn."
    Billy: "For wheaties."
Looking at the flour,
    Connie said, "Flour goes in cakes in the oven."
    Miss O'Dell: "What else can we make from flour?"
    Connie: "Bread."
    Miss O'Dell: "When we put bread in the oven, what happens?"
    John: "We make toast."
Looking at the wheat plants growing,
    Jack: "Some plants take a long time to sprout. My bean plants didn't come up for a long time."

Many possibilities for meaningful experience are evident to the adult who gives thought to children's responses such as these. Cues concern

Figure 64. Sense of touch, sense of sight, and muscular adjustment are used as this child perceives texture, form, color and weight of sand and water.

the importance of providing opportunities for preschool children to have a part in activities such as planting seeds, caring for plants, helping to bake bread or cake. In the course of these activities, the children quoted would discover many facts. The older child, of school age, was at another stage of development. His "exhibit" had meaning for him but was less appropriate than other experiences for the young children.

Development of Language

What Language Is.   Language is generally understood to include any and all means of expressing feeling and thought: facial expression and gesture, as well as spoken and written words.* Many writers consider that the child's language development begins at birth. Philosophers like Kant have suggested that the birth cry expresses "wrath at the catastrophe of birth." Psychologists would deny that the newborn baby has enough development to express a particular emotion. Physiologists, however, attribute to even the earliest vocalizations a function in the beginning of developing mechanical control over the vocal apparatus.

Speaking consists of a complex muscular coordination which involves voluntary muscular actions of the abdominal wall, the thorax, larynx, soft palate, and tongue and lips, and it is performed without conscious thought. Voice sounds are emitted from the mouth because a regulated expiration of breath forces air past the vocal cords, which vibrate variously in response, on through a passage which can be modified to produce the exact sound desired.[453] From the moment of birth the waking hours of the infant are occupied with vocal activities as well as with activity of the arms and legs. In the sense that the skills of walking can be said to develop from apparently instinctive beginnings in locomotion displayed in random muscular activity, so the skills of talking can be said to develop from the apparently instinctive beginnings in vocalization displayed in vocal sounds.

Concepts and theories of language development refer to stages and to processes through which various forms of language are achieved. Inherent orderliness is evident in the *vowel and consonant usage* of the infant and child in the first two and one-half years of life (Irwin[398]), and in the sequences in articulation, sentence structure and functions of the speech of children as they grow older (McCarthy,[528] Piaget,[661]

* Bibliographies concerning language development are in Dawe,[194] Goodenough[303] and McCarthy.[527, 528] McCarthy[528] reviews research on language.

Templin[830]). Changes in early infancy "seem to harmonize . . . with the theory of motor development proceeding from mass activity through control of gross muscles to the finer muscular coordinations."* Later changes involve selection of sounds to be repeated. "The hearing of the adult word can merely stimulate the child to the utterance of his *own* babbling sounds and . . . from this the child may become trained to respond with a particular sound to a particular heard sound."† Imitation such as this, seems related to the closeness of the association between the child and the adult (the affective or feeling quality). Because of the closeness of the association, the child may identify himself with and want to be like the adult. Or, in terms of learning theory, "initially neutral sounds, by virtue of their occurrence in temporal contiguity with primary reinforcements, have acquired secondary reinforcing properties. . . . Words or other human sounds are first made by infants, it seems, because the sounds have been associated with relief and other satisfactions and, as a result, have themselves come to sound good. . . . Human infants . . . in the course of random activities . . . will eventually make sounds somewhat similar to those which have already acquired pleasant connotations and will . . . have a special incentive for trying to repeat and refine these sounds. Soon, however, the infant discovers that the making of these sounds can be used not only to comfort, reassure, and satisfy himself directly but also to interest, satisfy and control mother, father and others."‡

Comprehending words as well as *saying words* are parts of the child's language development. In the development of comprehension "the child responds affectively both to the intonational pattern of what he hears and to the situation in which he hears it. And at this very same time he hears a phonetic pattern. . . . When at last the phonetic pattern acquires dominance so that irrespective of the intonational pattern it evokes the appropriate response from the child, we say that he has understood the conventional word."§

As the child becomes more able to speak‖ and to comprehend that which is complex, the *variety of functions* of language increases. This includes expression of feelings, wants, desires, information and thoughts.

---

* McCarthy[528] (p. 512).
† Lewis[511] (p. 80).
‡ Mowrer[603] (pp. 264-265).
§ Lewis[511] (p. 122).
‖ For further details on the child's learning to talk see Van Riper[868] (pp. 92-129).

Word functioning in thinking (i.e., in use of symbols instead of actual objects and situations) appears fairly late. This use of language in thought processes has egocentric and social functions. In egocentric speech, according to Piaget, the child "does not bother to know to whom he is speaking nor whether he is being listened to. He talks either for himself or for the pleasure of associating anyone who happens to be there with the activity of the moment . . . He does not attempt to place himself at the point of view of his hearer."* In socialized speech the child addresses his hearer, considers his point of view, tries to influence him or actually exchange ideas with him.

Early Stages of Speech. Within the first month or so mothers usually feel that they can interpret the nature of the child's crying. Sounds can express emotional states. They are, in fact, to be thought of as part of a total bodily reaction elicited in exciting or strenuous situations. Variations occur in an individual's voice quality and intensity under different circumstances. It is to be expected, then, that early in the development of language in the individual baby the emotional tone of the cry, the quality and intensity of the voice, indicate something of his inner needs and feelings. The actual control of muscles which push air over the voice mechanism and the control of the vocal apparatus which produces crying are present at birth. In the sense that the ability to cry at all is the more mature stage of many complex coordinations, even newborns are mature.

The variations of crying which express needs and emotions, however, seem to develop only after a month or so of life. Gesell[291] says that at about eight weeks the hunger cry which has until that time been universal in infants now tends to diminish in intensity and frequency. The child begins to substitute fussing for crying, and he is quiet for longer periods of time when he is awake because he is becoming interested in various forms of nonfeeding behavior. During the first six weeks of life the baby cries not only because of hunger but also when his diaper is wet or soiled, sometimes even crying out in his sleep for this reason.

In the vocalization of infants, certain sequences or patterns of development occur (Irwin[396, 397]). Irwin and Chen[399] report great expansion in the mastery of sounds during the first six months of life. Only about half of the vowels and very few of the consonants are present in the

* Piaget[661] (p. 9).

first month of life. During the second quarter of the first year of life, infants produce most of the vowel elements and about half of the consonant elements. In newborns there is a deficit of back vowels and an absence of consonants formed by the forward mouth parts; æ is the most frequent vowel sound (Irwin[398]).

Little active participation of the tongue and mouth muscles is required. Among the earliest noncrying sounds, heard during the first month or two, are "grunts, gurgles, burbles, or sighs," which are comfort vocalizations (Van Riper[869]). Many but not all of the vowel and consonant sounds and sound combinations have been mastered by normally maturing infants by one and one-half years (Irwin[398]). In this stage of random articulation or babble stage of language development the basis for later speech is laid.

These random sounds become organized vocal habits, depending on whether or not they produce satisfying results for the child and on the pattern or model of language the child hears around him.

By the age of nine to twelve months the random and meaningless character of the babblings seems to become softened into rhythm somewhat similar to the rhythm of flowing speech, and it closely resembles the rhythm of whatever speech the child hears. It is not unusual to hear a child of ten or twelve months cooing or jabbering to himself with a rhythm which sounds like a free-flowing conversation. Most parents have an impulse to talk to their children while bathing or tending them. This parental impulse provides the child not only with a model for rhythm during early infancy, but with a model for vocabulary as his development progresses.

Most children have developed a sufficiently discriminating reaction to language to permit recognition of their own names by the time they are six or eight months old, and by the time they are eight or nine months old they understand either the word "no" or the tone in which it is spoken when it is used to forbid action. Just how this attachment of meaning to definite words occurs in the brain is not yet known.[453]

Development of Passive Vocabulary. The process of attaching meaning to the sounds heard, leads the child to the understanding of words spoken to him. Thus he develops a *passive* or understanding *vocabulary*. As we have seen, most infants recognize their own names (or the much more frequently used word "baby") by the time they are six or eight months old. They usually come to understand that "no" means "stop what you are doing" by eight or nine months. From this stage on, passive vocabulary develops rapidly, the speed of its development depending on maturation and also, to an important degree, on how much language the child hears. By twelve to fifteen months most children understand a fairly wide assortment of simple concrete or action words like "ball," "dinner," "drink" and "bye-bye." Within two or three months of this stage they understand and react to simple sentences like "Where is baby's ball?" "Give mother the spoon," "Want to go bye-bye?" In the earlier stage the response to "Give mother the spoon," is an undifferentiated reaction to the single word "mother," or perhaps "spoon." The baby might have looked at his mother, held out his arms to her or leaned forward expectantly with his mouth open for food. In the later stage he understands the whole sentence and picks up the spoon to hand it to his mother.

He can be given a good deal of help at this stage if we speak slowly, clearly, and very simply to him, providing him with plenty of language to listen to and fitting the word or phrase to the appropriate object or action. For example, when dressing him we may speak of "shoes," "dress" and "socks" as each is used. In feeding him we may refer to "spoon," "milk" and "orange juice," thus associating the right sound with its appropriate object. If we say, "Throw the ball," as he throws it or "No," as we draw his hand away from a forbidden object, we help him to associate certain sounds with their appropriate action. Practice with "Where is baby's nose?" "Cover up your dollie," and "Show mother the book," provides the child with a pleasant game—unless, of course, it is overdone—and gradually increases his understanding or passive vocabulary which he is soon to put into active use. Children react to tones of voice at this stage of language learning. Since the child is not yet able to clearly differentiate separate words and sentences to any great extent, he reacts to much of what is said to him largely by implication from the tone of voice used.

The child understands the simple, concrete words first as he learns to speak them first. He understands simple action phrases and sentences before he can comprehend and react to more complex sentences. Prepositions, and phrases of relationship, like "in," "on," "under," "on top of" follow later. Although children of two years demonstrate that they can understand a wealth of words and phrases and sentences of action and concrete situations, in one study they understood and reacted correctly to an average of only three prepositions (Gesell[285]). By three to four years, however, most children understand the basic vocabulary of their native language, although their intellectual capacity to handle complex thoughts is still very limited (see Development of Reasoning, pp. 360 ff.). They can seem "snowed under" with too much talking. **Development of Active Vocabulary.*** At about one year, children have already a fairly wide active vocabulary of gestures and facial expressions, but their active vocabulary of spoken words is seldom more than two or three such simple words as "ma-ma," "da-da," or "bye-bye." Although passive vocabulary seems to develop quite rapidly from a year of age on, active vocabulary does not move forward as long as the child is using his energy in the achievement of upright locomotion. Most children are deeply absorbed in the achievement of the stepping and independent walking stages of locomotion between twelve and eighteen or twenty months of chronological age. Their acquisition of active vocabulary is ordinarily slow at this time. Shirley[753] has reported that the children studied by her showed a lull in vocabulary increase during the learning of each new motor skill. Hull and Hull[375] report a slowing of vocabulary learning during the period when toilet reliability is being established. This slowing down in the acquisition of active vocabulary occurs particularly in boys. There are distinct sex differences in the rate of acquisition of active vocabulary, girls acquiring speech sooner than boys. McCarthy,[528] in reviewing data in which girls proceed more rapidly than boys in a number of phases of linguistic development, refers to the sex difference as present but small.

Some girls, and a few boys, have from 10 to 100 words in the active vocabulary at around eighteen months of age. The average for children in a number of different studies is about five words. Some children, more boys than girls, do not have as many as five words in their active vocabularies until they are two or two and one-half years of age. When upright locomotion is reasonably well under control, the active vocabulary spurts forward.† Gesell[285] expresses this rapid growth before five years of age: "Indeed within his limits, he (the child) becomes an entertaining raconteur, whereas four years earlier he was unable to articulate a single word."‡ The rate of acquisition is around 500 to 600 words per year (Smith[775]) and the increase continues usually

---

* For details from a number of studies of language development, see Tables 1 through 10 in McCarthy[528] (pp. 500-575).

† Studies of increase in vocabulary with age are reported by Bayley,[85] Gesell,[285] McCarthy,[527] and Smith.[775]

‡ Gesell[285] (p. 221).

until well into adolescence in our society in which children go to school. Unless the child continues to have exposure to vocabularies larger than his own, however, his vocabulary increases will cease. Even with good or superior general intelligence, he does not learn the meaning of words which he never hears or reads.

One stage of language acquisition, which has been recognized by most authors, but carefully studied as yet by only a few, occurs when the child is first acquiring active words at a rapid rate. At this stage he is likely to modify his pronunciation of words to fit his own individual pattern of vocalization. In this stage the child, having acquired the new word, often with correct pronunciation in the first few repetitions of it, proceeds to distort the pronunciation while still using it correctly. The distortion takes a characteristic form which fits into the child's whole pattern of vocalization at the time. Words containing phonetic elements difficult for the child are modified to make for easy vocalization. In this so-called "baby talk" distortions may sound "cute," and tempt adults to talk to the child using the same distortions. This robs the child of the correct model for learning and unnecessarily delays his emergence from this stage of language learning.

In the usual course of events children around this stage of language learning discover that everything has a name. When this happens, they plague adults with the eternal query, "What's that?" Some children discover this to be a means of getting attention and rather "overwork" the situation, but reasonable answers to these queries usually serve to extend active vocabulary at a rapid rate. Often, given the answer, the child repeats the word himself, thus giving himself practice with it.

This echoing of the adult sometimes contributes to the child's natural confusion about pronouns at this stage. He hears himself referred to as "baby," or as "John." He echoes by referring to himself, "Baby wants a drink," or "John wants to go bye-bye." He soon corrects this, however, so that we should spare him the strain of nagging him constantly with the corrected form: "No, you mean, *I* want a drink." Confusion between such pronouns as "me" and "I," "him," "her," "his" and "hers" is natural at this stage of language development. Among the first words to be acquired, verbs, adjectives, and adverbs appear correctly, but articles, conjunctions, the more advanced forms of adverbs and the correct use of pronouns and prepositions appear late in the development of speech forms. Some children of three to five years still fail to use many prepositions accurately.

When any new form is acquired, however, it is usually practiced vigorously, as is any new learning in any area. Since language is very much in the making during the preschool years when increasingly new forms of language learning take place, there is much practice by most children. The impression most people have of preschool children as being talkative and on the move physically is an accurate one. They may use as many as 11,000 to 12,000 words in a day at three years of age and around 15,000 in a day at four years. In the studies in which these figures were established,* the three-year-olds used 37 per cent of their total vocabulary in one day, and the four-year-olds used 23 per cent. Few older children or adults use any such proportion of their total potential vocabularies, even in a period of weeks or months.

Articulation.   In referring to articulation, Van Riper[869] says:

"Many of the errors made by little children are due to their perceiving words as lumps of sound. They often omit the sounds that are of low intensity. They say 'ike' for 'like,' 'way' for 'away'; they omit the final *s* sounds from plural words; they may even omit a whole syllable if it is unstressed in the word. . . .
"The little child tends to use the sounds he knows best, the *w* instead of the unfamiliar *r,* the *t* instead of the *c.* . . ."

Later

"They find great interest in comparing and contrasting words which provide a small difference in a larger similarity. They are fascinated by 'fee, fie, fo, fum,' by 'eeny, meeny, miney, mo,' by 'Humpty Dumpty.'
"At first, the child prefers exact duplication, but he passes through that stage and comes to love rhyming for its own sake. If you eavesdrop on the child playing with his toys you will hear him practicing his vocal phonics: 'Foggie, old foggie foggie, you old goggie you, boggy-boggy, boo, boggie-bogguh.' This is vocal play, but a much more purposive type. Inflections abound! Word stems are isolated and different beginnings and endings are practiced. You can hear the child stressing certain parts of a well known word: 'Yesss, ssss, yessyess. . . .'
"By these activities the child learns to observe all the features of a given word. He plays with its beginning, he twists its tail. He becomes familiar with the fact that 'n. .o. .z' comes together to name a part of your face, while 'r. .o. .z' means a flower. He comes to attend to the way words begin. He notices the first sounds of words when he begins to vary them: 'teeny-weeny; teeny-weeny.' Children who practice such combinations in their word play soon begin to correct their initial errors in words they mispronounce. Children who practice spontaneous rhyming soon stop omitting the final consonants."†

The advisability of recognizing length of time that many children need to perfect their enunciation is suggested by Wellman's study.[886] At the age of five most sounds were given correctly, but some were

---

* Brandenburg and Brandenburg[129]; Nice.[633]
† Van Riper[869] (pp. 86-90).

still difficult. At three years almost one half of the consonant blends and approximately one third of the consonant elements were incorrect.

Vowels and diphthongs are articulated correctly at an earlier age than consonants, single consonants somewhat later, and two and three consonant blends still later.[830, 886] Templin[830] refers to growth in articulation as quite rapid between two and a half years and four and a half years but then continuing more slowly until at least eight years of age. Metraux[577] presents profiles of what the speech of the child sounds like, i.e., phonetic reports, over the age range, 18 months to four and one-half years.

Building of Sentences.   Building of phrases follows soon after the stage of repeating words after the adult and often overlaps it. Such phrases as "pretty flower," "no, don't want to," "all gone," and "it broke" characterize this stage, the first real sentences being characteristically made up of noun-verb combinations. At this stage children are usually willing to add "please" to the frequent "give me" or "help Bobby." More complex sentences soon follow although complex compound sentences do not appear in most children's speech before four or five years.* Almost every complete form of sentence structure appears by six years of age among children who will ever use such complex sentences. Some people, of course, never learn to speak with any but a limited vocabulary and use fairly simple sentence forms. Sex differences appear here as in all early language stages.

When we consider that command of a variety of sentence forms means that the child's command of the mechanics of language is nearly complete, we can appreciate something of the amount of language learning that has taken place during the preschool years. Written language follows the preschool stage if children are given formal schooling.

Content of Children's Speech.   At about the time the child can put together enough words to form a question beyond the simple "What's that?" mentioned earlier, he feeds his growing intelligence by asking innumerable questions. Although occasionally for other purposes, his questions are usually a serious effort to extend vocabulary and to gain information. Brandenburg and Brandenburg[129] found that in a single day a three-year-old child asked 376 questions and that a four-year-old child asked 397. Most questions are attempts to gain information and to clarify the hazy territory between reality and imagination, but they are

* Studies of grammatical form are reported by Fisher[258] and Smith.[776]

sometimes attempts to seek justification for an act or for an idea. "What" and "where" questions are more frequent among young children; "why," "how," and "when" seem to be more frequent as age increases (Smith[777]).

SOME QUESTIONS HAVE SPECIAL SIGNIFICANCE. Among the questions which are usual to three- and four-year-old children are questions about sex, death, and God. "What is the difference between boys and girls?" "Where do babies come from?" "What does it mean to die?" "What is God like?" are almost inevitable questions during the period of widespread interest in words and in facts. The child learns "Mr." and "Mrs.," "yes, ma'm" and "yes, sir," "him" and "her," "he" and "she." It is to be expected that in the course of his inquiries about everything that interests or puzzles him he will ask questions about differences between boys and girls. Or, a new baby may arrive, or someone may die in the child's own home or in the neighborhood. We do not regard the child as morbid, but rather as intelligent, if he asks "where" or "what" in such an instance. When these questions, like all his other questions, are answered truthfully, simply, and without sentimentality or tense emotional accompaniment, the adult's reply tends to reflect the child's purpose in asking. He is seeking information. Sometimes, of course, in order to answer truthfully, we must answer that we do not know, but this answer can stifle or distort the child's interest if it is substituted for information which we do have and which we could give the child in simple form when he asks for it.

The content of a child's speech is significant not only as a measure of his language growth and his interests but also as a measure of personality growth. Piaget[661] studied the language of two children in Geneva and has published one of the most comprehensive analyses of the language content of young children. He found two distinct classifications of language as it functions in relation to thought, namely, egocentric speech and socialized speech. Egocentric speech is speech which has no social function, such as the monologues which accompany action or which verbalize fantasies, and the soliloquies which take place either when the child is alone or when he is with others, but which are addressed to no one and are not intended to give information or to solicit an answer. This egocentric speech according to Piaget, occupies approximately 50 per cent of the total speech of young children and still plays an important part in the speech of six-year-old children. As the child matures his speech shows more attention to socialized language or thought which can be communicated; greater emphasis is laid on understanding by someone else and by oneself, in the sense of reasoning or logic which is more explicit; "logical systematization" is desired. Additional study is needed concerning sequences of language and thought content, egocentric and socialized, in older children and in adults. Study of these and other classifications would provide information on various forms and functions and their proportions over a span of years.

Many Uses Made of Language.   We have considered the uses of language *to secure information,* as for example in naming and in asking questions, and in *thinking aloud* with no desire to give anyone any particular information. In addition, the child uses it almost from the beginning *for the purpose of transferring information and securing what is wanted.* To accomplish these purposes he gives commands and expresses wants. "Go bye-bye," "mine" and "Bobby wants a drink" are examples of this.

Soon, however, language begins *to serve the purpose of simple narration.* The child tries to tell things that happened to him or that he has imagined. At first these narratives are extremely simple. One two-year-old child who had witnessed an accident in which there had been a good deal of excitement told breathlessly that "Bobby falled out of the bus," but could give no further detail when asked if Bobby was hurt, or who had come to help. His only answer to any question was reiteration of the statement, "Bobby falled out of the bus." At three years these narratives become somewhat more detailed. An occasional three-year-old child can tell a fairly well connected story: "I went to Grandmother's house. She lives on a farm. I saw pigs and chickens and a baby cow. Grandpa said it was a calf. It walked funny, like this," whereupon an apt demonstration of a wobbly calf-walk is given.

Imaginative elements often creep into these narratives: "I saw a big, black bear. It was in the yard by the lilac bush." Such statements do not warrant being treated as untruths, but can be regarded as natural play of imagination to be treated in the spirit of play. If direct falsehoods persist and come to be used to escape responsibility or fact, the situation is different. When such situations arise, consideration of their underlying cause usually suggests ways of discouraging the child from falsification for nefarious ends.

Once the child has achieved a basic language facility, imagination can produce a whole original story: "Once there was a great big engine,

difficulty because the child, being deaf, learns to compensate for his deficiency by extra alertness in his other senses. Even supposedly expert examiners sometimes have difficulty in diagnosing sensory defects because the special methods for examining very young children are not widely known, nor is the required equipment generally available.

VOCAL APPARATUS. Defective vocal apparatus is sometimes responsible for inability or unwillingness to attempt speech.

CENTRAL NERVOUS SYSTEM. Occasionally trouble lies in the nerve centers which control speech. Rarely the difficulty is one known as *word deafness*—a defect in which, although sounds are heard, the associations necessary to lend meaning to word sounds cannot be formed.

MENTAL ABILITY. Mental retardation is in some cases the cause of retardation in language development. Many studies of the relationship between general intelligence level and acquisition of language have been made, but the exact degree of association is difficult to state. All studies of mentally deficient children show language retardation, whereas all studies of superior children show language acceleration. It is safe in this connection to assume that children who talk unusually early are probably superior mentally and that mentally deficient children are always late in talking, but it is not to be assumed that all children who are late in talking are mentally retarded.

MODEL. Some children of average or even of superior mental capacity are late in talking because they do not have a model which is adequate in amount or in kind. Children who live in institutions for dependent children during the first three years of life are more often slow to acquire language no matter what their intelligence may be. Wooley's[926] case-study, *David,* was an example of this sort of handicap. David, a child of normal intelligence, at two years and ten months could speak only one phrase, "good morning," and understood little else. He had until this age been in an orphanage where he received good physical care, but where he heard little more than the "good morning" to the children.

On the other hand, children of superior inheritance and general intelligence are sometimes slow to talk because they are cared for by those who do not appreciate the need of talking, or who, when talking, are limited in expression.

Occasionally the model for language is one in which there seems to be too much language. The parents or nurse may speak too rapidly for the child to isolate from the general flow of conversation any specific and understandable words or phrases. Reasonable speed and clearness of enunciation are essential when addressing young children. On the subject of bilingualism Arsenian says detrimental effects do not occur in the learning of two languages from infancy, if "(1) . . . a consistent method of source and presentation of the two languages is observed, i.e., une personne, une langue. (2) . . . psychological barriers or negative affective conditions, such as inferiority or superiority of the languages involved, or national and religious animosities sometimes associated with language are absent, and (3) . . . the languages are learned by spontaneous, informal or play methods, and not by formal and task methods."[*]

NEED TO LEARN. Occasionally children do not learn to talk because they do not need to learn. They receive such constant attention and affection that they have no occasion to seek verbal communication, and their wants are so constantly anticipated that no need arises to express wants verbally. Twins, able to communicate with each other, sometimes are slow in developing aspects of language which enable them to communicate easily with others (Day[196]).

EMOTIONAL INFLUENCE. Occasionally parents are overanxious for evidences of development, forcing the child beyond his ability or rejoicing too enthusiastically over his successes. If a child is urged beyond his ability, realizing that more is expected of him than he can give even though he makes his best effort, he soon becomes discouraged and may perhaps refuse to try because he would rather have it appear that he "won't" than that he "can't." Children need praise for their efforts, for if reproof and correction alone meet their attempts to speak, they may stop trying. On the other hand, if too great praise is attached to effort or if the child is made to repeat the new word or phrase or story for every newcomer, he may become self-conscious or inhibited in his attempt to use the partially formed skill. If too great importance is attached to his every word, he may become conscious of his power over his parents, feeling that he can control their happiness by speaking or by refusing to speak, or by choosing one word or phrase instead of another.

---

[*] Arsenian[50] (p. 81). A bibliography on bilingualism and its effects is included in Arsenian. Effects of bilingualism on measurement of intelligence are reviewed by Darcy.[186]

EXPERIENCES. Some children have enough need to help them develop the type of language to express their wants, but are so limited in general experience that they have nothing to express in narrative and are lacking the knowledge of perceptions and judgments which provides material for reasoning. A fairly wide general experience is necessary if the child is to have a desire to express himself and his relation to the world about him. The richness and variety of his vocabulary, the fertility of his ideas, and the accuracy of his expression all depend on the richness and variety of his experience. A home which is rich in language model and in varieties of experience provides a background for language growth.

Much practice in language takes place when children play with other children, since, although children chatter away to themselves when learning language, they do not talk with the same need to be understood as they do when with other children, nor do they talk as much (Williams and Mattson[906]).

Interest in enriched experiences which facilitate the acquiring of language in the preschool and kindergarten years seems to be increasing. Dawe[195] reported greater gains on tests of vocabulary on home living information and on general science information in an experimental group of preschool and kindergarten children, than in a control group; the experimental group had an educational program which stressed training in the understanding of words and concepts, looking at and discussing pictures, listening to poems and stories, and going on short excursions. Van Riper[868] refers to "speech-play experiences which will facilitate fluency." For example, in a speech play game the Indians say "ugh," holding the hand under the chin, and thus practice saying the "g" sound and also "feel the 'g' sound." In one kindergarten study[909] children in an experimental speech improvement group showed greater decrease in articulation errors on sounds included in the program, and also on sounds not included in the program; pictures, stories, cards and articles, involving practice of particular sounds were presented to the experimental group.

Importance of Stories. A child is very responsive to stories appropriate to his stages of development. He enjoys them "for the fun of it." Hearing and seeing, speech, thought, imagination, and sometimes sociability all play a part in his joy when a story is told to him and when he "tells" it to himself as he looks at the book. The variety of stories and books of quality is great.* There has been a good deal of discussion as to whether children should hear fairy stories or not. Certain children may be frightened or confused; others may find in fairy stories further material for imaginations already overstimulated. On the whole, however, traditional fairy stories and stories with an imaginative aspect which are well selected provide a great deal of joy. Probably no writer, however, would recommend a steady diet of fairy stories or use of them without discrimination. Children are too easily entertained by stories from everyday life to permit neglect of this rich field. Simple stories about boys and girls who get up cheerfully in the morning and go on through the routines and other activities of the listener's day or stories about their world will also engage the attention of nearly all children from two to four or five years of age. The effect of an example or moral in a story is difficult to measure; certainly moralizing can be overdone. In providing books for the young child, the adult may want to ask: is the book beautiful, meaningful, durable, available and individually appropriate?

Stuttering.   TENSIONS AS POSSIBLE CAUSES.   Self-consciousness or fear of the listener's response discourages effort and tends to produce silence; or it may provide one cause of stuttering. The motor control which regulates speech is the finest in balance of any motor control in human behavior and it is the most easily disturbed. It seems more easily disturbed in boys than in girls, since there is considerably more stuttering among boys. One study[896] showed the ratio of boys to girls among stutterers to be from three to one to eight to one, depending on the age. Any tension, whether due to shock, self-consciousness, fear of ridicule, or fear of failure, may upset this balance in motor control. Stuttering or other speech disturbance may result from a death or financial strain in the family, overfatigue, the pain or shock of an accident to the child, fear of too severe discipline, fear of the listener's response, emotional conflict or strain of any kind. When due to such causes, methods of dealing with stuttering take into account the inciting cause. Nagging the child, or calling attention to his difficulty can only make him more self-conscious and more tense, and can, therefore, not cure, but only aggravate the difficulty.

* Books for children of preschool age are listed in Association for Childhood Education[53] and Updegraff.[866] *The Horn Book* published six times a year by The Horn Book, Inc., 248 Boylston St., Boston, Mass., reviews new books. Methods of selecting and presenting stories are presented in Arbuthnot,[45] Dalgleish,[179] Duff,[228] Mitchell,[593] and Sawyer.[721]

Wendell Johnson[430] stresses effect of labeling the child a stutterer and refers to speech and personality disorder as developing after diagnosis. Parental tensions created by the diagnosis create tensions in the child.*

CHANGING HANDEDNESS. Stuttering has sometimes been attributed to attempts to change the child from left-handed to right-handed motor performance. After years of research the relation between handedness† and stuttering is still confused. However, several studies‡ offer fairly convincing evidence that stuttering is associated with handedness and with motor facility in general. Other studies emphasize other influences.[432]

AN ASPECT OF GROWTH. One of the peaks of the curve of incidence of stuttering occurs at the stage in language growth when the child has more to say than he has vocabulary with which to say it. One study (Johnson[430]) revealed that 15 to 25 per cent of the words used by young children figure in some kind of repetition. This is at the stage of beginning to say words for many children, at the beginning of putting words into sentences for many others, or at the beginning of greater use of language in complex situations for others away from home or parents. The difficulty at this stage seems to occur because of natural aspects of growth. The child is reaching out socially and is discovering the use of language as a medium of social communication. Many children find the urge to communicate ideas to others so great that it outruns their active vocabulary. The result is that there is often an urgent need to reach others with language, but a shortage of words with which to do it. Stuttering or hesitation and uncertainty about words results. Fortunately the growth of the active vocabulary, being rapid from two years on, soon catches up with the social growth, and the stuttering disappears, having lasted from two or three weeks to two or three months.

The method of procedure in this type of stuttering is to avoid nagging or anxiety, and to help the child to acquire the vocabulary necessary to meet his needs. This is of great importance, since it is recommended

---

* Descriptions of different kinds of speech disorders, and suggestions for parents and teachers, are included in Johnson,[431] Van Riper,[868] and Beasley.[100] Research on stuttering is reported in Johnson.[432]

† Handedness is discussed on pages 315-316.

‡ Brill and Seidemann;[135] Cross;[176] Spadino;[784] Westphal;[888] Kopp;[474] Cobb and Cole;[166] Orton.[644]

that no negative emotions or lack of self confidence occur in connection with this temporary uncertainty about words if permanent stuttering is to be avoided. The whole problem is one of keeping the child from becoming self conscious about his speech, and of helping him to develop the vocabulary and feelings of ease needed to facilitate his social expression.

Enjoyment of Language. Concepts concerning language and its development were stated at the beginning of this section and followed by information on stages and influences upon them. An attempt to pull together the connotation of this material for use by adults in their association with children suggests the importance of *facilitating the child's use of speech sounds and language with ease and without self consciousness.*

Development of Reasoning

How Do Children Reason? When there is dispute about whether or not young children reason it usually hinges upon the question of what is called reasoning. Some writers have said that reasoning is a complex mental process impossible for young children; others have said that it is a mental process which grades in complexity from the simple trial-and-error problem solving of animals through the intricate associations and insight involved in the solution of subtle mathematical and philosophical problems. Thorndike[841] said that very young children possess not only the requisite elementary processes involved in reasoning, but also the interest in reasoning. He said that in the usual formal schoolroom reasoning is discouraged by neglecting their questions, by making them accept mere words as explanations, by feeding to them the dry bones of mathematics and grammar, and by teaching them to accept everything upon authority. "It is not the case that interest in reasoning comes late in youth; it comes early, but we restrain and dwarf it."

Anderson[40] says "While some problems are met by pure manipulation of physical objects, most are met by a process called *thinking,* which to many is a remote activity carried on in an ivory tower far from life. Actually, thinking is a universal process present in the infant as well as the adult, in the feebleminded as well as the bright. It is closely connected with ordinary living and usually involves symbolic processes.

Life, to most persons, is a succession of problems that are met and solved in work and in play."*

What the child knows, or his cognition, grows and develops as his motor, sensory, language and other aspects of behavior grow and develop. What the child brings before his mind, or his thinking,† may be that remembered or that newly apprehended. What the child uses with a view to attaining a conclusion, or his reasoning, may have more knowledge and thought in it as he grows and develops. Behavior and these processes of cognition, thinking and reasoning, could, of course, continue to change in quality throughout the life of the individual. Their interrelationships are evident in the concepts and theories stated about them from a developmental point of view (Baldwin,[65] Piaget,[660] Russell[715]). In consideration of the reasoning ability present in the early years, knowledge of the ways the child solves his problems or meets situations which are new to him is useful; explanations for these are being sought.

Changes in ways the young child deals with situations pertain, according to Piaget,[660] to the development of a concept or idea of an object as connected with space, causality and time. "Permanence" of this kind does not exist for the young infant. This begins when, for example, he prolongs the movements of grasping; it has proceeded further when he searches for objects that have disappeared; and it is more complete when the infant takes account of the change of position outside the field of direct perception (beginning at 16 to 18 months).

Development of "conceptual schemata" from the specific to the general is emphasized by Baldwin.[65] He refers to the young child's stage as one in which he "may understand in a specific concrete situation the invariance of a total when the parts are rearranged but fail to recognize the general applicability of the schema."‡ Also, he may be "so bound to his own point of view that he cannot be detached enough to recognize the objective logical relations among the elements of a problem."‡

Young Children Reason by Problem-Solving in Actions and in Words. It is evident that reasoning of a rudimentary sort is within the ability of fairly young infants if we consider the following examples.

---

* Anderson[40] (p. 177).
† For statements of theory and review of research on children's thinking, see Russell.[715]
‡ Baldwin[65] (p. 357).

Although not using the term "reasoning," Gesell[285] describes under "adaptive behavior" how nine- to twelve-month-old babies recover a cube which has been covered over by an enamel cup. The test is described as follows: "The examiner takes one of the small red cubes and casts it upon the table to entice the child's attention. He may even allow the child to handle the cube for a moment. While the attention of the child is directed to the cube, the examiner swiftly covers it with an inverted enamel cup and placing the handle of the cup at the child's right, he notes first the reaction of the child to the cup." Gesell's comment on this test is enlightening: "This is undoubtedly a valuable performance test. Complicating and distorting factors are relatively few. The test is placed near the beginning at each of the schedules when nearly every child is much interested in the red cube. The mental processes required for the solution of this situation follow closely the paradigm of Binet's definition of intelligence, and it was most astonishing to find one six-month-old child who solved the situation unmistakably, not only once but six times in immediate succession, exhibiting great zeal and concentration."*

Richardson,[701] Bayley,[85] Bühler,[144] and Shirley[753] all studied this type of simple, concrete problem solving by infants. They agree that pulling a coveted object toward one by means of an attached string is common in babies of one year, and that nearly all children will resort to the use of a chair in order to reach something before they are two years of age. Instances of such solutions of situations can be cited from samples of observations of the behavior of children from a few months of age through childhood. Whether or not young children reason is then not an argument of fact but a dispute over definition.

In studies of preschool children in which solution of the problem involved securing an object not easily reached, "exploration and elimination," "manipulation," "pointing and reaching" (also designated as "trial and error") were more frequent than insight, or "solution without previous manipulation" (Alpert,[15] Matheson[561]).†

Most children of twelve or fourteen months have discovered that they can bring a dish on the table nearer by pulling the whole table cloth toward them; they have discovered the relation between tilting the bottle and getting more milk; they have made the association between having

---

* Gesell[285] (p. 113). By permission of The Macmillan Company.
† Research on problem solving is reviewed by Munn[606] (pp. 428-434).

a hat on and going out-of-doors. Long before twelve months they have discovered the relation between arm movements and the noise produced by a rattle, between releasing their hold of a ball and its falling on the floor. These are all examples of an understanding of *cause* and *effect*.

Generalization and *application* come somewhat later. One need only to watch young children to conclude that their ability to generalize is not well developed. They must meet many specific situations and must be told about numerous specific instances before they are able to draw conclusions from them.

The child who has a horn and lets another child, John, blow it may stop at the adult's suggestion. But he is likely to let another child, Mary, blow it, unless the generalization has been added that the horn should be blown only by one person and the reasons presented in so far as he can understand. He may also understand, through discussion, why putting the horn away instead of having it in a group may be desirable. Attempts to draw conclusions are suggested by the following quotations:

> Lynn: My father doesn't like chocolate pudding.
> Debbie: My father doesn't either. Boys don't like chocolate pudding.
> Tommie: I like it. I'm a boy.
> Lynn: Yes, you're a boy. Then men don't like chocolate pudding.

And

> Bob: I have ten fingers (after counting).
> Bill: I have six fingers (after counting inaccurately). You must be older than I am.

The young child has not met situations in sufficient number to permit cognizance of the similarities and differences by which general classifications are made. He does not realize, for example, that combs, toothbrushes and wash cloths belong to the general class of "personal belongings" and are things that each individual uses for himself alone; whereas most chairs, books and other household furnishings belong to the general class of "family belongings" and are things which can be used by the family at large. Personal belongings are alike in the fact that they are used in the care of the person, and are different from family belongings as a class.

Further thought beyond the immediate situation is suggested in the following illustration. Barbara's playmate, Blanche, looked out of the window at heavily falling snow and said, "Oh, see the feathers." Barbara said, "They're not feathers, are they?" and received from an adult the answer, "No, Blanche is using her imagination." Barbara was apparently much impressed with the word "imagination" and went about repeating it over and over. Later in the day she said, "If Blanche had said, 'That is snow,' would that have been imagination?" In commenting on causal relations, children at kindergarten age are able to give mechanical and logical answers which are more often materialistic than nonmaterialistic (Deutsche[214]).*

In studies of preschool children in which solution of the problem involved learning the principle, i.e., generalizing, amount of experience the child needed for success varied greatly from one individual to another and from one age group to another (Heidbreder,[347] Pyles,[677] and Roberts[703]). Success in several experiments depended on discovering a basis for securing a doll or toy even when materials were rearranged. For example, in some experimental situations, solving the problem meant learning that the right hand box contained the doll, or that a certain color or figure was a key to securing a toy. Solving the problem was possible at an earlier age than statement of the principle (Roberts[703]). For the adult to encourage the child to verbalize his solution seemed to aid in generalizing (Pyles[677]).

In Kuenne's experiment,[483] for children to be able to verbalize the cue aspects of the stimulus situation, either in response to questioning afterwards or spontaneously during the trials, aided in far transposition. For example, children who verbalized "always the smaller square for a toy" were ones who also selected the smaller square of two, even when the actual size of the pair was far from that of the pair with which training took place. When actual size of the second pair was near that of the pair with which training took place, children who did not verbalize explicit association of size with success, were also successful. "Results revealed a highly significant relationship between mental age and the occurrence of far transposition and a low relationship between mental age and near transposition."† Most children of mental ages three to six years succeeded in the near test. Per cent succeeding in the far test increased as mental age increased from three to six. The mechanisms of discrimination and transposition were considered different in

---

* Research on children's reasoning is reviewed in Deutsche.[214] Russell[715] has a section on problem-solving of preschool children (pp. 270-273). Templin[831] considers the development of reasoning in children with normal and defective hearing.
    † Kuenne[483] (p. 471).

the verbal type of control. Transposition when the difference is near instead of far was considered to resemble mechanisms of animals.

Experience Necessary as Basis for Correct Generalization. As the child gains experience with a wide variety of situations, he becomes familiar with the elements of each, and gradually comes to discover how closely similar or how widely different the elements in several given situations must be to permit classification or generalization. We can help him in this by extending his general experience, and by recognizing his increasing power to verbalize essential similarities and differences upon which classifications are built. This needs to be done gradually, however, since young children are usually more confused than helped by detailed explanations and complex patterns of thought, and can reach only the simplest and most obvious conclusions. It is important to realize in this connection that many of the experiences and conclusions familiar and obvious to adults are new and strange to young children; the very strangeness of details often requires the child's entire attention at times when we expected his attention to be occupied with conclusions.

Experience Necessary for Application of General Principles to Specific Situations. The child suffers a similar handicap in his attempts to apply general principles to specific situations. He lacks experience, and hence often cannot decide whether or not a given situation comes under a general ruling, or, still more often, he does not even try to decide since the association between situation and principle never occurs to him. We explain to a three-year-old about keeping floors clean and not tracking mud on them and ask him to remove his galoshes on entering the house. He seems to understand and abides by the request for several weeks. When the weather becomes less severe, however, and galoshes are replaced by rubbers, we are surprised one day when, apparently forgetting our request and his own good habit, he appears in the house wearing rubbers and leaving muddy tracks behind him. He is puzzled when we ask if he has forgotten that muddy overshoes are not to be worn into the house, and replies, "But, mother, you said galoshes. You didn't say anything about rubbers."

Wishful Thinking Common in Children. The child's inability to generalize and to apply principles may also be due to an attitude which leads him to think what he wishes to think rather than what the situation demands. Wishful thinking, as this is called, is found not only among children but among adults who, even though brilliant in mental accomplishment, may be immature in this respect. The child, wearing his rubbers into the house because he has misunderstood the generalization involved, may have thought that rubbers were not included partly because he wished to think it. Four-year-old Betsy illustrated this type of wishful thinking when, during a game of papa and mama, the papa wanted a gun which she had found. She carried her point by saying, "No, you can't have it because I'm the mama and mamas carry the guns." In such an instance the child is not to be condemned for compromising with truth, nor even for a refusal to face facts, but can be encouraged to think more clearly in the matter.

A Growing Repertoire for Problem Solving.   Whenever a new situation for which the individual has no habitual reaction presents itself, the individual is said to be faced with a problem. As long as life flows along familiar channels where no new or unaccustomed action is demanded, habit may serve. But whenever a strange situation arises, habit is insufficient. A new solution or a new pattern of action is needed, and reasoning becomes important. The steps in such problem solving are usually listed as follows:

1. Location of the problem and determination of its nature.
2. Survey of possible solutions.
3. Selection of the most promising solution.
4. Trial of chosen solution.

EXAMPLE OF PROBLEM SOLVING BY THREE-YEAR-OLD.   These steps of reasoning are illustrated in an incident in a nursery school where each morning the children are served tomato juice in small glass cups.

The glasses were being served from a low serving table to children seated in groups of four at individual tables. One child from each table was serving his table. Jimmy, aged three years, having been chosen to serve, carried glasses from the serving table to his individual table until everyone in his group had been served. But he did not count correctly and appeared at his table carrying a fifth glass, which he discovered was not needed and had to be returned to the serving table. Meanwhile the children at all the other tables had been served, had drunk their tomato juice and had returned their empty glasses to a serving tray. Upon reaching the serving table Jimmy was faced with a problem. He must return his extra glass of juice to the serving tray, but the tray was full of empty glasses. He achieved step one in reasoning immediately: He realized where his problem lay and was able to see exactly what the nature of his problem was.

He surveyed the situation (step two) as he stood holding the glass of juice and trying to figure out what he could do about it. An idea which promised to work occurred to him (step three); and he took the glass by its handle and tried to use it as a pusher (step four), pushing the other glasses about in an attempt to crowd them a little closer and thus to make room for his glass. This solution failed. He returned to step two, considering other possible solutions as he stood thoughtfully holding his glass. Once more an idea occurred to him (step three), and he tried (step four again) to pile his glass on top of one of the empty glasses on the tray. But the handle on the side of his glass caused it to tilt, and threatened to spill the juice. At this point experience with similar situations led him to realize that this solution was a failure because, although putting his glass of juice on top of another glass would get his glass on the tray (one aspect of his goal), it would spill the juice and thus defeat another important aspect of his goal.

Once more he stood holding his glass as he surveyed other possible solutions (another return to step two). Suddenly his face beamed. Apparently he had discovered another possibility (step three). He reached out and poured his juice into one of the empty glasses thus "saving it," and triumphantly set his now empty glass upon another thus getting it upon the tray. It could tilt now with no loss of juice. In his own mind he had achieved success in his problem.

In this illustration of problem solving of a three-year-old, his repertoire of possible solutions was incomplete. His adding another possibility for use next time, instead of repeating his solution of this time, seems to hinge upon adult guidance of a kind which encourages further thought on his part.

An important contribution to the child's mental growth can be made if we permit freedom for wide experience with things, with people and with situations. *He learns through opportunity to solve his own problems, to do his own thinking whenever the situation involved is simple enough to permit a reasonably sound solution* from the background of his limited experience, or whenever the risk of a wrong solution is not too great; *guidance in accordance with language ability may be in the form of encouragement of further thought.* In a list of dominative and integrative categories of adult behavior with children Anderson[32] included "build up," meaning the encouragement of the child to solve his own problem without giving him the solution. In a study of college students in their association with nursery school children, only 2 per cent of all their integrative contacts (which were more frequent than the dominative contacts) were of this "build up" type (Nesbitt[627]). If a child has caught a wheel of his tricycle while riding between a box and a bench, the adult's comment can help him select the pertinent facts instead of giving him the solution.

If, for example, the eight-month-old baby drops his rattle, he is faced with the problem of recovering it. Unaided, he will make a variety of attempts to reach it, and will finally select through trial and error a good solution (steps two, three, and four of problem solving). Moreover, if he succeeds as a result of his own effort he has the satisfaction of finding his own solution, and this will make him more eager to attempt solution of the next problem that confronts him. If, however, we rush to him when he drops his rattle, restoring it to his grasp before he has had an opportunity to sense his problem, we rob him of a chance to learn.

If, when he is eighteen months old, we permit him to handle his own spoon or cup, he will soon select from all the possible ways of holding them the one or two ways which solve the problem of giving him food or drink successfully. If at three years he is permitted to cope with the problem of getting his blocks into a box, he will soon learn the best way to fit them together. Consider the problem of an eighteen-month-old child who has been playing horse and who has been running about dangling the reins behind him. He gives his imagination free play until the reins catch over a stake in the ground, thus impeding his progress. He is now faced with a problem. At first he is likely to behave much as an animal would under the same circumstances; he tugs and jerks at random, trying to pull himself free. If he has not had the satisfaction of attacking his own problems he may set up a lusty cry when he fails thus to free himself, expecting some adult to solve the situation for him. If, on the other hand, he has become accustomed to facing his own difficulties, he may pause in his struggles, examine the situation, discover that he must back up in order to release the reins, and then do so, extricating himself in this way.

When To Help Children in Their Thinking.   It is in accordance with our knowledge for adults to let children work on problems unaided if there is some appreciable chance that success will come with reasonable effort; but we will give aid rather than to allow failure to occur too often. Failure means dissatisfaction and an increasing unwillingness to attempt solution of problems, whereas success, especially success which comes as a reward for one's own effort, is a keen stimulant to further attempts. Aid seems warranted, too, whenever it becomes apparent that lack of motor ability or lack of ideas is about to produce discouragement leading to abandonment of the attempt, or irritation resulting in an explosion of temper. Learning, which it is hoped the problem-solving experience will provide, is not occurring if the child has a feeling of failure because he is too often faced with problems too difficult for his ability; if he gives up before reaching solutions because solutions are too long delayed; or if he frequently has explosions of temper because his drive for success outruns his motor ability. Instead of failure, giving up and annoyance, he can rather, through ample experience with problems within the scope of his ability, have responses of success, of persistence, of versatility in thought, and, most important, the attitude of attacking his own problems willingly. His level of aspiration is related to his problem-solving experience.

Experience Necessary for Decision Making. Decision making is an essential part of step three in problem solving and, like all other aspects of reasoning, depends for its development upon practice and success.

How To Make Decisions. 1. For deciding between choices A, B, and C, it is necessary to examine the advantages of A, of B, and of C, and also the disadvantages.

2. The advantages inherent in choice A must be weighed against the advantages inherent in the other two choices, and also against the disadvantages inherent in the same choice; the same must be done for B and C.

3. The individual making the decision must choose, knowing that by virtue of his choice he is giving up the advantages of the choices he decides against, and accepting the disadvantages of the choice that he decides for along with its advantages.

4. The individual must believe in his decision sufficiently to act upon it.

Causes of Indecision. This sounds complicated in a discussion which deals with young children who do not, of course, make decisions "by technique." But if we are to encourage them we must understand something of what is involved. Indecision may be due to failure in any of these steps.

Decisions Can Be Adapted to Ability. Children have many possibilities in their day for making many decisions apparently trivial to adults, but important to them. "What shall I play now?" "How can I make this tower of blocks stand straight?" "Where shall I keep my dollie?" Such decisions need not be made by adults but can be made by the child himself. When decisions for which he has sufficient experience and judgment are left for him to make he not only has practice in making decisions but also feels "less pushed around" or "pressed" by others. As suggested in the concept of the personality component "sense of autonomy," children seek or need to decide for themselves what they are able to decide; this means recognizing greater wisdom of others when it is appropriate.

Development of Imitation

Children Tend To Copy Things Seen around Them.   There is some dispute as to why children imitate movements they see or sounds they hear or values of other people. In the consideration of concepts concerning emotional influences and learning in Chapter 1 and in the section on language in this chapter, references were made to the child's identifying himself with another person, and to the satisfactions which he received in his learning as possible explanations of this. Most writers seem to assume that at least part of the child's tendency to duplicate the behavior and attitudes of those about him is due to a conscious imitation. Close observation of infants may reveal instances of direct imitation of movements before nine months. Gesell says that a new capacity for imitation develops at around nine months, and that the year-old child may be a prodigious imitator. "Demonstrate the ringing of a bell and he will wave it furiously by way of social reciprocity." At fifteen months the child enjoys imitating smoking, coughing, nose-blowing, sneezing and other such activities. By fifteen months "bow-wow," mewing like a cat, "peek-a-boo," "pat-a-cake," imitative crushing of paper, and throwing a ball all are familiar in behavior. "Bye-bye," imitative combing of hair, kissing of a doll, and scribbling with a pencil are also common at this age.

By the time most children are two years old they begin to reflect adult mannerisms. One little girl learned to greet everyone with the same swinging gesture and the same strident-voiced "How's evabody?" that her father used. Many mothers learn for the first time of the querulous tone which creeps into their "discipline voice" when they hear the three-year-old disciplining her doll in imitation of the adult manner.

MODEL IS OF GREAT IMPORTANCE.   From two years onward play time is much occupied with "housekeeping," "traffic cop," "hospital," "shopping tours"—play in which the child duplicates as faithfully as he can the activities, gestures, tones, and other incidents of adult behavior which have happened to attract his fancy. He is rude with the rudeness of adults whom he admires, or courteous with the easy grace of the fine example of those whom he loves. He speaks clearly and accurately, or mumbles bad grammar and profanity; he is neat or untidy, quiet or boisterous, truthful or sly, at least in some measure according to the examples set for him. Whether he reproduces the behavior and attitudes of the people about him by instinct or by selected habit is not so important to our consideration as the fact that he does reproduce them. In accordance with knowledge of imitation, ways of teaching courtesy involve being courteous before the child and to him; ways of teaching good English involve speaking it to children while they are in the early learning period of language development; ways of teaching attitudes toward health, authority, truth, and society are related to the attitudes we ourselves have, since children reflect these subtleties as inevitably as they imitate the more obvious gestures and tones of voice.

The model for imitation may not, of course, always be the parent. It will, however, always be someone whom, for some reason, the child loves or admires. This will be the parent or person who takes care of him until the child begins to meet other people. As contacts widen, potential models become more numerous. The strident profanity of a truck driver in the street may appeal to the child as "grown-up" and prove an attractive model. The pranks of the neighborhood "bad boy" may receive so much attention and create so much excitement that they appeal to all the other children in the neighborhood as worthy of duplication.

It would not be possible to protect the child from all undesirable models. Furthermore, unless he has some experience in the selection of standards, he can scarcely be expected to use good judgment in the matter when he no longer has his parents to think for him. He could be overwhelmed by too sudden or too constant exposure to undesirable models if he were not being constantly exposed to enough attractive and desirable models, either in life or in literature, to keep the balance a favorable one. Parents, being his first and his closest models, have a great balance of power.

Development of Imagination

Development of Imagination Important to Many Aspects of Growth. Much as the child imitates the models around him, every child adapts what he takes from his environment not only to his own inner pace of growth (or maturational patterns) but also to his own individuality. As pointed out in discussion of the development of language, for example, children take words, often use them correctly for a short time, and then adapt them to their own developmental pattern. They listen to stories, then dramatize them according to their own interpretation. As pointed out, each child has an inner pattern of personality or emotional tone which colors the ideas that come to him and the manner in which he reacts to the world around him. Thus he creates the world in terms of his own inner life, and absorbs from life the things he needs to fulfill his inner development. He also expresses back to the world varying interpretations and evidences of his own inner personality. He is creative, in this sense, just as he is in the things he does with paints and clay, with rhythms and bodily movement, and in story telling and dramatic play.

Ability to express imagination with any fluency, however, depends on the acquisition of controls over the body, on accumulation of knowledge which will permit one to judge and to handle objects intelligently (sense perceptions and judgments), on language facility and on increasing capacity to have and use ideas (reasoning). It is easy to understand, then, why the child's ability to express himself in what people usually regard as imaginative or creative behavior should increase steadily with age, at least in the early years of life (Markey[554]), and why the relationship between imaginative behavior and mental age is close enough to be demonstrated statistically. The more intelligent children show a somewhat higher amount of imaginative play. In this capacity of imagination, as in many areas of growth, there are no appreciable sex differences, since both boys and girls display wide individual variations and neither sex seems in the main to have more capacity in this direction than the other.

Imaginative Behavior Adjusts to Real World.   Life in our society is such that one cannot give full vent to one's imaginative tendencies.* Thus there can be seen in the development of the child's imagination, first the crescendo of increasing ability to be imaginative or creative and to express this, a peak time when imagination seems to occupy more time and energy than the world of facts; then a gradual diminuendo, as life forces the acceptance of the idea that one must adjust to the real world of routines and of other people's needs and desires.

What pattern the crescendo takes and how long it lasts will depend on the motor skills, language facility and other requisite maturings of the child and on the ways with which his parents introduce him to reality. The problem for parents and educators becomes one of foster-

---

* For further detail concerning imaginative behavior see Isaacs,[401] Piaget,[663] Wickes.[899]

ing the creative imagination and inner resourcefulness and initiative on the one hand, while at the same time teaching the child to cooperate with the necessary routines, to tell the truth, and to face facts realistically. In most children's lives, as they live with and adjust to most parents, the pattern of imaginative behavior begins gradually at about one year to eighteen months, mounts rapidly from then to three or four years and remains at a fairly high point for several years until around ten or twelve years of chronological age, when it gradually begins tapering off into the mature balance between imagination and adjustment to the real world.

Imaginative Behavior Can Have Many Forms. At around three years many children discover the fun of such dramatic play as living out simple stories by playing that they are the animals of a story or of playing mother or father in the role of housekeeping (see Figure 65). The child's doll becomes a live baby at this stage; a row of blocks becomes a train; a child pretends to eat sand pies and cakes with gusto.

Imaginary companions are frequent, especially if the three- or four-

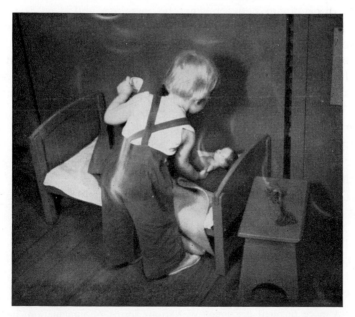

Figure 65. This two-and-one-half-year-old enjoys pretending to be the mother. The bed is big enough so that some of the time she can pretend she is the baby.

year-old child is deprived of the opportunity to play with other children at this stage of his social development when other children are becoming important to his growth (recall here the effect of companionship on his language development). Even in nursery schools, however, imaginary companions are found, since children sometimes provide a baby brother or a parent who has attributes the child considers important.

All imaginative play fills some kind of need in the child. It should be permitted expression and outlet. An outlook of this kind carries with it a *recognition of the importance of self-expression through imaginative play and other creative activities.* This attitude may include such aspects as the following. Even exaggerations of fact and apparent lies should be dealt with gently since they relate to the child's need or wish, and are usually innocent expressions of imagination or the confusions of imagination with fact in young children. Exaggerations or distortions are not to be encouraged unless the child is obviously enjoying the game and expects us to realize that he is only pretending, in which case we may join him in the play without further confusion for him. Guidance concerning use of imagination should come when the child obviously fails to discriminate between what he imagines and what is real, or when he is obviously trying to fool us or to win an undesirable advantage through the lie.*

Ames and Learned describe "a suggestive gradient . . . which indicates the several threads or general kinds of imaginative behavior which go to make up the total 'imagination gradient.' These threads are:

"1. Possessing an imaginary animal, or human, companion, or 'boy or girl' friend.

"2. Playing the role of a baby, an animal, a person.

"3. Imaginative play with some specific object (animates object, has a specific imaginary object, personalizes object).

"4. The various types of imaginative dramatic play and creative story telling and writing, and composing poems and songs.

. . . . Any or all parts (of this imagination gradient) . . . may quite normally occur in any one child."†

Imaginative Play Can Have Various Functions. In Figure 66, possibilities for development of various abilities are suggested. Children who are having a "tea-party" are holding tea cups, pretending to drink

---

* For a more detailed discussion of various forms of imagination, including children's lies, see Breckenridge and Vincent[131] (pp. 307 ff.).

† Ames and Learned[27] (pp. 165-166).

water from them, and deciding who will have the cubes that are to be "cookies." Reference has been made earlier to the child's learning through play. In his play, which involves use of his imagination, not only the joy of it but other values also may be present. Hartley, Frank, and Goldenson,[337] in referring to dramatic play, say:

"Through this activity the child is given an opportunity (1) to imitate adults; (2) to play out real life roles in an intense way; (3) to reflect relationships and experiences; (4) to express pressing needs; (5) to release unacceptable impulses; (6) to reverse roles usually taken; (7) to mirror growth; and (8) to work out problems and experiment with solutions."*

Referring to growth of a certain child revealed over a period of time, these authors say:

Figure 66. Children learn through play. These children are learning to use different abilities such as hand coordination, sense perception, language, imagination and social skills.

* Hartley, Frank, and Goldenson[337] (p. 27).

"The fourth scene finds Perry playing with boys and blocks and dealing with airplanes, a favorite instrument of power among normally masculine little boys. He seems well on his way toward achieving the male role.

Episode 4. . . . Tip and Melvin have each made a beautiful plane out of blocks. Perry goes over and does the same. He tries to fix some blocks on the tail and three smaller ones on top. Everything falls down and he starts again, completely undisturbed. Crawling on his knees he pushes his plane slowly forward, saying, 'Prrrr! Prrrr!' Melvin's and Tip's planes start to move also; Perry's is faster and he now races Tip's. 'Look at this,' he says, 'this is the propeller.' It falls down and he fixes it quickly again. He laughs when other boys start to throw blocks around and says, while moving it slowly forward: 'Mine is a fighter plane! Mine will be beating up the whole world in a few minutes. Burr! Burr!' "*

Development of Additional Creative Abilities

Widening Horizons for Children.   Imagination is the faculty of mind behind any understanding of an experience one has not actually had, or behind the capacity to feel how other people must be feeling when one sees them or hears about their being in a situation one has not actually lived through oneself. Children develop this quality of their minds which can carry them beyond the limitations of their own personal experience. Dramatic play in which they imagine themselves in someone else's situation helps this. Being read stories of animals or other boys and girls also helps. The possession of live animals to be interested in and to care for helps, although children under six rarely prove capable of being entirely responsible for the care of any animal. The children in Figure 67, in their experience with animals, are adding details of information which may be used in a variety of ways.† Occasional trips beyond house and yard include new and interesting things to think about and to ask questions about.

Adults play an important part in providing situations in which various abilities of the child are used. Parents and teachers determine to some extent opportunities the young child has to express and value his imagination, to learn new facts about the world, and to use play equip-

---

* Op. cit. (p. 58). Other references (335, 336) give additional details concerning progress of individual children and play materials useful in imaginative play.

† Children's experiences with nature are discussed in Bacmeister,[59] and Landreth and Read.[493] A useful source book for information is Comstock.[168] Science references are in Fuller.[620] Science experiences for children are discussed in Haupt.[341]

ment and creative materials. In his discussion of creative thinking*
Russell describes it as "problem solving plus." He says problem solving
is usually "more consonant with the facts. Creative thinking is more
personal, less fixed. It achieves something new rather than coinciding
with previously determined conditions."† *Originality may be in the
thinking; or it may be in the use of materials.*

Some parents, in an eagerness to provide adequate challenge to
growing motor skills and developing intellects, may provide too many
toys, or plan the child's time too completely, trying to see that no hour
is lost educationally. An overcluttered environment distracts and con-
fuses children. A year-old child responds well to only two or three
things at a time in the play pen; two- to five-year-olds concentrate best
when there are not too many choices of activity available. One should
remember, however, that children need a sufficient variety of choices
in order to leave the way open for them to choose according to their
own needs. The child can use simple "do-with" toys in a variety of ways
and can develop imaginative play around them. Adult supervision can
be sufficient to keep him safe from injury, but not so close as to inter-

Figure 67. Live animals widen the horizon for these four-year-olds.

* For discussion of concepts of creative thinking and references to research
see Russell.[715] For consideration of imagination in education see Associates of
Bank Street.[52]

† Russell[715] (p. 306).

fere with the free play of initiative and imagination. Dolls, blocks, equipment with which to pretend to be keeping house, doing the marketing, building a bridge, or landing an airplane, opportunities for water play and use of paper, paste, crayons, paint and finger paint, clay, and wood, as well as music, offer many possibilities for a variety of responses over a fairly wide age range.*

Development of Children's Paintings.   As an illustration of the type of maturity stages through which even creative abilities seem to grow, let us consider the development of children's paintings. Given the requisite motor and intellectual maturities, nearly all children enjoy an opportunity to use poster paints (which wash out of clothing if spilled) and paper. Few educators of young children attempt to force this play into the more formal lines which sometimes characterize the teaching of drawing and painting in schools. The pure joy of handling paints or clay, or of experimenting with a piano keyboard, can be destroyed by the parent or teacher who either insists that one "stop that messing," or forces one to "copy the bunch of carrots exactly as it is" or to practice the scales. We now know that free experimentation with the various art media, of which the piano keyboard is one, leads many children through certain preliminary stages of creative development which prove to be a sound foundation for later formal teaching. Even more desirable than the sound basis for formal teaching, however, is the joy the child comes to associate with the use of the art medium. If he learns to love what he is doing, he will later work intensely through the endless hours of "developing the techniques" which most formal teachers rightly insist on. Both children shown in Figure 68 are discovering the joys of painting.

Many two- and three-year-old children, properly covered to protect clothing and placed in an environment where spills are not serious, will spend long periods at "painting." Given freedom to experiment as they will, nearly all children pass through rather definite stages in their use of this art medium.†

First, there is relatively uncoordinated scrubbing and sweeping about

---

* Creative activities are discussed in Fuller,[620] Helping Children Grow,[54] Haupt and Osborn,[342] Heffernan,[346] Landreth and Read[493] and More Than Fun.[51] Excellent bibliographies on various activities (dramatic play, blocks, water play, clay, graphic materials, finger paint, music) are in Hartley, Frank, and Goldenson.[337] Staples and Conley[798] include a bibliography on finger-painting.

† Developmental aspects of children's art are described by Beach and Bressler,[96] Hildreth,[354] and Lowenfeld.[519]

with the brush, spreading color on the page, learning not to drip the paint, not to scrub through the paper, and mastering other such elementary factors. Body movements are random. Results are chaotic and are not intended to express anything more significant than sheer joy in color and activity.

Second, body movement is more coordinated. Lines, strokes and distinct color areas appear. An accidental design may develop, and may be the product of an interruption in the work or a disturbance developing from a paint run or a blot or other distracting occurrence. Even a slight shift of the child's mood may change the tone or the intention of the activity.

Third, consciously sought design appears. At this stage most children implicitly fill up the whole page before announcing themselves as "done." The design is often conscious in the sense that it develops as

Figure 68. This child, three and one-half years old, is in stage 2 of her experiments with paint. Her design was not planned ahead of time. The two-year-old watches, fascinated, and later asks to try it.

the painting proceeds. This is a transition from no design to pre-planned design. In this stage certain areas of the painting often emerge and call for a plan of design. The child often plans one area to balance another accidentally developed area.

Fourth is the stage of preplanned design, in which the child deliberately sets out to paint "a man" or "a house," these two being the most frequently announced subjects of first consciously planned paintings. Some children who have had plenty of opportunity to progress through the earlier stages arrive at this fourth stage as early as four or five years. With less opportunity most children do not arrive at it before six or seven years of age. Inexperienced children of six or seven will be likely to scrub in a sky or other large area in their pictures, or they may start to paint a scene and lapse into pure design. These children show by this that they need more experience in the earlier phases, and should be given freedom to experiment with these phases as they feel a need to do so.

The fifth and mature stage of painting is one in which the idea or feeling is more highly developed, and expression is more purposeful than in the earlier stage. Increasing perfection of art techniques and skills move forward in this stage, but according to students* of children's art, there is no further development in the basic approach to painting.

Children do not move smoothly through these stages, some skipping backward and forward. They spend varying lengths of time, from two weeks to two years in each stage, depending on the inner maturational factors and opportunities to practice.†

As a part of an interest in the child's emotional well-being, provision of opportunity for creative activities is stressed. They are important not only because of the joy the child may have in them, but also because of aspects of his personality they may reveal, and opportunities for personality growth they may provide. Alschuler and Hattwick,[16] in their study of children's paintings, emphasize these values. They warn against attempts at simple diagnosis of a particular child's feelings and needs from his paintings and say "in the analysis and interpretation of a given painting it is more often in the interrelationships of several aspects than in any simple characteristic that the distinctive and telling qualities

---

* Beach and Bressler.[96]

† A very complete review of research in the psychology of children's drawings and bibliography are in Goodenough and Harris.[306]

of the child's products are likely to lie."* Further discussion of projective techniques is on pages 440 to 442. Therapeutic values the child gains through graphic arts can be similar to those previously mentioned with regard to dramatic play (Hartley, Frank, and Goldenson[337]). Attitudes of parents and teachers toward these indications of the child's emotions are considered on pages 449 to 451.

Development of Musical Ability. Although children seldom develop any capacity which would be considered musical in the sense of performance on an instrument in the preschool years, much growth occurs which lays the foundation for the enjoyment or the performance of music in the later years.† In the singing field, especially, much can be done in the earliest years of life to prevent the development of monotone singers which teachers of elementary schools find so frequently among their pupils. In one study of three-year-old children‡ it was found that training caused a marked improvement in the number of notes and intervals the children could produce. In another study of three- to five-year-olds,§ it was found not only that ability to sing improved noticeably with training, but also that interest, satisfaction, and enjoyment increased as ability improved. Training seemed to give the children more self-confidence in singing, more interest in learning, and more enjoyment in participating in group musical activities. Preschool training in music activities seemed to carry over into school music activities, and interest gained seemed to persist. These are, of course, the achievements of children in the ordinary activities of a nursery school musical program. There is substantial evidence that any above average or genuinely unusual musical performance depends on above average or unusual inherited gifts‖ and cannot be forced through teaching. Ordinary ability to beat rhythms and to move the body rhythmically is more dependent on inner maturational factors than is the ability to sing. Much can be done, however, to help children to sing if songs are presented to them in the voice range natural to them. Jersild and Bienstock,¶ whose work in the study of the musical ability of young

---

* Alschuler and Hattwick[16] (p. 4).
† Music, like the learning of language at the reading and writing stages, seems to be an area of learning which, although dependent on inner maturational factors and on the possession of a modicum of talent, is subject to teaching.
‡ Jersild and Bienstock.[425]
§ Updegraff et al.[865]
‖ Scheinfeld.[723]
¶ Jersild and Bienstock.[424, 425, 426]

children is outstanding, have found that children have the following numbers of notes in the voice range at the given ages:

Age	Number of Tones in Range
2	5
3	7
4	9
5	10
6	13

This shows a rapid development of range through the preschool years, and permits the singing of many songs if they are written in the proper range. The two-year range included D, E, F, G, and A above middle C. By three years, middle C was included, and at six years the range included the scale from A below middle C to the second G above middle C. Ascending notes from middle C to A are sung readily by very young children and narrow intervals are sung more readily than wider ones.

Appreciation of and Response to Music.   Although individual children differ tremendously in capacity to enjoy and to respond to music, most children of three years have learned to recognize a few simple tunes, can beat a fairly good simple rhythm, and can detect the difference between high notes and low ones, between slow and rapid rhythms, and between loud and soft intensities in music. In this, as in all other aspects of learning, skill depends not only on original endowment but on opportunity to learn as well. In some homes where children hear a great deal of music, sharing it with people who appreciate it, they learn a genuine appreciation at an early age.*

Advance in the appreciation of music and rhythm is rapid from three to five years of age. Ability to discriminate pitch, timbre, intensity, and interval, as well as skill in pitching the voice, all grow quickly if the child has any special ability in this direction and if practice is given. Some children of three or four years have a response to rhythm which enables them to stamp, march, or sway in perfect time to simple music. A few can beat drums, clap cymbals or shake a tambourine accurately enough to accompany music. There is danger here, however, in the temptation to teach children "parlor tricks" in music. Many four-year-old children, having only a slight gift in music, can be taught to sing

* Research on music and educational methods, covering a wide age range, are presented in Krevit[476] and Mursell.[616] Methods appropriate for young children are discussed in Music for Children's Living,[55] Coleman,[167] Landeck[489] and Sheehy.[748] Song and rhythm books are listed in Music for Children's Living.[55]

dozens of nursery rhymes or to dance an entertaining variety of jigs to music. Average or slightly superior children can, if sufficiently coached, be taught to recognize scores of victrola or piano selections, reciting even long French or Italian names glibly before they are four years old. This sort of thing gives the impression of great precocity; it sometimes even deludes adults into expecting brilliant musical futures for such children.

The Surette School of Music at Concord, Massachusetts, made an admirable contribution to the teaching of music for young children when it took a stand against such artificial performances as those cited above. Mr. Surette believes that a feeling for music is more important than the mechanics of performance. Too great an emphasis on academic memory tricks or on mechanical reaction to music, he thinks, often interferes with true appreciation of music. Children must "experience" music with their minds, their bodies and their emotions. He advises letting children hear good music, sometimes listening quietly, sometimes expressing themselves in bodily movement; but "coaching" should be avoided until the foundation in appreciation has been laid.

Individual Differences in Creative Capacities.   Children differ widely in native gift in the creative areas of intellectual development, some children having little or no interest in music, painting or the crafts, and others having outstanding gifts in one or more of these fields. Given a reasonable exposure to the possibilities of expression in any one of these areas, the child himself will reveal what his native gift is by the interest and concentration he displays. Poor teaching will sometimes discourage a child by forcing him into specific patterns of expression, so that occasionally genuinely gifted children may refuse to respond. If the teaching is even reasonably well adapted to the growth patterns of the child, however, the gifted child seldom needs to be urged to use his abilities in the situation, informal at the preschool age, but still providing opportunity for practice. Children whose abilities are not exceptional also respond almost universally if the setting is appropriate.

Measurement of Intelligence in Young Children

For a number of years attempts have been made to measure intellectual development* in very young children.

* For reviews of research on measurement of intellectual development and variables related to it, see Goodenough[304] and Jones.[434]

Gesell* evolved a developmental scale with standards for one month and intervals thereafter. These standards are, however, in no real sense a test of intelligence *per se*. They are, rather, evaluations of the general developmental level the given infant has achieved at the time of evaluation. Gesell and his co-workers have refused to call their scale anything but a developmental scale, and have purposely avoided translating this scale into any form which could be regarded as a mental age scale.†‡ Bayley,[80] at the University of California, published a Scale of Motor Development which is standardized for infants. Several other tests or sets of standards for use with infants have been published.‡

Research has shown, however, that these tests of very young infants cannot be relied on for prediction of future mental ratings. Results of tests on children under two years of age do not correlate closely with tests made at later ages, nor do the results of one test agree closely with the results of other tests at the same age. Particularly unreliable are the results of tests of infants under three months of age.§ After three months of age several of the more carefully constructed tests show consistent, although not high, correlations with each other and with later tests. We do not yet know how much of this unreliability of the infant tests is due to the fact that different tests stress different aspects of intelligence, or perhaps to the fact that certain aspects of intelligence do not begin to mature in the earliest months of life and hence do not show up in the various tests.|| Most of the tests used in earliest infancy contain many motor items which do not tap more than a segment of the development of intelligent behavior. In man, intelligent behavior appeared with the development of the cerebral cortex (higher brain centers), the development of the sense organs, upright posture and the use of language; so, in the infant, intelligent behavior develops in its most "human" form with the achievement of these maturities.¶ Another way of saying this is to say that there appear to be two main factors which make up the mental organization of the child: the motor (non-mental) and the alertness or "mental" (nonmotor) factors. Whether the alertness (nonmotor) factor is present to any measurable degree

---

* Gesell;[292] Gesell and Amatruda.[288]

† Nelson and Richards[625] have translated the Gesell Developmental Schedule results into mental age values.

‡ For a bibliography of Mental Tests and Rating Scales for children under six years of age, see Hildreth.[352, 353]

§ Campbell and Weech.[152]

|| Bayley.[81, 86, 87]

¶ Irwin.[394]

before three months of age is questionable.* In proportion as the tests of early infancy are weighted with the motor factor, they will fail to correlate with later tests which are weighted increasingly with the alertness factors.

Tests of children from two to five years of age are somewhat more reliable than those of younger infants, and they appear to be increasingly reliable as they involve more alertness and fewer motor items.† Several intelligence tests have been widely used at this age level: the lower levels of the Stanford-Binet (1937 Revision), the Minnesota Preschool Scales, and the Merrill-Palmer Scale of Mental Tests being perhaps the most widely used, in addition to the upper levels of the Gesell Developmental Scale. It seems clear that the present scales are not as satisfactory for research and service purposes as would be desired, and that further work in the evaluation of the intelligence growth of younger children needs to be done.

Despite this unfavorable picture of standards and tests now in current use, many social agencies and physicians use these scales for helpful leads about infants. It must be assumed that no prediction is even approximately valid unless the examiner is well trained in the test techniques and has had fairly extensive experience in the testing of young children. Young children require special handling, and the results of their tests require special interpretation. Trained examiners should, and do, refuse to predict with any assurance the future mental development of children from a single examination. Reliability increases if two or more tests are used and checked against each other. Reliability also increases if the child is tested again after an interval of several weeks or months. It is particularly helpful in adoption cases to have the child examined by a trained and experienced infant examiner, then given a trial period of several months in the new environment, followed by a re-examination, if possible by the same examiner.

Influence of Training on Intelligence. Whether training can influence intelligence is a disputed question.‡ Some writers have claimed

---

* Richards and Nelson,[698] Black,[113] Anderson,[31] Ebert and Simmons,[237] Bayley.[81, 86, 87]

† For an extensive review of these tests see Goodenough and Maurer,[308] and Hildreth.[353] Research concerning mental tests and prediction is reported in Bradway,[127, 128] Bayley,[81] Goodenough and Harris,[305] and Worcester.[927] Information on psychological testing is in Anastasi.[29]

‡ For summary see: 39th Yearbook, Nat'l. Soc. for the Study of Educ.; Intelligence: Its Nature and Nurture, Pub. Sch. Pub. Co., Bloomington, Ill., 1940, and Jones.[434]

stoutly that such experiences as attendance at nursery school raise children's test scores.* Other writers† deny that this is the case. The dispute seems to depend on the interpretation given to test findings and to implications drawn from statistical handling of data. The relationship between health and test scores, between physical maturity level and test scores and other such factors seems clouded by issues over the validity of tests and of the statistical devices used to analyze the data. The general implication from the studies available seems to be that inner maturational factors outweigh environmental training in determining intelligence level as measured by the present intelligence tests. There is reason to believe, however, that seriously limited or sterile environments prevent any given potential intelligence from reaching its optimum in functioning. There is also evidence‡ that continued malnutrition and illness interfere with the mental alertness of children, if not with basic mental capacity. It is reasonable to suppose, too, that good teaching, if it does not actually raise the level of basic mental capacity, most certainly provides a wider knowledge and experience as materials to be used by whatever capacity is present.§

It should also be recognized that intelligence as measured by standardized intelligence tests is not always the true picture of the actual working intelligence of the child. What is usually measured by the standard test are those verbal abstract factors of intelligence such as the factors of language ability, memory, and other aspects of intellect which get along best in the formal schoolroom. Few standard intelligence tests measure the valuable aspects of intelligence which make some people intensely practical or which make others keenly creative. Selection of test items may not have included adequate recognition of effects of differences in experience of children.

Then, too, standard intelligence tests contain only those maturity indicators which can be set up in controlled test situations. They miss the numberless life responses which are the actual tests of intelligent or unintelligent adjustment to life. Again, the standard test results are usually computed in terms of the age-scale concepts discussed in

---

* Wellman.[885]

† Goodenough and Maurer,[308] Bayley.[86]

‡ Blanton.[115]

§ References concerning children who differ markedly (both above and below the majority in intelligence, and in particular talents) are included in Carmichael,[221, 586] and in the Forty-ninth Yearbook.[621] Points of view useful to parents of retarded children are presented in Woods School publications,[924, 925] and in Kirk.[455] Witty[916] discusses and includes bibliographies on the gifted child.

Chapter 1. They have the basic fallacies of these concepts, since they do not make enough allowance for individual variations of pattern and pace of growth. Free observation of children can reveal the individual patterns of the sequences of stages of development which are more important in individual guidance than the chronological age at which any of the particular stages may appear. Tests, however, are useful as general checks on accomplishment, and can give general guides on what to expect in over-all intellectual achievement, especially of the kind that adapts well to school situations.

Developmental-Dynamic Aspects of Intellectual Behavior and Development. The aspects of intellectual behavior are more frequently referred to today according to a developmental-dynamic concept, than was done in previous years. One aspect is more often explained in terms of other aspects. Numerous concepts and theories pertain to the interrelatedness of the aspects of intellectual behavior in sequence and in their interactions at a particular stage. For example, motor and sensory behavior are tied together;[606, 660] language is referred to along with motor and sensory, as well as emotional and social, behavior;[528, 830] sensory perception and judgment, language, thinking and reasoning are interwoven.[65, 661, 715] Likewise, evidence of the processes of maturation, of maturation and learning, of learning and of emotional influences, all tend to be referred to together more frequently.[65, 434, 528]

We hope that inclusive research on the same individuals over a period of time will be forthcoming. In the meantime, concepts and theories emphasize looking at the various aspects of intellectual development in an individual child together, as well as separately. Throughout this chapter on intellectual development, in statements of broad concept, in descriptions and explanations of behavior, and in the implications which this knowledge holds for adults associated with children, has run a continuous reference to the potentialities of growth and development within the child in his early years and to the influence of general experience on the child as contrasted to specific teaching. *Provision of a setting which facilitates growth and development* includes almost intangible adult attitudes as well as the more tangible elements.

Topics for Study and Discussion

Sensory Judgments

1. If you are studying an individual child, record behavior observed indicative of stages of development of his various sensory judgments (use of sense of touch, smell, taste, hearing, sight; judgment of size, shape, weight, distance, number,

time). When possible include enough detail to provide a basis for discussion of how the child is learning to make various judgments.

2. Discuss a number of pieces of play equipment in terms of sensory acuity and judgments which they encourage.

Language

1. If you are studying an individual child, quote what he says to give an indication of different aspects of his language ability (passive vocabulary, active vocabulary, pronunciation, sentence structure, grammar, language stages, language uses, original stories and poems, response to stories). Consider effect of the situation on his responses.

2. Examine several children's books. Discuss their characteristics by referring to the child's development of sensory perception, language, and imagination during the preschool years.

Reasoning

1. If you are studying an individual child, report incidents illustrative of different types of reasoning (problem solving in actions and in words, understanding of cause and effect, generalization and application, decision making). Indicate effect of the situation upon the child's use of his ability.

2. Describe several incidents in which the child's use of reasoning ability could be encouraged. Discuss ways of encouraging it.

Imagination and Creative Activities

1. If you are studying an individual child, report illustrations of his dramatic play, his use of materials (such as paint, paper and paste, crayons, clay, wood), and his response to music. Indicate ways of "building onto" his particular interests.

2. Discuss "cues" to feelings which imagination and creative activities suggest. Consider ways of using understanding of the child gained from these activities.

Selected Readings

Sensory Judgments

Barker, R. G., Kounin, J. S., and Wright, H. F.: Child Behavior and Development. New York, McGraw-Hill, 1943. Chaps. 4, 5, and 6.
Landreth, C., and Read, K. H.: Education of the Young Child. New York, John Wiley & Sons, 1942. Chap. 11.

Language

Childhood Education, Vol. 26, No. 3. Theme of entire November, 1949, issue, Using What We Know about Children in Developing Language Arts.
Dawe, H. C.: The Child's Experiences in Communication. Chap. 7, Part III, pp. 193-208. Forty-sixth Yearbook, Part II, National Society for Study of Education. Chicago, University of Chicago Press, 1947.
Journal of Speech and Hearing Disorders, Vol. 17, No. 3, Sept. 1952 (pp. 263-285). Three papers are presented from a Symposium, Speech Development in the Young Child: 1. The Autism Theory of Speech and Development and Some Clinical Applications. O. H. Mowrer. 2. Some Factors Related to the Speech Development of the Infant and Young Child. O. C. Irwin. 3. The Development of Certain Language Skills in Children. M. C. Templin.
McCarthy, D.: Language Development in Children, in Carmichael, L.: Manual of Child Psychology. New York, John Wiley & Sons, 1954. Chap. 9.

Reasoning

Baldwin, A. L.: Behavior and Development in Childhood. New York, Dryden Press, 1955. Chap. 13.

Barker, R. G., Kounin, J. S., and Wright, H. F.: Child Behavior and Development. New York, McGraw-Hill, 1943. Chap. 8.

Childhood Education, Vol. 23, No. 7. Theme of entire March, 1947, issue, Working with Children as Thinkers and Planners.

Munn, N. L.: Learning in Children, in Carmichael, L.: Manual of Child Psychology. New York, John Wiley & Sons, 1954. Chap. 7.

Russell, D.: Children's Thinking. Boston, Ginn and Company, 1956. Chap. 9.

Imagination and Creative Activities

Hartley, R., Frank, L. K., and Goldenson, R.: Understanding Children's Play. New York, Columbia University Press, 1952.

More Than Fun; Creative Activities for All Our Children. New York, Arts Cooperative Service, 1950.

Russell, D.: Children's Thinking. Boston, Ginn and Company, 1956. Chap. 11.

Intelligence

Jones, H. E.: The Environment and Mental Development, in Carmichael, L.: Manual of Child Psychology. New York, John Wiley & Sons, 1954. Chap. 10.

10

The Child's Emotional, Social, and Spiritual Growth

Development of a Healthy Personality

Personality has been described as "the thinking, feeling, acting, human being."* The two previous chapters have dealt with thinking and acting, with the recognition that feeling was a part of them. One way to begin the study of emotional, social and spiritual growth is to consider what underlies behavior usually described in these terms. For example, the child's expression of anger or affection, his response to other children, his comments about a world beyond his comprehension, can be viewed from the outside. But if the behavior is to be understood it needs to be thought of as coming from something inside the person, from his feelings. Description of feelings and of behavior accompanying them appears in the Fact Finding Report of the Midcentury White House Conference on Children and Youth.[583, 915] Certain "senses" are referred to as components of healthy personality. They are, of course, components of particular aspects of personality, such as the emotional, social and spiritual aspects, with which this chapter deals.

Components of a Healthy Personality. According to this report, components of a healthy personality are: (1) sense of trust, (2) sense

* Midcentury White House Conference Fact Finding Report,[583, 915] (p. 3). Further description refers to the individual as one who "varies in his behavior from time to time and from situation to situation. . . . Nevertheless, from an early age, perhaps even from birth, there is continuity in his behavior."

of autonomy, (3) sense of initiative, (4) sense of accomplishment, (5) sense of identity, (6) sense of intimacy, (7) parental sense, and (8) sense of integrity.*

How the person feels in terms of these particular senses affects his personality. He needs them. He struggles to secure them. They matter to him as he grows from infancy into adulthood. If the individual's needs for a sense of trust, autonomy, and the others are met more than not at the stage where they matter most, then he has more of a feeling of harmony with regard to himself and his world. According to an outline worked out by Erik H. Erikson, healthy personality development means the solving of a central problem of a particular stage so that the child can "proceed with vigor and confidence to the next stage."† For example, after a sense of trust emerges for the infant, he continues to need it, but another need tends to predominate (although all the others are also present), and so "the struggle for the next component of the healthy personality begins,"‡ i.e., the sense of autonomy.

"SENSE OF TRUST. The component of the healthy personality that is the first to develop is the sense of trust. The crucial time for its emergence is the first year of life. As with the other personality components to be described, the sense of trust is not something that develops independent of other manifestations of growth. It is not that the infant learns how to use his body for purposeful movement, learns to recognize people and objects around him, and also develops a sense of trust. Rather, the concept 'sense of trust' is a short-cut expression intended to convey the characteristic flavor of all the child's satisfying experiences at this early age. . . .

"Trust can exist only in relation to something. Consequently a sense of trust cannot develop until the infant is old enough to be aware of objects and persons and to have some feeling that he is a separate individual. At about three months of age a baby is likely to smile if somebody comes close and talks to him. This shows that he is aware of the approach of the other person, that pleasurable sensations are aroused. If, however, the person moves too quickly or speaks too sharply the baby may look apprehensive or cry. He will not 'trust' the unusual situation but will have a feeling of uneasiness, of mistrust, instead.

* A popular version of part of the Midcentury White House Conference Fact Finding Report[583, 915] is called A Healthy Personality for Your Child.[253] It includes the following descriptions: For a sense of trust—that sure feeling: everything is O.K. Autonomy—that strong feeling: I-I-I. Initiative—that more clean-cut feeling: my plans and ideas. Accomplishment—that feeling of importance: I can do. Identity—that new-old feeling: who am I really? Those later feelings: I am one with others and I care for others.

† Midcentury White House Conference Fact Finding Report[583, 915] (p. 6). Quotations which follow are taken from the publication of the Health Publications Institute.[583] Variations in Witmer and Kotinsky[915] are extremely slight, and page references are the same except where differences are noted.

‡ Op. cit. (p. 11).

"Experiences connected with feeding are a prime source for the development of trust. At around four months of age a hungry baby will grow quiet and show signs of pleasure at the sound of an approaching footstep, anticipating (trusting) that he will be held and fed. This repeated experience of being hungry, seeing food, receiving food and feeling relieved and comforted assures the baby that the world is a dependable place.

"Later experiences, starting at around five months of age, add another dimension to the sense of trust. Through endless repetitions of attempts to grasp for and hold objects, the baby is finally successful in controlling and adapting his movements in such a way as to reach his goal. Through these and other feats of muscular coordination the baby is gradually able to trust his own body to do his bidding."*

"SENSE OF AUTONOMY. The sense of trust once firmly established, the struggle for the next component of the healthy personality begins. The child is now twelve to fifteen months old. Much of his energy for the next two years will center around asserting that he is a human being with a mind and will of his own. A list of some of the items discussed by Spock under the heading, 'The One Year Old,' will serve to remind us of the characteristics of that age and the problems they create for parents. 'Feeling the oats.' 'The passion to explore.' 'He gets more dependent and more independent at the same time.' 'Arranging the house for the wandering baby.' 'Avoiding accidents.' 'How do you make him leave certain things alone?' 'Dropping and throwing things.' 'Biting humans.' 'The small child who won't stay in bed at night.'

"What is at stake throughout the struggle of these years is the child's sense of autonomy, the sense that he is an independent human being and yet one who is able to use the help and guidance of others in important matters. This stage of development becomes decisive for the ratio between love and hate, between cooperation and wilfulness, for freedom of self-expression and its renunciation in the make-up of the individual. The favorable outcome is self-control without loss of self-esteem. The unfavorable outcome is doubt and shame.

"Before the sense of autonomy can develop, the sense of trust must be reasonably well established and must continue to pervade the child's feeling about himself and his world. Only so dare he respond with confidence to his new-felt desire to assert himself boldly, to appropriate demandingly, and to hurl away without let or hindrance.

"As with the previous stage, there is a physiological basis for this characteristic behavior. This is the period of muscle-system maturation and the consequent ability (and doubly felt inability) to coordinate a number of highly conflicting action patterns, such as those of holding on and letting go, walking, talking, and manipulating objects in ever more complicated ways. With these abilities come pressing needs to use them: to handle, to explore, to seize and to drop, to withhold and to expel. And, with all, there is the dominant will, the insistent 'Me do' that defies help and yet is so easily frustrated by the inabilities of the hands and feet.

"For a child to develop this sense of self-reliance and adequacy that Erikson calls autonomy, it is necessary that he experience over and over again that he is a person who is permitted to make choices. He has to have the right to choose, for example, whether to sit or whether to stand, whether to approach a visitor or to lean against his mother's knee, whether to accept offered food or whether to reject it, whether to use the toilet or to wet his pants. At the same time he must

* Op. cit. (pp. 8 and 9).

learn some of the boundaries of self-determination. He inevitably finds that there are walls he cannot climb, that there are objects out of reach, that, above all, there are innumerable commands enforced by powerful adults. His experience is much too small to enable him to know what he can and cannot do with respect to the physical environment, and it will take him years to discover the boundaries that mark off what is approved, what is tolerated, and what is forbidden by his elders whom he finds so hard to understand.

"As problems of this period, some psychologists have concentrated particularly on bladder and bowel control. Emphasis is put upon the need for care in both timing and mode of training children in the performance of these functions. If parental control is too rigid or if training is started too early, the child is robbed of his opportunity to develop, by his own free choice, gradual control of the contradictory impulses of retention and elimination."*

"SENSE OF INITIATIVE. Having become sure, for the time being, that he is a person in his own right and having enjoyed that feeling for a year or so the child of four or five wants to find out what kind of person he can be. To be any particular kind of person, he sees clearly, involves being able to do particular kinds of things. So he observes with keen attention what all manner of interesting adults do (his parents, the milkman, the truck driver, and so on), tries to imitate their behavior, and yearns for a share in their activities.

"This is the period of enterprise and imagination, an ebullient, creative period when phantasy substitutes for literal execution of desires and the meagerest equipment provides material for high imaginings. It is a period of intrusive, vigorous learning, learning that leads away from the child's own limitations into future possibilities. There is intrusion into other people's bodies by physical attack, into other people's ears and mind by loud and aggressive talking. There is intrusion into space by vigorous locomotion and intrusion into the unknown by consuming curiosity.

"By this age, too, conscience has developed. The child is no longer guided only by outsiders; there is installed within him a voice that comments on his deeds, and warns and threatens. Close attention to the remarks of any child of this age will confirm this statement. Less obvious, however, are experts' observations that children now begin to feel guilty for mere thoughts, for deeds that have been imagined but never executed. This, they say, is the explanation for the characteristic nightmares of this age period and for the overreaction to slight punishment.

"The problem to be worked out in this stage of development, accordingly, is how to will without too great sense of guilt. The fortunate outcome of the struggle is a sense of initiative. Failure to win through to that outcome leaves the personality overburdened, and possibly overrestricted, by guilt."†

"SENSE OF ACCOMPLISHMENT. The three stages so far described probably are the most important for personality development. . . . The fourth stage, which begins somewhere around six years of age and extends over five or six years, has as its achievement what Erikson calls the sense of industry. Perhaps 'sense of accomplishment' would make the meaning clearer. At any rate, this is the period in which preoccupation with phantasy subsides, and the child wants to be engaged in real tasks that he can carry through to completion."‡

"SENSE OF IDENTITY. With the onset of adolescence another period of personality development begins. . . . The central problem of the period is the establish-

* Op. cit. (pp. 11-12;583 pp. 11-13915).
† Op. cit. (pp. 14-15;583 p. 15915).
‡ Op. cit. (pp. 16-17;583 p. 17915).

ment of a sense of identity. The identity the adolescent seeks to clarify is who he is, what his role in society is to be."*

"SENSE OF INTIMACY. After the sense of identity, to a greater or less extent, is achieved it becomes possible for the next component of the healthy personality to develop. This is the sense of intimacy, intimacy with persons of the same sex or the opposite sex or with one's self. The youth who is not fairly sure of his identity shies away from interpersonal relations and is afraid of close communion with himself. The surer he becomes of himself, the more he seeks intimacy, in the form of friendship, love and inspiration.†

"THE PARENTAL SENSE. 'Parental sense' designates somewhat the same capacity as that implied in the words, creativity or productivity. The individual has normally come to adulthood before this sense can develop fully. The parental sense is indicated most clearly by interest in producing and caring for children of one's own. It may also be exhibited in relation to other people's children or by a parental kind of responsibility toward the products of creative activity of other sorts."‡

"SENSE OF INTEGRITY. The final component of the healthy personality is the sense of integrity. . . . The individual, in Erikson's words, 'becomes able to accept his individual life cycle and the people who have become significant to it as meaningful within the segment of history in which he lives.'

"To continue Erikson's description, 'Integrity thus means a new and different love of one's parents, free of the wish that they should have been different, and an acceptance of the fact that one's life is one's own responsibility. It is a sense of comradeship with men and women of distant times and of different pursuits, who have created orders and objects and sayings conveying human dignity and love. Although aware of the relativity of all the various life styles that have given meaning to human striving, the possessor of integrity is ready to defend the dignity of his own life style against all physical and economic threats. For he knows that, for him, all human dignity stands or falls with the one style of integrity of which he partakes.' "§

These quotations from the Midcentury White House Conference Fact Finding Report have been presented here because of the perspective they provide as one views behavior of all kinds which emerges in the preschool years. In the remainder of this chapter, emotional, social and spiritual responses will be considered. A close look at the child's emotions, his awareness of himself, of people, and of the cosmos, can shift to a more encompassing look in which their relation to components of a healthy personality is considered. Figure 69 has a number of possibilities for thought on what a situation includes which seems related to personality components.

What it is deep within the human being that makes feelings such as those of the personality components matter (whatever they are called) defies complete understanding and certainly complete description. If one

* Op. cit. (p. 19).
† Op. cit. (p. 22).
‡ Op. cit. (p. 23;[583] pp. 23-24[915]).
§ Op. cit. (p. 24;[583] pp. 24-25[915]).

meditates about it, he gropes for a *connection between emerging abilities of different stages of development and energies which lead to satisfying action.* The baby has needs and seeks to satisfy them; likewise, the older child and the adult. To try to answer why has been the concern of philosophers for a great many years. Religions deal with the question. Scientists have also attempted to inquire into it.

Emotional Development

How the child feels about what happens to him seems more related to his personality than the particular words or actions which he experiences. It is interesting to try to relate this point of view concerning feelings as components of healthy personality to the usual vocabulary regarding emotion. It seems logical to say the infant's expressions of emotion suggest more acceptance of his world than rejection of it when a sense of trust is being established. When differentiation of emotional behavior can be noted, the child seems to have more of such

Figure 69. These children are using a variety of emerging abilities with possibilities for feelings of trust, autonomy, initiative, accomplishment, identity, closeness to others and integrity.

responses as delight or affection when trust, autonomy, initiative, and accomplishment predominate; he has more of such responses as anger, fear and distress when they do not predominate.*

Earliest Emotion Nonspecific.   The newborn infant is capable of emotional response apparently so complicated in its mechanism that it calls into play almost every part of the body. Just what arouses his emotions and just what emotion he shows as the result of specific stimuli are matters of dispute.† But that he becomes roused to emotion by remarkably few types of stimuli and that the number of his emotional reactions is limited seem to be agreed on by recent writers. We see, then, that the emotional behavior of infants is limited; it is roused by probably not more than four or five distinct stimuli; it becomes varied in kind and amount, depending on the constitution and experience of the child.

The extent to which early emotional experiences may make deep impressions which last into childhood and adult life, molding later ideas and behavior, still requires scientific study. It would be helpful to have research on effect of experience in infancy and on extent to which persistence of patterns in the individual may be due to persistent factors in the environment. After a review of studies concerned with questions such as these, Orlansky says, "In the normal range of infant experience . . . we believe that events subsequent to the first year or two of life have the power to 'confirm or deny' the personality of the growing infant, to perpetuate or remake it, depending upon whether the situation of later childhood perpetuates or alters the situation in which the infant was reared."‡

Physical Care Important in Early Emotional Development.   Presentation of information concerning emotional behavior carries with it presentation of experience which seems related to it. One important

---

* For detailed information about emotional development and an extensive bibliography, see Jersild.[422] On page 833, he refers to emotion as "a label for a vast range of psychosomatic states." On the subjective side he considers it as involving feeling, which may be clearly defined or vague, and perception or awareness; bodily features involve visceral activities and activities of the skeletal muscles; total response may be disorganized or organized.

† Studies of emotions of infants during the first months of life include Bühler,[144] Bridges,[134] Dennis,[206] Irwin,[395] Jones,[436, 437] Landis and Hunt,[490] Pratt et al.[671] and Brody.[140] Psychoanalytic interpretations are presented in Isaacs[402] and Josselyn,[441] and Brody.[140] Discussions of findings are in Jersild,[422] Jones,[437] and Orlansky.[643]

‡ Orlansky[643] (p. 35).

factor in the development of the child's emotions is his physical care. If his life is smooth, with intelligent management of feeding, sleeping and elimination, he experiences a sense of well-being which is conducive to the free flow of his emotional life. Evidence in support of emphasis on physical care comes from such studies as those of young infants in which the amount of crying decreased when the amount of nursing care in the hospital increased, and when the newborn had been discharged from the hospital and was at home (Aldrich, Sung and Knop[8]). One of the seven factors isolated in a recent report of mothers' child-rearing practices has been called "orientation toward child's physical well-being" (Sears, Maccoby and Levin[733]). It is hoped that information on its effects on the children will be forthcoming. Inadequate physical care thwarts the meeting of the child's inner needs and results in accumulation of inner emotional tensions. Sick children who, even with the best of care, cannot utilize food well suffer emotional frustration of the first order. If these children are left to cry as little as possible and have a maximum of physical love and comfort this may compensate for the inner pain and tension which unsatisfied hunger produces. The disposition may thus be bent from a fretful dissatisfaction with life toward a contented acceptance of it. Accumulation of inner frustration and tension may create a tense way of responding which continues in years to come, whereas a relaxed inner contentment in the earliest years may contribute to a pattern of relaxed and comfortable reaction to each day as it comes. Adequate relief of physical tensions thus becomes an important part of emotional development.

Parental Love also Basic. As emphasized earlier, and discussed in greater detail in the following chapter, parental love, expressed in terms which no child can doubt, is also of paramount importance in contributing to an early pattern of relaxed, contented ease. Children, normally, given reasonably adequate physical and psychological care,* develop a happy disposition. More of the early evidence in support of emphasis on the importance of personal association with one person, usually the mother, came from studies in which children were reared away from their families. Bakwin[63] describes as outstanding features of infants under six months of age who have been in an institution for some time, "listlessness, emaciation and pallor, . . . unresponsiveness

* Studies of infant relationship formation are in Soddy[781] (vol. 1, pp. 103-160) and in Rheingold.[694] Research on infant relationship to the mother is reviewed in Brody[140] (pp. 84-109).

to stimuli like a smile or a coo, indifferent appetite, failure to gain weight properly despite ingestion of diets which are entirely adequate. . . ."* Spitz[790] refers to the great increase in manifestations of emotions of displeasure and to arrested development of infants under one year of age separated from their mothers and having institutional care. Freud and Burlingham[270] describe infants and children under the age of five who were away from their families in residential nurseries in England during World War II by saying they enjoy companionship of children their own age but "search further for objects toward whom they can direct all these emotional interests which they would normally direct toward their parents."†

Some writers believe that change of experience, especially at certain ages, as children go from happy association with their mothers to a situation without them, is the key to the signs of disturbance they show.

More of the recent evidence concerns children reared with their families. Brody refers to the "mature social responsiveness and/or superior confidence in bodily movement and/or a high quality of interest in and concentration upon the mastery of objects"‡ in infants whose mothers' feeding practices were "conspicuous for their ability to accommodate to the needs of their infants,"§ and to differences in behavior among groups whose feeding experience (considered as a measure of infant and mother relationship) differed.

Sears, Maccoby and Levin found the warmth of the mother's feeling for her child "pervasive in its effects on the child. Maternal coldness was associated with the development of feeding problems and persistent bedwetting. It contributed to high aggression. It was an important background condition for emotional upset during severe toilet training, and for the slowing of conscience development."‖

Patterns of Emotional Development.   Variations in points of view about the emotional development of the infant, concern the bases for his feeling of well-being when his needs are met, or the bases for the affectional tie or interaction with the mother and its relation to forces within him and to experience. Expectations that the child will proceed through particular stages, and explanations of these stages vary ac-

---

* Bakwin[63] (p. 35).
† Freud and Burlingham[270] (p. 65).
‡ Brody[140] (p. 334).
§ Brody[140] (p. 265).
‖ Sears et al.[733] (p. 482-483).

cordingly. When attention focuses on the behavior of the infant, it is evident that he will express emotion vigorously and primitively. When unhappy or frightened, a young infant cries, clutches and struggles physically. When he is happy, he relaxes contentedly, or later coos and laughs to express his joy. He is roused by immediate things. As he grows older he gradually shows emotional differentiation.[134, 144] He reacts less to immediate and physical stimuli and is more responsive to psychological stimuli, as well as to remote aspects distant in time. As goals* change due to maturation and learning, changes also occur in the stimuli which arouse emotion. The child learns to control his expression of emotion, crying less easily, holding his temper, combating fear with growing courage, and directing joy and eagerness into constructive work. Not only control, but also expression is part of development.

In *affection,* as in other emotions, development can be considered in terms of what arouses emotion and in terms of how it is expressed. Descriptions of responsiveness to others are included in a later section on the concept of self.

Controls and variations in expression come gradually. Most preschool children have made beginnings only in the process of growing up emotionally. Three-year-olds, for example, are normally quite emotional in their reactions to life, being made glad or sad or angry by slight happenings, and expressing these emotions obviously and openly. Murphy[611] explains this as follows: "By and large it pays to be suspicious of a 'matter-of-fact' three-year-old. The age of three is a time when a child has a right to have emotions—he has only recently acquired his sea-legs, language is still being acquired with startling rapidity, new discoveries in the world are being made daily. The child who goes through all this without due emotion is missing as much as the person who marries without love. Few three-year-olds have a right to be unemotional; when they are completely matter-of-fact, it is worth asking whether this isn't a specious and external 'adjustment.' "† Yet, even at three years the processes of self control have begun. In most

* For discussion of drives and needs and their development, see Jersild[422] (pp. 834-837) and Baldwin[65] (pp. 170-208 and 457-481). On page 171, Baldwin refers to need "as any psychological condition that makes the child more easily motivated by one instigation than another." He refers to physiological and non-physiological bases for needs. For illustrations of hypotheses related to the study of individual differences, see Escalona[247] (pp. 2-7 and 21-24).

† Murphy[611] (p. 406).

children of this age the ability to wait to eat when hungry has been educated to three meals and two or three snacks a day; crying over trivial hurts has been overcome; and other beginnings in emotional control and relationships with people have been made.

Insight into causes of emotional outbursts and aids in establishment of control can be gained by reference to feelings important for the child at different stages. Findings concerning changes in emotional responses with age seem to agree with current emphases on feelings the child needs. For example, in several studies reported by Jersild and Holmes,[427] *fears* in response to noise and agents of noise, and in response to strange objects, situations, and persons were among those decreasing with age. These situations may arouse fear in the infant in whom a sense of trust of his tangible world is not yet well established. His sense perceptions for objects do not yet include a "permanence" in space, causality and time. For the older child who has established trust in material things, his fears have more of an imaginary angle. Fears of the dark, of being alone and of imaginary creatures in the dark were among those increasing during the preschool years. Imagination is increasing in these years. Gaining competence and skill, finding practical methods of one's own for dealing with the feared situation, and having, by degrees, active experience with, or successful directed participation in, the feared situation were especially effective ways of overcoming fears. All seem related to the child's sense of trust, autonomy, initiative and achievement.

Likewise, findings about *anger,* hostility and aggressiveness seem allied to knowledge about feelings of particular importance at certain stages. For example, anger outbursts related to establishment of routine and physical habits and to conflicts with authority, reported by Goodenough[302] at two years, seem connected with the child's need for a sense of autonomy. While his social difficulties of the next few years are undoubtedly related to the need for time as he learns to associate with other children, they may also be a reflection of his seeking the feelings already mentioned. Difficulties in social situations and disagreements with playmates were most frequent sources of provocation of anger between the ages of three and four. Although outbursts were less frequent by the age of four, social situations were still the most frequent source. Convictions that feelings of achievement are important at all ages are borne out by a study reported by Keister and Updegraff.[448] Anger was one of the outcomes in situations where the child was called upon to perform difficult tasks. His anger in response to a particular event decreased as he gained skill in handling it.

In any discussion of general pattern of emotional development, presence of conflicting feelings (ambivalence) should be mentioned. For example, a child may seem hostile and affectionate toward the same person within a comparatively short period of time. Knowledge of patterns, gradients or stages, is incomplete; variations with age are not clear.

Values in Expression of Feelings. What is known about emotional behavior and its development suggests that the child's expressing his feelings instead of keeping them "bottled up" inside himself can have advantages for him and for those associated with him. Many adults have wished they knew what an aloof, restrained, silent and tense child was concerned about. If he talked, played, expressed himself through creative activities, or "exploded," he might ease the tension and also straighten out his own thoughts in the process. Also, in so doing, he might reveal to the adult what it was that bothered him, or what he needed a better grasp of. On the other hand, many have wished for more restraint, for his own sake and the sake of others, in the child whose frequent intense emotional reactions jeopardized the safety and well-being of others. In children with responses of these kinds, and in children "who seem to be getting along very well," *insight is gained by considering feelings beneath the surface responses.* Furthermore, acceptance of the premise that expression of feelings and consideration for other people can both be present decreases confusion which current emphasis on expressiveness sometimes gives.

The adult's understanding and acceptance of the way the child feels are being stressed today. These attitudes encourage the child's expression of his feelings—a step toward handling them. For example, Read says, "A child may want the attention of the teacher and, not getting it, may attack the child whom he feels is his rival or the teacher whom he feels is deserting him. A child like this needs to have his confidence built up so that he will see others as less of a threat to him. He needs help in accepting and finding better outlets for his feeling. When it is all right to admit the feeling of wanting the teacher all to yourself, it becomes easier to work out a better solution than attacking others."*

The child's realization that his feelings are understood may come

* Read[684] (pp. 160-161).

in different ways. Baruch tells of a child who clung to his mother. She tried mirroring his feeling (thinking what he was feeling and saying it aloud). "Ronnie was nodding soberly each time she mirrored his feelings and in a subdued small whisper he was repeating, 'Ronnie want his mommie. Ronnie doesn't want his mommie to go 'way.' Came a day when his voice was no longer small and subdued. . . . And then, suddenly, . . . 'Mommie knows now. . . . Now Ronnie go play.' Without another glance in her direction, he turned and trudged out to the yard and his sandbox, secure in his mind that his mother did know and understood."*

Balance in use of this point of view which stresses expression of feelings comes through reference to other points of view also. The child's need to grow in self discipline is discussed in the following chapter. Possibilities of assisting in the child's development of feelings of confidence through use of his abilities were included in discussions of learning through play in the chapters on motor and intellectual growth. Along with increase in skill seemed to come an increase in social poise and self-confidence as evidenced by increased ascendance, according to studies by Jack[405] and Page.[647]

Indications of Feelings.   The term "general emotional tone" was used in the first chapter to describe an aspect of the individual which is receiving much attention today. It involves feelings regarding one's self and one's world not entirely of the obvious intensity that anger, fear, affection and other emotions often are. It may be described in terms of personality components, such as a sense of trust, etc. Feeling secure, confident, adequate, belonging, are other terms sometimes used. Agreement on the importance of understanding these feelings is general, but knowledge of how to do it is limited.

Everyday behavior of the child is one source of information about his feelings. Read says characteristic attitudes "may be seen in such things as in the way the child walks, runs, holds his hands, in his posture, etc. . . . One child clutches our finger tightly as we walk along with him, . . . Another lets his hand lie limply in ours, . . . Voice quality and speech offer clues to feelings. . . . One can get valuable clues by observing the way a child reacts to the approaches of another child as well as the way he himself approaches others."†

Responses in free play may also be revealing of emotional tone.

* Baruch[77] (p. 27).
† Read[684] (pp. 131-133).

For example, the following description suggests the happy tone which those associated with this particular three-year-old, Jerry, sensed repeatedly.

Jerry comes in from another nursery school room. Drops down on his knees and begins to play with Don's train. Don has left it to put blocks away and pays no attention. Jerry straightens the train. It has an engine in front and a caboose in back; he puts on another engine in back of the caboose. He begins to choo choo in a very low tone. Goes from front to back engine. Makes each one choo choo in its turn. Gets very close to the teacher and Don who are putting blocks away on the shelves. When the blocks are all up, Don begins to straighten toys on the shelves. Looks at the train Jerry is pushing and says, 'I'm going to put that away,' and begins taking the train up, car by car. Jerry continues ch! ch! Then helps put the train away. Jerry continues his ch ch after the train is put up and he has begun work on a puzzle. As he succeeds with the puzzle, the ch sounds become very loud and he smooths the finished puzzle hard with both hands.

Expressions of imagination, such as dramatization, and creative activities, such as painting, may sometimes reveal feelings in less direct ways than actions of the previous description seem to reveal them. For example, one may wonder what it means, if anything, for a particular child, when she always wants to be the mother in housekeeping play, when hospital play occupies a large proportion of her play time, or when she always covers over fresh bright colors in a painting until they become dark. Thought about questions such as these may lead to further understanding of the individual.

To assume that particular responses convey indirectly certain meanings is part of the thinking involved in use of projective techniques. (See pages 440 to 442.) Possibilities for understanding individuals based on interpretation of their paintings are reported by Alschuler and Hattwick.[16] Use of children's drawings as indications of the measure of security is described by Wolff.[919] Study of doll play is a frequent approach (Sears,[735] Murphy,[612] Moustakas[598]). In these attempts to learn about emotions, as in attempts to learn about intelligence through tests, training of those arranging the situation or administering the tests and interpreting the responses is very pertinent. Those qualified are in professional fields such as psychiatry, psychology, psychoanalysis and psychiatric social work.

Without venturing into a professional field for which he is not qualified, a person seeking understanding of a child's feelings can interest himself in what it is that the child seems to be responding to, what it is that he seems to be needing and seeking. This is a warm and human response, not an analytical one. There is no intention of studying every action and word to discover feelings they reveal, but there is genuine respect and concern for the feelings of another individual, i.e., of the child.

Reaction to Emotional Difficulty.   When young children experience emotional difficulties they may show physical symptoms of loss of appetite, wakefulness, irritability or restlessness. Nightmares in children of all ages call for an investigation of the child's emotional well-being.* Release of their emotional difficulties may be in imaginative play,† through which they can get rid of tension arising out of stress or of anxiety. Or accumulated emotional tensions may be released in explosions of temper or fear or in destructive play. Such behavior needs to be understood as a symptom to be studied to find out what the child is trying to say through such behavior.‡ Play techniques and play therapy are useful here. Study of such explosive or such retreat behavior involves attempting to find the cause and removing it if possible. Meanwhile, when the cause is not yet found, or, if found, cannot be removed, the child can be given every possible emotional security and emotionally constructive experience (of joy, rest, and peace). How love and understanding, which give the child affectional security and personal status, can restore preschool children who have lacked it, is frequently reported in case histories.

Causes of Behavior Difficulties.   Thwarting of emotions or inner anxiety are not the only causes of behavior difficulties in young children. Gesell states the case for the type of behavior problem which occurs as a result of sheer growth, the type which appears at certain stages of growth in most children as a result either of an inner disequilibrium in growth or of some error we in our present culture are making in what we expect of children. Gesell and Ilg say: "A developmental approach is of supreme importance in the management of those variations of conduct which are sufficiently atypical or pronounced to deserve the designation of behavior deviations. In infancy and early childhood it is especially difficult to draw a sharp line between normal and abnormal behavior. In a sense all children are problem children, because none can escape the universal problem of development which always presents some difficulties. On the other hand, there are few forms of malbehavior which are not in history

---

* Regarding nightmares, further discussion is in Josselyn[441] (p. 58).
† Levy,[507] Murphy.[612]
‡ Erikson.[245]

and essence a variation or deflection of normal mechanisms. . . . Many behavior deviations have their inception at a specific age when a mild degree of manifestation is well nigh universal. The deviation is in the nature of an exaggeration, or an 'overindividuation.' Overindividuation means that in a period of normal disequilibrium, the behavior did not become duly subordinated to the total action system: it grew out of proportion."*

Whether or not thumbsucking or stuttering is serious must be judged by their relation to the developmental pattern. In our culture most children suck thumbs for longer or shorter periods. In our culture also, transient speech defects such as stuttering often make their appearance at the stage of development when the child has more urge to say things than he has words with which to express himself. (See Chapter 9.) Such stuttering represents a disequilibrium in growth which occurs in the majority of children at about two and one-half to three years of age.

For children from one to three years of age, or at the period when routines are being established, even so-called stable children can be thrown off balance by a simple interruption in routine like a visit from Grandma or having to take a nap at an unaccustomed hour. The mother who understands these periods of disequilibrium and the forms the child's behavior deviation may take at the various periods is spared much anxiety. Growth has a strong impetus, so that the child can be expected to pull through these periods of disequilibrium by sheer inner or inherent sense of direction which works in line with his own unique pattern of development. The better we understand this fact of child development, the more we are inclined to trust inner development and the less we are given to the old methods of pouncing upon the so-called behavior problems with vigorously enforced campaigns of correction.

However, whenever a behavior problem† is prolonged or whenever it is severe, one should always bear in mind that such a behavior problem is probably due to more than a temporary disequilibrium in growth. For example, many six- to eighteen-month-old children rock themselves in bed. One should not be too disturbed when this occurs. Some writers recommend rocking such children to sleep in order to

---

* Gesell and Ilg[291] (p. 295).

† For additional information on behavior problems see research reported by Macfarlane, Allen and Honzik,[523] A Development Study of the Behavior Problems of Normal Children between Twenty-one Months and Fourteen Years.

satisfy the desire to be rocked. However, some children indulge in strenuous body rocking to the point of physical exhaustion, or in severe head bumping. These are not to be regarded as common aspects of growth in our culture but, rather, as evidence of great inner tension. Most children suck thumbs for longer or shorter periods of time, as has been said, but thumbsucking which absorbs the child's attention over long periods in the daytime in competition with normal play interest means that the child is in need of some change in routine or of personal relationships.

Various theories to explain *thumbsucking* are now being investigated.* Explanations offered include inadequate feeding in infancy, inadequate satisfaction of the sucking impulse, unsatisfied craving for affection, and chance habit established perhaps in the eating process or when the baby's fist comes by chance into contact with his lips with resultant sucking and satisfaction. One attitude toward thumbsucking is to consider it as fulfilling some basic need in the child's life. When it first appears, some shift in time, amount or quality of feeding may correct it, or some adjustment in sleeping hours or situation may cause it to disappear. Plenty of love and affection, balanced by a gradually increasing adjustment of the child to a workable routine for him and his family, are usually recommended.† It is the provision for the child's basic growth needs rather than a direct attack upon the habit itself which is now the generally accepted method of meeting the situation.

As the deeper meanings of the child's emotional and behavioral development have come to be understood, it has become increasingly clear that aggressive attack upon such behavior as thumbsucking, masturbation, nail-biting, stuttering, and other such manifestations not only is largely futile, but can also increase tensions. When the cause is of a deep-rooted emotional nature, as contrasted to persistence of a habit after its original basis has disappeared, mechanical devices, reminders and rewards are "surface approaches" which can increase strain. There is accumulating evidence that when the physical and emotional needs of children are met adequately any behavior manifestations which appear on the way will adjust themselves to the total

---

* Different studies of thumbsucking are presented in the Journal of Pediatrics, 39:4, 1951, and in Orlansky,[643] and Sears.[734, 737]

† Attitudes toward thumbsucking are discussed in Ridenour,[702] Spock,[792] and Wolf.[917]

growth complex and will disappear spontaneously in due time.[270, 291, 695]

There is one situation which can impede this spontaneous adjustment. In any form of behavior, such as thumbsucking, masturbation, stuttering, and the like, if the parent becomes tense and anxious, or if severe discipline or persistent nagging occurs, the behavior pattern tends to become fixed so that when the time comes for the growth pattern to straighten itself out it is less easily done. If children show emotional reaction clearly by negativism, defiant resistance, by sneaking under cover with the behavior, or by other signs of strain, they are telling adults their treatment is not only futile but perhaps dangerous. Among apparently "corrected cases" breaking one bad habit may mean another will appear soon.

On the other hand, exploring the child's readiness to proceed to another stage of response may reveal the child easily accepting new forms of behavior. Approaches with the child who is "ready" to proceed but has not, may have a connection with the findings of Sears and others concerning weaning practice. "None of the children who weaned themselves showed any upset." When mothers took the initiative, the children were studied for signs of emotional upset or frustration. Variations were found according to age, with the reduction of upset among children weaned between eight and eleven months not yet explained; it was also found that "the more preparation a child has, and the more gradually his mother makes the shift, the less disturbance he will show;" a third factor is "the mother's decisiveness in weaning. She can be absolutely adamant about the process, never reversing herself, or she can be very sensitive to the child's expressions of discomfort, and go back to bottles over and over again. These two extremes in training would produce comparable differences in *the child's expectancies*. The former mother would create certainty for the child while the latter mother would create uncertainty. Her child would be placed in a greater state of conflict about what to expect from her. Since conflict is itself frustrating, we would expect such backing-and-filling by the mother to produce greater upset than a more direct approach to the matter. . . . This dimension of decisiveness is not to be confused with . . . preparation and gradualness."*

Most children need time in learning to keep a bed dry, but some children have still not learned this by four years of age, boys char-

---

* Sears[733] (pp. 88-89).

acteristically having more difficulty with this learning than girls. When the learning is very slow, one may assume that something in the physical or psychological setting of the child needs attention.*

Some children show prolonged and violent temper tantrums which are more intense than those of most children and which do not taper off as normal growth occurs. These should be regarded, not as normal growth behavior, but as symptoms of an inner disturbance which requires attention.

One study† of 555 nursery school children gives some help in knowing what to expect as usual or growth behavior in preschool children, since each item on the list occurred in 50 to 90 per cent of the children studied. The list of behavior found in this high proportion of children is presented in the table.

Behavior in Nursery School Children

Per Cent of Children Showing the Behavior	Behavior	Peak
80	Ask unnecessary help	2½-3 yrs.
85	Leave tasks incomplete	2-3½ yrs.
90	Waste time at routines	2-4 yrs.
80	Ignore requests	2½-3 yrs.
85	Dawdle at meals	2½-3½ yrs.
75	Wriggle a great deal while sitting	2½-3½ yrs.
60	Resist at rest	2-4 yrs.
50	Fear strange people or objects	2-3½ yrs.
70	Laugh, squeal, jump around	2-4 yrs. (consistent)
70	Slur or speak indistinctly	2-2½ yrs.

Twenty per cent or more of the children studied showed tendencies toward all of these forms of behavior. Children of two years of age exhibit many tendencies which, in the normal course of events, tend to decrease gradually and regularly throughout the preschool period. The authors conclude by saying that preschool children are necessarily dependent on adults, have inadequate motor control and short attention span, are very active, negativistic and self-centered. These characteristics cause the responses listed in the table.

Different classifications were included in a study by Macfarlane, Allen and Honzik.[523] In reporting information on behavior problems shown by one-third or more of the boys and girls whom they studied

---

* For further discussion of these points see: Spock,[791] Spock and Huschber;[795] also Tomkins et al.[844]

† Hattwick and Sanders.[339]

longitudinally, they say, "It can be seen that some problems were present early—at 21 months, diurnal and nocturnal enuresis and restlessness in sleep, and thumbsucking in girls at 21 months and 3 years—but never reached the one-third-of-the-children level again. Other problems started later—food finickiness, negativism, and lying—and were given up by the children after a relatively brief trial run and did not recur at the one-in-three level. These were largely coping devices which apparently outran their usefulness for most children relatively quickly.

"Some problems were much later in appearing at the one-out-of-three level—reserve, and still later, nailbiting, mood swings, disturbing dreams, and, in the boys, jealousy. Other patterns, once started, continued throughout most of the age span—tempers for boys (girls at age 7 gave them up except for one age level), and oversensitiveness, the most continuous for girls and second to tempers for boys who largely dropped this pattern at age 12. Temper appears as both a coping technique and an expressive reaction, and oversensitiveness as largely a coping device although in a few children it was associated with real tension. Specific fears, though not lasting as long as either oversensitiveness or tempers, occurred in nine out of fourteen age levels for both the boys and the girls."*

Unstable Period of Learnings. Many of the emotional manifestations of preschool children characterize later periods of children's lives as well. They occur, apparently, whenever the child is learning new things so that his psychological energy is being diverted into a number of channels at once.

It is characteristic of learning that it reaches an apparently smooth, finished result on the surface before it has been practiced in the nervous system long enough to make it truly automatic. This unstable stage which is inherent in most, if not all, types of learning is likely to come to light whenever the child is asked to make a new adjustment before given learnings are fixed. For example, children who seem to be trained for the toilet so that they no longer have accidents demonstrate this principle when they "relapse" if a baby is born into the family, or if they are entered in nursery school or if some other basic and demanding adjustment is required of them.

Such relapses sometimes occur after the learning has had several

* Macfarlane et al.[523] (p. 154).

months to crystallize. When the child is exposed to new demands shortly after a skill or learning has first appeared to be accomplished, a partially fixed learning may be "jarred loose" by an added distraction or pressure made upon it.

The difference in approach to behavior problems implied here is important. When the problem is simply an aspect of growth or is a breakdown of a learning still in the unstable stage, the approach would be one of giving natural growth an opportunity to correct the difficulty. When, however, the behavior problem is due to inner tensions or anxieties, to physical difficulties or maladjustment in some other area, the approach is one of therapeutic treatment. A high proportion of the behavior problems of preschool children are of the former sort.

Integral Stage of Learnings.   Each learning probably has this unstable stage, when strain will break up the as yet not quite automatically fixed pattern. When, however, the pattern has had sufficient practice for it to function automatically, conscious attention to it or strain are no longer required. Change to another level of organization takes place; synthesis occurs. Psychological energy is then released to undertake new learnings or to produce a relaxed period of enjoyment of previous learnings.

In our culture, with the demands we characteristically make on young children, there appears to be a period at around eighteen months to three years of age when several basic learnings are in the unstable stage. At around three years, or if not at this chronological age then at the stage of learning which most children reach at around this age, there seems to be a period in which fewer learnings are being newly mastered. At this time earlier learnings are accomplished, and a total integration of previous learnings seems to occur. This is in many senses a "breathing spell" for the child, and, needless to say, for the mother as well. Four year olds are sometimes described as "bursting with powers." Entrance to kindergarten, and again to the first grade, may demand a great deal of attention and emotional energy.

Progressive Unstable and Integrated Stages of Learnings.   Many of the most basic of human learnings have a long series of maturity levels. The more complex the ability, the longer the ultimate integration stage is delayed. Such learnings would be the learning of social responsibility, the use of money, continued improvement in the use of language, the constant refinement of self-controls, and so on. In such learnings it would appear that the human being progresses a step at a time, each step having its stage of instability followed by crystallization into automatic, integrated smoothness as a part of the person and his behavior.

For example, one step in social responsibility pertains to whimsical demands upon other people. The baby learns not to fuss too much when he needs attention and to adapt his hunger and his sleepiness to routines which fit into the larger routines of the family as a whole. A little later he learns to feed himself, still later to dress and undress himself and to take complete toilet responsibility, thus relieving his mother of much of his care. Along the way he makes a beginning toward doing his share in the running of the family machinery. He may pick up the newspapers in the daily housecleaning; he may dry the silver and the pans at dishwashing time. The child in Figure 70 enjoys helping her mother. Each new task requires a learning process. Each

Figure 70.   This two-and-one-half-year-old girl helps put away the table silver and thus takes one step in learning to assume responsibility.

learning will have a period of only apparent finish, which will be thrown off balance by distraction. Yet with practice (particularly if the practice is companionable and fun) each will eventually find a state of integration and automatic smoothness as a part of the individual.

Each stage of instability in the learning may produce some emotional repercussions; each stage of integration will result in emotional freedom and rest. Some personalities absorb the emotional repercussions of new learning in their stride, showing, in periods of strain, little more maladjustment than slight extra fatigue. Other personalities take each of the new learnings required by life so hard that they seem constantly upset emotionally. Such children require a longer time in which to integrate or stabilize learnings before new demands are made upon them. Almost every person has some areas of learning in which integration comes more easily than in others. For example, some children take to intellectual learnings with great ease, yet take unusually long periods to stabilize motor learnings. Other children find the reverse true. Some children find social adjustments no demand to speak of, yet find every habit-training adjustment difficult to make. Here, as everywhere in child care, an awareness of individual differences is of extreme importance. Each child is in many ways a law unto himself, yet each belongs to the human race and grows according to certain fundamental laws. Each can, therefore, be understood better if these laws of growth are understood.

Developing Awareness of Self

In the course of his emotional development, and the unstable and integrated steps in learning referred to in the previous section, the child is making discoveries about himself. Attitudes toward himself and his place in his world are being developed. These attitudes change as different feelings become of particular importance at different stages of development. For example, when a sense of autonomy is of paramount importance the individual's views of himself and other people differ from those of a later stage when a sense of identity is the special need. Description of the development of awareness of self involves consideration of the widening horizon of the person's interest in others and his relation to them. This pattern of development is sometimes referred to as a pattern of love development. The term, psychosocial development, is sometimes used.* In its connotation behavior setting is taken into account. Wolff says that from his "observations there emerged a unifying concept of the viewpoint of the child, in that all expressions of personality by the young child seemed to be variations on one theme: the child's search for his self. The child's imagery, his spoken language, and the language of his behavior appear as a continuous questioning: Who am I? What am I for? The child does not explore the world only in order to gain knowledge, but also to differentiate himself from his environment."†

Children in many ways develop awareness of other people before they develop awareness of themselves. The infant seems unaware of himself as a body or as a person during the first two or three months of life. However, he can soon be seen in the process of developing self awareness. At around four months he may be seen lying in his crib in rapt attention as he regards his own hand or foot waving about before his eyes. By six or seven months a look of wonder may go over his face as he pinches his own toes and becomes aware of the resulting sensation as belonging to himself. Gradually he defines his own body as he handles his hands, his feet, his ears, pats his own head on "How tall is baby?" and finds his genitals, which he is likely to handle off and on for a period of several weeks at this stage of his growth.

Intense Self-centeredness a Stage of Growth. Even though self-awareness seems to develop slowly in the first year of life, the child seems suddenly very aware of himself. At around eighteen months to two years "me," "mine," "I want" begin to be outstanding in his language and in his action. He appears to be extremely self-centered. It is as if he had suddenly discovered himself and had become the focus of his own universe. As previously stated, he attempts to make a part of himself, that which his expanding world includes. (See sections on motor development, sense perceptions, language and reasoning.)

This self absorption has its roots in growth. As early as six or seven months he is experiencing the intense thrill of conquest over his own body and is so absorbed in his newly acquired control of eyes, head, arms and hands that he pays slight attention to other people, except,

---

* Josselyn;[441] McCandless;[526] Barker and Wright.[74]
† Wolff[919] (pp. xiii-xiv).

perhaps, to "play to the galleries"* for a moment at a time. This self absorption is especially evident at eighteen months to two years, or at the stage of development when the child has achieved upright loco-motion and spends prodigious amounts of energy "getting into things," exploring, handling, and manipulating everything he can lay his hands on, and seeming almost oblivious to the adult "No, no, don't touch." At this stage in the pursuit of his own objective he seems stubborn to the adult who tries to side-track or distract him. There is, however, a constructive side to this stubborn self-absorption; the child, faced with mastering control of his own body and learning to understand and to speak language, and also to discriminate size, shape, weight, color, and so on, would probably not accomplish the necessary learn-ings unless he were completely absorbed in these problems. If he were too reactive to people, he would probably accomplish these motor, language and perceptual learnings much more slowly.

This self-absorption is modified somewhat as the child completes his mastery over elementary motor processes and intellectual learn-ings, especially in the sense perception area. It persists, despite the widening social horizons of the three-year-old, and not until four or five years of age does the child begin clearly to sense himself as part of a group. At around three years of age most children begin to use "we," "us" and "ours" instead of the previous "I," "me," and "mine," which at two years are used predominantly.

At around four and thereafter through age six, boasting is a form of play and conversation. At this stage the expanding sense of self leads to the persistent "look at me, see me," and to the exaggerations which seem to be lies but are really attempts to have more and be more than the other children. It also leads to an urge to widen physical horizons, to break out of bounds, both physical and psychological, so that unless the adults expand the play and space and provide oppor-tunities for exploration of that which is new, running away may occur. Along with perception of his own size[445] in reference to others there seems to be an interest in "growing up" which, again, warrants study.

In this development of self the child sometimes relives his babyhood at around two and one-half to three years of age, and may even express a desire to be a baby again. Some parents meet this stage by respond-ing to the child's "Let's play I'm a baby;" they feed him if he desires, rock him on their laps and pick him up and carry him as if he were

* Gesell.[292]

tiny again. In doing this it is possible to regard the activity as a game, thus working on the assumption that although this is fun we are really growing up and that is even more fun. The response can be viewed as one in which the child is seeking something he needs; as he gains reassurance through it he will be more ready for the more complex situation. Not infrequently this stage develops at the time a new baby has been added to the household, and bears some of the elements of a desire to return to babyhood in order to command Mother's attention once more. However, it occurs in only children, and seems to express some aspect, as yet not quite understood, of the developing awareness of self. The child's interests in being independent and dependent conflict. He wants to be and is both.[104, 345]

Early Expansions of Self. As the self develops it expands beyond one's self, so that the child is affectionate toward the people who are close to him, who love and care for him. He may also at around eighteen months become closely attached to some such possession as a soft doll or toy animal. He may pet, hug and kiss the object, and like having it near him, sometimes insisting upon taking it to bed with him. As play interests develop the daytime attachment to these objects becomes less intense. However, he may continue over a period of time to want to have it nearby when the situation is a strenuous one for him.

Development of Ability to Love Someone Else. Affection for others is shown in the first year of life.[134, 144, 597] Jersild refers to the fact that "there is very little systematic information concerning the development of affection, concerning the way in which the child's capacity for loving, and the range or scope of his affections, wax and change in the process of development."*

The newborn infant, as we have seen, loves no one except in a most self-centered sense. He feels his own world of sensations; he finds comfort when cared for, but he has no respect for the comfort or well-being of others. This is to be expected from tiny infants. As time goes on, however, this self-centered being has potentialities and experiences which help him to develop an ability to consider others, to feel sympathetic toward them, to be happy at their happiness or sad at their sadness, and to enjoy contributing to their happiness and well-being (Murphy[613]).

* Jersild[422] (p. 893).

PSYCHOANALYTIC AND OTHER VIEWPOINTS. Description of the way this development occurs and the conditions conducive to its growth is to be found in psychoanalytical writings.* This school of thinking emphasizes the importance of the young infant's relationship to the mother, the importance later of the child's attachment to the father, the importance of early childhood manifestations of the sexual impulses and the need to deal with these wisely and wholesomely. The writers point out the many cases of adult neuroticism which can be traced to inadequate relationships between mother and young child or father and young child.

As previously stated, additional knowledge of aspects of emotional development and processes is to be desired. Information from Sears[733] concerning the importance of warmth in the mother's relationships with the child and the absence of punitiveness, is thought-provoking in terms of the concept of himself and the model to be imitated which it provides for the child.

PATTERNS OF LOVE DEVELOPMENT. As the child's concept of himself and his closeness to others develops, certain patterns can be seen through which nearly all children grow. At first, for both boys and girls, a close attachment to the mother is characteristic in infancy. She is the source of food and comfort. First love goes to her. Fathers who share in the physical care and social play with their babies also share in this first capacity to love.

Gradually the child learns to include others besides his mother in the circle of his expanding affections. The father is usually included next, even though he may not spend a great deal of time with the baby. At around eighteen months to three years girls are likely to attach themselves closely to the father emotionally, sometimes refusing to let the mother do anything for them if the father is around. Boys identify themselves with the father, as a rule, at a little later age, their attachment being at a peak around four to five years of age. As the child enters school he develops a more casual, less dependent attitude toward his parents, yet is likely still to cling to the intimate moments at bed time or at other times when comfort and assurance are needed. In adolescence there is again a period of shift of the child's most intense love.†

---

* A. Freud;[269] S. Freud;[272] Ribble;[695] Isaacs;[402] Horney;[370, 371] Josselyn.[441]

† For further discussion of development of sex interests and the need for sex education, see Breckenridge and Vincent,[131] Chapter 14. References on sex education include Child Study Association[163] and Hymes.[384]

In accordance with information concerning emotion, the ability to express affection is of great importance to normal and happy living. Again, we desire more information to explain behavior such as the following, which sometimes occurs at preschool ages:

All of the children were running to the steam shovel. Nicoli stood by the swing holding her toy animal. Laura came close to her and said "Come along. Let's go see the shovel." Nicoli took Laura's hand and together they went over to the fence to watch the steam shovel go by. The driver waved.

Ability to be Accepting of Oneself. In accordance with information concerning needs, the ability to "accept oneself" in harmony with the world or to integrate experience as part of oneself is important. Again, explanations of such behavior as the following which occurs frequently at preschool years would be interesting:

"La, la, la, la, I'm taller than you are. La, la, la, la, I'm taller than you are." Johnny is at the top of the slide. Later, "Hi, Mother Hubbard, I'm up in the tree cupboard," he calls to his mother from the tree.

These illustrations from observational records suggest many possibilities for the adult who *recognizes that it is important that the child feel adequate about himself as contrasted to his feeling criticized.* It seems logical to assume that the child will be interested in proceeding to new competences with such recognition.

Developing Awareness of Others

Previous discussion has implied that a concept of self and of others is interwoven and connected closely with emotion, as well as with intellect. These ideas need to be included in a concept of social behavior and development.* The newborn infant has no conception of himself as a person or of other people as different from any of the sense impressions which come to him. When he is hungry or in discomfort, he cries with no thought that a person or persons must come to his relief, but only that eventually he is relieved. He has only the sensations from his own body and the vague conglomerate sensations from the external world.

Reactions to People Begin Early. Strange as it is, the infant seems to become aware of other people sooner than he becomes aware of himself as a clearly defined entity. Morgan and Morgan[597] found that

* For discussion of theoretical concepts of social development see Anderson[34] and Sears.[732]

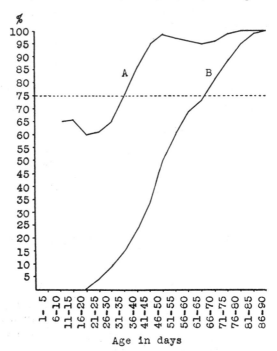

Figure 71.   Reactions of infant to talking by examiner. A, Passive attention to talking. B, Active attention to talking. (Morgan, S. S., and Morgan, J. B.: Adaptive behavior patterns in infants, Journal of Pediatrics 25:168-177, 1944, C. V. Mosby Company.)

most infants react to people as early as the thirty-fifth day by giving passive attention such as looking, making small movements with arms or legs, or turning eyes to follow someone. Some children react this way much earlier; all children examined reacted this way by three months. By a little over two months of age most children were found to react actively to being talked to by the examiner (Fig. 71). This active reaction consisted of smiling, cooing, laughing aloud or waving arms and legs in an excited manner. Some children reacted actively in this way as early as twenty to thirty days of age; all children examined did so by three months. When approached quietly by these examiners, the babies were more likely to react passively; when talked to they were more likely to react actively. When actively played with, most of the infants in this study reacted passively by fifty to seventy-five days of age; all of them did so by three months. A few of them reacted actively as early as twenty to twenty-five days; most of them did so by eighty days; all of them did so by ninety days. Most of the children reacted to being played with by a social smile before sixty days of age, and with cooing by seventy days.

Forms of Social Behavior. Several investigators[*] have found infants of two to three months of age reacting to being approached socially by *smiling* in return. Even when infants had less human contact than usual, they showed social responsiveness.

By three or four months of age infants have begun to progress from a general reactivity to anyone at all who happens to be near them to the differential reactivity which depends on *discrimination between persons*. At this time most babies begin to discriminate between one familiar person and another. They give clear evidence that they recognize mother as different, for example, from father. After the fourth month, the baby "begins at this time to show, in addition to physical growth and health, the first specific emotional responses to his mother. His eyes focus for an appreciable time on her face and he smiles in response to her presence, his entire motor system gradually becoming tense with excitement and anticipation."[†] *Social initiative* on the part of the child himself may occur at four or five months when he smiles a recognition of familiar persons whether these persons have taken the initiative in playing with him or not. By five or six months he shows his resentment at being parted from a familiar person by crying; withdrawing from strangers may appear at about this time.

"Sociable" behavior develops rapidly from nine or ten months on. By one year many babies, if given sufficient previous social experiences, have developed a high degree of *"social reciprocity"*[‡] as compared with babies of three, six, or nine months of age. Waving bye-bye, playing pat-a-cake, showing "how tall is baby" by patting his own head, are all usual at this time if the child has had a satisfactory kind of social experience. "Give Mamma the ball," or whatever else he happens to have in his hand, will get a reaction of giving at around one year if one reaches toward the child gently and smiles encouragingly. At this time, too, a quick gesture of giving or handing something to other people is a favorite social gesture on the part of the baby himself. However, the object proffered as a gesture of social behavior is more likely than not

[*] Bühler;[144] Gesell;[291] Jones and Burks;[438] Morgan and Morgan.[597]
[†] Ribble[695] (p. 83).
[‡] Gesell.[292]

to be hung on to, and a howl will ensue if the adult or another child takes the gesture seriously and tries to part the baby from the proffered toy.

By the time most children are a year old they show definite preferences and dislikes for people. They do not remember people long, however, unless they have had some unusually emotional experience with them. They may as late as eighteen months seem to forget even their mother if she is away for a week or more. Reacquaintance is rapid, however, when she returns.

A child of nine months seems to know when the conversation concerns him. If adults make a practice of addressing all the conversation to the child or of letting it all center around him whenever they are near him, the child may develop the false idea that conversation must be about him, since all the conversation that he hears centers around him. He can learn early that people talk about other things and have other interests, even when he happens to be awake.

It seems important to social development that babies be played with from three or four months of age on, or at the stage when they show reaction to being played with. Some people think that since small babies are, as they say, "mainly in the business of growing physically," they need only to be fed, bathed, changed and left to themselves. These people are likely to consider that "personality," as they conceive it, develops at two years or later, the period when "children become interesting as persons." Such an attitude is questionable. Although evidence of effect of early personal associations on personality is not clear-cut,* no one doubts the joy that the parents and the baby can have in their natural, easy response as they are sociable according to their temperaments. Figure 72 suggests that these social times of parents and children and the development of a sense of trust are related. Importance of joy of this kind in early associations is emphasized by the following report.

Bob's mother believed that learning to be happy, resourceful and sociable began early. From the sheer joy of motherhood she patted and talked with Bob from the time she took over his care after arriving home from the hospital. As soon as she caught his first social smile, she talked with him again as she was talking when he first smiled, thus beginning in Bob the awareness that it is fun to communicate with people. Some suitable toy, though never more than one or two at first, was always at hand when Bob was awake. His mother stopped by his crib as she went about her work, handing him the rattle he had let drop, rattling the

* Dennis,[206] Orlansky,[643] and Ribble[695] discuss this question.

string of wooden beads, or otherwise calling his attention to the toy. Thus he learned how to use and to enjoy toys. She talked with him, at first leaning over his crib, then from a greater distance as she worked, so that he could continue his smiling and wriggling reactions, and later could coo or babble in reply. This also added to his sense of nearness to her, and kept him assured that he was not alone. Gradually she increased the length of time she left him alone with his toys, but she seldom failed to speak to him or to smile or to sing a snatch of song whenever she passed near him. Occasionally she changed the toy he was playing with or had dropped because of boredom. Thus she taught him how to be alone with his toys, yet she gave him increasing experience in social relationships. When she had to be away to shop or for relaxation, she left some congenial substitute person near. Thus Bob learned not to be too dependent on her presence, yet was never left without protection and a friendly presence. This also widened his circle of desirable acquaintances. He was never allowed to become a "demanding baby," who expected adults to respond to his every whim and to furnish amusement at all times.

Bob became a socially delightful child. By the time he was two years old his lively "Hi, Mummy!" "Hi, Daddy!" sent himself and his parents off to a good start in the morning. A firm, "That's all. Now we must do this," brought occasional resistance, but offered opportunity to teach Bob that the world of adults must sometimes move on despite his wish to keep on playing.

Not aggressive or demanding, Bob greeted most people with a gay grin which won him innumerable friends. His alert interest in the things about him and his

Figure 72. Social times with her father develop responsiveness to people in this seven-month-old baby. She is developing a sense of trust.

wide resourcefulness with even the simplest materials attracted to him the friendship of a wide variety of adults. For example, on a four-hour automobile trip, Bob practiced language while watching "Cows," "Car," " 'Nother car," "Big truck." When tired of this, he accepted a piece of hard candy wrapped in paper, unwrapped it, sucked the candy for several minutes, enjoying its taste and feel in his mouth, and then made a game of holding the paper in the breeze, moving it up and down to get variations.

How much of Bob's personality is inborn and how much is due to experience is an open question.

Reactions to other children begin as early as three or four months, when one infant may react to others by brief notice, such as a smile at the other baby's wrigglings.[144] By six or seven months infants may show a brief interest in each other and will reach for each other's toys or poke a finger at each other in a playful gesture. By a year, if they have had previous experience with other children, they will offer each other playthings in the same spirit of social gesturing mentioned above, but will usually hang on or cry if the other infant tries to take possession of the proffered object. Around twenty-one to twenty-four months babies will play briefly with each other (see discussion of individualistic and parallel play later), though it is not until considerably later that they play together in any truly social interchange.

At two years, children are not usually successful in eliciting a desired response from another child.[610] However, the social interchange with them develops rapidly from two to four years of age. At four or five the socially experienced child shows much awareness of and ability to stimulate other children's reactions. They respond to distress in other children, make requests for assistance, and take social initiative in "Come on, let's play" and in making definite suggestions as to what to play. In response to other children they utilize varied techniques of acceptance, refusal, evasion, or changing of the situation.*

Development of Relationships to Social Groups.† As we have seen, the infant recognizes another infant in play only by a brief contact, or by using the other infant as a play object. However, if two or more children are together, after the first novelty of the association wears off the play becomes highly *individualistic,* each child occupying him-

---

* Murphy and associates[610] review research up to 1937. Bibliographies and reviews of later research on social growth are presented in Anderson,[34] Chittenden,[620] Goodenough,[303] Murphy,[614] and Parten and Newhall.[652] Bibliographies on development of personality and social behavior of the child according to social contexts are in Heinicke and Whiting.[348]

† Sequences of social behavior are in Ames.[24]

self with his own activities in almost complete disregard of the other. From eighteen months to two years the child continues to be absorbed in individual play but is more influenced by the presence of another child. Characteristic play of this age is sometimes referred to as *parallel play,* for each child, although apparently playing quite by himself, usually plays at the same type of activity that occupies the other children of the group. Not only does he play with the same material, but he plays at it longer and has more resourceful ideas than he would if playing alone. A favorite situation at two years is digging in sand or dirt. One child fills his pail, carries it a short distance, and empties it. Another child, who has been digging only, adopts the idea of filling a pail and fills his pail, carries and empties it. There has been no exchange of words, but simply an exchange of ideas. In Figure 73 one two-year-old has paused to watch the other, who continues to be absorbed in her play.

BEGINNINGS OF COOPERATIVE PLAY. The next step to greater socialization may come when the second child conceives the idea of

Figure 73. Parallel play. Children play together, yet are absorbed in their own activities. One pauses occasionally to watch the other.

Figure 74. A shifting-group activity: children come and go in this game, yet the game goes on.

emptying the pail on the same pile of sand with the first child, thus changing the activity from a purely individualistic emptying of pails into a cooperative building of a mound of sand. This change may take place in silence or occur after an exchange of words, and may last for several minutes or relapse into individual activity almost immediately. Sometimes a brief socialization, evident when one child says, "Let's play in the sand," dissolves when the idea is carried out, since each child occupies himself in almost complete disregard of the others.

There is a gradual transition from solitary and parallel play to more cooperative forms of play.[37] As time goes on and as the child gains experience with other children, there is more exchange of ideas and more cooperation in play. One child says, "Let's play blocks. I'll build a garage." Another child answers, "All right. I'll build mine over here." Again separate projects will be undertaken, but now there is an almost constant recognition of the presence of each other, and a flow of conversation. "See, mine's big." "Oh, look, I made a roof." Perhaps there will be a temporary merging of projects. "Look out, my car's going to visit your garage."

A little later, among experienced children around three to five years

Developing Awareness of Others

of age, the *shifting group* is conspicuous (Fig. 74). Under this arrangement a fairly loosely organized game may grow up, lasting throughout a whole morning or even for several days, embracing the activity of a number of children, but depending on the presence of no particular child. For example, child A may say, "Let's play store." Child B and child C like the idea and join with A to build walls and counters with the blocks. D may appear, watch for a moment, and, having learned what is happening, begin to carry blocks. The project is so loosely organized that his appearance causes no confusion, nor is the absence of B felt when he drops away to play for a time with his wagon. Child E may join the game, and A and C may go off on some individual project, leaving the store game intact with D and E but with none of the original children. Later B may return. The play goes on with one child or with several, each individual coming or going at will. This type of game is typical when children are getting their first practice at socialized play yet still feel the charm of solitary play in which they can execute their

Figure 75. The beginning of well-organized group play. Here three children are cooperating closely in a project which could not go on without them. One loads pine cones on a truck. Another "drives" the truck to the stationmaster. Two other children are watching the activity.

own ideas in their own way. Such semiorganized play is possible despite the fact that at about this stage of development most children, with growing sureness of their knowledge of the world and with their increasing ability to express themselves in language, tend to be bossy and dogmatic in their play with other children.

From this shifting group type of play there finally develops *well-organized group play* (Fig. 75). However, during the preschool period these groups are never very complex or stable in their organization. The literature* shows that in day-to-day groups in the preschool period there may be found a semblance of the leadership-followership structure of the later organized "gangs." These relationships are extremely unstable, however, often changing completely in structure in a three month period. In some preschool groups the removal of a single member can dissolve whatever group unity exists. In the University of Iowa Preschool Laboratories Parten[651] found a trend toward development of leadership throughout the year, with leaders excelling nonleaders in intelligence and occupational level of parents, but with individual differences outweighing age differences. She also corroborates the majority of other studies in finding some children able to dominate for a time but unable to retain this status for long. She also found two types of leadership even in the preschool years: the "artful diplomat," and the child who attempts to lead by brute force.

VARIOUS POSITIONS IN GROUP.   Frequently as children play together they fall into various positions within the group. A particular child may have one position more often than others, but he can usually be found in each of the other possible positions or relationships over a period of time. Bühler† refers to these relationships as those of leader, of cooperating companion, tolerated companion or rejected companion.

The *leader* is the child who furnishes most of the accepted ideas and whose wish dominates the play. He may bring forth from others further use of their powers. He is acceptable to the other children. The child who dominates a group through bullying, and hence who rules by fear, cannot be called a leader in any constructive sense. Leading in a constructive way may take many different forms.

The *cooperating* companions stand in a position of cooperation with the leader, often offering him acceptable ideas, and sometimes as the game changes or a special type of leadership is required, stepping tem-

* See footnote on page 422.
† Bühler, C., in a lecture given at Merrill-Palmer School.

porarily into a position of leadership. The *tolerated* companions, though seldom sought when ideas are being discussed, are needed to "fill in." They play when their services are not particularly needed. The *rejected* companions may wish to play but have had too little experience to know how. They are rejected, sometimes because they are lacking in skills and ideas and sometimes because they lack an acceptable kind of social behavior. Most children occasionally are in each of the positions described.* Adults who find a child in the tolerated or rejected position frequently can, after thought as to why, give assistance in developing abilities which make him more likely to occupy other positions more frequently.

Children have preferences. Northway[636] in reporting on sociometric studies says, "with children, there is considerable variation, but even at the nursery school level, there is some tendency for a child to maintain his sociometric level."† Referring to "facts of social life" and emphasizing the importance of a person's finding his own situation satisfying, she says, "the child who has a low social potential can be just as satisfied and as satisfactory as the one who has a higher, provided he is not made to feel he should be more popular, or that he would be, 'better off' if he were."‡

Sympathetic Behavior Appears Early. Important to social participation of young children is development of the ability to be aware of and reactive to the feelings of others. Murphy,[613] in a study of the development of sympathy in preschool children, reviews the fact that the first awareness of the feelings of other children in the group she studied was shown in a tendency to help others when it was convenient or when it did not interfere with the given child's self-absorbed plans. The second stage was marked by a tendency to stop what one was doing in order to help another child, or to respond to the distress of another. Bridges[134] noted marked individual differences among children in this behavior. Some preschool children show sympathy only by staring or crying in sympathetic imitation. A more advanced stage of expression of sympathy is to try to comfort the distressed child by putting an arm around him, or saying "Does it hurt?" or, "What are you crying for?" Only later in social development is sympathy expressed

---

* Relative frequencies of different kinds of social participation are reported by Parten and Newhall.[652]

† Northway[636] (p. 10).

‡ Northway[636] (p. 11).

by more active measures to relieve the distressing situation, by such intuitive understanding as is shown by being kind to newcomers and helping them with their new tasks, by offering to share materials, by getting a toy to give to a child, or by defending the rights of smaller children. Murphy reports that three-year-olds notice the clothing and routines of other children, which shows a definite advance in social interest beyond the two-year level. In a rudimentary way the social conversation of three-year-olds is adult-like in its inclusion of discussion of clothes, likes and dislikes of people, where one lives and ordinary matters of daily routine.

Murphy[613] further reports that sympathetic behavior in very young children seems to arise from a number of different sources. In one instance it may represent the desire of a child to please a superior member of his group; in another instance it may represent the projection of his own anxiety; again, behavior like fighting, which is usually forbidden by adults, may be permitted because it appears to be in defense of someone else. Sympathetic behavior may also represent a spasmodic spill-over of behavior when one is too frightened to get into the swim, or it may represent genuine warmth and friendliness for the injured child or a desire to be sympathized with one's self. Murphy adds that no form of social behavior can be rightly understood apart from the underlying motive behind it.

Despite the self absorption of the preschool child which often appears as selfishness and quarrelsomeness, Murphy[613] and Bridges,[134] as well as other investigators,[313, 428] find that cooperative, sympathetic social behavior is emerging in the early years, and with satisfactory social experiences in the preschool years can proceed in the direction of further social insight and human understanding.

Sharing and Social Experiences Should Be Fun. "Sensitiveness to the needs and desires of others and a willingness to adjust one's own needs and desires to them"* is an important characteristic of sharing. In discussing the provision of environment conducive to sharing, Chittenden says the first responsibility is to create an environment where young children can feel secure and happy. The second responsibility is to introduce physical and social factors conducive to the child's learning to share.

Even the secure and happy child may not seem generous at first. One needs to remember that young children are self absorbed because

* Chittenden[620] (p. 182).

of the many demands which learning makes on their attention. Imagination has not yet reached the developmental level where true insight into other people's feeling is possible. Time concepts are also extremely limited at this age. When, therefore, we ask a young child to lend his toy "for five minutes" he has no idea that this is a short time. If he gets it back soon he may feel more willing to part with it the next time. In order to learn to share, it is important to see that the child gets plenty of satisfactory fun experiences in sharing with both adults and other children. Children are not discovering the joy of sharing if their social and sharing experiences are turned into unnecessarily painful periods when one is constantly nagged to be "nice to your little guest," or to give up precious possessions. Having to stand aside and see one's favorite doll or other cherished possession broken by another child does not result in the desire to share or even to have other children around. Thus joy in being with people and in sharing one's possessions with them can be fostered only by having social experiences which produce more fun than pain.

When two or more young children play together, it seems in accordance with their stage of development to have a tricycle or wagon apiece, a doll for each or a pail for each for digging in the sand. This does not mean cluttering up the play space of young children with excessive equipment, since too much equipment stultifies the development of imagination. It does mean, however, that if there is only one wagon or one tricycle between two or more young children, there will be more quarrels over its use. The sense of "mine" is acute at this age. The stage of learning the difference between "mine" and "yours" usually precedes the stage of taking turns. When visiting another home the mother who takes along one or two of the child's favorite play possessions so that he may play happily without being nagged to keep his hands off the knickknacks on the parlor table or to leave his host's possessions alone provides a setting in which happy associations are more likely to occur.

Children are naturally kind and generous if they are permitted to make gestures of kindness and generosity on their own level. They spontaneously want to see their own joy shared with adults or children. A well disciplined yet well loved child finds life with adults and other children good. A so-called response of "being mean" may grow out of inexperience or previous experience without practice of adaptation to others, in the sense of overindulgence. Or, the child may have felt forced to grab and fight in order to have a reasonable sense of possession of his own things. Or, in the child who does not feel well loved, it grows out of deep emotional disturbance. Well loved and well disciplined children with a reasonable supply of possessions which they can have, yet share, usually develop evidences of generosity fairly early.

Understanding of Individual Differences. Understanding of the individual is an important part of an adult's attitude toward a child. It is important in relationships of people, whatever their ages. It is interesting to speculate on how the child begins at an early age to acquire such an attitude. The point to stress in this section on the child's social growth is his potentiality for understanding and respect for each person, if he has the opportunity to reflect such a point of view from other people. Many parents and nursery school teachers can report illustrations of these potentialities in responses of an individual child to a child who is younger, or slower, a child who is different physically, or a child whose race or religion is different. One illustration will serve to suggest, and probably to raise questions about, potentialities and influences of the situation. In one nursery school a Chinese child entered a group of three-year-olds who had never known a Chinese person. Two children looked at her closely and one said, "Her eyes look sleepy." The teacher explained that eyelids looked different; the three children looked at theirs in the mirror. Then the teacher said, "She is Chinese." Twice during the morning and later at the luncheon table with her, the two children repeated this statement. At the table when they said it, the Chinese child smiled and said, "I am Chinese."

The need for early experience and discussion concerning individual differences is suggested by Stendler's report[806] that mothers found the greatest difficulties of children in beginning first grade were in understanding behavior differing from the child's own standards of goodness and badness.

Many Potentialities Present. It seems the nature of two- to four-year-olds to show all types of social behavior, both constructive and friendly, and destructive and self centered. One thing that puzzles many people who do not understand the beginnings of social development and who do not appreciate the intellectual and emotional limitations of young children is their apparent display of strangely contradictory behavior. Preschool children, for example, fight their best friends more than they fight other children.* This, to the person who understands,

* Murphy;[613] Isaacs.[402]

is not as contrary as it appears, since the child naturally more often "runs afoul" of the child he sees and plays with most than he does with other children. The children's self absorption and aggressive possessiveness run into each other in proportion as the children are exposed to each other in play.

It should be recalled here, too, that the quarrels of preschool children, although frequent, are brief, and children recover from them quickly, as a rule harboring no resentment. One study* showed that the average quarrel of a group of preschool children lasted only twenty-three seconds. The younger the child in this study, the more frequently he started quarrels, but the less aggressive he was. As the children grew older in the preschool age group, they quarreled less frequently, but were more aggressive when they did quarrel. The majority of the quarrels in this study started with a struggle for possessions. Quarrels as a rule led to pushing, striking, or other motor activities. Most such quarrels settle themselves without adult interference, although some adult supervision is necessary to keep older and bigger children from bullying younger and smaller children.

Another apparent contradiction in social behavior is revealed in Murphy's study.[613] She showed that children who had high scores in sympathetic behavior also showed considerable unsympathetic behavior and frequently had high scores in aggressive behavior. Here again the amount of social contact was high for some children who, in their many contacts, had wide opportunity to display the whole repertory of preschool social behavior, both good and bad; whereas less active children simply had fewer contacts. In other words, one can expect all sorts of social behavior from young children who, as a rule, react to each other impulsively and hence both kiss and strike other children, depending on the situation.

There seems little sex difference in this, boys showing as frequent sympathetic and friendly behavior as girls; girls striking, shouting and grabbing as frequently as boys. Before long, however, the cultural pattern becomes manifest, and the general expectation that boys must look out for themselves leads to greater tolerance of aggressive behavior for boys; on the other hand, the expectation that girls must be mellow and motherly emphasizes the sympathetic in their behavior and weeds out the aggressive patterns of behavior. Boys who display too much

* Dawe.[193]

sympathetic and too little fight behavior are likely to be branded as "sissies;" girls who are too aggressive and not tender enough are likely to be called "tomboys."

Success in Adjustment to Peers Important Step in Growth. As the child meets his contemporaries on an acceptable level, he progresses in the emotional weaning from his family, and builds extensions of his spiritual and of his social self. The period from three to five years of age is ordinarily one of rapid development in this respect. It is a time when the child asserts himself as an individual with at least some degree of success. It is fairly usual for these independent strivings to take the form of boisterousness, of "showing off," and of fighting. Values of parents and other adults come into focus as the child senses from them what is important in individuality and what is important in conformity. It seems possible to encourage individuality without tolerating rudeness to adults or to other children, nor should fundamental disrespect toward others be tolerated in any instance. Most mental hygienists consider a certain amount of competition and striving among contemporaries a thoroughly wholesome stage of development.*

Shyness. Another impact of our American social culture may hit hard on the shy child. America places a great premium on the socially "go-getter" type. The result is that adults may become disturbed when preschool children display shyness in social relationships in the sense of wanting to make few contacts with people. Nearly all children experience a period of shyness with strangers sometime between nine months and two years of age; some children experience it as late as three years of age. Many children are shy also with familiar persons.

Shy behavior may change, depending on the reason for the shyness as well as on the treatment the child receives. Nagging a shy child or forcing him seldom results in anything but increased social self consciousness and awkwardness. If the child already finds it hard to face people socially, he is not going to be put at ease by having his social reticence made the focus of attention before other people. Quietly giving the child an "easy setting" where others are present and he can proceed according to his inclinations without being forced and without conflicting with others will usually take care of the cases of "growth shyness" or the type of shyness described earlier as an aspect of social growth. However, shyness is sometimes the result of other inner tensions, the

---

* For further discussion of later social development see Breckenridge and Vincent.[131]

root of which needs to be discovered. Quiet drawing-out, combined with an easing of the inner tension, can accomplish the desired result.

One such child, Barbara, "ruled the roost" of her home during the first two and one-half years of her life, being coddled, shown off, and made the center of attention not only of her parents but of visitors to the home. At the age of two and one-half she suffered two disasters within three months: her father went into military service, and her mother's attention became deeply absorbed not only in the loss of her husband's companionship but also in the tending of a new baby sister. As the baby sister reached six months of age it became clear that she was a "charmer" socially. Already Barbara, in her emotional bewilderment, had passed through the stage of frantic bids for her mother's attention by toilet relapse, refusal to go to sleep at night and refusal to eat, one device after another being adopted in an effort to focus her mother's attention upon herself, each device being abandoned as it failed to win her mother away from the baby. During this interval Barbara clung pathetically to other people whenever they appeared, climbing on their laps and chattering feverishly to hold their attention. When the baby sister developed power to command the attention of visitors, Barbara began to sulk in dejected silence. Mother and visitors noticed and played with the baby more and more and ignored Barbara in proportion. Soon she began to withdraw whenever visitors appeared, and in time she actually hid when they came. Some children at this point, or sooner, would have attacked the baby physically in an uncontrollable desire to dispose of the interloper, or at least to express some of the resentment felt. Barbara, however, at no time did this. Rather, she soon found that she could win a word of approval from her mother by "being nice to the baby," and in time found that the baby's smile eased her loneliness, so she came to spend more and more time in the nursery.

When she began to hide, her behavior came sharply to the mother's attention and it was not long until Barbara's unusual social behavior drew comment and was talked over thoroughly and frequently in the child's hearing. Pressure began to be exerted to make her speak to visitors. In time her silence spread to include her mother, and her conversation with her mother began only after several minutes of quiet, unconcerned social sharing, as, for example, reading her a story.

The mother loved Barbara deeply and attempted to be understanding of her in the matter. With sincere thought on the subject and some quiet watching of the child's reactions, she realized much of what had happened. As soon as she could feel that she understood, she did two things. First, whenever visitors arrived she quietly slipped her arm around Barbara and picked up a topic of conversation which would distract the visitor's attention from the fact that the child had not spoken to them. Thus Barbara began to feel less defeated by her social failure, and came to be less afraid that she would be forced to greet people when she could not find it in her power to do so. Second, the mother carefully planned her day to give the child more attention. Barbara, now four, could help her mother in many ways, thus creating a situation of relaxed companionship in which she could talk naturally. With each week the periods when she found it difficult to talk and be with others shortened, and the ease of natural conversation became greater.

The mother also talked with one or two of her most understanding friends who came frequently to the home. These people, accepting Barbara's silence, quietly included her in the conversation from time to time, but always under circumstances which required no answer. In time Barbara began to feel "at home" with these friends and found conversation possible with them. It was over a year, however, before she could muster a social greeting even for these people when they first appeared or when they were leaving. It was two years before this carefully planned program produced ease of first greetings and farewells for most of the familiar persons in the social circle of the family. Barbara by that time had again built inside herself the conviction that, although she did not charm people as her little sister did, she could have satisfying social contacts.

Friends appreciate in Barbara her vivid imagination and her fine physical skills. These people find her fun socially as well as the younger sister. From these people she feels cherished for something fundamental in herself. This has done much to decrease her sense of inadequacy. The mother also appreciates individuality in the child and loves her with warmth.

One study on shy and aggressive behavior in preschool children (Murphy[613]) shows that children not only develop shyness for varied reasons, but also overcome shyness in varied ways. Many children, for example, who are solitary and quiet at first become socially at ease partly as the result of growth and partly because of social experience. Other children, whose shyness is more than mere passivity or quietness, are shy as the result of active self depreciation which involves deeper ego feelings or anxiety. These children may recover from their shyness by becoming aggressive, teasing, proud, swashbuckling or domineering.

Overaggressiveness. Some children are aggressive socially. They approach any and all people with self confidence. These children are sometimes so aggressive with things that they are destructive, pulling, throwing and hauling at objects with vigor. In their approach to people they may "rush in where angels fear to tread," bursting into rooms without waiting to be invited, pelting people with questions, and pushing, grabbing, hitting, and bossing other children. Occasionally this aggressiveness is a short-lived overreaction to previous shyness and uncertainty. Sometimes it is the result of parents who have let the child believe that he is lovable and irresistible no matter what he does. Sometimes it is the result of deep uncertainty or other emotional anxiety, the child's aggressiveness being either a cover-up, or a sheer explosion of pent-up feeling.

Like shyness, overaggressiveness takes various forms and works itself out in different ways and with various patterns.* There is the blustering, "showoffy" child, who, with experience, becomes affectionate and social. Some aggressiveness which appears destructive is only creative ability which has found no satisfactory outlet; once directed into chan-

---

* Appel;[44] Brody;[140] Fite;[259] Jersild and Markey;[428] Murphy;[613] Roff and Roff;[710] Sears;[736] Walters.[877] A socioeconomic variable is considered in McKee.[541]

nels it becomes the source of creative and original productivity. Another type of aggressiveness is to be found in the scattered, tense, disorganized child. This, when organized or directed in more peaceful and relaxing channels, may become the source of a work drive.

It is clear that neither shyness nor aggressiveness can be properly understood unless one can translate them into terms which will explain what they mean to the individual child who displays them, terms which will reveal the child's inner self, his immediate feelings and persistent needs. What appears to be socially undesirable behavior may prove to be the only available satisfaction in some area important to the child where more constructive satisfactions are not available at the time. In this sense, the reactions are distortions of usual ways of behaving. As in any behavior difficulty, solution lies in discovering what need the child is endeavoring to fulfill through his behavior, and in helping him to find ways of filling this need which are satisfying to him and acceptable to other people.*

Friendship Contacts of Preschool Children. There have been a number of studies of the friendship contacts of preschool children.† They do not all agree in their findings. Several studies found that *chronological age* was an important factor in the choice of friends, children tending to gravitate to other children of like age, even in the preschool years. However, propinquity is of great importance, and if children cannot find other children of similar age to play with they will seek companionship with older or younger children, whichever are available. Under free conditions of choice children tend more and more to seek other children of similar age as they grow older. Young preschool children of two years trail older ones of four to six or eight years fairly happily, but as the ability to participate socially on a more give and take level develops, the child tends to seek other children of his own *developmental level.* This shows in several studies in which the children studied offered a wide range of mental ability. Dull children tended to gravitate to younger normal or superior children; more advanced children mentally tended to seek companionship with equal mental rather than chronological age; hence they often played with chronologically older children quite happily and were accepted by them.

---

* Ridenour[702] presents suggestions concerning attitudes toward the child who hurts others, is destructive, uses bad language and won't share.

† Beaver;[101] Challman;[158] Green;[313] Hagman;[326] Hubbard;[373] Koch;[467] Lippitt;[515] Loomis;[518] Thomas.[836]

Children of more highly accelerated mental development tended to seek more friendships than did the average or dull children.* A few studies† show that even in the preschool years girls prefer to play with girls and boys with boys. Other studies, however, show that boys and girls play freely together during the preschool years, refusal to play with the opposite sex developing as a rule only at the school age level. No study shows a sex preference in play before the late preschool level, around four years of age.

Studies of *acceptance* of preschool children have not included the number of variables which would yield insight explaining children's acceptance of and by others. One study‡ on *popularity* among pre-school children found that among four-year-olds the more popular children were ones who conformed to routine, who showed respect for property rights, and tended to seek commendation. Those who tended to tattle were more popular than average. On the other hand, children were unpopular who tended to attack, to escape or to offer no resistance when attacked, who dawdled and who ignored other children. This study reports that sociable children were not necessarily the popular ones. A study§ at the Iowa Child Welfare Research Station found that children who cooperated with routines were more popular than those who did not, and that physically attractive children were more popular than unattractive ones.

One lead to helping children achieve self assurance socially comes from studies‖ in which it was found that *self assurance tends to increase as children learn skills,* both of body control and of language. As children learn how to do things, they become more at ease with themselves as well as with others. This is a corroboration of work done with older children, in which children were found to take leadership positions in groups whenever they had skills or knowledge which other children wished to share. Skills naturally develop with increasing age if children are given reasonable opportunity to learn, but much can be done to help them acquire definite controls over body and language. Children should not, of course, be forced in any learning, but care in developing new skills can be taken to discover capacities in which the child has some interest and can, therefore, develop some degree of skill. It seems

* Beaver;[101] Hubbard.[373]
† Challman;[158] Green;[313] Koch;[467] Hagman.[326]
‡ Koch.[467]
§ Lippitt.[515]
‖ Emmons;[242] Jack;[405] Keister;[446] Page.[647]

important to understand that self assured outer behavior can be achieved only when the child feels inner assurance. He will feel greater assurance as a rule when he becomes more skillful, but he cannot acquire an inner feeling of assurance if he is forced to practice skills which are not easy and natural to him.

Developmental-Dynamic Aspects of Social, Emotional, and Spiritual Growth. Since the area of social, emotional and spiritual behavior and development is comprehensive enough to include "personality," "experience with self," "experience with people" and "awareness of the cosmos,"* information showing sequence and interaction will come slowly. More precise methods and a more thorough study of segments are being undertaken. Attempts are being made to grasp "the essence" of the subject as contrasted to "meaningless" figures. A number of rather subtle aspects are being considered. For example, subtle aspects in the child are being studied by Brody,[140] Escalona[247] and Murphy;[612] in the parent by Brody[140] and Sears;[733] in the family and community by Barker.[71] Interest in the depth of the explanations of behavior is evident in studies of antecedents and sequences, constitutional and environmental. For example, Pasamanick[653] reports on prenatal and paranatal factors associated with certain forms of behavior such as tics; Fries[274] considers the role of congenital activity type in personality development; Jones[435] reports the relation of motor factors, such as strength, with social aspects and personal adjustment; Macfarlane[523] reports on the persistence of certain behavior problems according to a pattern; and Neilon[623] reports fifteen years later on children who were studied as infants (Shirley[753, 754]). A larger number of, or different, variables are being considered in studies of immediate behavior, experience or learning; for example, in attention seeking (Gewirtz[294, 295]) and in the relation of language to transposition behavior (Kuenne[483]).

Methods of Studying Emotional and Social Development

The measurement of emotional and social growth including concepts of self and of others, presents problems of even greater complexity than the measurement of physical growth. Emotional and social growth data are far less definite than height, weight, the appearance of teeth, or even

---

* See pp. 443-446 for discussion of spiritual growth.

an x-ray plate of bones. Children's behavior varies from situation to situation and depends on the form of stimulation, the state of physical fatigue and many other factors. Particularly difficult to evaluate, or even to see, is the force of inner drives and wishes which are often the strongest motivation behind a given piece of behavior. Because of these factors it is very difficult to standardize procedures for the description of behavior, and even more difficult accurately to evaluate such a description.

More needs to be known about the patterns which social and personality growth take. We know, for example, that children play with one or two children and enjoy these before they are able to participate in larger groups. And we know that as they adjust to larger groups they are likely to follow various patterns in their attempts to do so. We know, also, that children express emotion openly, vigorously and without control before they proceed to stages where inner feelings are less evident.

Those interested in studying this development have tried many devices, ranging all the way from attempts to create exact age scales based on open or overt and hence observable behavior, to attempts to understand the deep, inner emotional life of the child.

The devices for studying outer or observable behavior are defended by some workers in the field as being the only methods for studying social and personality development that "can be counted upon." The feeling of these workers is that what can be seen and heard one can be sure of, whereas one can only guess at what goes on inside the child. Others scoff at this idea, saying that it is exactly what is seen and heard that cannot be counted on, since one has no idea what the child meant to say or do, or what inner feelings and attitudes are being expressed in any given piece of behavior, no matter how obvious it may appear to be on the surface.

There is something to be said for both viewpoints, as there is something to be said for most of the devices employed by both groups. In actual fact, most of the methods developed for the observation of outer behavior and for the study of inner feelings and attitudes have something of the other viewpoint in them. Observers of outer behavior know that they cannot be sure, but must, nevertheless, be aware of the inner drives. Conversely, inner drives and meanings can be discovered only by the observation and study of what the child does and says.

Devices Used Primarily for Study of Outer Behavior.   We cannot attempt even to summarize the wide variety of methods which have been tried, and often discarded as ineffective, in the past thirty years to get concrete and definite pictures of children's behavioral growth. For many years attempts have been tried which would obtain data as definite as a height or weight figure and hence could be handled statistically. Of these attempts some have survived. There are now available a number of *check lists* of personality traits, or descriptions of behavior reactions on which a teacher or parent may check or report on those traits or reactions which they think apply to the particular child under consideration.* These are useful for reminding the adult to look for and observe certain traits or situations which, in a free-running description of the child, they might forget to mention. The assumption on these check lists is that if an item has not been checked, it was not present in the child at the time the observation was made. Kept over a period of years these checked lists thus serve as a rough record of the time certain traits appeared and how long they lasted.

Some of these descriptive check lists have been "weighted" numerically, thus not only giving the observer a numerical value to use statistically, but giving a rough estimate of the degree of the trait present. For example: "Plays with other children: always (5) usually (4) average (3) seldom (2) never (1)" gives not only the fact that he does or does not play with other children, but roughly how much, and assigns a numerical value which can be handled statistically.

Justification of the check-list method lies in the fact that case studies which are chiefly descriptions of children are not sufficiently quantitative to be used in statistical studies, or for objective comparison of one child with another. Check lists permit groupings of traits to be studied, and give a short and easy-to-see summary of material which in descriptive case studies often takes up many pages. Changes in an individual from one age to another can be considered according to the same "yardstick." Numerical evaluations attached to the check lists provide data which can be handled statistically; they are sufficiently convenient, however, that they may tempt investigators to an indiscriminate overuse or misuse of the device.

Observational records† in which detail is collected at the time the

* Examples of check lists of emotional and social behavior are the Bridges scale,[134] the Fels scales,[700] and the Read-Conrad I inventory.[686]

† Observational records of behavior of the baby with the mother are in Brody.[140]

behavior occurs are sometimes used. Interviews* and questionnaires†
involve recollection of detail.

Another device which has had, and still has, a good deal of use in
studying the social group relationships of children is the *sociometric
technique.*‡ In this method *groups* of children are watched closely, and
each contact any child makes with any other child is recorded. With
these observations in hand a sociogram can be sketched, revealing the
number of contacts made by any given child, as well as which children
he sought and which children sought him. Another way of studying
group interrelationships involves the naming of children preferred. It
can also indicate, as can the sociogram, which children tend to cluster
into small play groups or preferred cliques. These devices and many
others like them have helped our understanding of group formation
as well as our knowledge of how individual children adapt to group
associations.

A number of other methods are used for studying the outer behavior
of children, but these mentioned will suffice to indicate the type of
devices in current use. They have yielded information about children's
social and personality growth and are means by which many of the
things we know about overt social behavior were discovered.

Evaluation and Interpretation of Inner Emotional Life. As we have
seen, the behavior of a child, even the part we can see and hear, is
extremely complex and, therefore, hard to measure. Still more complex
and still harder to evaluate is the vitally important inner aspect of
behavior which we cannot see. This is the child's inner world that he
creates for himself in terms of the meanings and feelings which his
experiences produce inside of himself. Until we understand these inner
meanings and inner feelings, we cannot truly understand him, nor can
we interpret with even reasonable accuracy what he does. More and
more we are realizing the deep and significant relationship between the
inner world of the child and his outer behavior; we are also gathering
substantial evidence that this inner world of thoughts and feelings is
closely related to his physical growth and well-being. On the one hand,
the nature of his inner emotional harmony or disharmony is affected
by his inner physical harmony or disharmony. On the other hand, his

---

* A parent interview schedule is in Sears.[733]

† A questionnaire is in Knoblock and Pasamanick.[463]

‡ A review of the literature about sociometric methods can be found in Frankel
and Potashin,[268] and in Jennings.[419] Usefulness of sociometric techniques with
preschool children is reported by Marshall and McCandless.[557]

physical well-being is affected by his emotional well-being or conflict.

A number of methods have been tried in the attempt to understand and to interpret this inner or private world of childhood.* There are the *nonschematic methods* which, like methods used to study the outer behavior of the child, consist simply of careful observations of free play of children in nursery school or other play groups. Trained observers can often gain valuable clues to inner behavior and feelings in this way. Another method is studying children's spontaneously produced creative products, like paintings, spoken or written stories, or models made in clay. As in interpretation of children's free play, only trained observers should attempt to interpret meaning from paintings or other creative products.†

In addition to these methods and other nonschematic approaches to interpretation of children's inner life, there is a rapidly increasing number of devices for studying children under more *systematic and controlled conditions.* Play with selected materials or under standardized conditions often reveals inner thoughts and feelings, since the materials or conditions can be set up so that they stimulate and call out responses in specially selected areas of thought and feeling. For example, a set of dolls which includes a papa doll, a mama doll, a little boy doll, and a little girl doll may be given a child when we wish to study his relationship to and hence his feelings about his father, mother, himself, and his little sister. In his spontaneous dramatic play with these particular dolls he often reveals his true feelings, and sometimes is able to express pent-up emotion which has been denied outlet in his family life. Among the techniques now in use are play with puppets or dolls, with housekeeping toys, and with clay, paints, and other creative materials. Another device is to ask the child to name three wishes (or several wishes). Still another device is to start a story for the child, asking him to complete it for you, as for example: "Once there was a little girl who lived with her Mother and her Daddy. She had a little brother. Now you tell me the rest of the story."

These play techniques or *projective techniques,* as they are often

* Summaries of these methods and a set of excellent references can be found in Anderson,[33] Lerner and Murphy,[500] and in Symonds and Krugman.[824] Temple and Amen[829] and Winstel[913] have reported interesting studies based on a projective technique.

† Illustrations and discussion of interpretation of children's paintings are in Alschuler and Hattwick;[16] of children's play in Hartley, Frank, and Goldenson,[337] and in Murphy.[612]

called, permit the child to project outward some of the thoughts and feelings which he does not reveal in ordinary situations. They have been used extensively in the analysis of children's inner motives and feelings, both when the child is troubled and needs correctional treatment, and as a means of investigating the inner development of normal children. In correctional treatment the play situations have been used not only to reveal the source of the difficulty but also to help the child express pent-up emotion and to help him replace destructive feelings with constructive ones. When used like this as a treatment device, the procedure is referred to as *play therapy*.* When used simply as a means of investigating personality development or emotional reaction, the device is usually referred to as the play technique or as the projective technique.

As emphasized earlier, only well trained observers should attempt to interpret the inner life of children as revealed in play, in creative products, or in controlled situations. Even trained specialists need to be warned against the temptation to overgeneralize about the personality of the subject in general from the application of a single projective technique.† All projective methods should be subjected to careful validating studies to test their findings against the results of all available descriptions and general information about any child being studied. One session with a child in which one or several projective methods are used is not an adequate basis on which to draw sweeping conclusions about that child.

RORSCHACH AND WORLD TESTS.   One so-called test of personality, the Rorschach test,‡ is coming into wider use each year. It is actually a method of analyzing personality through a careful study of the reactions of the subject to a series of "ink-blot" cards. It has been standardized on adults, but in recent years several workers have been studying the reactions of children to the test. Longitudinal studies of children from two to ten years suggest that the test can be used effectively with children as young as three years if scored by "child" norms (Ames et al.[28]). The World Test§ is also being used with young children. In it, the child's arrangement of miniature parts of the world, such as people, houses, fences, animals and trees, is scored.

---

* Play situations employed to reveal personality and to assist in bringing about better adjustment are described by Axline[58] and Moustakas.[598]
† Macfarlane,[524] Murphy.[612]
‡ References to these methods are in Anderson,[33] Ames and Learned,[28] and Moustakas.[598] Nine quarterly records of a young child are in Allen.[11]
§ Copyrighted by Charlotte Bühler, Los Angeles, Calif.

Developing Awareness of the Cosmos

The components of healthy personality, emotional development, development of awareness of self and of other people, discussed in the previous sections of this chapter, have a connection with spiritual growth. The way in which the individual views these experiences, which are close at hand, is one part of his spiritual growth. Another part concerns his beginning to have feelings about, and to seek knowledge of, that which lies beyond his immediate experience or beyond his grasp in a tangible sense. At a simple level, the young child begins to acquire that which man has always sought, not only some understanding of a world which is big and beyond his immediate or complete comprehension but also some understanding of his relation to it in the sense of the spirit or the material.*

Concepts of Spiritual Growth. Growth of the spirit suggests something in addition to growth of a more material kind. Quality of thought and feeling are involved. For some, spiritual growth means appreciation and understanding of, and participation in the good, the beautiful and the true. Another attempt to describe it concerns appreciation and understanding of one's immediate world, the broader world, and the cosmos. These references to the spirit with which one views his world and has feelings about it suggest that the terms spiritual growth and religious growth are related. Being religious, in a broad sense, concerns a person's way of living, his way of looking at his world, acting in it, viewing and feeling that beyond his complete comprehension. Or, in a conventional sense, being religious concerns a person's acceptance of a particular religion; allegiance is to organized statements of man's place in the world or his relation to the infinite, as formulated in a particular religion and adhered to through its organization or church. Not only attitudes toward God, prayer, the source of order or power in the world, immortality and the Church, traditionally thought of as religious, but also attitudes of appreciation in everyday living are involved. Whether views in these fields are personal or in accordance with a particular religion, they can be thought of as spiritual or religious.

* Observational records of concept formation of one child beginning at the age of three and continuing for over two years are in Navarra.622 This reference also includes a review of the research on concept formation and a bibliography.

In thinking of the young child's spiritual or religious growth, it is recognized that individual families will wish emphases in accordance with their own conviction. Reflection of these family attitudes is a very significant part of the child's spiritual growth. Consequently, discussion here will not deal with attitudes but rather with the child's potentialities for attitudes of many different kinds, and with methods appropriate for his stage of development. Reference will be to responses which seem to be of a spiritual nature in infancy and preschool years and to methods of the adult which seem to warrant consideration, whatever the aims of guidance may be.

For the baby, the tender loving care of his family can mean the beginning of his spiritual growth. He has a feeling of harmony with his world. A sense of trust and a realization of the lawfulness of the universe can have their foundations laid early. For the older child, who is walking around, talking, or playing in a group, there are many additional possibilities for spiritual growth. The following record of an observer illustrates a few.

Five four-year-old girls are playing near an indoor sand box. (It could be at home, in a church school, or a nursery school.) Colleen empties the sand out of the train car that Sara has filled. Becky gets the brush and begins to sweep the spilled sand. Kay gets the dust pan. They clean up the sand, then go on sweeping other parts of the floor. They sing together as Kay sweeps, keeping time with the broom. Finished, they go to the sand box and smooth the sand flat with their hands. Margo joins them. They cover their hands, saying, "Can't see mine." Then, "I got one hand." Finally, "I got two," as they pull hands out of the sand. Now Becky gets a shovel, Margo a pan, and Kay a small wheel. They play vigorously and sand begins to fly. The adult talks with them about use of sand. Then the adult walks over to a bowl of pussy willows and forsythia. The children gather around her and begin to handle them eagerly, pulling their hands along the stems. Sara tells of flowers at her home. Becky asks whether she can have a "pussy."

Anyone looking for possibilities for experience and discussion encouraging spiritual growth can find many in the brief period described here. Signs of interest in sand or the earth, one's self, other people, flowers or nature, are all there.

The child's use of vocabulary concerning particular religious concepts often reveals his interest. An example is the following conversation of four-year-old boys:

Dickie: "There isn't really any sky. The air just goes up and up. I can touch the sky."
Paul: "I can see the sky. There is a sky and it is blue. That is heaven."
Jimmie: "If there weren't any sky, what would God sit on?"

Inclination to state the familiar rather than the unknown is illustrated by the Iowa children whose teacher listened carefully to what they were singing and found it was "Oh East Des Moines" instead of "Oh Easter Morn." Signs of reverence, whatever the words, signs of interest, confusion, and clarification about the world, heaven, God, and days of particular religious significance, such as these illustrations suggest, are part of the potentialities of the preschool child for spiritual growth.* One group of parents kept a record of their children's questions because they, the minister, and the teacher were interested in studying their Church School program.† Their three- to four-year-olds asked the following questions concerning particular religious concepts: Who is God? Where does God live? What does God look like? Where is Jesus? Where is heaven? Where did daddy go? (asked after father's death). Who made the hills? Who made the trees? The four- to five-year-olds asked: Where is God? Where did Jesus live? Will you die? What is an angel?

Methods of Encouraging Spiritual Growth. As previously stated, anyone aware of social and spiritual potentialities such as those demonstrated in these quotations would respond to them according to his own convictions. Methods emphasized here could be appropriate, whatever the convictions of the adult. One point of emphasis is on the importance of recognition of signs of interest and readiness with regard to spiritual growth which appear at the preschool age. The second point of emphasis is on the importance of adaptation of experience to the child's stages of development. Both of these approaches stress thought on the adult's part as to what is done and why. This thought about meaning of experience provided may or may not mean routine following of tradition and convention, but, if it does, it will be with insight. A few illustrations of these approaches, rather than a more complete discussion,‡ will be presented here.

For example, for one mother who considered respect for the dignity of each person important in her child's spiritual growth, the following incident prompted thought.

* Study of religious interests is summarized in Hurlock[381] and Jersild.[421]
† Additional information about this experimental approach is in Murray and Tyler[615] and Smart.[764]
‡ Discussions of spiritual growth are in Bro,[138] and Fahs,[250] McDowell,[532] Manwell and Fahs,[552] Munkres,[605] and Perry.[657]

John, who was three and a half years old, had two visitors, Stanley and Sue. While the children were drinking milk and eating crackers, Stanley spilled a few drops of milk on the linoleum floor. Sue told him to wipe it up with his paper napkin. When he sat, doing nothing, she began to push him, saying, "You spilled your milk, you must wipe it up." John began to imitate the pushing. His mother said, "Everybody spills things sometimes. Stanley knows about wiping things up. It's all right if he doesn't feel like doing it now. He may or he may not. We might think about his wanting to decide things for himself. We could also think about our helping by saying nothing, or by wiping it up for him."

In another family, in which the parents considered a concept of God and of the Bible important, the four-year-old child began to ask questions about them. The parents answered his questions simply and told him what others thought as well as their own ideas. They wondered whether use of books would add to this discussion. They tried to consider values of pictures and stories with simple phrasing and specific statements meaningful in terms of the child's experience. Values of Biblical language were also considered.*

In one Church School, where meaningful experience and happy associations were stressed, the children had activities such as the following: sharing toys, sharing "news" (telling of experiences of the preceding week), going into the church to look at the colors in the stained glass windows, having the minister tell them a story in their play room, hearing the organist play songs they knew, including the "Big Tall Indian Beats upon His Drum," watching the recessional, planting flower bulbs, dramatizing stories, having a few of the choir members visit them in their room, going with the sexton when he fired the furnace. Some of the more usual Church School experiences were also included. A variety of resources in the children and the setting was used.

The illustrations presented here have concerned traditional religious concepts and experiences: i.e., the dignity of man, God, church attendance, not because the aspect of spiritual growth called "appreciation" is less important. Other appreciations have already been referred to in considerations of the child's intellectual, emotional, and social growth.

---

* Books written for children which illustrate different presentations include *The Lord's Prayer,* by I. and E. D'Aulaire (New York, Doubleday, Doran & Co., 1934); *Prayer for a Child,* by Rachel Field (New York, Macmillan, 1944); *One God,* by F. Fitch (New York, Lothrop, Lee & Shepard, 1944); *Small Rain,* by J. and E. Jones (New York, Viking Press, 1944); *Tell Me About God,* by M. A. Jones (New York, Rand McNally, 1943); *I Wonder,* by A. Munkres (New York, Abingdon Press, 1930); and *The Christ Child,* by M. and M. Petersham (New York, Doubleday, Doran & Co., 1931).

Topics for Study and Discussion

The following suggestions concerning study of an individual child are arranged in an order which follows the sequence of the chapter. Consequently, (a) can parallel the section on personality components, (b) and (c) the parts on emotional development and awareness of self, (d) and (e) the part on awareness of people, and (f) and (g) the section on spiritual growth. All of (a) and (b) and parts of (c) and (d) are appropriate for study of an infant as well as of a child of preschool age.

1. For the individual child, who is being studied, make a record of:
   (a) behavior which seems related to his sense of trust, autonomy, initiative, and achievement;
   (b) expressions of affection, anger, fear, and other emotions;
   (c) responses considered revealing of emotional tone, in motor activities, speech, free play, expressions of imagination and creative activities;
   (d) social behavior illustrative of reactions to people, relationships to social groups (individualistic, parallel, and cooperative play), and positions within the group (leader, cooperating, tolerated, and rejected companion);
   (e) responses considered revealing of sympathy, ability to share, and understanding of individual differences;
   (f) responses indicative of interest in and appreciation of the immediate world and a broader world, with regard to nature and science;
   (g) responses concerning specific religious concepts (such as concept of God, Jesus, prayer, immortality, church).

Recall points of view and facts from this chapter which seem useful in understanding behavior recorded.

2. Select a particular aspect of a child's behavior about which there are questions, such as hesitancy to join a group, use of force, seeking attention, or interest in prayer. Discuss references in the footnotes and in the following list in terms of their usefulness to parents. (Additional discussion questions and references are in the *Discussion Aid* for "A Healthy Personality for Your Child," Children's Bureau Publication No. 338, 1952.)

3. Students may wish to pretend to be (take the roles of) the mother, father, child, and teacher, in a discussion of a particular situation concerning emotional, social, or spiritual growth.

4. Select from the discussion or from a footnote, a reference to research to consider thoroughly. Report on it in terms of its connection with a particular area, point of view, or question.

Selected Readings

Emotional Development

Baruch, D.: New Ways in Discipline. New York, McGraw-Hill, 1949. Chaps. 2 and 3.

Brody, S.: Patterns of Mothering. New York, International Universities Press, 1956. Chaps. 1, 2 and 3.

Children's Bureau: A Healthy Personality for Your Child. Children's Bureau

Publication No. 337. Washington, D. C., Supt. of Documents, U. S. Government Printing Office, 1952.

Frank, L.: The Fundamental Needs of the Child, Mental Hygiene 22:353-379, 1938. Reprint distributed by New York Committee on Mental Hygiene, New York City.

Jersild, A. T.: Child Psychology, ed. 4. New York, Prentice-Hall, 1954. Chaps. 9, 10 and 11.

Read, K. H.: The Nursery School. Philadelphia, W. B. Saunders Co., 1955. Chap. 7.

Ridenour, N., and Johnson, I.: Some Special Problems of Children Aged Two to Five Years. National Mental Health Foundation, Inc., in association with New York Committee on Mental Hygiene, 1947.

Wolf, A.: The Parents' Manual; A Guide to the Emotional Development of the Child. New York, Simon & Schuster, 1941. Also in Popular Library Edition, New York, Popular Library, Inc. Chap. 9, Psychological Growing Pains (including section, Some Common Problems).

Social Development

Anderson, H.: Social Development, in Carmichael, L.: Manual of Child Psychology. New York, John Wiley and Sons, 1954. Chap. 19.

Barker, R. G., Kounin, J. S., and Wright, H. F.: Child Behavior and Development. New York, McGraw-Hill, 1943. Chaps. 20 through 23, and 27 through 29.

Chittenden, G.: Experiences in Which Young Children May Learn to Share. Chap. 7, Part II, pp. 179-193, Forty-sixth Yearbook, Part II, National Society for Study of Education. Chicago, University of Chicago Press, 1947.

Goodman, M.: Race Awareness in Young Children. Cambridge, Mass., Addison-Wesley Press, 1952.

Jersild, A. T.: Child Psychology. ed. 4. New York, Prentice-Hall, 1954. Chaps. 6, 7 and 8.

Josselyn, I.: Psychosocial Development of Children. New York, Family Service Association of America, 1948.

Read, K. H.: The Nursery School. Philadelphia, W. B. Saunders Co., 1955. Chaps. 8 and 10.

Strain, F. B.: Your Child, His Family and Friends, New York, D. Appleton Century, 1943. Chaps. 4, 6, and 9.

Wolf, A.: The Parents' Manual; A Guide to the Emotional Development of the Child. New York, Simon & Schuster, 1941. Also in Popular Library Edition, New York, Popular Library, Inc. Chap. 5, The Child and His Friends.

Spiritual Development

Bro, M.: When Children Ask. New York, Harper & Brothers, 1956.

Hurlock, E. B.: Child Development. ed. 3. New York, McGraw-Hill, 1956. Pp. 443-453.

Manwell, E., and Fahs, S.: Consider the Children—How They Grow. ed. 2. Boston, Beacon Press, 1951. Chaps. 1, 3, 4, 6, 12 through 15.

Perry, E.: Children Need Adults. New York, Harper & Brothers, 1943. Chap. 5.

Also current issues of *Children, Childhood Education, Child Study,* and *Parents' Magazine,* which usually contain articles related to the content of this chapter.

11

Philosophy of Adult-Child Relationships

Aims for Child and Methods of Adult

Balance in Adult Attitudes. The picture of growth and development of the young child, presented in the preceding chapters, contains implications for the adult in his associations with a particular child. The importance of certain adult attitudes for the child's growth is suggested by current thinking and knowledge. Description of five attitudes in the following way represents one of many possible formulations of point of view. These attitudes overlap, are interrelated, and their order could be rearranged, but separate statement of them seems to suggest balance in the adult's methods.

1. *Recognition of the child's stages of development* has a particular connection with Chapter 1, on concepts of growth. This chapter suggests the extent to which intrinsic factors responsible for the child's unfolding warrant consideration. They warrant consideration in every aspect of growth referred to in all of the other chapters because they not only limit what is to be expected but also give cues as to readiness for new learning.

2. *Provision for meeting the child's basic needs* is stressed in Chapter 1, with its reference to emotional tone which frees the child to use his emerging abilities, and also in Chapter 10, with its reference to loving care which concerns both the physical and the psychological

care of the child. The importance of the adult's relating what he does
to the child's basic needs in a physical sense is suggested in discussion
of eating habits, habits of rest and sleep, and toilet habits in Chapters 6
and 7. The importance of the adult's relating what he does to the child's
needs in a psychological sense is suggested in these same chapters and
is further emphasized in Chapters 8 and 9 on Motor and Intellectual
Development. Important keys to the adult's effective use of this second
attitude, included in Chapter 10, are: discrimination in recognizing
what needs are basic and realization not only that a number of feelings
are needed as components of a healthy personality but also that feelings
of particular importance vary with developmental stage.

3. *Study of patterns of growth to increase understanding of the individual child* may be approached in light of the content of Chapters 4,
5, 8, 9, and 10, on physical, motor, intellectual, emotional, social, and
spiritual growth. Knowing what the individual child is like (for example,
being aware of details about his physical growth, health, habits of eating, rest and sleep, toilet habits, motor ability, language, reasoning
ability, imagination, emotional, social and spiritual development) provides facts in the light of which to consider stages of development and
needs.

4. *Provision of opportunity for the child to enjoy using his emerging
abilities* is cued to change with age and experience from one stage to
another stage. Cues about opportunities to be provided and behavior
to be expected are gained through the attitudes stated in the three previous paragraphs. This fourth attitude encourages functioning on the
level of which the child is capable, rather than on one above or below
it. Use of knowledge about how learning takes place was suggested in
all of the chapters.

5. *Recognition of the importance of influences of the family on the
child's growth* was stressed in a general way in Chapter 2 by reference
to family setting and emotional climate. In the following pages it is
stressed in a more specific way by reference to behavior of parents and
children in their relationships with each other. Specific areas often considered in study of parent and child relationships are affection, discipline and ambition. Focus on effects of these three factors is gained
through a more specific statement of this fifth adult attitude, such as
the following: Recognition that relationships within the family affect
the child's senses of trust, autonomy, initiative, achievement, feeling of
being one with others, and integrity.

Philosophy as referred to in the title of this chapter concerns not only attitudes of the adult, in the sense of methods to be used in association with a particular child, but also aims for the child toward which these methods are to contribute. Both aims and methods are included in a philosophy. Reference to aims, goals, or hopes of the adult for the child, and to methods or ways in which the adult contributes to these goals in the child, may be misunderstood. It is a misconception to think of them as being fixed instead of flexible, or as being similar from one child to another or from one adult to another, instead of being unique for each.

In writings about child development a number of different aims for the child have received attention.* Health, in the sense of physical well-being, has been recognized as very important. In the Children's Charter of the White House Conference Report of 1930,[894] a number of the items refer to health and its protection. Emphases of this book on the child's physical health and growth, his being well nourished and well cared for physically are a reflection of recognition of importance of this aim. Goals of democracy were stressed in the 1940 White House Conference.[897] To refer to additional factors, healthy personality was the theme in 1950.[583, 584, 915] Components of a healthy personality (which is a growing personality) as the individual develops from infancy into childhood and adulthood were described in Chapter 10.

Aims concerning physical aspects of the child and what the adult provides with regard to them, were included in earlier chapters; aims regarding personality aspects of the child were presented in Chapter 10. What the adult provides with regard to them, in immediate personal associations, will be included in this chapter. Such a consideration of relationships of people and what they provide for personality growth requires as a preliminary a review of general principles concerning personality. For related theories, see Chapter 1.

Use of General Principles About Personality Growth

Expectation of Progress from Infantile Behavior to Maturity in Various Phases of Physical, Motor, Intellectual, Social and Emotional Life. Physical growth brings about conspicuous changes which can

---

* Aims and methods of philosophers and educators writing about young children in previous centuries as well as in the twentieth century are reviewed in Forest.[263]

be detected by everyone. Physical growth as a phenomenon of human life is, therefore, recognized and accepted by everyone. Mental growth, being somewhat less conspicuous in its manifestations, is nevertheless fairly evident. That personality grows, however, is not so evident to many people. The general belief of the public at large is that personality is just something that descends upon us and about which we can do nothing. Actually, according to knowledge in various fields, including the child development field, personality grows and develops in the sense of the continuous integration of various aspects which are changing with age and experience. Growth of this kind can continue over a long period of time, and can follow certain clearly defined patterns. It continues throughout life, and its 100 per cent maturity level thus is not reached. This is true because this is the area of growth most subject to continuous development through changes in the attitudes and habits of the individual.

Continuous growth as contrasted to almost reaching a so-called ceiling of development early in life varies from one individual to another. Some persons, in other words, become rather fixed or static early in life; others continue to grow, acquiring continuously better integrated personalities. The 99 per cent maturity level for such continuously developing personalities is achieved only very late in life, after the individual has met the various vicissitudes of life as they occur, taking from each the richness and meaning which enable one to meet each successive stage more fully. The ultimate level of development for such a personality is quiet acceptance of old age, in which joy and fulfilment are as real or more real than in earlier stages; it means ultimately an acceptance of death as the final fulfilment of life. For such a person there is no longing to go backward in life, no childish clinging to immature aspects of personality and experience. There is, rather, a looking forward and a fulfilled living at every stage of life.

Development of personality in the sense of change of qualities and attitudes is, of course, most rapid in childhood, since the individual is in the most malleable or formative stage then. Habits, ways of responding, attitudes, and feelings are in the making, particularly in the preschool years. Everything is new; first experiences are many, and important first emotional overtones are being laid in. Although these important "firsts" may be, and will be, added to and changed as time goes on, the fact remains that they *are* firsts and that, being there, they tend to color reactions to later experiences and hence to influence a great deal of practice unless something happens to change them.

Parents and teachers as persons can do much more to affect the course of personality growth than to alter physique or intellect, since children reflect or respond according to the attitudes and feelings of the adults forming their social and emotional environment. Personality is, in important ways, the result of experience. However, it is also the result of the child's own inner reaction to his social and emotional experiences, since each child takes from his environment the things which fulfill his own inner needs, and each reacts to events and patterns in his environment in his own particular way. The child's experiences cannot be determined entirely by parents and teachers, but they can in many ways be outlined and steered into certain general channels. Just as the child's physical development can be directed by the richness or inadequacy of his food, by the fulness or the restrictions of his activities and other factors, so the child's personality development is affected by the stage set for him, the variety and quality of his experiences with people and with things, and by the way the adults in his environment deal with him in the routines and experiences of his day. Loved and cared for, he can in turn love others; denied love and security he may either seek it frantically or withdraw into an inner world that cannot hurt him. Given varied and rich experiences shared with enthusiastic adults, he will learn to seek experiences and to be enthusiastic about learning. Forbidden activity, scolded and punished for adventuring into new learnings, he may rebel or withdraw, becoming overaggressive in his seeking of adventure or coming to dread and fear new experiences.

Recognition of Constitutional Factors in Personality Development. * What any given child will take out of his social and emotional environment will in a measure be determined by the basic or constitutional personality he happens to have. Some children are *phlegmatic*, taking changes and adjustments to routines, accidents, and other events in their stride. Others tend to be more *excitable* and to be more easily thrown off balance by changes and the need to adjust to new situations. Each child is complex and cannot be labeled; however, he may show more responses of one kind and less of another.

This shows in both physical and psychological reaction. The more phlegmatic children tend to be stabilized in total metabolic reaction;

* See Chapter 1 (pp. 24-25) and Chapter 2 (pp. 32-33).

they sleep well, tend not to run a high temperature when ill, and adapt to routines readily. As a baby* this kind of child is the so-called "good baby." He does not cry easily, he takes the breast easily, has slight trouble learning to drink from a bottle or eat from a spoon, and is not easily upset by changes in food or changes in light or temperature. He sleeps soundly through ordinary noises or distractions, is not particularly upset by physical pain, and is not especially liable to disturbances of digestion. As he grows older he is steady going, adaptable and usually happy.

The more excitable or less steady child has more of the reverse qualities. He is likely to have trouble in learning to take the breast, is inclined to be easily upset by change of any kind, cries easily, fatigues easily, runs a temperature with slight cause, and is susceptible to digestive disturbances. As he grows older he gives evidence of over-excitability and hyperactivity which often lead to excessive fatigue. This fatigue is of the type that deceives parents, since an overexcitable child when tired does not as a rule become sleepy, but is likely to run faster, shout more loudly, and appear unusually alert. When finally put to bed he may, if overtired, take a long time to go to sleep and after the first exhaustion is slept away, spring into action again, driven by an over-excited nervous system to seek activity at four or five o'clock in the morning. It is sometimes hard for parents to realize that these symptoms point to a need of more rather than less rest. The unsteady child is likely to be changeable in mood, and is particularly likely to over-react to any nervous strain or emotional tension in the family atmosphere.

The foregoing description does not necessarily imply that the child with more of the steady responses has a more desirable personality than the less steady child. Stability may or may not amount to flaccid indifference and to stolid lack of imagination. Excitability may or may not include increasing discrimination and competence in the child who reacts keenly to sensory stimuli, who sees and hears things that others fail to, and who has an alert and fertile imagination.

One aspect of the excitable child's history is that he is usually born of excitable parents. Not only must he bear his heredity, he must, if he lives with his parents, spend his most impressionable years in the environment which excitable parents produce. Thus he may not find his environment an ally to help him in adjusting easily. Tension can

* Rating of these differences in newborn babies is described by Aldrich.[6]

continue to mount in the child who, needing more than most children a quiet stability of environment, is surrounded by persons who are also tense. The excitable child, most in need of regularity in routine, and most easily disturbed by irregularity of feeding, of sleep hours, and of elimination, is more likely to be the child whose parents provide interruptions in routine.

Charles and Sally illustrate this point. Charles, a tense, high-strung boy of three, is constantly on the move. He runs about, seldom slowing his movements down to a walk, is likely to shriek with excitement every few moments in his play, cries easily when hurt, and finds it almost impossible to relax at nap time. He is never ready to go to bed at night, often lying awake until ten or eleven o'clock, even though put to bed early. In spite of this he is usually to be found jumping about in his bed or running about his room ready for action at five o'clock in the morning. His family seem unable to help him achieve rest. Both his father and mother are quick-moving, high-strung people whose voices are inclined to shrillness and whose presence adds tension and excitement rather than relaxation and quietness to the family atmosphere. The mother has tried rubbing Charles' back at night in order to help him to relax, but her own tenseness serves only to key him to a still higher pitch. The remedy for Charles' excitability is not to be found in rigorous insistence that he sit quietly for certain periods of the day or that he spend more hours in bed, although this would help. The real solution lies in a change of family atmosphere—a reorganization of family routine to minimize hurry and fatigue and to build up more of a feeling of leisure.

Sally, on the other hand, is a child who plays hard but who stops to sit quietly when she becomes tired. She alternates quiet periods of handiwork or of looking at books with periods of vigorous play. Her voice has the quiet pitch of a rested child and is seldom shrill or whiny as is the voice of an overexcited or overfatigued child. She is hungry at meal time, eating her meal with dispatch, and trots off quietly to nap or to bed where she drops to sleep within five or ten minutes. She wakens refreshed and smiling. Sally's parents are relaxed people who have a great deal of pleasure but who seldom become overfatigued to the point of irritability and tension. The mother plans the day's routine so that breakfast can be an unhurried meal, and so that dressing, toilet, and other essentials are allowed for in time, thus minimizing the feeling of tension and hurry which plays so large a part in Charles' life.

It must be remembered, however, that these two children represent extremes of personality. Most children lie somewhere between these extremes in their reaction to the usual stimulations of life.

The phlegmatic child, reacting to changes of routine as he does, can be subjected to more irregularity than can the excitable child. The excitable child, once he has settled upon a reasonable regularity (see Chapter 6 on self-regulatory schedules), has more possibility for not being overly tense if given a fairly regular and undisturbed life. No child, however, grows well in a setting which is overroutinized or overprotected to the extent that he becomes habit-bound or inflexible in a changing world. A fairly safe guide for any child, phlegmatic or excitable, is to let him settle into his own routine and to see that this routine remains adaptable to his growth needs as he changes and develops. Children prosper in growth better if they have a fairly regular life, yet one which is not devoid of interest. Protection from exposure to nervous strain, emotional tension, or overstimulation seems sound. Yet their lives must be interesting and intellectually stimulating, offering enough demands for adaptation and adjustment to encourage the ability to meet difficulties when they arise.

Another way of considering personality besides phlegmatic and excitable is to think of persons as tending toward introversion or extroversion. These words mean to *turn in* or to *turn out,* and when applied to people mean that some people have a tendency to turn their attention and interests toward a center inside themselves, and some toward a center outside themselves. Individuals whose predominating attitudes and feelings turn in are more often interested in ideas than in people or things. Persons whose attitudes and feelings turn outward are more often interested in people and things than in ideas. Most people are neither one nor the other but have some traits of both. In so far as the child leans in one direction or another, however, he is likely to react to specific situations in one way rather than in another. To use this discussion as indication of a basis for diagnosing personality types would be to presume too greatly upon the scientific knowledge now available about personality. The aim of such a discussion is to correct the false idea that specific situations in family life will give rise to specific and predictable behavior reactions in all children. Not all children react to given situations in the same way, but they will differ at least somewhat in accordance with the tendency to turn inward or to turn outward.

If a child has, for lack of companionship, developed imaginary companions, the more introverted child will find such companions very real and so satisfying that he is inclined to cling to them even when flesh and blood children are provided for him to play with. The more extroverted child, however, finds imaginary companions a pale substitute for live children, and when exposed to other children abandons his shadows promptly in favor of real substance.

If a parent nags his child, the more introverted child is likely to give submission in action but to withdraw to his world of dreams for interest and satisfaction in life; whereas the more extroverted child is likely to fight his parents, to become "negative" and resistant, because he can find interest and satisfaction only in the real world, a world in which he finds himself so constantly intruded upon that he must resist. Effects of "sitting and thinking" after difficulty would be different, according to temperament of the child.

The child who is quiet and withdrawn usually slips past his parents and teachers without attracting much attention or causing much anxiety. He is not troublesome. He usually meets his problems alone and unaided, burying his difficulties within himself or retreating from them to his day dreams. On the other hand, in the child who meets his troubles in the open, symptoms of conflict or of unsolved problems are immediately evident. If he finds life unchallenging or unsuccessful, he responds in an active way by probing and investigating—often in forbidden places—or seeks success in mischief. He throws equipment in school or incites rebellion. He may "tell tall tales" or run vigorously and create excitement. In any case, he finds something to do which, although often producing trouble, at least provides a growing mind with something substantial to feed upon or permits a real outlet for emotion. The more introverted child, unchallenged or unsuccessful, retreats quietly. He is no trouble, so we miss the fact that he may be feeding his mind on shadows, or collecting steam from unsatisfied longings which occasionally bursts forth in explosions or resentments. The psychologist is more likely to worry about the future of the child who is docile and withdrawn.

We must bear in mind that there is no clear-cut demarcation between phlegmatic and excitable, or between introvert and extrovert. The great mass of people are somewhat phlegmatic and somewhat excitable, somewhat introvert and somewhat extrovert.

Neither extreme of phlegmatism or of excitability, of introversion or of extroversion, occurs frequently; more often each is achieved to some extent: phlegmatism is seasoned with adaptability, and excitability with a basis of sound habits; introversion and extroversion can temper each other. Wickes states the case thus: "Introversion must be guided so that it may not become morbid introspection, which shuts the person away from the world of human activity and human relationships, but rather a process making for the understanding of these and leading at last to a realization of the good within. Extroversion must be controlled so that men may not become lost in the multiplicity of things, but may be able to meet squarely the responsibilities of adaptation to the world.

Neither of these two forms of psychic activity may be emphasized at the expense of the other if man is to develop as a whole. Any attempt to stimulate the growth of one side while suppressing the other must result in frustration."*

Only a few of the many ways of thinking of personality have been mentioned here. To use these terms alone in describing an individual would be an oversimplification. Again, uniqueness of each child in his particular combination of qualities should be stressed. This uniqueness can be a constant source of interest to the parent in his attempts to understand his child. We can remember when dealing with the child to watch for tendencies in various directions, and to accept such tendencies as important in producing behavior and determining reaction to guidance. We can take them into consideration in our expectations of the child and in our accepting him as he is.

Recognition of Drives† as Factors in Personality Development. Personality is the by-product of the interplay between the child's constitutional personality, his inner instinctive drives or emotional needs, values or goals, and his experiences. All people have certain inner emotional needs which motivate behavior and color the form of reaction to environmental experience. Certain basic longings must be fulfilled if life is to be satisfying. Some of these, like the *hunger for food* and the *need of rest after activity* must be fulfilled if physical existence is to be maintained. These have been discussed in Chapters 6 and 7.

The *need for physical and psychological activity* is almost as demanding in children as is the need for food and rest. The waking time of even the tiny infant, if he is not physically ill or psychologically handicapped, is occupied with almost continuous activity. Arms and legs wiggle and jerk about in uncoordinated but continuous movement which gradually comes under control and assumes the coordinations of skilled movement (see Chapter 8 on Development of Motor Skills). Vocalizations are also almost constant as the child begins his gradual mastery of the spoken language (see Development of Language in Chapter 9). By the time the child is "run-about" age he is constantly on the move, running, climbing, poking and prying into everything in the house. His mind is also constantly on the alert, so that his general bodily and manual activity is providing his intellect increasing knowledge of the properties of the objects around him. Throughout early

* Wickes[899] (pp. 12 f.).
† See Chapter 1 (pp. 19-20).

childhood this drive for physical and intellectual activity increases. It cannot be denied without stress. To curb it beyond reasonable demands for self control would repress this inner drive and could result in withdrawal for the more introverted child or rebellion for the more extroverted.

It is helpful to the child and his family if space, materials and guidance are provided for activity. These have been discussed in Chapters 8 and 9.

Just as the child needs space and equipment for bodily activity both indoors and out, and just as he needs ample opportunity to exercise his increasing skill and to expand his knowledge in the use of his hands and his mind, so also does he have *needs in social contacts*. Some concern the company of other children. Infants, as we have seen earlier, do not respond very much to association with other infants, but by the time most children are two to three years old they show further signs of interest in other children, preferably children somewhere near their own developmental age. The longing for companionship is so genuine that the imaginative child will invent imaginary companions if real ones are lacking (see Development of Imagination in Chapter 9). Many of the happy associations with people can come from adults, particularly from parents. However, some aspects of social and personal adjustment are learned from other children. Much of the physical activity sought by growing children can be supplied best by other children, as can much of the knowledge of give and take socially. There is, beyond this, a simple urge for sociable exchange which seems to be a basic emotional drive in children.

One most important need of children seems to supersede all others if personality development is to be optimal. It is so important that a child could have all the above needs provided for and still be badly stunted or warped in personality development if he does not have the warm love of his parents. Even though children are meticulously cared for physically and have their needs for activity and for other children conscientiously met, if they lack close *warmth and love,* personality development will suffer. Parental love fills so great a need in children's lives that many children, lacking what appears to be even the essentials of food, warmth, protection, thrive because they have the warm love of both parents. Further discussion of affection follows on pages 461 to 468.

Because so much of nature's functioning has law and order in it, it seems logical to include in this section on drives a reference to discipline. The child needs more from his parents than security in love. He also needs a steady *discipline* which helps him to adjust his own inner needs and wishes to the needs and wishes of other people and to the facts and situations of the real work-a-day world. The world cannot be made up entirely of people who love him as his parents do; there are certain real situations like grief, hard work, the convenience of other people, and so on, which cannot be evaded but which must be faced. In discussing child care, Senn says, "discipline is seen first as something which reaches the infant from the external world, yet early in life becomes incorporated within the child. This point marks the beginning of self discipline, which is necessary for the happy and creative life of the individual in the social group."* Further discussion of discipline follows on pages 468 to 476.

Recognition of Dynamics of Learning Process† as Factor in Personality Development. What the child learns from experience needs to be considered in the light of his constitution, drives and previous experience. Insight into his learning may be furthered by consideration of such questions as the following: What impels the child to respond? What situations produce what responses? What seems rewarding or satisfying to him? What strengthens the probability of his responding in a similar way another time? What lessens the probability of his responding in a similar way another time? Ausubel[57] suggests the attempts to answer questions such as these will follow a different pattern, according to whether the person is secure or insecure. Stendler[805] suggests that different effects on personality will occur according to the time at which disturbances affecting the child's dependency drive occur.

Rewarding or satisfying experience has been described in many different ways. Stendler's[805] discussion of the child's learning related to dependence and independence includes reference to various aspects of the mother to which the child reacts. Aspects of the mother which acquire value in the child's eyes are: physical contact, proximity, paying attention, verbal praise, "helping" when the child has begun a task and has encountered difficulties in repeating it. "Thus the three-year-old may put on his own shoes but his mother helps by

* Gruenberg[320] (p. 116).
† See Chapter 1 (pp. 19-20).

pointing out which shoe goes on which foot and by tying the laces."* Associations with the adult, such as these, affect the child. In addition, it seems helpful to think of the feelings described as components of a healthy personality as rewarding to the child. For example, fitting together a nest of boxes, graduated in size, may be thought of as giving the child a sense of achievement; being rewarded in this way may be a factor in his wanting to put the boxes together again. These references to possible sources of satisfaction are incomplete; they are included here to suggest the importance of further knowledge about learning as a way of understanding the individual child.

Keeping in mind the general principles about personality which have been mentioned on this and preceding pages, it seems justifiable to attempt to be specific about parental attitudes and practices concerned with affection, discipline and ambition. The attempt is made with a recognition of the subtleties of emotional relationships between parents and children, and a realization of the greater significance of how the person feels about it than of what he says or does.

For a number of years, those interested in relationships of parents and children† have thought affection, discipline and "ambition," or expectations, were key parts of the relationship and consequently parts of the child's growth and development. Such a concept includes the idea that qualities in parents' affection, discipline and "ambition" are related to qualities in the child's behavior, growth and development. Gradually, research is providing information pertaining to this concept and to points of view related to it, such as those in the following pages. Previous chapters have also included reference to research on parent-child relationships.

Affection Conducive to Growth

Emotional Climate of the Home. The general atmosphere of the family, or the emotional climate of the home, is to the growing child what weather and climate are to the growing plant. Because of it the child grows and prospers socially and emotionally, or he is stunted

---

* Stendler[805] (p. 4). This point of view is presented in further detail on pages 465-466.

† Bibliographies on research in parent-child relationships are in Brody,[140] Martin,[558] Sears.[733]

and warped. In the young infant, that in his being which is considered physiological may be responding more than that which is psychological (Pinneau[664]). But even then, he seems to be affected by emotional climate conveyed to him through the care he receives. When the infant is made comfortable physically and administered to with a kind hand, he responds positively to personal contacts. In his well-being on a physiological plane, there seems to be a harmony with his world.

The emotional climate in most homes is, fortunately for the children in these homes, one in which more experience is on the side of warmth, understanding and mutual support. In it the child usually finds some bases for emotional security, a good pattern of adult behavior and personal relationship, sound discipline and the fulfilment of his major physical and emotional needs. Some homes, unfortunately for the development of the children in them, create an atmosphere that is too far on the side of antagonism, suspicion, distrust, selfishness and mutual competition to be conducive to growth. In such homes the children suffer from lack of sound affectional security, steady discipline, and an inspiring pattern for personal behavior.

AMOUNT AND KIND OF AFFECTION. One way to encourage thought about the important aspects of affection is to refer to ideas about amount and kind of affection. Perhaps the first thing parents think of in connection with their relationship to their child is how much they love him or, as sometimes happens, how much bother it is to have him about. It seems impossible to most people that parents could fail to love their children, yet a few parents do fail in this respect.

So much has been said about the necessity for loving children enough that it is sometimes pointed out that too much of some forms of love is hampering, particularly if the overloved is at the same time an underdisciplined child. Ribble,[695] having emphasized the need of ample and continuous loving, points out the danger of spoiling a baby: "It is obviously true that unwise attention prolongs dependency and thus spoils a baby. But mother love is a good deal like food; we do not stop giving it because the child may get too much or the wrong kind." She goes on to say that love should be abundant and consistent; it should not be given, then withdrawn, put on and off as the mother happens to feel in or out of the mood. "Babies become demanding when they are given a great deal of attention and then deprived of it."

In some families affection may be in the form of constant deference to the child, showering gifts, protecting him too much from the ordinary hardships of life, and kissing and caressing him excessively; this hampers the child's development.

DEMONSTRATIVENESS. On the subject of demonstrativeness in affection, much was said at one time about the child's learning to be independent. Advocates of the behavioristic school of psychology[882] recommended that children be given no physical demonstrations of affection at all. There was to be no kissing, petting, rocking, or holding of the child. The danger, they claimed, was in making the child too dependent upon the parent, and in the possibility that the child would become emotionally fixed upon the parent and unable later in life to free himself from this "silver cord." Psychoanalysts point to cases of unhappy marriage and of adult neuroticism which are due to over-possessiveness of children by parents. At the present time, the individual adult's ease with the baby and young child is emphasized. Most parents kiss, pat, rock and cuddle their children because they love them. In such demonstrations of affection the young child who understands concrete situations, has a concrete demonstration of love and of love freely expressed.

Children differ in the amount of love they seem to need. Some children need little more than kind treatment and a loving tone of voice; they are so busy with their own affairs that too much caressing becomes an interference with their activities and they tend to brush it off in a self sufficient manner. Other children are very dependent upon demonstrations of love and constant reassurance that they are secure in affection.

INDICATIONS OF AFFECTION WHICH MEETS NEEDS. We may turn for guidance in the matter of desirable amount and kind of parental affection to a brief survey of symptoms which may appear in the child's behavior if all is not well. Any deviation from the usual in a child's emotional expression suggests to the parent, teacher, or clinical examiner at least the possibility that the environment of affection needs investigation. Emotional apathy, emotional instability, excessive shyness, excessive boldness, negativism, feelings of inadequacy, excessive demands for attention, jealousy and too great or too little dependence on adults may any of them indicate difficulty in this field. Simply to judge one's affectional relationship to one's child by watching for such symptoms is, of course, a negative approach. A positive approach is obviously better, for if we wait for symptoms of unsatisfactory relations to appear we will probably find it exceedingly difficult to bring about changes in these relations. Well loved children are busy with their own affairs, yet reach out for adult support when in difficulty; they are happy, reasonably calm emotionally, accept physical routines, and give evidence that life is good. Prevention is important because of its connection with human happiness. A balance can be maintained so that expression of affection in either adult or child shall neither be rebuffed nor constantly sought for reassurance.

LOVE AS AN INSTRUMENT FOR DISCIPLINE. Abuse of the love relationship between parents and children can come through the use of love as a disciplinary measure. "Mother loves you when you're good," "Daddy can't love you if you are bad," raise questions for the following reasons. If we love a child at all we must of necessity lie to him when we say that a single bit of behavior can win or destroy that love. He can gain from such statements an example of lying, or a false notion that love is something to be lightly given or withdrawn as a reward or punishment for trivial bits of behavior. On the other hand, the child may sense what we mean, which is different from the particular choice of words.

Sears et al.[733] found a patterning of maternal behavior into "love-oriented techniques" (praise as a means of reward, isolation as a punishment, withdrawal of love as a punishment) and "object-oriented techniques" (tangible rewards as incentives and rewards, deprivation of privileges as a punishment, physical punishment). They report "some relationship between the mother's high use of love-oriented techniques and the occurrence of confession and guilt about misbehavior in her child . . . and . . . apparent relevance of the dimension or trait to conscience development."* Their reference to these dimensions as "fallible indicators of other—'deeper'—dimensions"* is a useful point in thinking of implications of this finding.

Constancy in Administration of Care. Particular practices (in the sense of recipes) cannot be singled out as the only effective ones or the most effective ones for parents to use with their children. The uniqueness of the child, his parents, and his own setting are variables which make different practices warranted. Whether infants treated differently in different cultures grow up into normal healthy adults or not, does not seem to be because of any single type of treatment.†

* Sears[733] (p. 478-479).
† Orlansky.[643]

Some writers* stress the importance of physical contact as the infant is cared for. Others† stress what is sometimes called emotional interchange between child and mother. Rather frequent appearance in the literature of the words *loving care* suggests that they have a breadth, acceptable to many, to encompass both the idea of personal attention to basic needs and also the idea of variations in the form it takes according to the individuals and the culture.

Agreement on the importance of constancy for the child of his particular type of care seems rather general.‡ For example, the infant with colic may later seem so content and well adjusted because his type of care has been constant. The child who was a "good" baby may be a very different two-and-one-half-year-old if a situation such as the illness of his mother separated him from her at a crucial time. Changes in type of care seem especially disturbing at particular stages. According to the Fact Finding Report of the Midcentury White House Conference,

"Reactions (of disturbance) are most likely to occur in children who up to the time of separation at six to nine months of age had a happy relation with their mothers, while those whose relations were unhappy are relatively unaffected. It is at about this age that the struggle between trusting and mistrusting the world comes to a climax, for it is then that the child first perceives clearly that he and his environment are things apart. That at this time formerly happy infants should react so badly to separation suggests, indeed, that they had had a faith which now was shattered. Happily, there is usually spectacular change for the better when the maternal presence and love are restored."§

Stendler[805] refers to two critical periods in socialization when overdependency seems more apt to occur. She says,

"Two critical periods for the formation of overdependency are proposed. The first critical period begins when the child begins to test out the mother to see if he can depend upon her. For most children this occurs toward the end of the first year of life. Earlier the infant has been learning to be dependent upon the mother. Now he shows his sudden recognition of the importance of his mother by his demands upon her and especially for his mother's proximity. In effect, he tests out his mother, to see if he really can depend upon her and to see if he can control her. He cries when she leaves his presence and demands that she be in sight or readily available when he needs help. Gesell[291] reports that as early as 28 weeks the baby 'demands more of the one who feeds him.'

* Ribble,[695] Maloney.[551]
† Spitz,[790] Bakwin,[63] Horney,[371] Baker,[62] Goldfarb,[301] Rheingold.[694]
‡ Spitz,[790] Ribble,[695] Orlansky.[643]
§ Midcentury White House Conference on Children and Youth; Fact Finding Report (p. 10[583] and, with slight change in wording, p. 10[915]).

Bowlby[122] (p. 122) suggests that the most critical time for the production of anxiety concerning the mother is after eight months, 'When the child's first object relationship (to his mother) is developing in a specific way.'

"Severe traumatic experiences involving separation from the socializing agent are important to consider, then, during this period when the child has become aware of his dependency upon the mother and is testing his control of her. During this critical period it is necessary that the infant have his dependency needs met in a manner to which he has become accustomed. . . .

"The next critical period for the formation of *over*dependency comes during the two- to three-year-old period. As we have already indicated, this is the time in our society when demands upon the child to change his old ways of doing things increase tremendously. Now the child must give up his control of his mother and come to accept his dependence upon her, yet at the same time learn to be independent in culturally approved ways. Again, anxiety arises because important goal responses are being interfered with. In normal socialization the anxiety generated produces the right amount of dependency. But where disturbances of a traumatic nature occur so that important habits must be suddenly and drastically changed, so much anxiety may be generated that overdependency will result."*

Authorities disagree on the extent of the effect of the infant's experience on his personality at later stages. Opinions vary widely. Evidence is incomplete. The importance of infancy as a period and also the resiliency of human beings both seem implied in a statement such as the following,

"We conclude that the rigidity of character structuring during the first year or two of life has been exaggerated by many authorities, and that the events of childhood and later years are of great importance in reinforcing or changing the character structure tentatively formed during infancy."†

Warmth. Warmth in the relationships of parents and children has been referred to a number of times. Sears, Maccoby and Levin[733] in their study of the patterns of child rearing found warmth of mother-child relationships to be one of seven factors or underlying traits.‡ They say, "Mothers who were high—toward the warm end—can be described as follows:

"1. Much affectionate interaction with the baby.
"2. High affectionate demonstrativeness toward the child.

* Stendler[805] (pp. 7-8).
† Orlansky[643] (p. 38).
‡ Reference to another factor in Sears,[733] in addition to the warmth of mother-child relationships, i.e., orientation toward child's physical well-being, is found on page 397. Others, i.e., permissiveness-strictness, aggressiveness and punitiveness will be considered in the discussion of discipline; the reponsible child training orientation and the general family adjustment are in the discussion of "ambition." The seventh, perception of husband, has less information available on it.

"3. Found ample time to play with the child.
"4. Reacted acceptingly to child's dependency.
"5. Praised the child when he showed good table manners.
"6. Used reasoning as a method of training."*

Maternal coldness was associated with behavior difficulties.

In considering the effects of child-rearing which includes this factor, they say, "There is no clear evidence in our findings to explain why warmth should have such widespread influence. We can speculate, on the basis of our general theory of the learning process, about the possibility that it may play several roles. A warm mother spends more time with her child. She offers him more rewards, technically speaking, and gives him more guidance. He develops stronger expectancies of her reciprocal affection, and thus is more highly motivated to learn how to behave as she wants him to. He becomes more susceptible to control by her, for he has more to gain and more to lose. It seems likely, too, that he gets proportionately more satisfaction and less frustration from his growing desire for affection.†

Meaning of Affection. Thinking not only of the infant but also of years beyond the first one or two, one can attempt to clarify what it is the adult does that makes the child feel sure of his affection (see Fig. 76). One observer, trying to identify it in adults with reference to the preschool child's sense of trust, autonomy, initiative, achievement and other personality components, noted the following behavior in children of preschool age in a short period of time: A child about to go down a slide asked the adult to stand near her, which she did. When a child discovered that his teacher who had been absent had returned, he came and stood beside her; she picked him up and held him on her lap as they both sat watching the block building of two other children. When a boy heard other children talking about Halloween, he turned to his mother and seemed reassured by her answer to his question, "Will it be Halloween for me too?"

Trying to put into words what it was that mattered with regard to affection, in relationships of adults and children, one group of students listed the following attitudes which are specific expressions of the more general ones previously listed.

1. Loving the child for himself (for what he is which is different from anyone else).

* Sears[733] (pp. 474-475).
† Sears[733] (pp. 483-484).

Figure 76. Responsive to their children's interests, these parents have made equipment for them. The two-year-old is using the climbing box and sliding board for the first time.

2. Being natural, understanding, sincere and consistent.
3. Realizing that children respond to interest and companionship and not to words, demonstrativeness or gifts alone.
4. Not being overly protective and stifling independence but showing a readiness to help when needed.
5. Letting the child feel sure of affection whether he is "good" or "bad." (Not using affection as an instrument of discipline.)
6. Recognizing the influence on the child of a harmonious relationship of the parents.

Discipline Leading to Self-Discipline

Views about Discipline. In beginning to think about important aspects of discipline, it is useful to review the range of ideas. Some parents seem to think that if one loves a child one cannot or must not expect discipline in behavior contrary to his inclination or wish. Or, vice versa, that if one is firm with a child one cannot love him. This is an assumption, very different from the one in which the parent believes he can love his child through any and all vicissitudes, yet provide reasonable discipline whenever it is needed. It is not a question of love *or* discipline; it is, rather a question of love *and* discipline. Growth in the direction of self-discipline is the adult's aim for the child. As the child grows older, it is hoped that he will assume more responsibility for his actions and will rely less on authority outside himself. Effective methods encouraging growth in this direction fit the child's stage of maturity, his personality and temperament, his particular actions, and the situation of the moment.* The parent who loves his child and observes him enough to see the effect of various methods can usually provide for continuous growth in which self-discipline is increasing.

One of the most frequently discussed topics of parents concerns obedience in relation to growth in self discipline. "How can I make my child mind me?" "When should I insist?" Some parents, of course, do not stop to think about the matter at all, but live with their children from moment to moment, exacting behavior or excusing it by whim rather than by principle. If a discussion on the subject arises, however, there usually develop two extreme viewpoints and all grades of variation in between. On the one hand, some parents will say that they expect instant and unquestioning obedience from their children, and will give as their defense a statement that obedience is a difficult but necessary life lesson which must be learned early and thoroughly. On the other hand, some parents will say that the most important thing for children to learn is to make intelligent and independent decisions and to express their inner thoughts freely. Obedience as such, they say, has no place in child care and should never be exacted; all behavior should flow freely from within outward. "Self expression," in other words, should be supreme.

As a general principle in child care, it can be said that *extreme views are seldom right*. So, in this case, neither extreme has the advantage of "reasonable limits." Parents represent all authority to the young child. The attitudes which he develops toward them are important to his attitude toward all authority in adulthood. How he obeys the laws of his state or church, whether he obeys the dictates

* Smart and Smart;[765] Gruenberg;[319, 320] Washburn.[880]

of convention, of society at large, or of his own immediate group, or of his own convictions, or whether he defies these laws and dictates, will be influenced by his attitude toward the authority represented by his parents, his home and his school. Many believe that the child who loves and respects his parents as worthy ideals and as worthy censors of his natural behavior, has a sound basis for growth. Parents serve, then, as important influences as the child develops an effective "super-ego" or "conscience" with which to discipline and control his behavior.

INSTANT AND UNQUESTIONING OBEDIENCE UNDESIRABLE. If, as the result of a program of extreme rigidity in discipline, an individual goes through childhood yielding instant and unquestioning obedience to authority, we can scarcely expect him to behave differently toward authority in adulthood. He will, if sufficiently trained in docility, do anything he is told. He will, if trained to depend on other judgments than his own, be unable to think for himself. The freshman who enters college unable to decide where to live, what courses to take, what clothes to buy, and which friends to make is a familiar spectacle to every dean. Being unable to resist commands he does as nearly as he can whatever he is told to do by anyone, no matter how unwise for his own welfare the commands may be. Such docility may be the reaction of the more introverted child brought up under a regimen of instant, unquestioning obedience.

The child who tends to turn inward may, however, react to rigidity in quite a different way. Instead of becoming docile he may develop the habit of sullen withdrawal, growing up to resent direction and to react to it by pouting or sulking, or he may give surface obedience but live in reality a life of stubborn resistance. In this case he becomes apt in the art of deceit, appearing to do what he is not really doing and appearing to think what he is not really thinking.

On the other hand, another type of child is likely to react to repressive authority by open rebellion, and may grow to adulthood with a completely negative attitude toward authority. Such people are familiar to us as needing to be "handled with gloves." They "fly off the handle" when given orders; they "simply can't stand to be bossed." They are the anarchists of the world, the typical "agin-ers," being against anything which smacks of authority. Every college dean knows these people, too—the students who want to cast aside everything that is upheld by convention or tradition for the naive reason that they "can't tolerate being dictated to."

UNLIMITED FREEDOM OF BEHAVIOR ALSO UNDESIRABLE. Perhaps enough has been said to make it clear that the "instant and unquestioning obedience" program is not conducive to sound growth for any type of child. Let us analyze the program at the opposite extreme where unlimited "self expression" is encouraged. The child who gets the idea that he need obey no dictates but those of his own impulses is indeed in a false position. He may soon discover that even though his impulse may crave flying across the room as if he were riding an airplane, he may not do so because the physical law of gravity is more powerful than his wish. More serious than this, he may wish to live his days without eating vegetables and other nutritious foods only to learn too late that impaired health results. He may try to express his impulses of snatching toys or of striking other children, only to learn that he is soon ostracized and left to play alone. Breaking the neighbor's window or pulling up his father's garden is hardly to be condoned simply because he happens to feel that he is expressing something inside himself. Yet, hard as it is to believe, there are parents who actually fail to see that such extravagant "self-expression" does not free the child but only makes him the slave of his own whims. Impudence or lack of consideration for other people may be confused with independence or creative expression. They are utterly different.

NECESSITY OF BOTH FREEDOM AND SELF CONTROL. Sometimes this attitude of reverence for the child's wish is only a compensation on the part of parents who, refusing to work on the old principle of despotism in child training, feel the necessity of working on some sort of principle, and have found nothing less extreme than a complete "hands off" policy. Few parents have the courage to exercise this policy to its natural conclusion. They give the child extreme liberty until they find him about to learn a severe lesson as the result of some inexpert choice of behavior; then they step in to protect him from the natural consequence of his action, and hence deprive him of the opportunity to learn *the need of natural restraint within liberty.* Parents who give verbal loyalty to the principle of "self expression" but who lack the courage to let the child learn the discipline inherent in such a policy are doubtless the parents to whom Seabury refers when he says: "Thousands of American homes are without the ancient despotism in child training. There is only an empty void in its place. These parents cannot accept or successfully apply old ideas, and so they apply none. Son and daughter grow up in a protected, loose, undirected liberty, sure that they will be supported, taught not to exert themselves, made to be parasites, permitted to be self-indulgent, helped to be indolent. Tragedy results."*

WISDOM IN UNDERSTANDING REASONS. There are also parents who think that obedience should never be expected unless the child understands the full reasons for his action. On the whole this is an excellent principle, but ability to grasp reasons which are not immediately evident changes with age. The eighteen-month-old child and the four-year-old tend to differ greatly in this respect. Furthermore, most children soon learn that if parents are always ready to explain reasons they may be side-tracked from carrying out commands or persuaded to withdraw them altogether when bombarded with enough "whys." Children then are using "why" as a means of postponing obedience once they really understand the nature of the command given. We must, of course, make sure that commands are really understood before we become arbitrary about seeing that they are executed. We must realize, too, that there are certain emergency occasions when commands must be obeyed instantly for the sake of safety as well as other occasions when the reasons behind commands would be incomprehensible to the child. Implied in both of these cases is a habit of obedience to an authority which the child has learned from experience is reasonable, consistent and interested in his own ultimate welfare. To delay obedience under such circumstances because of insistent "whys" would be either dangerous or unreasonable. In other instances, the reasonableness of the authority may be based, not on the child's own safety and well-being, but rather on the welfare of others, or occasionally on convention.

SOME GENERAL GUIDES FOR OBTAINING OBEDIENCE. A few guides may help in this respect:

1. Before making a request take care to gain the child's attention.

2. Use language the child can understand. A four-year-old, for example, does not understand "in the upper right-hand drawer you'll find so-and-so."

3. Enunciate slowly enough and clearly enough to be sure he follows you. Children under five are still learning to distinguish the meanings of individual words.

4. Do not give too many suggestions at once. A child of five can execute three exceedingly simple directions at once, but only if they are repeated at least once under concentrated attention before he sets out to obey.

* Seabury.[730]

5. Be consistent. Do not tell him to do one thing today and a contrary thing tomorrow.

6. Ask him to do only the things you consider important and really intend to have him do. Do not, because you have not stopped to think, or simply to show your authority, give needless commands which you do not carry to completion or which you lightly withdraw when you realize their uselessness.

7. Be sure that you are reasonable and fair in your requirements; then see that they are carried out.

8. Do not make requests or allot punishment in anger.

9. Do not use threats or bribes as a means of gaining obedience.

10. Do not make misbehavior interesting by making it exciting or profitable.

DEVELOPING DESIRABLE ATTITUDES TOWARD AUTHORITY. On the whole the child can have a gradually developing experience in independent judgment of authority, since adjustments to authority comprise one large class of adjustments necessary in adult life. Whether we wish to admit it or not, no individual can do as he pleases. He may fondly imagine that there is no authority outside the realm of his own individual autonomy, but in practical living he must constantly make adjustments to physical and to social law. He recognizes that, no matter how much he may wish to place his hand on a hot stove without burning it, he may not do so because physical law dictates that flesh becomes injured by burning when exposed to a given temperature. He learns that society has organized itself according to a mutually agreed on set of traffic rules, and that, even though he as an individual may wish to disregard a red traffic light, he may not do so without danger to his life and the lives of other people because the rest of society regards the counter green light as a "go" signal. The same principle holds for the less codified social laws. Individuals are not autonomous in themselves but accept the inevitable consequences which follow, entirely regardless of individual wish, on the heels of specific types of behavior. For example, there are certain rules for friendship—rules of fair play, of generosity, of respect for other people's wishes as well as for one's own—rules which can be broken only at the cost of loss of friendship. Thus, infringement on social law or rule, like infringement on physical law, entails specific consequences. It is no good to say, "I am a law unto myself." No one is a law unto himself. Adjustment to law and authority is a part of sound mental health.

Each individual can learn what constitutes a desirable adjustment to authority. This includes learning what constitutes a "good and desirable" authority: What kind of law it is wise to obey; what kind of superior wisdom and experience it is desirable to consult. It also includes learning what constitutes a bad authority: What kind of opinion it is wise to disregard; what kind of advice is worthless or vicious. He proceeds toward self-discipline enough to comply with a "good" authority.

Wisdom in judgment of authority and courage in acting on such judgment come only as the result of practice. Children can be encouraged to assume such responsibility as rapidly as they have achieved enough experience to make their judgment sound; they can weigh facts and wisdom of others, yet value their own experiences for whatever those experiences may be worth.

Variation of Amount of Self-Discipline with Age. In the process of growing up, situations involving adjustments to authority and obedience to it are always present. Control by nature, society, another person and one's self are all a part of the situation. On the other hand, decision to act in acceptable or responsible ways, whether or not authority in the form of another person or an immediate consequence is present, can increase with age. Ability of this kind is allied to the sense of integrity. For example, in handling a book appropriately, a young child may at first have his hand guided by an adult's, later he may respond to verbal suggestions, a glance, the mere presence of the adult. Still later, his response is similar even when the adult is not present. One observer looking for illustrations of different stages of self discipline in a group of preschool children found the following in a short period of time; child throwing a piece from a puzzle into the sandbox, then walking with adult to get it to put back into the puzzle; child pushing doll buggy without bumping into others; child hanging up wraps without reminder; child playing in accordance with suggestions of another child, taking "tickets" for a "train" ride.

As ways of encouraging growth in self discipline, the following methods of the adult might be added to methods previously listed as encouraging obedience and discrimination in response to authority. Again, these are specific expressions of the more general attitudes listed at the beginning of this chapter.

1. Recognizing what the child is and is not able to do and enabling him to do for himself what he can.

2. Helping the child to learn what to do, instead of what not to do.

3. Making plans for constructive activities.

4. Being openminded and relaxed, willing to discuss reasons and reconsider.

5. Practicing as an adult aims set up for the child.

6. Praising when it is justified.

7. Expecting "good" behavior and making it interesting but not always entertaining.

8. Being logical: having the sequence of events related whether commendable or questionable behavior is involved, trying to avoid arbitrary punishment.

9. Being honest.

Intentions or Qualities of Parents. Guiding the child in learning what he needs to learn as he proceeds toward greater self discipline and thinking, can be done through methods which are not harsh, but which show an interest in the positive rather than the negative approach. Variations in the use of these methods are reported by Sears who says there is "evidence for the existence of a permissiveness-strictness dimension in respect to standards set up for the child's guidance."* The permissiveness-strictness factor concerned such practices as play in the house and with furniture, table manners, noise, being neat and orderly, toilet training, strict obedience, doing well in school, response to dependency, use of physical punishment, response to aggression, immodesty, masturbation, sex play.† Findings on the effects of this factor on children are not extensively reported in this study.

In connection with another factor, aggressiveness and punitiveness, findings are definitely stated: "Our measures of punishment, whether of the object-oriented or love-oriented variety, referred to levels of punitiveness in the mothers. That is, the amount of use of punishment that we measured was essentially a measure of a personality quality of the mothers. Punitiveness, in contrast with rewardingness, was a quite ineffectual quality for a mother to inject into her child training.

"The evidence for this conclusion is overwhelming. The unhappy effects of punishment have run like a dismal thread through our findings. Mothers who punished toilet accidents severely ended up with bed-wetting children. Mothers who punished dependency to get rid of it had more dependent children than mothers who did not punish.

* Sears[733] (p. 313).
† Sears[733] (p. 472).

Mothers who punished aggressive behavior severely had more aggressive children than mothers who punished lightly. They also had more dependent children. Harsh physical punishment was associated with high childhood aggressiveness and with the development of feeding problems.

"Our evaluation of punishment is that it is ineffectual over the long term as a technique for eliminating the kind of behavior toward which it is directed."*

Ambition or Expectations Adapted to Child's Own Pattern

Parental Ambitions for Child. Every child has the need to grow at his own rate. Furthermore, he has his own unique pattern of growth. Occasionally parents try to force growth into a more rapid pace or into a pattern different from the child's own. In the interest that parents have in their children, the children, being the first extension of their parents' egos, are sometimes allied to the most intimate thoughts and secret ambitions of those parents. This may involve the parents' refusal to grant the child an individual personality of his own. It may mean the parents are self-effacing and make every sacrifice that their child may have possessions and privileges denied them in their own childhood. We hear these parents say, "Bob will never have to work as I had to," or "Betty is going to have all the good times I missed when I was a girl."

In so far as work and suffering are a detriment to growth, children should, of course, be protected from them. We must not, however, lose sight of the fact that a certain amount of striving for achievement, of struggle for fulfillment is fundamental to rapid and desirable growth.† Overprotected children, like overindulged children, suffer a handicap for the very reason that they have been denied the opportunity for strength which struggle gives.

Refusal to understand the fact that children are not duplicates of parents may mean a refusal to grant the child individuality in wishes and desires. Sometimes we hear a mother say, "Betty wants a bicycle

---

* Sears[733] (p. 484).

† Adler develops this thesis clearly in his Practice and Theory of Individual Psychology.[2]

for Christmas, but when I was her age I was just crazy for a doll. I've the most beautiful doll for her; I just know she'll love it." And Betty's disappointment on Christmas morning leaves the mother with only a bewildered self hurt, but with no clearer understanding that Betty is not a duplicate of herself. One father who had always wanted to be a lawyer refused to permit his oldest son to study for medicine because "the young scoundrel doesn't know the thrill of arguing before a jury. Just wait until he's tried it; he'll be grateful to me for insisting." The father, denied expression of his own wish and intent on molding a law career through his son, failed to see that he was denying his son the same expression of an equally strong wish. This desire of parents to live again through their child, to find in him the pleasures they missed and the satisfactions they failed to achieve, is an urge to make up through the child for the disappointments and failures of their own lives, and is detrimental to the development of the child.

Less specific than these urges to live the detail of joy or disappointment through the child is the general urge to find success through the child in no matter what form. In this case the parents do not force any specific career on the child, but insist on success wherever the child seems most likely to achieve it. Difficulty often arises here when parents, refusing to recognize mediocre or inferior ability in the child, drive him far beyond his natural ability.

The urge of parents for the feeling of success through their child may take another form. If a child can recite an endless chain of nursery rhymes when he is two years old, or if he can graduate from high school at fourteen, thus persuading people to remark, "What a bright child!" parents can feel, "He is mine," in a way that may be overly gratifying.

It is a natural accompaniment of parental love to wish to see the child succeed. It is not the parental wish to see the child succeed that is dangerous; often the very wish for success and faith that it will come is the motive which produces it for the child. Trouble arises when the parental wish becomes selfish and the major drive behind the wish is gratification of the parent, or a desire to live again one's own life through the child. An illustration of the influence of external factors on the mother's behavior in an experimental situation, is in Merrill[112, 576] After being told the child had not realized his full capacities during a play period, the mother, in the next session, showed an increase in the following responses: directing the child's activity, interfering, criticizing, making changes in his activity. Mothers in the control group who did not receive the mild criticism did not show changes.

Trouble results whenever parents refuse to accept inherent limitations and continue to drive beyond native ability. No amount of hard work can make up for serious native deficiencies. Nothing but failure can come to a child driven beyond reasonable effort. Whenever a child has made a serious effort, the feeling that he has failed to meet the expectations of his parents is disastrous. Continued disappointment of parent in child produces a discouragement which inhibits even the measure of success that would otherwise be possible.

The subject of praise and blame is involved here. Too ready praise can breed habits of laziness and self complacency. Lack of serious competition or lack of sufficiently high standards of accomplishment is almost sure to leave wells of capacity undeveloped. On the other hand, too constant blame can breed habits of failure and self effacement.

The chief thing to be borne in mind in this connection is that parental ambition can be adjusted to the capacity and the interest of each individual child. Standards can be high enough to exact maximum development of native capacity, but flexible enough to adjust to incapacity. Praise and blame should be awarded according to effort as well as according to product, and the concept of success should be broadened to include the achievement of a good disposition and of a desirable individual and social viewpoint, and should not be limited to the attainment of material prosperity.

Growth through Expectation of Use of Ability.   Throughout this discussion it can be seen that parent-child relationships must change as the child grows. In early infancy the child is completely dependent on the parent for everything, his physical well-being, his psychological stimulation, and his emotional security. As he grows he gradually takes over for himself his own physical care, his pursuit of interest, and his social contacts; his emotional security passes gradually from being centered on his parents to being centered in things and situations under his own control. He is not grown up emotionally until he has learned to meet life on his own initiative and responsibility. There is, then, the problem of weaning him, at first physically from his mother's breast; also, as he grows, he must be weaned psychologically from dependence on his parents for economic support, for thinking and decision making, and for emotional security and satisfaction. Socially, his exposure to other people's standards and ideas comes at around two years or even sooner, when he meets other adults than his parents, if only during the brief hours when he is left in the charge of a person other than his mother. It progresses as he is exposed to other children and the patterns of behavior and standards the parents of these other children hold for them. In school he is legally under the control of teacher and principal; later he is deeply influenced by the ideas and ideals of his gang, especially of his adolescent gang. Ultimately he must live economically, socially and emotionally as an adult, fond of and respectful to his parents, yet independent in his decisions and his behavior, and in his choice of friends and of his mate. Parents can think of their children at all stages of growth as heading for an intelligent, independent adult existence.

The mother's acceptance of and confidence in both herself and her husband are referred to by Sears[733] as important in general family adjustment. Wanting her child to develop toward mature status is referred to by Sears[733] as a part of responsible child-training orientation. Both of these seem to have connotations related to parents' ambitions and expectations for their children. Achieving growth of independence need not mean the child is to be weaned away from love of parents and home. Quite the contrary, for the child who can gradually become an independent personality within his home seldom feels anything but devotion and loyalty for parents who understand him so well and who prepare him for life so wisely.

Parents who are wise grant freedom gradually and increasingly, and welcome rather than resent signs of a desire for independence on the child's part. The first contacts outside the home, even those made when the child is only two or three years old, almost inevitably mean exposure to behavior and to ideas that differ from the ones taught at home.

In encouraging growth in independence it is important to remember that the adult must not only earn a living and live happily with other people; he *must* also *live happily with himself.* In doing this he accepts himself with all of the assets and liabilities which he, along with everyone else, has. He discovers and trusts his talents and capacities, somehow fitting his own peculiar special skills and talents to the life demands around him. He also accepts whatever liabilities or handicaps there are in his own particular makeup. From the earliest adventures into living the infant can learn joy in using whatever ability he has, and can at the same time learn to accept the fact that he is not all perfect or all powerful. He is able to find pleasure in the exercise of his capacities, yet accept the fact that there are some things in which he cannot "be the best in the whole world." High standards which require genuine hard work to accomplish have a function; yet these standards should not be so high that the child develops a constant sense of failure and inadequacy. One of the greatest skills demanded of parents is the ability to gauge demands on the child to fit the child's maturity readiness (see Chapter 1), and yet to set the stage in such a fashion that the child learns early the supreme inner joy of success achieved through genuine effort. Adjustment of parental ambition for the child to the child's abilities is one of the important aspects of the parent's relationship to his child.

Studies of Parental Practice

Studies of relationships* between behavior of parents and behavior of their children based on observation of what the parents and children did and said have been comparatively few. Many more studies have used some method of reporting removed from the real situation. Interviews with parents have been one source of information about their practice. Questionnaires for parents, recalling their experiences or describing their attitudes about child rearing practices, have been another source of information. Classifications of ratings of parents' responses, as observed by someone else or as reported by themselves, and case studies have been used as a basis for conclusions. Ratings based on observation of children's behavior in natural situations and in experimental situations, and projective techniques have provided information about children's adjustment. Aspects of the parent have been related to aspects of the child. The following paragraphs are illustrative of findings of research which can stimulate thought about one's own procedures with children.

Permissiveness, or early self regulation and acceptance of particular forms of behavior has been studied.† With regard to practices affecting

---

* Methods of study of adult-child relationships are considered by Moustakas, Sigel and Schalock[601] and Highberger.[351]

† Aldrich,[6] Brim,[137] Brody,[140] Dameron,[180] Holway,[367] Newton,[630] Sears,[733] Sewell and Mussen.[746]

the child in the hospital before he came home to be with his parents, Aldrich[8] found that amount of crying decreased when personal attention the baby received increased. He supported his point of view about the importance of gratification, or satisfaction of emerging needs of the infant as they appear, by referring to studies of feeding activities.[5] Difficulties in eating habits decreased as attitudes of the mothers became more relaxed. In considering children three to five years of age, Holway[367] found satisfactory adjustment in nursery school and ability to face the home situation realistically occurring more frequently in children whose early life had lacked frustration (whose parents' philosophy was more permissive).

Brody found mothers could be grouped as follows:

"Group A: These mothers were sensitive, consistent and attentive.

"Group B: These mothers, in general, followed closely the pattern of the Group A mothers, but fell short of the mark in each index. They were less sensitive, less consistent, and somewhat overactive or overattentive.

"Group C: These mothers were insufficiently sensitive, moderately inconsistent, but adequately attentive.

"Group D: These mothers were hypersensitive, very inconsistent, and hyperactive."*

She concludes, "It appears that a mother may choose to breast feed, may try to give good physical support to her infant and may try to feed on a demand schedule—all popular and important criteria for adequate feeding—and yet she may unknowingly offer little satisfaction to her infant in the process. In all of these aspects of a feeding looms the problem of a mother's motives in adopting any of the procedures, and of her consciousness of conflict in this motivation. Direct observation may not reveal the presence of conflict, but a mother's capacity to make the early feeding experience of her child satisfying can probably be assessed if the observer bears in mind the three sets of criteria that have been brought forward: the first relates to the mother's *sensitivity to the infant's needs*; the second to her *use of physical space, time and communication* during feeding; and the third, to her choice of feeding methods and the *motives for her choice*. The three sets of criteria are recognized to contain overlapping features."†

* Brody[140] (p. 252).
† Brody[140] (p. 321). (Italics are ours.)

Reactions of children to particular actions of their parents have been studied.* With regard to *verbal and physical contacts* recorded during observations of mothers and children of preschool age, Lafore[485] made the following tentative generalizations.

Concerning interrelationships between parent practices and child behavior, she found:

"The parents who presented the smallest number of affectionate advances to their children received the largest number of affectionate advances from their children.

"The parents who presented the largest number of instances of dictating and interfering with their children received the largest number of expressions of hostility from their children.

"Parents who showed large numbers of instances of blaming, hurrying, punishing, threatening, and interfering, had children who presented large numbers of instances of crying.

"The parents who represented many instances of ignoring the child and diverting the child received many instances of teasing or nagging from the child.

"The parents who interfered most often with their children encountered large numbers of instances of resistance by them."†

Concerning relationships between parent practices and child characteristics, she found:

"The children who received the smallest number of affectionate advances were rated as least secure.

"Children who were frequently encouraged in academic learning scored high on ability.

"Children who were cautioned most often scored low on resourcefulness.

"Children who were frequently threatened scored high on fearfulness."‡

Responses of children growing up in different home atmospheres, in the sense of different personal relationships, have been studied.§ Baldwin[67] found relationships between certain conditions supplied by parents and behavior of the children. When *democratic handling* increased (with the factor of "control" of children constant) children's responses showed an increase in activity level, aggressiveness, fearlessness and planfulness. Such children were more likely to be nursery school leaders, were more likely to be cruel, were more curious, nonconforming, and disobedient. In homes where child *control* was high (with the factor of democracy constant) the children were relatively

---

* Lafore,[485] Hattwick and Stowell,[340] Tucker.[853]

† Lafore[485] (p. 141).

‡ Lafore[485] (pp. 141-142).

§ Baldwin,[66, 67, 68, 69] Champney,[159, 160] Macfarlane,[524] Sanford,[720] Sears et al.,[733] Wilkinson.[905]

less quarrelsome, negative and disobedient, they were also less aggressive, planful, tenacious and fearless.*

Other studies also concerned *authority or discipline.* Radke[679] found that children from homes having relatively autocratic discipline were "more frequently fighting and quarreling with the other children, more inconsiderate of others, more emotionally unstable, more uninhibited and daring, less rivalrous and more insensitive to praise or blame than children from the more democratic atmospheres."† When atmosphere of the home was considered, not in the way control was achieved but in the *amount of freedom* given to the child, a relation was found between the restrictive home and unpopularity and nonrivalrous passive behavior of the child. When home discipline was severe, the children were rated as hesitant in expressing themselves verbally and less affectionate. Radke found evidence that the child takes over, in his own behavior with other children, the behavior of the parent.

In a study of transmission of authority patterns in the family, Ingersoll[392] found matricentric authority patterns in the family relationships of adults whose own families had been matriarchal. The same reproduction of the pattern of the past was also true for patriarchal authority patterns. When children from opposite patterns married, a tendency to modify toward equalitarian relationships was found.

In a study based on observation of parents and children at home as well as at a university nursery school, factors were suggested which related to the children's behavior when the parents were, on the whole, democratic and understanding in their methods. Wilkinson[905] found that children rating high in social and emotional adjustment came from homes that were *active but not tense.* Their mothers were rated more *effective in gaining desired conduct from their children.* "Evidence of a relation was found between children rating high in social and emotional adjustment and the family that was interested in life outside the home, but not constantly seeking new contacts. The tendency was for children of parents who used moderate rather than lenient penalties to rate higher in adjustment. Children whose parents had given them experience in facing their own obstacles, rather than children who had been protected from difficulties, tended to rate higher. The parents who

---

* McCandless,[526] in reporting these findings, suggests that all of these behaviors of the children could be considered in terms of an aggression-passivity continuum.

† Radke[679] (p. 76).

satisfied their children's curiosity to the greatest extent had children with high adjustment scores."*

Parental *encouragement of expression of ideas, the fostering of social development,* and *overprotection* were related to children's behavior in a study by Grant.[311] Parental overprotection was related to children's dependent behavior, submissiveness and withdrawal from the group. Extremely overprotective parents had children showing nervous habits and insecurity. Encouragement of expression of ideas was related to cooperative self-reliant behavior, perseverance and resourcefulness on the part of the children. When social development was fostered, the children were ascendant, and cooperative, and played with the group.

Macfarlane[524] reported that fewer problems were found among children of *relaxed* mothers than among those of mothers who were worrisome, uneasy, or tense in their relationships to their children.†

In thinking about findings such as these reported, it is important to recall the complexity of relationships of parents and children and also the variations in ways of behaving and believing in different social groups. No simple cause-and-effect connections can be established. Sanford's[720] emphasis on syndromes seems very important. For example, he considers different patterns of "family press" in terms of different personality structures of the children. Again, the interrelationship of many factors is the pertinent point.

Captions, bold faced type and italics in this chapter have indicated some of the attitudes and practices of parents which affect their children's personality. Any review of them by leafing back through the pages suggests the importance of flexibility in the point of view.

Topics for Study and Discussion

Affection

1. Consider several publications of a popular type in an attempt to discover how suggestions to parents represent use of knowledge from research concerning children's stages of development, learning and responses to parental practice. For example:

    Children's Bureau Publication No. 8. Infant Care. Washington, D. C., U. S. Government Printing Office, 1955, pp. 48-56, How Your Baby Develops and Learns.

    Children's Bureau Publication No. 30. Your Child from One to Six.

---

* Wilkinson[905] (p. 87).

† Personality factors in the mothers are studied in Behrens[103] and Lakin.[488]

Washington, D. C., U. S. Government Printing Office, 1956, pp. 36-45, Constructive Discipline.

Hymes, J. L.: Being a Good Parent. New York, Bureau of Publications, Teachers College, Columbia University, 1949.

2. In observing relationships of children and adults look for illustrations of an understanding attitude concerning the individual child on the part of the adult and for illustrations of an understanding attitude concerning the individual adult on the part of the child.

Discipline

1. Consider several pamphlets or popular types of publications concerning discipline in an attempt to decide what in their points of view you agree or disagree with, and why. For example:

Discipline (Bulletin of Association for Childhood Education). Washington, D. C., Association for Childhood Education, 1957.

Hymes, J. L.: Discipline. New York, Bureau of Publications, Teachers College, Columbia University, 1949.

The Road Ahead in Discipline. Ames, Iowa, Agricultural Extension Service, Iowa State College, 1949.

2. In observing a group of preschool children, clarify aims in a philosophy of discipline by noting illustrations of self discipline in a child of two, three and four years. Clarify methods by noting effect on the child of different adult methods, such as explaining, using force, arranging for logical sequence of events, examples, expectation of a cooperative spirit, connection with reward, bribe, threat, deprival of privilege.

3. Report a situation or an incident with a child and an adult in which you were a participant or an observer, and attempt to decide what the child was seeking, what the adult was seeking and the effects of their behavior.

"Ambition" Adapted to Child's Pattern

1. Have a panel discuss ways of deciding whether or not a child is using his abilities. What are signs that standards are too high, too low, appropriate?

2. In observation of a child, in a particular situation consider what he seems to aspire to and what effect adults seem to have on his aspirations.

Parental Practice

1. Select from the discussion or from a footnote, a reference to research to consider thoroughly. Report on it in terms of its connection with a particular area, point of view or question.

Selected Readings

Frank, L., and Frank, M.: How To Help Your Child in School. New York, Viking Press, 1950. Chap. 2, How A Young Child Grows and Learns.

Gruenberg, S. A. (editor): Our Children Today. New York, Viking Press, 1952. Chap. 10 (Milton Senn), Permissiveness in the Early Years; Chap. 11 (Mary Fisher Langmuir), Discipline: Means and Ends.

Martin, W. E., and Stendler, C. B.: Child Development. New York, Harcourt, Brace and Company, 1953. Chap. 13, The Child in the Family.

Orlansky, H.: Infant Care and Personality, Psychological Bulletin 46:1-48, 1949.
Prescott, D.: Role of Love in Human Development, Journal of Home Economics 44:173-176, 1952.
Read, K. H.: The Nursery School. Philadelphia, W. B. Saunders Co., 1955. Chap. 9, Defining and Maintaining Limits for Behavior.
Sears, R. R., Maccoby, E. E., and Levin, H.: Patterns of Child Rearing, Evanston, Ill., Row, Peterson and Company, 1957. Chap. 13, The Sum and Substance.
Smart, M. S., and Smart, R. C.: It's a Wise Parent. New York, Charles Scribner's Sons, 1944.
Wolf, K.: There Is No One Way, Child Study 29:3-5, 1951-52.

List of Films

This list presents films about infants and young children which may be used with this text. Additional films may be found by consulting large annotated lists.* It is advisable that films be previewed before use and that an introduction to the film be given to the class before the showing, for the purpose of guiding the students' observations of the material shown in the film.

All films are 16 mm., sound film, and in black and white unless otherwise noted. The list is arranged alphabetically; the annotations are all taken from various lists of films.†

The films listed here can be obtained from the producer or the distributor named for each title. Films frequently may be obtained from local libraries or borrowed from universities with large film libraries.

Ages and Stages Series

> Produced by National Film Board of Canada, 1950.
> Distributed by McGraw-Hill Book Company.

> *He Acts His Age.* 14 min., color, 1949.

> Pictures how a child's emotional development keeps pace with his physical growth and the behavior he exhibits at certain ages. Examines the play habits of children from 1 to 15 years of age and shows some characteristics of each age group.
> Introduction to the series.

* Federal Security Agency: Motion Pictures on Child Life. A list of 16 mm. films. Compiled by Inez D. Lohr, Children's Bureau, Federal Security Agency. Superintendent of Documents, Government Printing Office, Washington, D.C. Supplement No. 1, 1954, and Supplement No. 2, 1956, U. S. Department of Health, Education and Welfare.

American Home Economics Association: Annotated List of Films Useful for Family Centered Teaching. American Home Economics Association, 1600 Twentieth Street, N.W., Washington 9, D.C.

† The Detroit Public Library: Films. Annotated catalog of films in the collection of the Audio-Visual Department of The Detroit Public Library, 1950, and a supplement, July, 1952, and January, 1957.

Terrible Twos and the Trusting Threes. 20 min., color, 1951.

Presents a close examination of the growing years between two and four.

The Frustrating Fours and Fascinating Fives. 25 min., color, 1952.

Depicts characteristic behavior of four- and five-year-old children.
Produced by Crawley Films for the National Film Board of Canada.

Baby Meets His Parents. 11 min., 1948.

Points out how differences in personality can be accounted for, not only by heredity, but also by the human relationships and environmental factors experienced during the first years of life.
Produced by Encyclopaedia Britannica Films in collaboration with Lawrence K. Frank, Director, Caroline Zachry Institute of Human Development.
Distributed by Encyclopaedia Britannica Films.

Design for Happy Mealtimes. 48 frames, 1954.

Ways by which a preschool child develops food habits and attitudes. Discussion guide included.
Produced by The Merrill-Palmer School. Direction and script by Muriel G. Wagner. Photography by Donna Harris.

Emergence of Personality. 30 min., 1948.

A combined version of the three films "Baby Meets His Parents," "Helping the Child To Accept the Do's," and "Helping the Child To Face the Don'ts."
Produced and distributed by Encyclopaedia Britannica Films.

Fears of Children. 29 min., 1951.

How parents, eager to raise their five-year-old correctly, learn to handle a particular situation. Paul, frightened with false warnings from the mother, is timid, sulky, and fearful. Father is impatient; he wants to encourage his son to do things for himself. These parents learn through similar experiences in another family that it is normal for children to become angry with their parents and that some rebellion should be tolerated.

Produced by Julien Bryan for the National Association for Mental Health. Third in a series *Emotions of Everyday Living.* Distributed by International Film Bureau.

Helping the Child To Accept the Do's. 11 min., 1948.

Portrays the child learning to live in a world defined by the "do's" and explains how his personality is influenced by the extent to which they are accepted.
Produced by Encyclopaedia Britannica Films in collaboration with Lawrence K. Frank, Director, Caroline Zachry Institute of Human Development.
Distributed by Encyclopaedia Britannica Films.

Helping the Child To Face the Don'ts. 11 min., 1948.

Reveals how the young child meets a world of "don'ts" and how he reacts in his own distinctive ways, thus forming his own individual personality.
Produced by Encyclopaedia Britannica Films in collaboration with Lawrence K. Frank, Director, Caroline Zachry Institute of Human Development.
Distributed by Encyclopaedia Britannica Films.

Human Reproduction. 22 min., 1950.

A film intended for college audiences which discusses the imminent birth of a child in a relative's household. The son approaches his father with the familiar question about the origin of babies. The film reviews for the benefit of the parents the basic facts of human reproduction, making use of models and animated drawings.
Produced and distributed by McGraw-Hill Book Company.

It's a Small World. 38 min., 1951.

Activities and routine of a day in a London Day Nursery photographed by a hidden camera. In detailed and leisurely fashion recounts all the events of the child's day—painting, building, sailing boats, cooking, playing games, eating and departure in the afternoon.
Produced by International Realist, 1950.
Distributed by British Information Service.

Life with Baby. 18 min., 1946.

Shows how children grow mentally and physically. A popular version and condensation of the Gesell Child Development Series.
Produced and distributed by March of Time Forum Films.

A Long Time To Grow. 35 min., 1951.

Shows in a series of incidents taken in a nursery school what children are like while they are learning and growing. The ways in which teachers help set limits, the effect of the variety and suitability of play equipment, how student teachers help are also pictured. This is the first of a series of three designed to show school experiences in the period of early childhood and is intended for teachers and parents.
Produced by the Department of Child Study at Vassar College.
Distributed by New York University Film Library.

Meeting Emotional Needs in Childhood: The Groundwork of Democracy. 33 min., 1947.

Attempts to help children develop positive attitudes toward other people and toward the community.
Produced by Department of Child Study at Vassar College.
Distributed by New York University Film Library.

Preface to Life. 30 min., 1951.

The story of a boy and two dreams. The boy is Michael Thompson, son of a typical young couple living in a small town or suburb. One dream is that of his father, a vision of Michael rising to be a strong and successful leader. The other dream is the mother's, the hope that Michael will always be her baby. It shows how attitudes may influence adult's actions in everyday situations and how trivial-seeming incidents may make a difference in the way a child develops. It promotes the basic idea that children must be understood and respected as individuals— growing personalities in their own emotional needs and rights.
Produced by National Institute of Mental Health.
Distributed by New York University Film Library.

Preschool Incidents (No. 1): When Should Grown-ups Help? 13 min., 1951.

> Shows four episodes in which an adult may not have inter-vened to assist the child. Intended to stimulate discussion on the issue and to provide an exercise in the observation and recording of behavior.
> Produced by Department of Child Study, Vassar College.
> Distributed by New York University Film Library.

Preschool Incidents (No. 2): And Then Ice Cream. 10 min., 1951.

> Presents episodes to stimulate discussion on the parental super-vision of children's meals.
> Produced by Department of Child Study, Vassar College.
> Distributed by New York University Film Library.

Principles of Development. 15 min., 1950.

> Outlines the fundamentals of growth and change from early infancy.
> Produced by Crawley Films.
> Distributed by McGraw-Hill Book Company.

A Two-Year-Old Goes To Hospital. 45 min., 1952.

> A little girl's reaction to an 8-day stay in the hospital shows some of the effects of her temporary separation from her parents. Because this film was part of a research project the child was photographed at the same time every day to secure a "daily time sample." The English hospital procedures de-picted are in many respects different from those in American hospitals.
> Produced by James Robertson, at the Tavistock Clinic, London, England, in the course of a research project directed by John Bowlby, M.D.
> Distributed by New York University Film Library.

Understanding Children's Play. 10 min., 1948.

> Shows how adults can understand and help children through observation of their use of toys and play materials. By in-creasing parents' awareness of children's play activities, they can function more effectively in guiding children.

Produced by Caroline Zachry Institute of Human Development.
Distributed by New York University Film Library.

Why Won't Tommy Eat? 19 min., color, 1948.

Uncovers both physical and mental causes of the problem of
the child who refuses to eat.
Produced by Crawley Films for Canadian Department of
National Health and Welfare.
Distributed by Sterling Films.

Your Children's Sleep. 23 min., 1947.

Discusses common causes of sleeplessness in adults: worry,
overfatigue, unfortunate incidents during the day. Focusing
upon the child, the film analyzes his difficulties in going from
active play to sleep and explains the role which dreams play
in the child's developing mind. Gives many good suggestions
for helping children to relax and accept sleep.
Produced by Realist Film Unit.
Distributed by British Information Service.

Distributors of Films Listed Above

British Information Service, 30 Rockefeller Plaza, New York 29, New
York, or 39 South LaSalle, Chicago 3, Illinois.
Encyclopaedia Britannica Films, 1150 Wilmette Avenue, Wilmette,
Illinois.
International Film Bureau, 60 Michigan Avenue, Chicago 2, Illinois.
McGraw-Hill Book Company, Text-Film Department, 330 West 42nd
Street, New York 18, New York.
March of Time Forum Films, 369 Lexington Avenue, New York 17,
New York.
New York University Film Library, 26 Washington Place, New York 3,
New York.
Sterling Films, Incorporated, 316 West 57th Street, New York 19,
New York.

Bibliography

1. Acheson, R. M.: A method of assessing skeletal maturity from radiographs. A report from the Oxford Child Health Survey, Brit. J. Anat. 88:498-508, 1954.
2. Adler, A.: Practice and Theory of Individual Psychology (translated by P. Radin). New York, Harcourt, Brace & Co., Inc., 1924.
3. Aisensone, M. R.: Closing of anterior fontanelle, Pediatrics 6:223-226, 1950.
4. Aldrich C. A.: Advisability of breast feeding, J.A.M.A. 135:915-916, 1947.
5. ———: Role of gratification in early development, J. Pediat. 15:578-582, 1939.
6. Aldrich, C. A., and Aldrich, M. M.: Babies Are Human Beings. ed. 2. New York, Macmillan Company, 1954.
7. Aldrich, C. A., and Hewitt, E. S.: Self-regulating feeding program for infants, J.A.M.A. 135:340-342, 1947.
8. Aldrich, C. A., Sung, C., and Knop, C.: The crying of newly born babies; the community phase, J. Pediat. 26:313-326, 1945.
9. ———: The crying of newly born babies; the individual phase, J. Pediat. 27:89-96, 1945.
10. ———: The crying of newly born babies; the early period at home, J. Pediat. 27:428-435, 1945.
11. Allen, R. M.: Nine quarterly Rorschach records of a young girl, Child Development 26:63-69, 1955.
12. Allen, W., and Campbell, D.: The Creative Nursery Center, a Unified Service to Children and Parents. New York, Family Service Association, 1948.
13. Allinsmith, W.: The Learning of Moral Standards. Doctoral Dissertation Series Publication No. 8266. Ann Arbor, Michigan, University of Michigan Microfilms, 1954.
14. Almy, M.: Child Development. New York, Henry Holt and Company, 1955.
15. Alpert, A.: The Solving of Problem Situations by Preschool Children. Contributions to Education, No. 323. New York, Teachers College, Columbia University, 1928.
16. Alschuler, R. H., and Hattwick, L. W.: Painting and Personality, a Study of Young Children. Chicago, University of Chicago Press, 1947. Two volumes.
17. Alvarez, W. C.: Digestive Tract; Motor Functions, in Glasser, O. (editor): Medical Physics, vol. I. Chicago, The Year Book Publishers, Inc., 1944.
18. American Academy of Pediatrics: Child Health Services and Pediatric Education. Report of Committee for Study of Child Health Services. New York, Commonwealth Fund, 1949.
19. ———: Round table discussion, Infant feeding (Gegenback, F. P., Chairman; Abt, I. A., Barbour, P. F., Durand, J. H., Associates; Garrison, H., Secretary), J. Pediat. 18:834-839, 1941.

493

20. American Academy of Pediatrics: Round table discussion, Nursing care in the newborn infant (Durand, J. H., Chairman; Christie, A. U., Assistant), J. Pediat. 13:434-444, 1938.

21. American Council on Education: Women in the Defense Decade. Series I, Number 52, vol. 16, Reports of Committees and Conferences. Washington, D. C., 1950.

22. Ames, L. B.: Bilaterality, J. Genet. Psychol. 75:45-50, 1949.

23. ———: Development of sense of time in the young child, J. Genet. Psychol. 68:97-125, 1946.

24. ———: The sense of self of nursery school children as manifested in their verbal behavior, J. Genet. Psychol. 81:193-232, 1952.

25. ———: The sequential patterning of prone progression in the human infant, Genet. Psychol. Monogr. 19:409-460, 1937.

26. Ames, L. B., and Learned, J.: Development of verbalized space in the young child, J. Genet. Psychol. 72:63-84, 1948.

27. ———: Imaginary companions and related phenomena, J. Genet. Psychol. 69:147-167, 1946.

28. Ames, L. B., et al.: Child Rorschach Responses. New York, Harper & Brothers, 1952.

29. Anastasi, A.: Psychological Testing. New York, The Macmillan Co., 1954.

30. Anderson, A.: Some observations on birth weights, Med. Officer 89:15-17, 1953.

31. Anderson, D. L.: Predictive value of infancy tests in relation to intelligence at five years, Child Development 10:203-212, 1939.

32. Anderson, H.: Measurement of domination and of socially integrative behavior in teachers' contacts with children, Child Development 10:73-89, 1939.

33. Anderson, H., and Anderson, G. (editors): Introduction to Projective Techniques. New York, Prentice-Hall, 1951.

34. Anderson, H., and Anderson, G.: Chap. 19—Social Development, in Carmichael, L.: Manual of Child Psychology. ed. 2 (155).

35. Anderson, H., et al.: Personality development in infancy and the preschool years, Rev. Educ. Research 25:453-468, 1955.

36. Anderson, J. E.: Child development: an historical perspective, Child Development 27:181-196, 1956.

37. ———: Development of social behavior, Am. J. Sociol. 44:839-857, 1939.

38. ———: Chap. 1—Methods of Child Psychology in Carmichael, L.: Manual of Child Psychology. ed. 2 (155).

39. ———: Personality organization in children, American Psychologist 3:409-416, 1948. Also in Dennis, W.: Readings in Child Psychology (208).

40. ———: Psychology of Development and Personal Adjustment. New York, Henry Holt & Co., 1949.

41. Anderson, M., et al.: Growth of the normal foot during childhood and adolescence. Length of the foot and interrelations of foot, stature and lower extremities as seen in serial records of children between 1-18 years of age, Am. J. Phys. Anthropol. 14 ns:287-308, 1956.

42. Andrews, V. L.: Infantile beriberi, Philippine J. Sci. 7:67-89, 1912.

43. Antonov, A. N.: Children born during siege of Leningrad in 1942, J. Pediat. 30:250-259, 1947.

44. Appel, M.: Aggressive behavior of nursery school children and adult procedures in dealing with such behavior, J. Exper. Educ. 11:185-199, 1942.

45. Arbuthnot, M. H.: Children and Books. Chicago, Scott, Foresman & Co., 1957.
46. Arey, L. B.: Developmental Anatomy. ed. 6. Philadelphia, W. B. Saunders Co., 1954.
47. Armbruster, A.: What about parent-cooperative preschool groups? Nat. A. Nurs. Educ. Bull. 7:5-9, 1952.
48. Armstrong, E. M., and Wagoner, L. C.: Motor control of children as involved in the dressing process, J. Genet. Psychol. 35:84-97, 1928.
49. Armstrong, W. D.: Radiotracer studies of hard tissues, in Recent Advances in the Study of the Structure, Composition and Growth of Mineralized Tissue. Annals of the New York Academy of Science 60, art. 5:670-684, 1955.
50. Arsenian, S.: Bilingualism in the postwar world, Psychol. Bull. 42:65-86, 1945.
51. Arts Cooperative Service: More than Fun. New York, Arts Cooperative Service, 1950.
52. Associates of Bank Street College of Education: Conference Proceedings, Imagination in Education. New York, 69 Bank Street Publications, 1956.
53. Association for Childhood Education: Bibliography of Books for Children. Washington, D. C., Association for Childhood Education, 1956.
54. ———: Helping Children Grow. Washington, D. C., Association for Childhood Education, 1951.
55. ———: Music for Children's Living. Washington, D. C., Association for Childhood Education, 1955.
56. Ast, D. B., et al.: Newburgh-Kingston caries-fluorine study. XIV. Combined clinical and roentgenographic dental findings aften ten years of fluoride experience, J. Am. Dent. A. 52:314-325, 1956.
57. Ausubel, D. P.: Ego-development and the learning process, Child Development 20:173-190, 1949.
58. Axline, V.: Play Therapy. New York, Houghton Mifflin Co., 1947.
59. Bacmeister, R.: The Young Child Learns about Nature. New York, Arts Cooperative Service, 1950.
60. Baehr, G.: The Peckham experiment, Milbank Mem. Fund Quarterly 22: 352-357, 1944.
61. Bain, K.: Death due to accidental poisoning in young children, J. Pediat. 44:616-623, 1954.
62. Baker, S. J.: Child Hygiene. New York, Harper & Brothers, 1925.
63. Bakwin, H.: Emotional deprivation in infants, J. Pediat. 35:512-521, 1949.
64. Bakwin, R. M., and Bakwin, H.: Accident proneness, J. Pediat. 32:749-752, 1948.
65. Baldwin, A. L.: Behavior and Development in Childhood. New York, Dryden Press, 1955.
66. ———: Effect of home environment on nursery school behavior, Child Development 20:49-61, 1949.
67. ———: Socialization and the parent-child relationship, Child Development 19:128-136, 1948.
68. Baldwin, A. L., Kalhorn, J., and Breese, F. H.: Patterns of parent behavior, Psychol. Monogr. vol. 58, No. 3, 1945.
69. ———: Patterns of parent behavior, Psychol. Monogr. vol. 63, No. 4, 1949.
70. Balfour, M. I.: Supplementary feeding in pregnancy, Lancet 246:208-211, 1944.

71. Barker, R. G.: Midwest and Its Children: The Psychological Ecology of an American Town. Evanston, Ill., Row, Peterson and Co., 1955.
72. Barker, R. G., Kounin, J. S., and Wright, H. F.: Child Behavior and Development. New York, McGraw-Hill Book Co., Inc., 1943.
73. Barker, R. G., and Wright, H. F.: One Boy's Day. New York, Harper and Brothers, 1951.
74. ————: Psychological ecology and problem of psychosocial development, Child Development 20:131-143, 1949.
75. Barnes, G. R., Jr., et al.: Management of breast feeding, J.A.M.A. 151:192-199, 1953.
76. Barton, M., and Wiesner, B. P.: Waking temperature in relation to fetal fecundity, Lancet 2:663-668, 1945.
77. Baruch, D.: New Ways in Discipline. New York, McGraw-Hill Book Co., Inc., 1949.
78. ————:Parents and Children Go to School. New York, Scott, Foresman & Co., 1939.
79. ————: Study of reported tension in interparental relationships as co-existent with behavior adjustment in young children, J. Exper. Educ. 6:187-204, 1937.
80. Bayley, N.: California Scale of Motor Development. University of California Syllabus Series 259, 1936.
81. ————: Consistency and variability in growth of intelligence from birth to eighteen years, J. Genet. Psychol. 75:165-196, 1949.
82. ————: Development of Motor Abilities during the First Three Years. Washington, D. C., Society for Research in Child Development, National Research Council, 1935.
83. ————: Growth curves of height and weight by age for boys and girls, scaled according to physical maturity, J. Pediat. 48:187-194, 1956.
84. ————: Individual patterns of development, Child Development 27:45-74, 1956.
85. ————: Mental growth during the first three years: developmental study of 61 children by repeated tests, Genet. Psychol. Monogr. 14:1-92, 1933.
86. ————: Mental Growth in Young Children, in Thirty-ninth Yearbook of the National Society for the Study of Education, Part II. Bloomington, Ill., Public School Publishing Company, 1940.
87. ————: On the growth of intelligence, American Psychologist 10:805-818, 1955.
88. ————: Skeletal maturing in adolescence as basis for determining percentage of completed growth, Child Development 14:1-46, 1943.
89. ————: Some increasing parent-child similarities during the growth of children, J. Educ. Psychol. 45:1-21, 1954.
90. ————: Studies in Development of Young Children. Berkeley, University of California Press, 1940.
91. Bayley, N., and Davis, D. C.: Growth changes in bodily size and proportion during the first three years, Biometrika 27:26-87, 1935.
92. Bayley, N., and Espenschade, A.: Motor development from birth to maturity, Rev. Educ. Research 11:562-572, 1941.
93. ————: Motor development from birth to maturity, Rev. Educ. Research 14:381-389, 1944.
94. ————: Motor development and decline, Rev. Educ. Research 20:367-374, 1950.

95. Bayley, N., and Stolz, H. R.: Maturational changes in rectal temperatures of 61 infants from 1 to 36 months, Child Development 8:195-206, 1937.
96. Beach, V., and Bressler, M. H.: Phases in development of children's painting, J. Exper. Educ. 13:1-4, 1944.
97. Beal, V. A.: Nutritional intake of children. I. Calories, carbohydrate, fat and protein, J. Nutrition 50:223-234, 1953.
98. ———: Nutritional intake of children. II. Calcium, phosphorus and iron, J. Nutrition 53:499-510, 1954.
99. ———: Nutritional intake of children. III. Thiamine, riboflavin and niacin, J. Nutrition 57:183-192, 1955.
100. Beasley, J.: Slow to Talk; a Guide for Teachers and Parents of Children with Delayed Language Development. New York, Bureau of Publications, Teachers College, Columbia University, 1956.
101. Beaver, A. P.: Initiation of Social Contacts by Preschool Children. Child Development Monograph, No. 7. New York, Teachers College, Columbia University, 1932.
102. Beck, A. C., Taylor, E. S., and Colburn, R. F.: Vitamin K administered to mother during labor as prophylaxis against hemorrhage in newborn infant, Am. J. Obst. & Gynec. 41:765-775, 1941.
103. Behrens, M.: Child rearing and the character structure of the mother, Child Development 25:225-238, 1954.
104. Beller, E. K.: Dependency and independence in your children, J. Genet. Psychol. 87:25-35, 1955.
105. Bender, L., and Frosch, J.: Children's reactions to the war, Am. J. Orthopsychiat. 12:571-587, 1946.
106. Benedict, F. G., and Talbot, F. B.: Metabolism and Growth from Birth to Puberty. Carnegie Institute Publication No. 302. Washington, D. C., Carnegie Institute, 1921.
107. Bernstein, R. L., and Borkowski, W. J.: Prenatal fetal electrocardiography, Am. J. Obst. & Gynec. 70:631-638, 1955.
108. Bernstein, P., and Mann, H.: Clinical evaluation of fetal electrocardiography: a study of 100 cases by a new technique and an improved instrument, Am. J. Obst. & Gynec. 43:21-32, 1942.
109. Bethell, F. H., et al.: Nutritional inadequacies in pregnancy correlated with incidence of anemia, J. Am. Dietet. A. 19:165-172, 1943.
110. Bibby, B. G.: Effect of sugar content of foodstuffs on their caries-producing potentialities, J. Am. Dent. A. 51:293-306, 1955.
111. Binning, G.: "Peace be on thy house." The effect of emotional tensions on the development and growth of children, based on a study of 800 Saskatoon school children, Health—Canada's National Health Magazine, March-April, 1948.
112. Bishop, B. M.: Mother-child interaction and the social behavior of children, Psychol. Monograph 65, No. 11, 1951.
113. Black, I. S.: Use of Stanford-Binet (1937 Revision) in group of nursery school children, Child Development 10:157-173, 1939.
114. Blake, R. B., and Ramsey, G.: Perception—An Approach to Personality. New York, Ronald Press, 1952.
115. Blanton, S. M.: Mental and nervous changes in children of Volkschule of Trier, Germany, Ment. Hyg. 3:343-386, 1919.
116. Blatz, W., and Bott, H.: Management of Young Children. New York, William Morrow and Company, 1930.

117. Block, J., and Martin, B.: Predicting the behavior of children under frustration, J. Abnorm. Soc. Psychol. 51:281-285, 1955.
118. Blum, A.: The value factor in children's size perception, Child Development 28:5-14, 1957.
119. Bodman, F.: Child psychiatry in war-time Britain, J. Educ. Psychol. 35:293-301, 1944.
120. Body, M.: Patterns of aggression in the nursery school, Child Development 26:3-11, 1955.
121. Bossard, J. H. S.: Sociology of Child Development. New York, Harper & Brothers, 1954.
122. Bowlby, J.: in Hoch, P. H., and Zubin, J. (editors): Anxiety. New York, Grune and Stratton, 1950.
123. ————: Maternal Care and Mental Health. New York, Columbia University Press, 1951.
124. Bowman, H. A.: Marriage for Moderns. New York, McGraw-Hill Book Co., Inc., 1954.
125. Boyd, E.: Weight of thymus and its component parts and number of Hassal corpuscles in health and in disease, Am. J. Dis. Child. 51:313-335, 1936.
126. Boynton, M. A., and Goodenough, F. L.: Posture of nursery school children during sleep, Am. J. Psychol. 42:270-278, 1930.
127. Bradway, K.: Experimental study of factors associated with Stanford-Binet I.Q. changes from preschool to junior-high school, J. Genet. Psychol. 66:107-128, 1945.
128. ————: I.Q. constancy on revised Stanford-Binet from preschool to junior-high school level, J. Genet. Psychol. 65:147-160, 1944.
129. Brandenburg, J., and Brandenburg, G. C.: Language development during the fourth year, Ped. Sem. 26:27-40, 1919.
130. Brash, J. M., McKeag, H. T. A., and Scott, J. H.: The Aetiology of Irregularity and Malocclusion of the Teeth. 44 Hallam St., London W.I, The Dental Board of the United Kingdom, 1956.
131. Breckenridge, M. E., and Vincent, E. L.: Child Development; Physical and Psychology Growth through the School Years. ed. 3. Philadelphia, W. B. Saunders Company, 1955.
132. Briant, W. W., and Henderson, S. G.: The colon in the healthy newborn infant, Radiology 39:261-272, 1942.
133. Brichetto, T.: Security of Children in Cooperative Play Group. Unpublished Master's thesis, Purdue University, 1947.
134. Bridges, K. M. B.: Social and Emotional Development of Preschool Child. London, Geo. Routledge & Sons, Ltd., 1931.
135. Brill, N. Q., and Seidemann, H.: Electroencephalograms of normal children; effect of hyperventilation, Am. J. Psychiat. 98:250-256, 1941.
136. Brill, N. Q., et al.: Electroencephalographic studies in delinquent behavior problem children, Am. J. Psychiat. 98:494-498, 1942.
137. Brim, O. G.: The acceptance of new behavior in child rearing, Hum. Relat. 7:473-491, 1954.
138. Bro, M.: When Children Ask. ed. 2. New York, Willett, Clark and Company, 1956.
139. Broadbent, B. H.: Ontogenetic Development of Occlusion, in Gregory, W. K., Broadbent, B. H., and Hillman, M.: Development of Occlusion. Philadelphia, University of Pennsylvania Press, 1941.
140. Brody, S.: Patterns of Mothering; Maternal Influence during Infancy. New York, International Universities Press, 1956.

141. Brooks, L. M., and Brooks, E. C.: Adventuring in Adoption. Chapel Hill, N. C., University of North Carolina Press, 1946.
142. Bryan, E. S.: Variations in responses of infants during first ten days of postnatal life, Child Development 1:56-77, 1930.
143. Bühler, C.: From Birth to Maturity. London, Routledge and Kegan Paul Ltd., 1935.
144. ————: The First Year of Life. New York, John Day Co., 1930.
145. Burgess, E. W., and Cottrell, L. S.: Prediction of Success or Failure in Marriage. New York, Prentice-Hall, Inc., 1939.
146. Burke, B. S.: Diet during pregnancy, Am. J. Clin. Nutrition 2:425-428, 1954.
147. ————: Need for better nutrition during pregnancy and lactation, J. Am. Dietet. A. 17:102-111, 1941.
148. Burke, B. S., et al.: Nutrition studies during pregnancy, Am. J. Obst. & Gynec. 16:38-52, 1943.
149. Burke, B. S., Harding, V. V., and Stuart, H. C.: Nutrition studies during pregnancy; relation of protein content of mother's diet during pregnancy to birth length, birth weight and condition of infant at birth, J. Pediat. 23:506-515, 1944.
150. Burke, B. S., and Stuart, H. C.: Nutritional Requirements during Pregnancy and Lactation, in Handbook of Nutrition; a Symposium. ed. 2. American Medical Association, published by Blakiston Co., 1951.
151. Caille, A.: Left-handedness as an educational problem, Ann. Clin. Med. 1:111-116, 1922.
152. Campbell, R. V. D., and Weech, A. A.: Measures which characterize the individual during development of behavior in early life, Child Development 12:217-234, 1941.
153. Cannon, W. B.: Wisdom of the Body. New York, W. W. Norton & Co., 1933.
154. Carlson, A. J., and Johnson, V.: Machinery of the Body. ed. 4. Chicago, University of Chicago Press, 1953.
155. Carmichael, L. (editor): Manual of Child Psychology. ed. 2. New York, John Wiley & Sons, Inc., 1954.
156. Carmichael, L.: Chap. 2—Onset and Early Development of Behavior, in Carmichael, L.: Manual of Child Psychology (155).
157. Castner, B. M.: Development of fine prehension in infancy, Genet. Psychol. Monogr. 12:105-193, 1932.
158. Challman, R. C.: Factors influencing friendships among preschool children, Child Development 3:146-158, 1932.
159. Champney, H.: Measurement of parent behavior, Child Development 12:131-166, 1941.
160. ————: Variables of parent behavior, J. Abnorm. & Social Psychol. 36:525-542, 1941.
161. Chant, N., and Blatz, W.: Study of sleeping habits of children, Genet. Psychol. Monogr. 4:13-43, 1928.
162. Chess, S.: War ideologies of children, Am. J. Orthopsychiat. 13:505-509, 1943.
163. Child Study Association of America: When Children Ask About Sex. New York, Child Study Association of America, Inc., 1953.
164. Christensen, H.: Marriage Analysis: Foundations for Successful Family Life. New York, Ronald Press, 1958.
165. Clements, E. M. B.: Changes in the mean stature and weight of British children over the past seventy years, Brit. Med. J. ii:897-902, 1953.

166. Cobb, S., and Cole, E. M.: Stuttering, Physiol. Rev. 19:49-62, 1939.
167. Coleman, S.: Your Child's Music. New York, John Day Co., 1939.
168. Comstock, A. B.: Handbook of Nature Study. ed. 24. Ithaca, N. Y., Comstock Publishing Co., 1947.
169. Conel, J. LeR.: Postnatal Development of Human Cerebral Cortex. vol. I, Cortex of The Newborn. Cambridge, Harvard University Press, 1939.
170. ———:Postnatal Development of Human Cerebral Cortex. vol. IV, Cortex of The Six Month Infant. Cambridge, Harvard University Press, 1951.
171. Coons, C. M., and Marshall, G. B.: Some factors influencing nitrogen economy during pregnancy, J. Nutrition 7:67-78, 1934.
172. Corner, G. W.: Ourselves Unborn. New Haven, Yale University Press, 1944.
173. Coursin, D. B.: Effect of vitamin B₆ on the central nervous activity in childhood, Am. J. Clin. Nutrition 4:354-362, 1956.
174. Cox, G. J.: Fluorine and Dental Caries, in Survey of the Literature of Dental Caries. Food and Nutrition Board, National Research Council Publ. 225. Washington, D. C., National Academy of Sciences, National Research Council, 1952.
175. ———: Oral Environment, in Survey of the Literature of Dental Caries. Food and Nutrition Board, National Research Council Publ. 225. Washington, D. C., National Academy of Sciences, National Research Council, 1952.
176. Cross, H. M.: Motor capacities of stutterers, Arch. Speech 2:112, 1936.
177. Daily, E. F.: Maternal mortality, 1939, Am. J. Obst. & Gynec. 42:352-354, 1941.
178. Dales, R.: Afternoon sleep in group of nursery school children, J. Genet. Psychol. 58:161-180, 1941.
179. Dalgleish, A.: First Experiences with Literature. New York, Charles Scribner's Sons, 1932.
180. Dameron, L. E.: Mother-child interaction in the development of self-restraint, J. Genet. Psychol. 86:289-308, 1955.
181. Dammon, V. I.: Developmental changes in attitude as one factor determining energy output in a motor performance: normal child development study of Department of Pediatrics, Columbia University and Babies Hospital, Child Development 12:241-246, 1941.
182. Danforth, C. H.: Hair. With Special Reference to Hypertrichosis. Chicago, American Medical Association, 1925.
183. Daniels, A. L., et al.: Calcium and phosphorus needs of preschool children, J. Nutrition 10:373-388, 1935.
184. Dann, W. J., and Darby, W. J.: Appraisal of nutritional status (nutriture) in humans, with special reference to vitamin deficiency diseases, Physiol. Rev. 25:326-346, 1945.
185. Darby, W. J., et al.: The Vanderbilt Cooperative Study of Maternal and Infant Nutrition. IX. Some obstetric implications, Obst. & Gynec. 5:528-537, 1955.
186. Darcy, N. T.: A review of the literature on the effects of bilingualism upon the measurement of intelligence, J. Genet. Psychol. 82:21-57, 1953.
187. Darner, C. B., and Hunter, G. W.: Importance of rest in initiation of breast feeding, Am. J. Obst. & Gynec. 45:117-120, 1943.
188. Davis, A.: Clinical experiences with children in wartime, Social Service Rev. 17:170-174, 1943.
189. Davis, W. A., and Havighurst, R.: Father of the Man: How your Child Gets His Personality. Boston, Houghton Mifflin Co., 1947.

190. Davis, C. M.: Chap. 30 (vol. 1)—Feeding After The First Year, in Breene-mann's Practice of Pediatrics, I. McQuarrie, editor. Hagerstown, Md., W. F. Prior Co., Inc., 1957.

191. ————: Practical application of some lessons of self-selection diet study to feeding of children in hospitals, Am. J. Dis. Child. 46:745-750, 1933.

192. ————: Self-selection of diet by newly weaned infants, Am. J. Dis. Child. 36:651-679, 1928.

193. Dawe, H. C.: Analysis of two hundred quarrels of preschool children, Child Development 5:139-157, 1934.

194. ————: The Child's Experiences in Communication, in Forty-sixth Yearbook of the National Society for the Study of Education, Part II. Chicago, University of Chicago Press, 1947.

195. ————: Environmental influences on language growth, in Kuhlen, R., and Thompson, G.: Psychological Studies in Human Development (484).

196. Day, E.: Development of language in twins: comparison of twins and single children, Child Development 3:179-199, 1932. Also in Dennis, W.: Readings in Child Psychology (208).

197. Dean, H. J.: Fluorine in the control of dental caries, J. Am. Dent. A. 52:1-8, 1956.

198. Dean, R. F. A.: XXVIII. The size of the baby at birth and the yield of breast milk. Studies of Undernutrition, Wuppertal 1946-1949, Special Report Series Medical Research Council, No. 275. London, Her Majesty's Stationery, 1951.

199. Dearborn, G. V. N.: Motor-Sensory Development. Baltimore, Warwick & York, Inc., 1910.

200. Dearborn, W. F., and Rothney, J.: Predicting the Child's Development. Cambridge, Sci-Art Publishers, 1941.

201. Decroly, O.: Comment l'enfant arrive à parler. Cahiers de la Centrale. Centrale du P. E. S. de Belgique, 8:(1-2):1-306, 1934.

202. DeHaas, J. H., and Posthuma, J. H.: Nederlandsche kinderen in Japansche interneerings kampen op Java, Nederl. tijdschr. v. geneesk. 90: 1530-1541, 1946.

203. Deischer, R. W., and Goers, S. S.: A study of early and later introduction of solids into the infant diet, J. Pediat. 45:191-199, 1954.

204. Deming, J., and Washburn, A. H.: Respiration in infancy; method of studying rates, volume, and character of respiration, Am. J. Dis. Child. 49:108-124, 1935.

205. Dennis, J. M., and Kaiser, A. D.: Are home accidents in children preventable? Pediatrics 13:568-575, 1954.

206. Dennis, W.: Infant reaction to restraint: evaluation of Watson's theory, Tr. N. Y. Acad. Sci. 2:202-218, 1940. Also in Dennis, W.: Readings in Child Psychology (208).

207. ————: On possibility of advancing or retarding motor development of infants, Psychol. Rev. 50:203-218, 1943.

208. ———— (editor): Readings in Child Psychology. New York, Prentice-Hall, Inc., 1951.

209. Despert, J. L.: Effects of war on children's mental health, J. Consult. Psychol. 8:206-217, 1944.

210. ————: Preliminary Report on Children's Reactions to the War, Including Critical Survey of Literature. New York, Cornell University Medical College, 1942.

211. ————: Sleep in preschool children: preliminary study, Nerv. Child 8:8-27, 1949.

502   *Bibliography*

212. Deutsch, H.: The Psychology of Women, vol. I. Psychoanalytic Interpretation. New York, Grune & Stratton, 1944.
213. ———: The Psychology of Women, vol. II. Motherhood. New York, Grune & Stratton, 1945.
214. Deutsche, J. M.: Development of Children's Concept of Causal Relations. Institute of Child Welfare Monograph No. 13. Minneapolis, University of Minnesota Press, 1937.
215. ———: Chap. 8—Development of Children's Concept of Causal Relations, in Barker, R. G., et al.: Child Behavior and Development (72).
216. Dewey, E.: Behavior Development in Infants. New York, Columbia University Press, 1935.
217. Dieckmann, W. J., et al.: Observations on protein intake and the health of the mother and baby. I. Clinical and laboratory findings, J. Am. Dietet. A. 27:1046-1052, 1951.
218. Dietrich, H. F.: Chap. 17, Section II (vol. I)—Accidents in Childhood, in Brennemann's Practice of Pediatrics, I. McQuarrie, editor. Hagerstown, Md., W. F. Prior Co., Inc., 1957.
219. ———: The role of education in accident prevention, Pediatrics 17:297-302, 1956.
220. di Sant' Agnese, P.: Combined immunization against diphtheria, tetanus, and pertussis in newborn infants, Pediatrics 3:20-33, 1949.
221. Doll, E. A.: Chap. 17—The Feeble-Minded Child, in Carmichael, L.: Manual of Child Psychology, ed. 2 (155).
222. Dollard, J., and Miller, N. M.: Personality and Psychotherapy. New York, McGraw-Hill Book Co., Inc., 1950.
223. Donelson, E., et al.: Metabolism of women during the reproductive cycle; calcium and phosphorus utilization in late lactation and during subsequent reproductive rest, J. Biol. Chem. 91:675-686, 1931.
224. Dreizen, S., et al.: The effect of nutritive failure on the growth pattern of white children in Alabama, Child Development 24:189-202, 1953.
225. ———: Maturation of bone centers in hand and wrist of children with chronic nutritive failure. Effect of dietary supplements of reconstituted milk solids, Am. J. Dis. Child. 87:429-439, 1954.
226. Dublin, T. D., and Fraenkel, M.: A Plan for Health Services for The Family, in The Family as The Unit of Health. New York, Milbank Memorial Fund, 1949.
227. Dudycha, G. J., and Dudycha, M. M.: Childhood memories: review of the literature, Psychol. Bull. 38:668-682, 1941.
228. Duff, A.: Bequest of Wings. New York, Viking Press, 1944.
229. Dunbar, F.: Emotions and Bodily Changes. ed. 4. New York, Columbia University Press, 1954.
230. Dunham, E. C.: Premature Infants. A Manual for Physicians. ed. 2. New York, Paul B. Hoeber, Inc., 1955.
231. Dunnington, M. J.: Behavioral differences of sociometric status groups in a nursery school, Child Development 28:103-111, 1957.
232. Dupertuis, C. W., and Michael, N. B.: Comparison of growth in height and weight between ectomorphic and mesomorphic boys, Child Development 24:203-214, 1953.
233. Duvall, E., and Hill, R.: When You Marry. Boston, D. C. Heath & Co., 1953.
234. Eastman, N. J.: Effect of interval between births on maternal and fetal outlook, Am. J. Obst. & Gynec. 47:445-466, 1944.

235. Eastman, N. J.: Expectant Motherhood. rev. ed. 3. Boston, Little, Brown & Company, 1957.

236. Ebbs, J. H., Tisdall, F. F., and Scott, W. A.: Influence of prenatal diet on mother and child, J. Nutrition 22:515-526, 1941.

237. Ebert, E., and Simmons, K.: Brush Foundation Study of Child Growth and Development; Psychometric Tests. Monograph 8 (2). Washington, D. C., Society for Research in Child Development, National Research Council, 1943.

238. Elftman, H.: Skeletal and Muscular Systems; Structure and Function, in Glasser, O. (editor): Medical Physics, vol. 1. Chicago, Year Book Publishers, Inc., 1944.

239. Eliot, M. M., and Jackson, E. B.: Bone development of infants and young children in Puerto Rico, Am. J. Dis. Child. 46:1237-1262, 1933.

240. Eliot, M. M., and Park, E. A.: Chap. 36 (vol. 1)—Rickets, in Brennemann's Practice of Pediatrics, I. McQuarrie, editor. Hagerstown, Md., W. F. Prior Co., Inc., 1957.

241. Ellenwood, J.: There's No Place Like Home. New York, Charles Scribner's Sons, 1940.

242. Emmons, A. L.: Study of relationship between self-assurance and skill in young children, Child Development 4:325-339, 1933.

243. Erikson, E. H.: Childhood and Society. New York, W. W. Norton and Co., 1950.

244. ———: Growth and Crises of The "Healthy Personality," in Symposium on The Healthy Personality. New York, Josiah Macy, Jr., Foundation, 1950.

245. ———: Studies in interpretation of play; clinical observation of play description in young children, Genet. Psychol. Monogr. 22:557-667, 1940.

246. Escalona, S.: Commentary upon some recent changes in child rearing practices, Child Development 20:157-162, 1949.

247. Escalona, S., Leitch, M., et al.: Early Phases of Personality Development: A non-normative study of infant behavior. Society for Research in Child Development Monograph, No. 54. Lafayette, Ind., Child Development Publications, 1952.

248. Espenschade, A.: Motor development, Rev. Educ. Research 17:354-361, 1947.

249. Evans, C. L.: Principles of Human Physiology, originally written by E. H. Starling. ed. 11. Philadelphia, Lea & Febiger, 1952.

250. Fahs, S.: Today's Children and Yesterday's Heritage. Boston, Beacon Press, 1951.

251. Federal Security Agency: Charts on Infant, Childhood and Maternal Mortality, 1949. Children's Bureau Statistical Series No. 9. Washington, D. C., Federal Security Agency, Social Security Administration, 1951.

252. ———: Good Posture in The Little Child. Children's Bureau Publication No. 219. Washington, D. C., Federal Security Agency, Social Security Administration, 1949.

253. ———: A Healthy Personality for Your Child. Children's Bureau Publication No. 337. Washington, D. C., Federal Security Agency, Social Security Administration, 1952.

254. Ferguson, A., Cutler, F., and Scott, R.: Growth and development of Negro infants. VI. Relationship of certain environmental factors to neuromuscular development during the first year of life, J. Pediat. 48:308-313, 1956.

255. Fiedler, M. F.: Deaf Children in a Hearing World, Their Education and Adjustment. New York, Ronald Press, 1952.
256. Finn, S. B.: Prevalence of Dental Caries, in Survey of the Literature of Dental Caries. Food and Nutrition Board, National Research Council Publ. No. 225. Washington, D. C., National Academy of Sciences, National Research Council, 1952.
257. ———: Second annual progress report on fluoride investigations, N. Y. State Dental J. 13:78-89, 1947.
258. Fisher, M. S.: Language Patterns of Preschool Children. Child Development Monograph No. 15. New York, Teachers College, Columbia University, 1934.
259. Fite, M. D.: Aggressive behavior in young children and children's attitudes towards aggression, Gen. Psychol. Monogr. 22:151-319, 1940.
260. Flory, C. D.: Osseous Development in Hand as Index of Skeletal Development. Monograph I (3). Washington, D. C., Society for Research in Child Development, National Research Council, 1936.
261. Food and Nutrition Board, National Research Council: Recommended Dietary Allowances, revised 1953. Reprint and Circ. Series 129. Washington, D. C., National Research Council, 1953.
262. Foote, N. N., and Cottrell, L. S.: Identity and Interpersonal Competence. A New Direction in Family Research. Chicago, University of Chicago Press, 1955.
263. Forest, I.: Early Years at School. New York, McGraw-Hill Book Co., Inc., 1949.
264. Forsham, P. H., and Thorn, G. W.: Chap. 4—The Adrenals, in Textbook of Endocrinology. ed. 2. R. H. Williams, editor. Philadelphia, W. B. Saunders Co., 1955.
265. Foster, J. C.: Hours spent in sleep by young children, in Proceedings Ninth International Congress of Psychology. Yale University, New Haven, Conn., Sept. 1-7, 1929, pp. 168-169.
266. Foster, R. G.: Marriage and Family Relations. ed. 2. New York, Macmillan Company, 1950.
267. Frank, L. K.: Working toward Healthy Personality, in Senn, M. J. (editor): Problems of Infancy and Childhood, Transactions of Fourth Conference, March 6-7, 1950. New York, Josiah Macy, Jr., Foundation, 1951.
268. Frankel, E. B., and Potashin, R.: Survey of sociometric and pre-sociometric literature on friendship and social acceptance among children, Sociometry 7:422-431, 1944.
269. Freud, A.: Psycho-Analysis for Teachers and Parents. New York, Emerson Books, Inc., 1935.
270. Freud, A., and Burlingham, D. T.: Infants without Families. New York, International University Press, 1944.
271. ———: War and Children. New York, Medical War Books, 1943.
272. Freud, S.: An Outline of Psychoanalysis. New York, W. W. Norton & Co., 1949.
273. Friedgood, H. B.: Chap. 10—Neuroendocrinology, in Textbook of Endocrinology, ed. 2. R. H. Williams, editor. Philadelphia, W. B. Saunders Co., 1955.
274. Fries, M., and Woolf, P.: Some hypotheses on the role of the congenital activity type in personality development. Psychoanalytic Study of the Child, vol. viii. New York, International Universities Press, 1953.

275. Fuerst, J. S., and Kaplan, R.: Chicago's Public Housing Program helps to save babies' lives, Child 15:178-181, 1951.
276. Fuller, E. H.: Injury prone children, Am. J. Orthopsychiat. 18:708-723, 1948.
277. Funkenstein, D. H.: The physiology of fear and anger, Scient. Amer. 192: 74-80, 1955.
278. Garn, S. M.: Individual and group deviations from "channelwise" grid progression in girls, Child Development 23:193-206, 1952.
279. Garn, S. M., et al.: Stature, body-build and tooth eruption in Aleutian children, Child Development 22:261-270, 1951.
280. Garry, R. C., and Stiven, D.: Review of recent work on dietary requirements in pregnancy and lactation, with attempt to assess human requirements, Nutrition Abstr. & Rev. 5:855-887, 1936.
281. Garvey, C. R.: Activity of Young Children during Sleep. Minneapolis, University of Minnesota Press, 1939.
282. Garvin, J. A.: Efficacy of Sauer's vaccine; comparison of incidence of preschool pertussis in city with high and in one with low percentage of immunization, Ohio State M. J. 36:738-739, 1940.
283. Geiger, A. J., Munroe, W. M., and Goodyer, A.: Clinical fetal electrocardiography; its practical accomplishment, Proc. Soc. Exper. Biol. & Med. 48:646-648, 1941.
284. Gentry, E. F., and Aldrich, C. A.: Toe reflexes in infancy and development of voluntary control, Am. J. Dis. Child. 76:389-400, 1948.
285. Gesell, A.: Mental Growth of Preschool Child. New York, Macmillan Company, 1925.
286. ————: Chap. 6—The Ontogenesis of Infant Behavior, in Carmichael, L.: Manual of Child Psychology. ed. 2 (155).
287. Gesell, A., in collaboration with Amatruda, C. S.: The Embryology of Behavior. New York, Harper & Brothers, 1945.
288. Gesell, A., and Amatruda, C. S.: Developmental Diagnosis. New York, Paul B. Hoeber, Inc., 1947.
289. Gesell, A., and Ames, L.: Development of handedness, J. Genet. Psychol. 70:115-175, 1947.
290. Gesell, A., and Ilg, F. L.: The Child from Five to Ten. New York, Harper & Brothers, 1946.
291. ————: Infant and Child in Culture of Today. New York, Harper & Brothers, 1943.
292. Gesell, A., et al.: The First Five Years of Life. New York, Harper & Brothers, 1940.
293. Gesell, A., and Thompson, H.: Twins T. and C. from infancy to adolescence, Genet. Psychol. Monogr. 24:3-121, 1941.
294. Gewirtz, J. L.: A factor analysis of some attention-seeking behaviors of young children, Child Development 27:17-37, 1956.
295. ————: Three determinants of attention-seeking in young children. Society for Research in Child Development Monograph 19: Serial No. 59, No. 2. Lafayette, Ind., Child Development Publications, 1954.
296. Giddings, G.: Effect of emotional disturbances on sleep, J. M. A. Georgia 25:351-357, 1936.
297. ————: Normal sleep patterns for children, J.A.M.A. 102:525-529, 1934.
298. Gilbert, M. S.: Biography of the Unborn. Baltimore, Williams & Wilkins Co., 1939.
299. Glick, P. G.: American Families. New York, John Wiley & Sons, Inc., 1957.

300. Goldenberg, M.: Adrenal medullary function, Am. J. Med. X:627-641, 1951.
301. Goldfarb, W.: Infant rearing and problem behavior, Am. J. Orthopsychiat. 13:249-265, 1943.
302. Goodenough, F. L.: Anger in Young Children. Inst. Child Welfare Monograph Series, No. 9. Minneapolis, University of Minnesota Press, 1931.
303. ———: Bibliographies in child development, Psychol. Bull. 41:615-633, 1944.
304. ———: Chap. 8—The Measurement of Mental Growth in Childhood, in Carmichael, L.: Manual of Child Psychology, ed. 2 (155).
305. Goodenough, F. L., and Harris, D. B.: Intellectual growth in childhood, Rev. Educ. Research 17:306-316, 1947.
306. ———: Studies in psychology of children's drawings, Psychol. Bull. 47:369-433, 1950.
307. Goodenough, F. L., and Leahy, A. M.: Effect of certain family relationships upon development of personality, Ped. Sem. 34:45-71, 1927.
308. Goodenough, F. L., and Maurer, K. M.: Mental Growth of Children from Two to Fourteen Years: Study of Predictive Value of Minnesota Preschool Scales. Minneapolis, University of Minnesota Press, 1942.
309. Goodman, M. E.: Race-Awareness in Young Children. Cambridge, Massachusetts, Addison-Wesley Press, 1952.
310. Goodrich, F. W.: Natural Childbirth. New York, Prentice-Hall, Inc., 1950.
311. Grant, E.: Effect of Certain Factors in Home Environment upon Child Behavior. Studies in Child Welfare, 17. Iowa City, University of Iowa, 1939.
312. Graubard, M.: Man's Food, Its Rhyme or Reason. New York, Macmillan Company, 1943.
313. Green, E. H.: Friendships and quarrels among preschool children, Child Development 4:237-252, 1933.
314. Green, M., and Woods, E.: A Nursery School Handbook for Teachers and Parents. Sierra Madre, California, Sierra Madre Community Nursery School Association, 1954.
315. Greenhill, J. P.: Obstetrics. ed. 11. Philadelphia, W. B. Saunders Co., 1955.
316. Greulich, W. W., and Pyle, S. I.: Radiographic Atlas of Skeletal Development of Hand and Wrist. Stanford, Stanford University Press, 1950.
317. Griffiths, R.: The Abilities of Babies: A Study in Mental Measurement. New York, McGraw Hill Book Co., 1954. (Also University of London Press.)
318. Gruber, S.: The concept of task orientation in the analysis of play behavior of children entering kindergarten, Am. J. Orthopsychiat. 24:326-335, 1954.
319. Gruenberg, S. A.: We the Parents. New York, Harper & Brothers, 1939.
320. Gruenberg, S. A., and the Child Study Association (editors): Our Children Today. New York, Viking Press, 1951.
321. Gutelius, M. F.: Modified self-selection method of feeding preschool children in the home, Am. J. Pub. Health 38:1118-1125, 1948.
322. Gutheim, F.: Houses for Family Living. New York, The Woman's Foundation, 1948.
323. Gutteridge, M.: The Child's Experiences in Bodily Activity, in Forty-sixth Yearbook of the National Society for the Study of Education, Part II. Chicago, University of Chicago Press, 1947.
324. ———: Study of motor achievements of young children, Arch. Psychol., No. 244, 1939.
325. Guy, L. P., et al.: The possibility of total elimination of retrolental fibroplasia by O_2 restriction, Pediatrics 17:247-249, 1956.

326. Hagman, E. P.: Companionships of Preschool Children. Studies in Child Welfare, 7 (4). Iowa City, University of Iowa, 1933.
327. Halverson, H. M.: Acquisition of skill in infancy, J. Genet. Psychol. 43:3-48, 1933.
328. Ham, A. W.: Histology. Philadelphia, J. B. Lippincott Co., 1950.
329. Hansen, A. E.: Nutritional Requirements, in Textbook of Pediatrics. ed. 6. W. E. Nelson, editor. Philadelphia, W. B. Saunders Co., 1954.
330. Haring, D. G.: Personal Character and Cultural Milieu. Syracuse, Syracuse University Press, 1956.
331. Harris, D. B. (editor): The Concept of Development. Minneapolis, University of Minnesota Press, 1957.
332. Harris, D. B., and Harris, E. S.: Study of fetal movements in relation to mother's activity, Human Biol. 18:221-237, 1946.
333. Harris, H. H.: Bone Growth in Health and Disease. London, Oxford University Press, 1933.
334. Hart, B. F.: Vitamin B in heartburn of pregnancy, Am. J. Obst. & Gynec. 45:120-122, 1943.
335. Hartley, R.: Growing through Play. New York, Columbia University Press, 1952.
336. Hartley, R., Frank, L. K., and Goldenson, R.: New Play Experiences for Children: Planned Play Groups, Miniature Life Toys and Puppets. New York, Columbia University Press, 1952.
337. ————: Understanding Children's Play. New York, Columbia University Press, 1952.
338. Hattwick, L.: Interrelations between preschool child's behavior and certain factors in the home, Child Development 7:200-226, 1936.
339. Hattwick, L., and Sanders, M. K.: Age differences in behavior at nursery school level, Child Development 9:27-47, 1938.
340. Hattwick, L., and Stowell, M.: Relation of parental over-attentiveness to children's work habits and social adjustment, J. Educ. Research 30:169-176, 1936.
341. Haupt, D.: Science Experiences for Nursery School Children. Kingston, R. I., National Association for Nursery Education, 1954.
342. Haupt, D., and Osborn, K.: Creative Activities. Detroit, Merrill-Palmer School, 1955.
343. Havighurst, R. J.: Developmental Tasks and Education. New York, Longmans Green & Co., 1950.
344. Havighurst, R. J., and Davis, A.: A comparison of the Chicago and Harvard studies of social class differences in child rearing, Am. Sociol. Rev. 20:438-442, 1955.
345. Heathers, G.: Emotional dependence and independence in nursery school play, J. Genet. Psychol. 87:37-57, 1955.
346. Hefferman, H. (editor): Guiding the Young Child. New York, D. C. Heath & Co., 1951.
347. Heidbreder, E.: Problem solving in children and adults, J. Genet. Psychol. 35:522-545, 1928.
348. Heinicke, C., and Whiting, B.: Bibliographies on Personality and Social Development of the Child. New York, Social Science Research Council, 1953.
349. Herdan, G.: The relation between birth weight and subsequent weight in childhood, Arch. Dis. Childhood 29:220-223, 1954.

350. Hicks, J. A.: The acquisition of motor skills in young children, Child Development 1:90-105, 1930.
351. Highberger, R.: Maternal behavior and attitudes related to behavior of the preschool child, J. Home Econ. 48:260-264, 1956.
352. Hildreth, G. H.: Bibliography of Mental Tests and Rating Scales. ed. 2. New York, Psychological Corporation, 1939.
353. ————: Bibliography of Mental Tests and Rating Scales: 1945 Supplement. New York, Psychological Corporation, 1946.
354. ————: Child Mind in Evolution; Study of Developmental Sequences in Drawing. New York, King's Crown Press, 1941.
355. ————: Development and training of hand dominance: characteristics of handedness; developmental tendencies in handedness; origins of handedness and lateral dominance, J. Genet. Psychol. 75:197-275, 1949.
356. ————: Development and training of hand dominance: developmental problems associated with handedness; training of handedness, J. Genet. Psychol. 76:39-144, 1950.
357. ————: Manual dominance in nursery school children, J. Genet. Psychol. 72:29-45, 1948.
358. Hilgard, J. R.: Learning and maturation in preschool children, J. Genet. Psychol. 41:31-56, 1932. Also in Readings in Child Psychology (208), Dennis, W. (editor).
359. Hill, L. F.: Infant nutrition, Am. J. Clin. Nutrition 3:75-83, 1955.
360. Hill, R.: Families Under Stress; Adjustment to Crises of War Separation and Reunion. New York, Harper & Brothers, 1949.
361. ————: Review of research on marriage and the family, Sociol. Rev. 16:694-701, 1951.
362. Hilleboe, H. E.: History of the Newburgh-Kingston caries-fluorine study, J. Am. Dent. A. 52:291-295, 1956.
363. Hirsch, M.: Mütterschaftsfürscorge, Arch. Gynakol. 144:34-85, 1931.
364. Hoeflin, R.: Child-rearing practices and child-care resources used by Ohio farm families with preschool children, J. Genet. Psychol. 84:271-297, 1954.
365. Hollingsworth, D. F.: Nutritional policies in Great Britain, 1939-1946, J. Am. Dietet. A. 23:96-100, 1947.
366. Holt, L. E., Jr.: Amino Acid Deficiencies in Man. Proceedings of Conference on Implications of Nutrition and Public Health in the Postwar Period. Research Lab. of Children's Fund, Michigan, Nov. 3, 1944.
367. Holway, A.: Early self-regulation of infants and later behavior in play interviews, Am. J. Orthopsychiat. 19:612-623, 1949.
368. Hooker, R. S., et al.: Maternal Mortality in New York City. New York Academy of Medicine, Committee on Public Health Relations. New York, Commonwealth Fund, 1933.
369. Horney, K.: The flight from womanhood, Internat. J. Psychoanalysis 7:324-339, 1926.
370. ————: Neurosis and Human Growth. New York, W. W. Norton, 1950.
371. ————: Self-Analysis. New York, W. W. Norton & Co., Inc., 1942.
372. Howorth, B.: Dynamic posture, J.A.M.A. 131:1398-1404, 1946.
373. Hubbard, R. M.: Method of Studying Spontaneous Group Formation, reported in Thomas, D. S.: Some New Techniques for Studying Social Behavior. New York, Columbia University Press, 1929.
374. Hubert, M. A. G., and Britton, J. H.: Attitudes and practices of mothers rearing their children from birth to the age of two years, J. Home Econ. 49:208-219, 1957.

375. Hull, C. L., and Hull, B. I.: Parallel learning curves of infant in vocabulary and in voluntary control of bladder, Ped. Sem. 26:272-283, 1919.
376. Hummel, F. C., et al.: Consideration of nutritive status in metabolism of women during pregnancy, J. Nutrition 13:263-277, 1937.
377. Hunscher, H. A.: The life cycle and its diet. A symposium on recent findings in human nutrition, J. Home Econ. 49:101-115, 1957.
378. ————: Metabolism of women during reproductive cycle; calcium and phosphorus utilization in two successive lactation periods, J. Biol. Chem. 86: 37-57, 1930.
379. Hunscher, H. A., et al.: Metabolism of women during reproductive cycle; nitrogen utilization, J. Biol. Chem. 99:507-520, 1933.
380. ————: Metabolism of women during reproductive cycle; case study of continuous nitrogen utilization of a multipara during pregnancy, parturition, puerperium, and lactation, J. Nutrition 10:579-597, 1935.
381. Hurlock, E. B.: Child Development. ed. 3. New York, McGraw-Hill Book Co., Inc., 1956.
382. Hyde, H. van Z.: World Health Organization—Progress of Plans. Dept. of State Bull. 3126. Washington, D. C., April 4, 1948.
383. Hymes, J. L.: Discipline. New York, Teachers College, Columbia University, 1949.
384. ————: How To Tell Your Child About Sex. Public Affairs Pamphlet No. 149. New York, Public Affairs Committee, Inc., 1949.
385. ————: A Pound of Prevention: How Teachers Can Meet Emotional Needs of Young Children. New York, Caroline Zachry Institute, 1947.
386. Igel, A.: Effect of war separation on father-child relations, The Family 26:3-9, 1945.
387. Illingworth, R. S., et al.: Relation of birth weight to physical development in childhood, Lancet. 2:598-602, 1949.
388. Illingworth, R. S., and Stone, D. G. H.: Self-demand feeding in a maternity unit, Lancet. 262:683-687, 1952.
389. Ingalls, T. H.: Anoxia as a cause of fetal death and congenital defect in the mouse, Am. J. Dis. Child. 30:34-45, 1950.
390. ————: Causes and prevention of developmental defects, J.A.M.A. 161: 1047-1051, 1956.
391. ————: Preventive Prenatal Pediatrics, in Advances in Pediatrics, vol. VI. S. Z. Levin, editor. New York, Yearbook Publishers, Inc., 1953.
392. Ingersoll, H.: Study of transmission of authority patterns in the family, Genet. Psychol. Monogr. 38:225-299, 1948.
393. Irwin, O. C.: The amount and nature of activities of new-born infants under constant external stimulating conditions during the first ten days of life, Genet. Psychol. Monogr. 8:1-92, 1930.
394. ————: Can infants have I.Q.'s? Psychol. Rev. 49:69-79, 1942.
395. ————: Infant responses to vertical movements, Child Development 3:167-169, 1932.
396. ————: Reliability study of speech sounds observed in crying of newborn infants, Child Development 12:351-368, 1941.
397. ————: Research on speech sounds for first six months of life, Psychol. Bull. 38:277-285, 1941.
398. ————: Speech development in the young child: some factors related to the speech development of the infant and young child, J. Speech and Hearing Disorders 17:269-279, 1952.

399. Irwin, O. C., and Chen, H. P.: Speech sound elements during the first years of life; a review of the literature, J. Speech Disorders 8:109-121, 1943.
400. Irwin, O. C., and Weiss, L. A.: The effect of darkness on the activity of newborn infants. Studies in Child Welfare, 9:163-175, Iowa City, University of Iowa, 1934.
401. Isaacs, S. S.: The Nature and Function of Phantasy. Developments in Psychoanalysis. London, The Hogarth Press, 1952.
402. ————: Social Development in Young Children; Study of Beginnings. London, Geo. Routledge & Sons, Ltd., 1946.
403. Ivy, A. C., and Gibbs, G. E.: Chap. 20 (vol. I)—Physiology of the Gastrointestinal Tract, in Brennemann's Practice of Pediatrics, I. McQuarrie, editor. Hagerstown, Md., W. F. Prior Co., Inc., 1957.
404. Ivy, A. C., and Grossman, M. I.: Chap. 20—Digestive System, in Cowdry's Problems of Aging. ed. 3. A. I. Lansing, editor. Baltimore, Williams & Wilkins Co., 1952.
405. Jack, L. M.: Experimental Study of Ascendent Behavior in Preschool Children, in Jack, L. M., et al.: Behavior of Preschool Child. Studies in Child Welfare, 9 (3). Iowa City, University of Iowa, 1934.
406. Jackson, E. B.: Childbirth Patterns in the United States, in Mental Health and Infant Development. Proceedings of the International Seminar held by The World Federation for Mental Health at Chichester, England, vol. I. K. Soddy, editor. New York, Basic Books, Inc., 1956.
407. Jackson, E. B., et al.: Statistical report on incidence and duration of breast feeding in relation to personal-social and hospital maternity factors, Pediatrics 17:700-715, 1956.
408. Jackson, E. B., and Trainham, G.: Family Centered Maternity and Infant Care. Report of Committee on Rooming-in of Josiah Macy Jr. Foundation Conference on Problems of Infancy and Early Childhood. New York, Josiah Macy Jr. Foundation, 1950.
409. Jackson, F. W.: Manitoba Health Plan and Its Effect Upon The Family, in The Family As The Unit of Health. New York, Milbank Memorial Fund, 1949.
410. Jackson, R. L., and Kelly, H. G.: Growth charts for use in pediatric practice, J. Pediat. 27:215-229, 1945.
411. Jacobson, E.: Progressive Relaxation; Physiological and Clinical Investigation of Muscular States and Their Significance in Psychology and Medical Practice. ed. 2. Chicago, University of Chicago Press, 1937.
412. Jay, P., and Bennett, A. S.: Role of diet in the control of dental caries, J. Am. Dent. A. 52:18-25, 1956.
413. Jeans, P. C.: Chap. XIV—Feeding of Healthy Infants and Children, in Handbook of Nutrition; a Symposium. ed. 2. American Medical Association, published by Blakiston Co., 1951.
414. ————: Chap. X—Vitamin D, in Handbook of Nutrition; a Symposium. ed. 2. American Medical Association, published by Blakiston Co., 1951.
415. Jeans, P. C., and Stearns, G.: Effect of vitamin D on linear growth in infancy; effect of intake above 1800 U.S.P. units daily, J. Pediat. 13:730-740, 1938.
416. ————: Retention of calcium with a pint and a quart of milk, Am. J. Dis. Child. 44:645-650, 1932.
417. Jeans, P. C., et al.: Incidence of prematurity in relation to maternal nutrition, J. Am. Dietet. A. 31:576-581, 1955.

418. Jennings, C. G., and Pyle, S. I.: The Merrill-Palmer logarithmic developmental graph, The Merrill-Palmer Quarterly I, Spring: 99-110, 1955.
419. Jennings, H. H.: Sociometry of Leadership. New York, Beacon House, 1947.
420. Jensen, K.: Physical growth, Rev. Educ. Research 25:369-414, 1955.
421. Jersild, A. T.: Child Psychology. ed. 4. New York, Prentice-Hall, Inc., 1954.
422. ———: Chap. 14—Emotional Development, in Carmichael, L.: Manual of Child Psychology. ed. 2 (155).
423. ———: Mental health of children and families in wartime, Rev. Educ. Research 13:468-477, 1943.
424. Jersild, A. T., and Bienstock, S.: Development of Rhythm in Young Children. Child Development Monograph, No. 22. New York, Teachers College, Columbia University, 1935.
425. ———: Influence of training on vocal ability of three-year-old children, Child Development 2:272-291, 1931.
426. ———: Study of development of children's ability to sing, J. Educ. Psychol. 25:481-503, 1934.
427. Jersild, A. T., and Holmes, F. B.: Children's Fears. Child Development Monograph, No. 20. New York, Teachers College, Columbia University, 1935.
428. Jersild, A. T., and Markey, F.: Conflicts between Preschool Children. Child Development Monograph, No. 21. New York, Teachers College, Columbia University, 1935.
429. Jersild, A. T., and Meigs, M. F.: Children and war, Psychol. Bull. 40:541-573, 1943.
430. Johnson, W.: People in Quandaries. New York, Harper & Brothers, 1946.
431. ——— (editor): Speech Problems of Children; a Guide to Care and Correction. New York, Grune and Stratton, 1950.
432. ———: Stuttering in Children and Adults: Thirty Years of Research at the University of Iowa. Minneapolis, University of Minnesota Press, 1955.
433. Joint Committee on the Economic Report: Characteristics of the Low-Income Population and Related Federal Programs. Selected materials assembled by the staff of the subcommittee on low-income families. Washington, U. S. Gov. Printing office, 1955.
434. Jones, H.: Chap. 10—The Environment and Mental Development, in Carmichael, L.: Manual of Child Psychology, ed. 2 (155).
435. ———: Motor Performance and Growth. Berkeley, University of California Press, 1949.
436. Jones, H. E., and Jones, M. C.: Genetic studies of emotions, Psychol. Bull. 27:40-64, 1930.
437. Jones, M. C.: Chap. 6—Emotional Development, in Murchison, C. (editor): Handbook of Child Psychology, ed. 2. Worcester, Clark University Press, 1933.
438. Jones, M. C., and Burks, B. S.: Personality Development in Childhood: Survey of Problems, Methods and Experimental Findings. Monograph I (4). Washington, D. C., Society for Research in Child Development, National Research Council, 1936.
439. Jones, T. D.: Development of Certain Motor Skills and Play Activities in Young Children. Child Development Monograph, No. 26. New York, Teachers College, Columbia University, 1939.
440. Josey, W. E.: The role of nutrition in the management of pregnancy: a review of recent studies, Am. J. Clin. Nutrition 2:303-315, 1954.

441. Josselyn, I.: Psychosocial Development of Children. New York, Family Service Association of America, 1948.
442. Kaiser, A. D.: Chap. 4 (vol. 2)—The Tonsil and Adenoid Problem, in Brennemann's Practice of Pediatrics, I. McQuarrie, editor. Hagerstown, Md., W. F. Prior Co., Inc., 1957.
443. Kaplan, B. A.: Environment and human plasticity, American Anthropologist 56:780-800, 1954.
444. Karger, P.: Ueber den Schlaf des Kindes, Abh. a. d. Kinderh. u. Grenzgebiet, pp. 1-50, 1925, cited in Kleitman, N.: Sleep and Wakefulness (459).
445. Katcher, A., and Levin, M.: Children's concepts of body size, Child Development 26:103-110, 1955.
446. Keister, M. E.: Chap. 25—Behavior of Young Children in Failure, in Child Behavior and Development, by Barker, R., et al. (72).
447. ————: Relation of mid-morning feeding to behavior of nursery school children, J. Am. Dietet. A. 26: 25-29, 1950.
448. Keister, M. E., and Updegraff, R.: Study of children's reactions to failure and experimental attempt to modify them, Child Development 8:241-248, 1937.
449. Kelley, I. B., and Nesbitt, M.: The family, education, and child adjustment, Rev. Educ. Research 16:71-80, 1946.
450. Kelley, V. C., and Bosma, J. F.: Chap. 22 (vol. 1)—Basal Metabolism in Infants and Children, in Brennemann's Practice of Pediatrics, I. McQuarrie, editor. Hagerstown, Md., W. F. Prior Co., Inc., 1957.
451. Kellogg, W. N.: Method for recording activity of human fetus *in utero* with specimen results, J. Genet. Psychol. 58:307-326, 1941.
452. Kendall, H. O., Kendall, F. P., and Boynton, D. A.: Posture and Pain. Baltimore, Williams and Wilkins Co., 1952.
453. Kerridge, P.: Recent advances in knowledge concerning hearing and speech, Physiol. Rev. 18:59-85, 1938.
454. Keys, A., et al.: Biology of Human Starvation, vol. II. Minneapolis, University of Minnesota Press, 1950.
455. Kirk, S. A., Karnes, M. B., and Kirk, W. D.: You and Your Retarded Child: A Manual for Parents of Retarded Children. New York, The Macmillan Co., 1956.
456. Klatskin, E. H.: Shifts in child-care practices in three social classes under an infant care program of flexible methodology, Am. J. Orthopsychiat. 22:52-61, 1952.
457. Klein, H.: Effects of pregnancy on incidence of tooth decay, Dental Cosmos 77:864-867, 1935.
458. Kleitman, N.: Mental hygiene of sleep in children, Nerv. Child 8:63-66, 1949.
459. ————: Sleep and Wakefulness. Chicago, University of Chicago Press, 1939.
460. ————: Sleep and Wakefulness, in Glasser, O. (editor): Medical Physics, vol. 1. Chicago, Year Book Publishers, Inc., 1944.
461. Kluckholn, C., Murray, H. A., Schneider, D. (editors): Personality in Nature, Society, and Culture. New York, A. Knopf, 1953.
462. Klump, T. G., and Neale, A. V.: Gastric and duodenal contents of normal infants and children, Am. J. Dis. Child. 40:1215-1229, 1930.
463. Knoblock, H., and Pasamanick, B.: A Developmental Questionnaire for Infants Forty Weeks of Age: An Evaluation. Society for Research in Child Development Monograph 20: Serial No. 61, No. 2. Lafayette, Ind., Child Development Publications, 1955.

464. Koch, H. L.: Attitudes of young children toward their peers as related to certain characteristics of their siblings, Psychol. Monogr. 70, No. 19 (whole No. 426), 1956.
465. ———: Children's work attitudes and sibling characteristics, Child Development 27:289-310, 1956.
466. ———: Emotional attitudes of the young child in relation to characteristics of his sibling, Child Development 27:393-426, 1956.
467. ———: Popularity in preschool children, Child Development 4:164-175, 1933.
468. ———: The relation of certain family constellation characteristics and the attitudes of children toward adults, Child Development 26:13-40, 1955.
469. ———: The relation in young children between characteristics of their playmates and certain attributes of their siblings, Child Development 28:175-202, 1957.
470. Koffka, K.: Growth of the Mind. New York, Harcourt, Brace & Company, Inc., 1925.
471. Kohn, J. L., Fischer, A. E., and Marks, H. H.: Case totality in infants and children with pertussis, 1942-1946, Pediatrics 5:840-852, 1950.
472. Koos, E. L.: Families in Trouble. New York, King's Crown Press, 1946.
473. ———: Marriage. New York, Henry Holt Co., 1957.
474. Kopp, H.: Relationship of stuttering to motor performance, Nerv. Child 2:107-116, 1943.
475. Koshuk, R. P.: Social Influences Affecting Behavior of Young Children; Review of Literature since 1925. Monograph VII (2), Washington, D. C., Society for Research in Child Development, National Research Council, 1941.
476. Krevit, W.: Music for Your Child. New York, Dodd Mead & Company, 1946.
477. Krogman, W. M.: The concept of maturity from a morphological viewpoint, Child Development 21:25-32, 1950.
478. ———: Handbook of Measurement and Interpretation of Height and Weight in The Growing Child. Monograph XIII (3). Evanston, Ill., Society for Research in Child Development, Inc., 1950.
479. ———: The Physical Growth of Children: An Appraisal of Studies 1950-1955. Society for Research in Child Development, Monograph XX (No. 1). Lafayette, Ind., Child Development Publications, 1956.
480. ———: The skeleton talks, Scient. Am. 159:61-64, 1938.
481. ———: Trends in study of physical growth in children, Child Development 11:279-284, 1940.
482. Krugman, S., and Ward, R.: The rubella problem. Clinical aspects, risk of fetal abnormality and methods of prevention, J. Pediat. 44:489-498, 1954.
483. Kuenne, M.: Experimental investigation of the relation of language to transposition behavior in young children, J. Exper. Psychol. 36:471-490, 1946.
484. Kuhlen, R. G., and Thompson, G. G. (editors): Psychological Studies of Human Development. New York, Appleton-Century-Crofts, 1952.
485. Lafore, G.: Practices of Parents in Dealing with Preschool Children. Child Development Monograph No. 31. New York, Teachers College, Columbia University, 1945.
486. Laird, D. A., and Breen, W. J.: Sex and age alteration in taste preference, J. Am. Dietet. A. 15:549-550, 1939.
487. Laird, D. A., and Drexel, H.: Experimenting with foods and sleep; effects

of varying types of food in offsetting disturbances caused by hunger pangs and gastric distress—children and adults, J. Am. Dietet. A. 10:89-99, 1934.

488. Lakin, M.: Personality Factors in Mothers of Excessively Crying (Colicky) Infants. Society for Research in Child Development Monograph, 22:Serial No. 64, No. 1. Lafayette, Ind., Child Development Publications, 1957.

489. Landeck, B.: Children and Music: An Informal Guide for Parents and Teachers. New York, Wm. Sloane Associates, 1952.

490. Landis, C., and Hunt, W.: The Startle Pattern. New York, Farrar & Rinehart, 1939.

491. Landis, J. T., and Landis, M. G.: Building a Successful Marriage. New York, Prentice-Hall, 1953.

492. ———— (editors): Readings in Marriage and the Family. New York, Prentice-Hall, 1952.

493. Landreth, C., and Read, K. H.: Education of the Young Child. New York, John Wiley & Sons, Inc., 1942.

494. Langdon, G., and Stout, I.: The Discipline of Well-Adjusted Children. New York, John Day, 1952.

495. Langford, W. S., et al.: Pilot study of childhood accidents. Preliminary report, Pediatrics 11:405-415, 1953.

496. Lasko, J. K.: Parent behavior toward first and second children, Genet. Psychol. Monogr. 49:97-137, 1954.

497. Lawrence, J. M., et al.: Human milk studies; comparative values of bovine and human milk in infant feeding, Am. J. Dis. Child. 70:193-199, 1945.

498. Leicester, H. M.: Dentistry, in Annual Review of Medicine. vol. 5, W. C. Cutting, editor. Standford, Annual Reviews Inc., 1954.

499. ————: Nutrition and the tooth. J. Am. Dent. A. 52:284-289, 1956.

500. Lerner, E., and Murphy, L. B.: Further report of committee for information on children in wartime, J. Social Psychol. 18:413-418, 1943.

501. ————: Methods for Study of Personality in Young Children. Monograph VI (4). Washington, D. C., Society for Research in Child Development, National Research Council, 1941.

502. Leverton, R. M., and Clark, G.: Meat in the diet of young infants, J.A.M.A. 134:1215-1216, 1947.

503. Leverton, R. M., et al.: Further studies of use of meat in diet of infants and young children, J. Pediat. 40:761-766, 1952.

504. Leverton, R. M., and Gram, M. R.: Nitrogen excretion of women related to distribution of animal protein in daily meals, J. Nutrition 39:57-65, 1949.

505. Levin, H., and Sears, R. R.: Identification with parents as a determinant of doll play aggression, Child Development 27:135-153, 1956.

506. Levine, M.: A modern concept of breast feeding, J. Pediat. 38:472-475, 1951.

507. Levy, D.: Maternal Overprotection. New York, Columbia University Press, 1943.

508. ————: Release therapy, Am. J. Orthopsychiat. 9:713-736, 1939.

509. ————: War and family life; report for War Emergency Committee, 1944, Am. J. Orthopsychiat. 15:140-152, 1945.

510. Levy, J., and Munroe, R.: The Happy Family. New York, Alfred A. Knopf, Inc., 1938.

511. Lewis, M. M.: Infant Speech: A Study of the Beginnings of Language. ed. 2. New York, Humanities Press; London, Routledge and Kegan Paul, 1951.

512. Lewis, S. J., and Lehman, I.: Observations on growth changes of teeth and dental arches, Dental Cosmos 71:480-499, 1929.

513. Linfert, H. E., and Hierholzer, H. M.: Scale for measuring mental development of infants during first year of life, Studies in Psychol. & Psychiat., Cath. Univ. Amer. 1:1-33, 1928.

514. Ling, B.: Genetic study of sustained visual fixation and associated behavior in human infant from birth to six months, J. Genet. Psychol. 61:227-277, 1942.

515. Lippitt, R.: Popularity among preschool children, Child Development 12: 305-332, 1941.

516. Lippman, H. S.: Certain behavior responses in early infancy, J. Genet. Psychol. 34:424-440, 1927.

517. Lombard, O. M.: Breadth of bone and muscle by age and sex in childhood, Child Development 21:229-239, 1950.

518. Loomis, A. M.: Technique for Observing Social Behavior of Nursery School Children. New York, Columbia University Press, 1931.

519. Lowenfeld, V.: Creative and Mental Growth. ed. 2. New York, Macmillan Company, 1957.

520. Lund, C. J., and Kimble, M. S.: Some determinants of maternal and fetal plasma vitamin C levels, Am. J. Obst. & Gynec. 46:635-647, 1943.

521. Maccoby, E., and Gibbs, P. K.: Methods of child rearing in two social classes, in W. E. Martin and C. B. Stendler (editors): Readings in Child Development (560).

522. Macfarlane, J. W.: Interpersonal relationships within the family, Marriage and Family Living 3:25-31, 1941.

523. ———: Problems of validation inherent in projective methods, Am. J. Orthopsychiat. 12:405-411, 1942.

524. ———: Chap. 18—Study of Personality Development, in Barker, R. G., et al.: Child Behavior and Development (72).

525. Macfarlane, J. W., et al.: A Development Study of the Behavior Problems of Normal Children Between Twenty-one Months and Fourteen Years. Berkeley, University of California Press, 1954.

526. McCandless, B.: Psychosocial development of personality, Child Development 20:123-129, 1949.

527. McCarthy, D.: Language Development of Preschool Child with Special References to Sentence Formation. Institute of Child Welfare Monograph, No. 4. Minneapolis, University of Minnesota Press, 1930.

528. ———: Chap. 9—Language Development in Children, in Carmichael, L. (editor): Manual of Child Psychology, ed. 2 (155).

529. ———: Language disorders and parent-child relationships, J. of Speech and Hearing Disorders 19:514-523, 1954.

530. McCaskill, C. L., and Wellman, B. L.: Study of common motor achievements at preschool age, Child Development 9:141-150, 1938.

531. McClelland, D.: Personality. New York, Dryden Press, 1955.

532. McDowell, J.: The Development of the Idea of God in the Catholic Child. Washington, Catholic University of America Press, 1952.

533. McFarland, M. B.: Relationships between Young Sisters as Revealed in Their Overt Responses. Child Development Monograph, No. 23. New York, Teachers College. Columbia University, 1938.

534. McGanity, W. J., et al.: The Vanderbilt Cooperative Study of Maternal and Infant Nutrition. VI. Relationship of obstetric performance to nutrition, Am. J. Obst. and Gynec. 67:501-527, 1954.

535. ———: The Vanderbilt Cooperative Study of Maternal and Infant Nutri-

tion. VIII. Some nutritional implications, J. Am. Dietet. A. 31:582-588, 1955.

536. McGraw, M. B.: Later development of children specially trained during infancy, Child Development 10:1-19, 1939.

537. ———: Chap. 7—Maturation of Behavior, in Carmichael, L.: Manual of Child Psychology. New York, John Wiley & Sons, 1946.

538. ———: Neural maturation as exemplified in achievement of bladder control, J. Pediat. 16:580-590, 1940.

539. ———: Neural maturation as exemplified in reaching-prehensile behavior of human infant, J. Psychol. 11:127-141, 1941.

540. ———: Neuromuscular Maturation of Human Infant. New York, Columbia University Press, 1943.

541. McKee, J. P., and Leader, F. B.: The relationship of socio-economic status and aggression to the competitive behavior of preschool children, Child Development 26:135-142, 1955.

542. McLellan, F. C.: Neurogenic Bladder. Springfield, Ill., Charles C Thomas, Publisher, 1939.

543. Macy, I. G.: Nutrition and Chemical Growth in Childhood. vol. 1. Springfield, Ill., Charles C Thomas, Publisher, 1942.

544. ———: Composition of human milk and colostrum, Am. J. Dis. Child. 78:589-603, 1949.

545. Macy, I. G., Kelley, H., and Sloan, R.: Composition of Milks. Bulletin No. 119. Washington, D. C., National Research Council, National Academy of Science, 1950.

546. Macy, I. G., and Mack, H. C.: Physiological Changes in Plasma Proteins Characteristic of Human Reproduction. Detroit, Children's Fund of Michigan, 1952.

547. Macy, I. G., et al.: Human milk flow, Am. J. Dis. Child. 39:1186-1204, 1930.

548. ———: Human milk studies, Am. J. Dis. Child. 42:569-589, 1931.

549. ———: Physiological adaptation and nutritional status during and after pregnancy, J. Nutrition 52: Suppl. 1, 1954.

550. Magnussen, G.: The sleep function and sleep disturbances, Ment. Hyg. 37: 89-118, 1953.

551. Maloney, J. C.: Psychiatric observations in Okinawa Shima, Psychiatry 8:391-399, 1945.

552. Manwell, E., and Fahs, S.: Consider the Children—How They Grow. ed. 2. Boston, Beacon Press, 1951.

553. Maresh, M. M.: Paranasal sinuses from birth to late adolescence, Am. J. Dis. Child. 60:55-78, 1940.

554. Markey, F. V.: Imaginative Behavior of Preschool Children. Child Development Monograph, No. 18. New York, Teachers College, Columbia University, 1935.

555. Marquis, D. P.: Can conditioned responses be established in the newborn infant? J. Genet. Psychol. 39:479-492, 1931.

556. ———: Learning in the neonate: modification of behavior under three feeding schedules, J. Exper. Psychol. 29:263-282, 1941.

557. Marshall, H., and McCandless, B.: A study of prediction of social behavior of preschool children, Child Development 28:148-159, 1957.

558. Martin, W. E.: Effects of early training on personality, Marriage and Family Living, 19:39-45, 1957.

559. Martin, W. E., and Stendler, C. B.: Child Development. New York, Harcourt Brace and Co., 1953.
560. ———— (editors): Readings in Child Development. New York, Harcourt Brace and Co., 1954.
561. Matheson, E.: A study of problem solving behavior in preschool children, Child Development 2:242-262, 1931.
562. Mattson, M.: The relation between the complexity of the habit to be acquired and the form of the learning curve in young children, Genet. Psychol. Monogr. 13:299-398, 1933.
563. May, C. D.: Vitamin B₆ in human nutrition: a critique and an object lesson, Pediatrics 14:269-279, 1954.
564. Mead, M.: From the South Seas. New York, William Morrow and Co., 1939.
565. ————: Male and Female. New York, William Morrow and Co., 1949.
566. ————: Chap. 12—Research on Primitive Children, in Carmichael, L.: Manual of Child Psychology. ed. 2 (155).
567. Mead, M., and Wolfenstein, M. (editors): Childhood in Contemporary Cultures. Chicago, University of Chicago Press, 1955.
568. Members of the Department of Experimental Medicine, Cambridge, and associated workers: Studies of Under-Nutrition. Wuppertal 1946-1949. Medical Research Council Special Report Series No. 275. London, His Majesty's Stationery Office, 1951.
569. Mercier, M. H., and Despert, J. L.: Psychological effects of war on French children, Psychosom. Med. 5:266-272, 1943.
570. Meredith, H. V.: Birth order and body size; neonatal and childhood materials, Am. J. Phys. Anthropol. 8:195-224, 1950.
571. ————: Body size in infancy and childhood; comparative study of data from Okinawa, France, South Africa and North America, Child Development 19:180-195, 1948.
572. ————: A chart on eruption of the deciduous teeth for the pediatrician's office, J. Pediat. 38:482-483, 1951.
573. ————: Order and age of eruption for deciduous dentition, J. Dent. Research 25:43-66, 1946.
574. Meredith, H. V., and Goldstein, M. S.: Studies on the body size of North American children of Mexican ancestry, Child Development 23:91-110, 1952.
575. Meredith, H. V., and Knott, V. B.: Changes in body proportions during infancy and preschool years; Skelic Index, Child Development 9:49-62, 1938.
576. Merrill, B.: A measurement of mother-child interaction, J. Abn. and Soc. Psychol. 41:37-49, 1946.
577. Metraux, R. W.: Speech profiles of the pre-school child—18-54 months, Journal of Speech and Hearing Disorders 15:37-53, 1950.
578. Metropolitan Life Insurance Company: Health of Teen-Agers. Metropolitan Life Insurance Co. Statistical Bull. 34, 1, August, 1953.
579. Meyer, L. F., and Nassau, E.: Physiology and Pathology of Infant Nutrition. ed. 2. Springfield, Ill., Charles C Thomas, Publisher, 1955.
580. Michelson, N.: Investigations in physical development of Negroes; Stature, Am. J. Phys. Anthropol. 1:191-213, 1943.
581. Michigan Department of Health: Michigan Health Statistics. Annual Statistical Report. Division of Disease Control, Records and Statistics, Michigan Department of Health, Lansing, Michigan, 1953.

518   *Bibliography*

582. Midcentury White House Conference on Children and Youth: Chart Book. Raleigh, N. C., Health Publications Institute, 1951.
583. ———: Fact Finding Report. Raleigh, N. C., Health Publications Institute, 1951.
584. ———: Proceedings. Raleigh, N. C., Health Publications Institute, 1951.
585. Milbank Memorial Fund: The Family Health Maintenance Demonstration. Proceedings of a Round Table at the 1953 Annual Conference of the Milbank Memorial Fund. New York, Milbank Memorial Fund, 1954.
586. Miles, C. C.: Chap. 16—Gifted Children, in Carmichael, L.: Manual of Child Psychology. ed. 2 (155).
587. Miller, H., and Baruch, D. W.: A study of hostility in allergic children, Am. J. Orthopsychiat. 20:506-519, 1950.
588. Miller, H. L., and Flannery, F. E.: Education for childbirth in private practice: 585 consecutive cases, Child-Family Digest 6(April):33-44, 1952.
589. Miller, J. G.: Toward a general theory for the behavioral sciences, American Psychologist 10:513-531, 1955.
590. Millis, J.: The influence of breast feeding on weight gain in infants in the first year, J. Pediat. 48:770-775, 1956.
591. ———: A study of the effect of nutrition on fertility and the outcome of pregnancy in Singapore in 1947 and 1950, Med. J. Malaya 6:157-179, 1952.
592. Mitchell, D. F.: The mechanism of dental caries, J. Am. Dent. A. 52:14-18, 1956.
593. Mitchell, L. S.: The Here and Now Story Book. New York, E. P. Dutton & Co., 1921.
594. Montagu, M. F. Ashley: Constitutional and Prenatal Factors in Infant and Child Health, in Senn, M. J. E. (editor): Symposium on The Healthy Personality. New York, Josiah Macy Jr. Foundation, 1950.
595. Montessori, M.: Pedagogical Anthropology (translated by F. F. Cooper). New York, Frederick A. Stokes Company, 1913.
596. Morgan, A. F., and Haynes, E. G.: Vitamin B_1 content of human milk as affected by ingestion of thiamin chloride, J. Nutrition 18:105-114, 1939.
597. Morgan, S. S., and Morgan, J. J. B.: Adaptive behavior patterns in infants, J. Pediat. 25:168-177, 1944.
598. Moustakas, C. E.: Children in Play Therapy. New York, McGraw-Hill Book Co., Inc., 1953.
599. Moustakas, C. E., and Berson, M. P.: The Nursery School and Child Care Center. New York, William Morrow & Co., 1955.
600. ———: The Young Child in School. New York, William Morrow & Co., 1956.
601. Moustakas, C., Sigel, I., and Schalock, H.: An objective method for the measurement and analysis of child-adult interaction, Child Development 27:109-134, 1956.
602. Mowrer, O.: Learning Theory and Personality Dynamics. New York, Ronald Press, 1950.
603. ———: Speech development in the young child. The autism theory of speech development and some clinical applications, J. of Speech and Hearing Disorders 17:263-268, 1952.
604. Moyer, E. Z., et al.: Nutritional Status of Mothers and their Infants. Detroit, Children's Fund of Michigan, 1954.
605. Munkres, A.: Which Way for Our Children. New York, Charles Scribner's Sons, 1936.

606. Munn, N. L.: Chap. 7—Learning in Children, in Carmichael, L.: Manual of Child Psychology, ed. 2 (155).
607. Munro, N.: Between meal feedings for preschool children, J. Home Econ. 46:724-728, 1954.
608. Munroe, M.: Drawings and Color Preferences of Young Children. Dissertation submitted to Graduate Faculty in candidacy for degree of Doctor of Philosophy, University of Chicago, 1929.
609. Murphy, G., and Hochberg, J.: Perceptual development; some tentative hypotheses, Psychol. Rev. 58:332-349, 1951.
610. Murphy, G., Murphy, L. B., and Newcomb, T. M.: Experimental Social Psychology. ed. 2. New York, Harper & Brothers, 1937.
611. Murphy, L. B.: The nursery school contributes to emotional development, Childhood Educ. 16:404-407, 1940.
612. ———: Personality in Young Children. New York, Basic Books, 1956, Two Volumes.
613. ———: Social Behavior and Child Personality: Exploratory Study of Some Roots of Sympathy. New York, Columbia University Press, 1937.
614. ———: Social and emotional development, Rev. Educ. Research 11:479-501, 1941.
615. Murray, B. F., and Tyler, D.: Study of religious education for young children, Relig. Educ. 32:55-61, 1937.
616. Mursell, J. L.: Education for Musical Growth. Boston, Ginn & Company, 1948.
617. Myers, G. C.: Education of Young Children through Celebrating Their Successes. City School Leaflet No. 26. Washington, D. C., Department of Interior, Bureau of Education.
618. National Association for Nursery Education: Essentials of Nursery Education. Kingston, R. I., 1948.
619. National Conference on Family Life: Dynamics of Family Interaction. Report of committee, edited by E. Duvall and R. Hill. Mimeographed, 1948.
620. National Society for the Study of Education: Forty-sixth Yearbook, Part II, Early Childhood Education. Chap. 6, Practices and Resources in Early Childhood Education, by E. Fuller and others. Chap. 7, Part II, Experiences in Which Young Children May Learn To Share, by G. Chittenden. Chicago, University of Chicago Press, 1947.
621. ———: Forty-ninth Yearbook, Part II, The Education of Exceptional Children, edited by Nelson B. Henry. Chicago, University of Chicago Press, 1950.
622. Navarra, J. G.: The Development of Scientific Concepts in a Young Child. New York, Bureau of Publications, Columbia University, 1955.
623. Neilon, P.: Shirley's babies after fifteen years, J. Genet. Psychol. 73:175-186, 1948.
624. Neisser, E. G.: Brothers and Sisters. New York, Harper & Brothers, 1951.
625. Nelson, V., and Richards, T. W.: Fels mental age values for Gesell schedules, Child Development 11:153-157, 1940.
626. Nelson, W. E. (editor): Textbook of Pediatrics. ed. 6. Philadelphia, W. B. Saunders Company, 1954.
627. Nesbitt, M.: Student and child relationships in the nursery school, Child Development 14:143-166, 1943.

628. Newberry, H.: Studies in fetal behavior; measurement of three types of fetal activity, J. Comp. Psychol. 32:521-530, 1941.
629. Newton, N.: Maternal Emotions. A Study of Women's Feelings toward Menstruation, Pregnancy, Childbirth, Breast Feeding, Infant Care and Other Aspects of their Femininity. A Psychosomatic Medicine Monograph. New York, Paul B. Hoeber, Inc., Medical Book Department of Harper & Brothers, 1955.
630. Newton, N. R.: The relationships between infant feeding experience and later behavior, J. Pediat. 38:28-40, 1951.
631. Newton, N. R., and Newton, M.: Relation of let-down reflex to ability to breast feed, Pediatrics 5:726-733, 1950.
632. ———: Relationship of ability to breast feed and maternal attitudes toward breast feeding, Pediatrics 5:869-875, 1950.
633. Nice, M. M.: Concerning all day conversations, Ped. Sem. 27:166-177, 1920.
634. ———: Length of sentence as criterion of child's progress in speech, J. Educ. Psychol. 16:370-379, 1925.
635. Norris, M., Spaulding, P., and Brodie, F.: Blindness in Children. Chicago, University of Chicago Press, 1957.
636. Northway, M., and Weld, L.: Children and their contemporaries, what has been learned from sociometric studies, Bulletin of The Institute of Child Study, University of Toronto, 18:8-16, 1956.
637. Norval, M. A.: Some factors which influence duration of breast feeding, J. Pediat. 31:415-419, 1947.
638. O'Brien, M. A., Edler, R. A., et al.: Developing creativity in children's use of imagination: nursery, ages two and three, Union Coll. Stud. Character Research 1:35-42, 1954.
639. Olmsted, R. W., and Jackson, E. B.: Self-demand feeding in the first week of life, Pediatrics 6:396-401, 1950.
640. Olson, W. C.: Child Development. Boston, D. C. Heath & Company, 1949.
641. Olson, W. C., and Hughes, B. O.: Concept of organismic age, J. Educ. Research 35:525-527, 1942.
642. Orent-Keiles, E., and Hallman, L. F.: The Breakfast Meal in Relation to Blood-Sugar Values. U. S. Department of Agriculture Circular No. 827, 1949.
643. Orlansky, H.: Infant care and personality, Psychol. Bull. 46:1-48, 1949.
644. Orton, S. T.: Physiological theory of reading disability and stuttering in children, New England J. Med. 199:1046, 1928.
645. Osborn, J. J., Dancis, J., and Juan, F. J.: Studies of immunology of newborn infant, Pediatrics 9:736-744, 1952.
646. Outhouse, J., et al.: The calcium requirements of five preschool girls, J. Nutrition 7:199-211, 1939.
647. Page, M. L.: Modification of Ascendant Behavior in Preschool Children. Studies in Child Welfare 12 (3). Iowa City, University of Iowa, 1936.
648. Paiva, S. L.: Pattern of growth of selected groups of breast fed infants in Iowa City, Pediatrics 11:38-47, 1953.
649. Palmer, A.: Basal body temperature in disorders of ovarian function and pregnancy, Surg., Gynec. & Obst. 75:768-778, 1942.
650. Park, E. A.: Bone Growth in health and disease, Arch. Dis. Childhood 29:269-281, 1954.
651. Parten, M. L.: Leadership among preschool children, J. Abnorm. & Social Psychol. 27:430-442, 1933.

652. Parten, M. L., and Newhall, S.: Chap. 29—Social Behavior of Preschool Children, in Barker, R. G., et al.: Child Behavior and Development (72).
653. Pasamanick, B., and Kawi, A.: A study of the association of prenatal and paranatal factors with the development of tics in children, J. Pediat. 48:596-601, 1956.
654. Pearse, I. H., and Crocker, L. H.: The Peckham Experiment; Study of the Living Structure of Society. New Haven, Yale University Press, 1945.
655. Peiper, A.: Der Sangvorgang, Ergebn. d. inn. Med. u. Kinderh. 50:527 ff., 1936, cited in Wolman, I. J.: Major motility patterns of child's digestive tract; review, Am. J. M. Sc. 207:782-804, 1944.
656. People's League of Health: Nutrition of expectant and nursing mothers in relation to maternal and infant mortality and morbidity, J. Obst. Gynaec., Brit. Empire 53:498-509, 1946.
657. Perry, E.: Children Need Adults. New York, Harper & Brothers, 1943.
658. Phillips, H. T.: Some social and ethnic variations in the physique of South African nursery school children, Arch. Dis. Childhood 28:226-231, 1953.
659. Phillips, P. H.: Recent progress in dietary research and dental caries, J. Am. Dietet. A. 32:110-114, 1956.
660. Piaget, J.: Construction of Reality in the Child. New York, Basic Books, 1954.
661. ———: Language and Thought of the Child. New York, Harcourt, Brace & Company, Inc., 1926.
662. ———: The Moral Judgment of the Child. New York, Harcourt, Brace & Company, Inc., 1932.
663. ———: Play, Dreams and Imitation in Childhood. New York, W. W. Norton, translation, 1951.
664. Pinneau, S.: Critique on articles by Margaret Ribble, Child Development 21:203-228, 1950.
665. Plant, J. S.: The Envelope. New York, Commonwealth Fund, 1950.
666. Plummer, G.: Anomalies occurring in children exposed in utero to the atomic bomb in Hiroshima, Pediatrics 10:687-693, 1952.
667. Pond, M. A.: How does housing affect health? Pub. Health Rep. 61:665-672, 1946.
668. Population Reference Bureau: College Study Report—1956. Population Bulletin, Population Reference Bureau, Inc., vol. XII, No. 6, 1956.
669. Potter, E. L.: Fundamentals of Human Reproduction. New York, McGraw-Hill Book Co., Inc., 1948.
670. Pratt, K. C.: Chap. 4—The Neonate, in Carmichael, L.: Manual of Child Psychology, ed. 2 (155).
671. Pratt, K. C., Nelson, A. K., and Sun, K. H.: Behavior of the Newborn Infant. Ohio State University Studies, Contrib. Psychol. No. 10, 1930.
672. Prentice, C. S.: An Adopted Child Looks at Adoption. New York, D. Appleton-Century Company, Inc., 1940.
673. Preston, M. I.: Late behavioral aspects found in cases of prenatal, natal, and postnatal anoxia, J. Pediat. 26:353-366, 1945.
674. Preyer, W.: The Senses and the Will (translated by H. W. Brown). New York, D. Appleton-Century Company, Inc., 1893.
675. Pyle, S. I., and Hoerr, N. L.: Radiographic Atlas of Skeletal Development of the Knee. Springfield, Ill., Charles C Thomas, Publisher, 1955.
676. Pyle, I., and Sontag, L. W.: Variability in onset of ossification in epiphyses and short bones of extremities, Am. J. Roentgenol. 49:795-798, 1943.

677. Pyles, M.: Verbalization as factor in learning, Child Development 3:108-113, 1932.
678. Rabban, M.: Sex-role identification in young children in two diverse social groups, Genet. Psychol. Monogr. 42:81-158, 1950.
679. Radke, M.: Relation of Parental Authority to Children's Behavior and Attitudes. Institute of Child Welfare Monograph Series No. 22. Minneapolis, University of Minnesota Press, 1946.
680. Ranson, S. W.: Anatomy of the Nervous System; Its Development and Function, revised by S. L. Clark. Philadelphia, W. B. Saunders Co., 1953.
681. Rapoport, M.: Prenatal Disturbance, in Textbook of Pediatrics. ed. 6. W. E. Nelson, editor. (626).
682. Read, G. D.: Childbirth without Fear. New York, Harper & Brothers, 1944.
683. ———: Observations on a series of labors with special reference to physiological delivery, Lancet 1:721-726, 1949.
684. Read, K. H.: The Nursery School. ed. 2. Philadelphia, W. B. Saunders Company, 1955.
685. ———: What about cooperative nursery schools? Nat. A. Nurs. Educ. Bull. 6:3-6, 1950.
686. Read, K. H., and Conrad, H. S.: Interpretation of behavior ratings in terms of favorable or unfavorable deviations; study of scores from Read-Conrad behavior inventory, Genet. Psychol. Monogr. 25:157-215, 1942.
687. Reinhold, J. G., et al.: Utilization of thiamine in the human subject; effect of high intake of carbohydrate or of fat, J. Nutrition 28:51-61, 1944.
688. Reynolds, E. L.: Bony pelvic girdle in early infancy; roentgenometric study, Am. J. Phys. Anthropol. 3:321-352, 1945.
689. ———: Bony pelvis in prepuberal childhood, Am. J. Phys. Anthropol. 5:165-200, 1947.
690. ———: Degree of kinship and pattern of ossification, Am. J. Phys. Anthropol. 1:405-416, 1943.
691. ———: Distribution of tissue components in female leg from birth to maturity, Anat. Rec. 100:621-630, 1948.
692. Reynolds, E. L., and Grote, P.: Sex differences in distribution of tissue components in human leg from birth to maturity, Anat. Rec. 102:45-53, 1948.
693. Reynolds, M. M.: Sleep of young children in 24-hour nursery school, Ment. Hygiene 19:602-609, 1935.
694. Rheingold, H.: The Modification of Social Responsiveness in Institutional Babies. Society for Research in Child Development Monograph, vol. 21: Serial No. 63, No. 2. Lafayette, Ind., Child Development Publications, 1956.
695. Ribble, M.: The Rights of Infants. New York, Columbia University Press, 1943.
696. Richards, T. W.: The relationship between bodily and gastric activity of newborn infants: I. Correlation and influence of time since feeding, Human Biol. 8:368-380, 1936.
697. Richards, T. W., and Irwin, O. C.: Studies in Infant Behavior; Plantar Responses of Infants and Young Children: Examination of Literature and Reports of New Experiments. Studies in Child Welfare 11 (1). Iowa City, University of Iowa, 1935.
698. Richards, T. W., and Nelson, V.: Abilities of infants during first eighteen months, J. Genet. Psychol. 55:299-318, 1939.
699. Richards, T. W., and Newberry, H.: Studies in fetal behavior; can per-

formance on test items at six months postnatally be predicted on basis of fetal activity? Child Development 9:79-86, 1938.

700. Richards, T. W., and Simons, M. P.: Fels child behavior scales, Genet. Psychol. Monogr. 24:265-274, 1941.

701. Richardson, H. M.: Growth of adaptive behavior in infants; experimental study of seven age levels, Genet. Psychol. Monogr. 12:195-359, 1932.

702. Ridenour, N., and Johnson, I.: Some Special Problems of Children Aged 2 to 5 Years. Published by National Mental Health Foundation, Inc., in association with New York Committee on Mental Hygiene. New York, New York Committee on Mental Hygiene of State Charities Aid Association, 1947.

703. Roberts, K. E.: Ability of preschool children to solve problems in which a simple principle of relationship is kept constant, J. Genet. Psychol. 40:118-133, 1932.

704. Roberts, K. E., and Schoelkopf, J. A.: Eating, sleeping, and elimination; practices of group of two-and-one-half-year-old children, Am. J. Dis. Child. 82:121-152, 1951.

705. Robinow, M., Johnston, M., and Anderson, M.: Feet of normal children, J. Pediat. 23:141-149, 1943.

706. Robinow, M., Leonard, V. L., and Anderson, M.: New approach to quantitative analysis of children's posture, J. Pediat. 22:655-663, 1943.

707. Robinow, M., Richards, T. W., and Anderson, M.: Eruption of deciduous teeth, Growth 6:127-133, 1942.

708. Rock, J., and Loth, D.: Voluntary Parenthood. New York, Random House, 1949.

709. Rockwood, L. D.: Trends in family life research, J. Home Econ. 34:647-654, 1942.

710. Roff, M., and Roff, L.: Analysis of variance of conflict behavior in preschool children, Child Development 11:43-60, 1940.

711. Rondell, F., and Michaels, R.: The Adopted Family: I. You and Your Child: A Guide for Adoptive Parents. New York, Crown Publishers, 1951.

712. Rose, M. S.: Feeding the Family. ed. 3. New York, Macmillan Company, 1929.

713. Rose, W. C.: Amino acid requirements of man, Federation Proc. 8:546-552, 1949.

714. Rowntree, G.: Accidents among children under two years of age in Great Britain, J. Hygiene 48:322-337, 1950.

715. Russell, D.: Children's Thinking. Boston, Ginn, 1956.

716. Salt selection by adrenalectomized rats, Nutrition Rev. 14:123-124, 1956.

717. Sanders, B. S.: Environment and Growth. Baltimore, Warwick & York, 1934.

718. Sandler, H. C.: Eruption of deciduous teeth, J. Pediat. 25:140-147, 1944.

719. Sanford H.: Care of skin of newborn infant; six-year study of 3500 newborn infants, J. Pediat. 11:68-76, 1937.

720. Sanford, R. N.: Chap. 32—Personality Patterns in School Children, in Child Behavior and Development by Barker, R. G., et al. (72).

721. Sawyer, R.: The Way of the Storyteller. New York, Viking Press, 1951.

722. Scammon, R. E.: Summary of Anatomy of Infant and Child, in Abt, I. A.: Pediatrics, vol. I, pp. 277-278. Philadelphia, W. B. Saunders Company, 1923.

723. Scheinfeld, A.: The New You and Heredity. Philadelphia, J. B. Lippincott Company, 1950.

524   *Bibliography*

724. Schlesinger, E. R., et al.: Newburgh-Kingston caries fluorine study. XIII. Pediatric findings after ten years, J. Am. Dent. A. 52:296-306, 1956.
725. Schoenheimer, R.: Dynamic State of Body Constituents. Monograph in Medicine and Public Health, No. 3, pp. 39-40. Cambridge, Harvard University Press, 1942.
726. Schour, I., and Massler, M.: Studies in tooth development; growth pattern of human teeth, J. Am. Dent. A. 27:1918-1931, 1940.
727. Schreiber, F.: Apnea of the newborn and associated cerebral injury, J.A.M.A. 111:1263-1269, 1938.
728. Scott, E. M., Verney, E. L., and Morissey, P. D.: Self selection of diet; appetites for calcium, magnesium and potassium, J. Nutrition 41:187-201, 1950.
729. Scott, R. B., et al.: Growth and development of Negro infants; growth during first year of life as observed in private pediatric practice, J. Pediat. 37:885-893, 1950.
730. Seabury, D.: Growing into Life. New York, Boni & Liveright, Inc., 1928.
731. Sears, R.: Ordinal position in the family as a psychological variable, Am. Sociol. Rev. 15:397-401, 1950.
732. ———: A theoretical framework for personality and social behavior, American Psychologist 6:476-483, 1951.
733. Sears, R. R., Maccoby, E., and Levin, H.: Patterns of Child Rearing. Evanston, Ill., Row, Peterson & Co., 1957.
734. Sears, R., et al.: Effects of cup, bottle, and breast feeding on oral activities of newborn infants, Pediatrics 2:549-557, 1948.
735. ———: Effect of father-separation on preschool children's doll play aggression, Child Development 17:219-243, 1946.
736. Sears, R. R., et al.: Some child-rearing antecedents of aggression and dependency in young children, Genet. Psychol. Monogr. 47:135-234, 1953.
737. Sears, R., and Wise, G.: Relation of cup-feeding in infancy to thumbsucking and the oral drive, Am. J. Orthopsychiat. 20:123-138, 1950.
738. Sedgewick, J. P.: Preliminary report of study of breast feeding in Minneapolis, Am. J. Dis. Child. 21:455-464, 1921.
739. Seeley, J. R., Sim, R. A., and Loosley, E. W.: Crestwood Heights; a study of the culture of suburban life. New York, Basic Books, 1956.
740. Self selection of diet by rats, Nutrition Rev. 9:26-28, 1951.
741. Selfridge, G.: Eighth nerve high tone deafness from nutritional standpoint, Ann. Otol., Rhin. & Laryng. 48:608-631, 1939.
742. Selye, H.: The Story of the Adaptation Syndrome. Montreal, Acta, Inc., 1952.
743. ———: Stress—The Physiology and Pathology of Exposure to Stress. Montreal, Acta, Inc., 1950.
744. ———: The Stress of Life. New York, McGraw-Hill Book Co., Inc., 1956.
745. Senn, M. J. (editor): Problems of Infancy and Childhood; transactions of the seventh conference, sponsored by the Josiah Macy Jr. Foundation. Josiah Macy Jr. Foundation, New York, 1954.
746. Sewell, W. H., and Mussen, P. H.: The effects of feeding, weaning and scheduling procedures on childhood adjustment and the formation of oral symptoms, Child Development 23:185-191, 1952.
747. Shaw, J. H.: Nutrition and Dental Caries, in Survey of the Literature of Dental Caries. Food and Nutrition Board, National Research Council Publ. 225. Washington, D. C. National Academy of Sciences, National Research Council, 1952.

748. Sheehy, D.: There's Music in Children. ed. 2. New York, Henry Holt & Company, 1952.
749. Sheldon, W. H.: Atlas of Men. A Guide for Somatotyping the Adult Male of All Ages. New York, Harper and Brothers, 1954.
750. Sherman, H. C., and Lanford, C. S.: Essentials of Nutrition. ed. 4. New York, Macmillan Company, 1957.
751. Sherry, S. N., and Kramer, I.: The time of passage of the first stool and first urine by the newborn infant, J. Pediat. 46:158-159, 1955.
752. Shinn, M.: Notes on Development of a Child. Berkeley, University of California Press, 1909.
753. Shirley, M. M.: The First Two Years; a Study of Twenty-Five Babies. Minneapolis, University of Minnesota Press, 1931.
754. ———: The First Two Years; a Study of Twenty-Five Babies' Personality Manifestations. Institute of Child Welfare Monograph, Series No. 7, University of Minnesota Press, 1933.
755. Shock, N. W.: Chap. 18—Ageing of Homeostatic Mechanisms, in Problems of Ageing by Cowdry. ed. 3. A. I. Lansing, editor. Baltimore, Williams & Wilkins Co., 1952.
756. Sigel, I. E.: The need for conceptualization in research on child development, Child Development 27:241-252, 1956.
757. Sillman, J. H.: Malocclusion in deciduous dentition; serial study from birth to five years, Am. J. Orthodontia & Oral Surg. 28:197-209, 1942.
758. ———: Thumbsucking and the oral structures, J. Pediat. 39:424-443, 515-516, 1951.
759. Silver, G. A.: Objectives of the Family Health Maintenance Demonstration, in The Family Health Maintenance Demonstration. New York, Milbank Memorial Fund, 1954.
760. Simchen, H.: Studien über Mehlverdauung beim Saugling, Arch. f. Kinderh. 75:6-12, 1925.
761. Simmons, K.: Brush Foundation Study of Child Growth and Development; Physical Growth and Development. Monograph IX (1). Washington, D. C., Society for Research in Child Development, National Research Council, 1944.
762. Simsarian, F. P., and McLendon, P. A.: Further records on self-demand schedule in infant feeding, J. Pediat. 27:109-114, 1945.
763. Skodak, M., and Skeels, H.: Final follow-up study of one hundred adopted Children, J. Genet. Psychol. 75:85-125, 1949.
764. Smart, M S.: Child development and religious education, Childhood Educ. 16:159-164, 1939.
765. Smart, M. S., and Smart, R. C.: It's a Wise Parent. New York, Charles Scribner's Sons, 1944.
766. Smith, C. A.: Effects of maternal undernutrition upon the newborn infant in Holland, J. Pediat. 30:229-243, 1947.
767. ———: Introduction to neonatal pediatrics, in Textbook of Pediatrics. ed. 6. W. E. Nelson, editor. W. B. Saunders Company, Philadelphia, 1954.
768. ———: The Newborn Infant, in Textbook of Pediatrics. ed. 6. W. E. Nelson, editor. (626).
769. ———: Physiology of the Newborn Infant. ed. 2. Springfield, Ill., Charles C Thomas, Publisher, 1951.
770. Smith, C. A., et al.: Maternal-fetal nutritional relationships. Effect of maternal diet on size and content of the fetal liver, Obst. & Gynec. 1:46-58, 1953.

771. Smith, D. A., and Woodruff, M. F. A.: Deficiency Diseases in Japanese Prison Camps. Medical Research Council Special Report Series No. 274. London, His Majesty's Stationery Office, 1951.
772. Smith, G. V.: Chap. 6—The Ovaries, in Textbook of Endocrinology. ed. 2. R. H. Williams, editor. Philadelphia, W. B. Saunders Co., 1955.
773. Smith, J.: University of Illinois nursery school for children of student war veterans, Nat. A. Nurs. Educ. Bull. 4:12-14, 1949.
774. Smith, L. H.: Care of skin of newborn infant; prevention of infection, J. Pediat. 12:603-604, 1938.
775. Smith, M. E.: Investigation of Development of the Sentence and Extent of Vocabulary in Young Children. Studies in Child Welfare 3 (5). Iowa City, University of Iowa, 1926.
776. ———: Grammatical errors in speech of preschool children, Child Development 4:183-190, 1933.
777. ———: Influence of age, sex, and situation on the frequency, form, and function of questions asked by preschool children, Child Development 4:201-213, 1933.
778. Smith, N., and Rosello, S.: Iron deficiency in infancy and childhood, Am. J. Clin. Nutrition 1:275-286, 1953.
779. Smith, S. L., and Goss, A. E.: The role of the acquired distinctiveness of cues in the acquisition of a motor skill in children, J. Genet. Psychol. 87:11-24, 1955.
780. Snyderman, S. E., et al.: Pyridoxine deficiency in the human infant, J. Clin. Nutrition 1:200-207, 1953.
781. Soddy, K. (editor): Mental Health and Infant Development; Proceedings of the International Seminar held by the World Federation for Mental Health at Chichester, England, vols. I and II. New York, Basic Books, 1956.
782. Sontag, L. W.: Significance of fetal environmental differences, Am. J. Obst. & Gynec. 42:996-1003, 1941.
783. Sontag, L. W., and Wines, J.: Relation of mothers' diets to status of their infants at birth and in infancy, Am. J. Obst. & Gynec. 54:994-1003, 1947.
784. Spadino, E. J.: Writing and Laterality Characteristics of Stuttering Children. New York, Columbia University Press, 1941.
785. Spector, W. E. (editor): Handbook of Biological Data. Philadelphia, W. B. Saunders Co., 1956.
786. Spier, L.: Growth of Japanese Children Born in America and Japan. Seattle, Wash., University of Washington Press, 1929.
787. Spies, T. D., et al.: Skeletal maturational progress of children with chronic nutritive failure: effect of dietary supplement of reconstituted milk solids, Am. J. Dis. Child. 85:1-12, 1953.
788. Spiker, C. C.: Experiments with children on the hypotheses of acquired distinctiveness and equivalence of cues, Child Development 27:253-263, 1956.
789. ———: The stimulus generalization gradient as a function of the intensity of stimulus lights, Child Development 27:85-98, 1956.
790. Spitz, R.: Role of ecological factors in emotional development in infancy, Child Development 20:145-155, 1949.
791. Spock, B.: Avoiding behavior problems, J. Pediat. 27:363-382, 1945.
792. ———: The Common Sense Book of Baby and Child Care. ed. 2. New York, Duell, Sloan and Pearce, Inc., 1957. Also in Pocket Book Edition. New York, Pocket Books, Inc.

793. Spock, B.: Round table discussion on present day attitudes toward breast feeding (Smith, C. A., Chairman; Heatos, C., Harsberger, R. N., Spock, B., Nathanson, I. T.; Bain, K., and Kimball, E. R., Secretaries), Pediatrics 6:656-659, 1950.

794. ————: in Symposium on The Healthy Personality, M. J. E. Senn, editor. New York, Josiah Macy Jr. Foundation, 1950. P. 74.

795. Spock, B., and Huschber, M.: Psychological Aspects of Pediatric Practice. New York State Committee on Mental Hygiene of State Charities Aid Association, 1938.

796. Staples, R.: Factors influencing afternoon sleep of young children, J. Genet. Psychol, 41:222-228, 1932.

797. ————: Responses of infants to color, J. Exper. Psychol. 15:119-141, 1932.

798. Staples, R., and Conley, H.: Use of color in finger paintings of young children, Child Development 20:201-212, 1949.

799. Stearns, G.: Chap. IV—Human Requirement of Calcium, Phosphorus and Magnesium, in Handbook of Nutrition; a Symposium. ed. 2. American Medical Association, published by Blakiston Co., 1951.

800. ————: Mineral metabolism of normal infants, Physiol. Rev. 19:415-438, 1939.

801. ————: Nutritional health of infants, children and adolescents, in Proceedings of Food and Nutrition Institute. Agriculture Handbook No. 56. Washington, D. C., U. S. Department of Agriculture, 1952.

802. Stearns, G., Jeans, P. C., and Vandecar, V.: Effect of vitamin D on linear growth in infancy, J. Pediat. 9:1-12, 1936.

803. Stearns, G., and Stinger, D.: Iron retention in infancy, J. Nutrition 13:127-141, 1937.

804. Stein, K. F., et al.: Influence of heredity in the etiology of malocclusion, Am. J. Orthodontia 42:125-141, 1956.

805. Stendler, C. B.: Critical periods in socialization and overdependency, Child Development 23:1-12, 1952.

806. Stendler, C. B., and Young, N.: Impact of beginning first grade upon socialization as reported by mothers, Child Development 21:241-260, 1950.

807. Stern, C.: Principles of Human Genetics. San Francisco, W. H. Freeman & Co., 1950.

808. Stevenson, S. S.: Adequacy of artificial feeding in infancy, J. Pediat. 31: 616-630, 1947.

809. Stewart, A., and Westropp, C.: Breast-feeding in the Oxford Child Health Survey. 2. Comparison of bottle-fed and breast-fed babies, Brit. Med. J. ii:305-308, 1953.

810. Stewart, H. L., Jr., and Pratt, J. P.: Influence of suckling stimulus on lactation, West. J. Surg. 49:98-103, 1941.

811. Stolz, L. M., et al.: Father Relations of War-Born Children. Stanford, Stanford University Press, 1954.

812. Stott, L. H.: The longitudinal approach to the study of family life, J. Home Econ. 46:79-82, 1954.

813. ————: The Longitudinal Study of Individual Development. Detroit, The Merrill-Palmer School, 1955.

814. ————: The persisting effects of early family experiences upon personality development, Merrill-Palmer Quarterly 3, Spring: 144-159, 1957.

815. ————: Problem of evaluating family success, Marriage and Family Living 13:149-152, 1951.

816. Stott, L. H.: Research in family life in Nebraska, J. Home Econ. 37:80-83, 1945.
817. Strain, F. B.: New Patterns in Sex Teaching. New York, D. Appleton-Century Company, Inc., 1951.
818. Strang, R.: Introduction to Child Study. ed. 3. New York, Macmillan Company, 1951.
819. Stuart, H. C., Hill, P., and Shaw, C.: Growth of Bone, Muscle and Overlying Tissues as Revealed by Studies of Roentgenograms of the Leg Area. Monograph 5 (3). Washington, D. C., Society for Research in Child Development, National Research Council, 1940.
820. Stuart, H. C., and Sobel, E. H.: Thickness of skin and subcutaneous tissue by age and sex in childhood, J. Pediat. 28:637-647, 1946.
821. Stuart, H. C., and Stevenson, S. S.: Physical Growth and Development, in Textbook of Pediatrics. ed. 6. W. E. Nelson, editor. (626).
822. Stutsman, R.: Scale of Mental Tests for Preschool Children. New York, World Book Company, 1930.
823. Swanson, W. W., and Iob, L. V.: Growth of fetus and infant as related to mineral intake during pregnancy, Am. J. Obst. & Gynec. 38:382-391, 1939.
824. Symonds, P. M., and Krugman, M.: Projective methods in study of personality, Rev. Educ. Research 14:81-98, 1944.
825. Talbot, N. B., Sobel, E. H., McArthur, J. W., and Crawford, J. D.: Functional Endocrinology from Birth Through Adolescence. Cambridge, Mass., Harvard University Press, 1952.
826. Tanner, J. M., et al.: Aberdeen Growth Study I. The prediction of adult body measurements from measurements taken each year from birth to 5 years, Arch. Dis. Childhood 31:372-381, 1956.
827. Taylor, K. W.: Parent Cooperative Nursery Schools. New York, Bureau of Publications, Columbia University, 1954.
828. Teel, H. M., et al.: Vitamin C in human pregnancy and lactation; studies during pregnancy, Am. J. Dis. Child. 56:1004-1010, 1938.
829. Temple, R., and Amen, E.: Study of anxiety in young children by means of projective technique, Genet. Psychol. Monogr. 30:59-114, 1944.
830. Templin, M. C.: The development of certain language skills in children, J. of Speech and Hearing Disorders 17:280-285, 1952.
831. ————: Development of Reasoning in Children with Normal and Defective Hearing. Minneapolis, University of Minnesota Press, 1950.
832. ————: Norms on a screening test of articulation for ages three through eight, J. of Speech and Hearing Disorders 18:323-331, 1953.
833. Terman, L. M., and Merrill, M. A.: Measuring Intelligence: A Guide to the Administration of New Revised Stanford-Binet Tests of Intelligence. New York, Houghton Mifflin, 1937.
834. Terman, L., and Tyler, L.: Chap. 17—Psychological Sex Differences, in Carmichael, L.: Manual of Child Psychology, ed. 2. (155).
835. Terman, L. M., et al.: Psychological Factors in Marital Happiness. New York, McGraw-Hill Book Co., Inc., 1938.
836. Thomas, D. S.: Some New Techniques for Studying Social Behavior. New York, Columbia University Press, 1929.
837. Thompson, H. M., and Rea, L. E.: Clothing for Children. New York, John Wiley & Sons, Inc., 1949.
838. Thoms, H.: Training for Childbirth. New York, McGraw-Hill Book Co., Inc., 1950.

839. Thoms, H., in collaboration with Roth, L. G.: Understanding Natural Childbirth. New York, McGraw-Hill Book Co., Inc., 1950.
840. Thoms, H., and Wyatt, R. H.: One thousand consecutive deliveries under a training for childbirth program, Am. J. Obst. & Gynec. 61:205-209, 1951.
841. Thorndike, E. L.: Unpublished statement quoted by consent.
842. Todd, T. W.: Objective ratings of constitution of growing child based on examinations of physical development and mental expansion, Am. J. Dis. Child. 55:149-159, 1938.
843. Todd, T. W., et al.: Atlas of Skeletal Maturation. St. Louis, C. V. Mosby Company, 1937.
844. Tomkins, S., et al.: Contemporary Psychopathology. Cambridge, Harvard University Press, 1943.
845. Tompkins, W. T., and Wiehl, D. G.: Maternal and Newborn Nutrition Studies at Philadelphia Lying-In Hospital. Maternal Studies III. Toxemia and maternal nutrition, in The Promotion of Maternal and Newborn Health. New York, Milbank Memorial Fund, 1955.
846. Tompkins, W. E., et al.: The underweight patient as an increased obstetric hazard, Am. J. Obst. & Gynec. 69:114-123, 1955.
847. Toverud, G.: Influence of nutrition on course of pregnancy, Milbank Memorial Fund Quarterly 28:7-24, 1950.
848. Toverud, K. U., Stearns, G., and Macy, I. G.: Maternal Nutrition and Child Health; Interpretative Review. Bulletin No. 123, Washington, D. C., National Research Council, National Academy of Science, 1950.
849. Toverud, K. U., and Toverud, G.: Studies on mineral metabolism during pregnancy and lactation and its bearing on disposition to rickets and dental caries, reported in Toverud, K. U., Stearns, G., and Macy, I. G.: Maternal Nutrition and Child Health (848).
850. Towle, C.: Effect of the war upon children, Social Service Rev. 17:144-158, 1943.
851. Trainham, G., et al.: A case history of twins breast fed on a self-demand regime, J. Pediat. 27:97-108, 1945.
852. Trotter, M., and Duggins, O. H.: Age changes in head hair from birth to maturity. I. Index and size of hair of children, Am. J. Phys. Anthropol. 6 ns:489-506, 1948.
853. Tucker, C.: Study of Mothers' Practices and Children's Activities in Co-operative Nursery School. Contributions to Education, No. 810, New York, Teachers College, Columbia University, 1940.
854. Turner, C. D.: General Endocrinology. ed. 2. Philadelphia, W. B. Saunders Co., 1955.
855. Tuttle, W. W., et al.: Effect of omitting breakfast in physiologic response of men, J. Am. Dietet. A. 26:332-335, 1950.
856. Tuttle, W. W., et al.: Effect of altered breakfast habits on physiologic response, J. Appl. Physiol. 1:545-559, 1949.
857. United Nations: Foetal, Infant and Early Childhood Mortality. vol. II, Biological, Social and Economic Factors. Population Studies No. 13. Department of Social Affairs, Population Division, New York, 1954.
858. United States Department of Agriculture: Posture in Housework. PA 186. Washington, D. C., U. S. Department of Agriculture, 1951.
859. United States Department of Health, Education and Welfare: Infant Care. Children's Bureau Publication No. 8. Washington, D. C., U. S. Department of Health, Education and Welfare, Social Security Administration, 1955.
860. United States Department of Health, Education and Welfare; Public Health

Service; National Office of Vital Statistics. Infant mortality; each state and territory and specified possessions, 1953. Vital Statistics—Special Reports, vol. 42, No. 15, January 4, 1956.

861. ———: Maternal mortality; each state and territory, and specified possessions, 1953. Vital Statistics—Special Reports, vol. 42, No. 12, November 23, 1955.

862. United States Department of Health, Education and Welfare: Your Child from One to Six. Children's Bureau Publication No. 30, Washington, D. C., U. S. Department of Health, Education and Welfare, Social Security Administration, 1956.

863. United States Department of Labor: Planning Services for Children of Employed Mothers. A Report Prepared by a Subcommittee of the Interdepartmental Committee on Children and Youth. Washington, D. C., U. S. Government Printing Office, 1953.

864. Updegraff, R.: The visual perception of distance in young children and adults: A comparative study. Studies in child welfare, 4, (4). Iowa City, University of Iowa, 1930.

865. Updegraff, R., et al.: Effect of Training upon Singing Ability and Musical Interest of Three-, Four-, and Five-Year-Old Children. Studies in Child Welfare, 14 (1), Part III. Iowa City, University of Iowa, 1937.

866. ———: Practice in Preschool Education, New York, McGraw-Hill Book Company, 1938.

867. Valentine, C. W.: Reflexes in early childhood; their development, variability, evanescence, inhibition, and relation to instinct, Brit. J. M. Psychol. 7:1-35, 1927.

868. Van Riper, C.: Speech Correction Principles and Methods. New York, Prentice-Hall, Inc., 1954.

869. ———: Teaching Your Child to Talk. New York, Harper & Brothers, 1950.

870. Vilter, R. W.: The metabolism of vitamin B_6 in human beings, Am. J. Clin. Nutrition 4:378-385, 1956.

871. Wachstein, M.: Evidence for abnormal vitamin B_6 metabolism in pregnancy and various disease states, Am. J. Clin. Nutrition 4:369-377, 1956.

872. Wagoner, L. C.: Construction Ability of Young Children. Studies in Child Welfare, III (2). Iowa City, University of Iowa, 1925.

873. ———: A Playgroup Handbook for Parents and Leaders. Bremerton, Wash., Olympic College Bookstore, 1954.

874. Wagoner, L. C., and Armstrong, E. M.: Motor control of children as involved in the dressing process, J. Genet. Psychol. 35:84-97, 1928.

875. Waller, H.: The early failure of breast feeding; clinical study of its causes and their prevention, Arch. Dis. Childhood 21:1-12, 1946.

876. Waller, W.: The Family, revised by R. Hill. New York, Dryden Press, 1951.

877. Walters, J., et al.: Affectional and aggressive behavior of preschool children, Child Development 28:15-26, 1957.

878. Waring, E.: Relation between Early Language Habits and Early Habits of Conduct Control. Contributions to Education, No. 260. New York, Teachers College, Columbia University, 1927.

878a. Warkany, J., Roth, C. B., and Wilson, J. G.: Multiple congenital malformations; consideration of etiologic factors, Pediatrics 1:462-471, 1948.

879. Washburn, A. H.: Chap. 8 (vol. 1)—Appraisal of Healthy Growth and Development from Birth to Adolescence, in Brennemann's Practice of Pediatrics, I, McQuarrie, editor. Hagerstown, Md., W. F. Prior Co., Inc., 1957.

880. Washburn, R.: Children Have Their Reasons. New York, D. Appleton-Century Co., Inc., 1942.
881. Watson, E. H., and Lowrey, G. H.: Growth and Development of Children. ed. 2. Chicago, Year Book Publishers, Inc., 1954.
882. Watson, J. B.: Psychological Care of Infant and Child. New York, W. W. Norton & Co., Inc., 1928.
883. Weinstein, B. B., et al.: Oral administration of pyridoxine hydrochloride in the treatment of nausea and vomiting, Am. J. Obst. & Gynec. 47:389-394, 1944.
884. Wellman, B.: Development of Motor Coordination of Young Children. Studies in Child Welfare, III (4). Iowa City, University of Iowa, 1926.
885. ————: I.Q. changes of preschool and non-preschool groups during preschool years; summary of the literature, J. Psychol. 20:247-268, 1945.
886. Wellman, B., et al.: Speech Sounds of Young Children. Studies in Child Welfare, V (2). Iowa City, University of Iowa, 1931.
887. Wenger, M. A.: An investigation of conditioned responses in human infants. Studies in Child Welfare 12:1-90, Iowa City, University of Iowa, 1936.
888. Westphal, G.: Experimental study of certain motor abilities of stutterers, Child Development 4:214-221, 1933.
889. Wetzel, N. C.: Assessing physical condition of children; components of physical status and physical progress and their evaluation, J. Pediat. 22:329-361, 1943.
890. ————: Growth, in Glasser, O. (ed.): Medical Physics, vol. 1. Chicago, Year Book Publishers, Inc., 1944.
891. ————: Physical fitness in terms of physique, development and basal metabolism, J.A.M.A. 116:1187-1195, 1941.
892. ————: The baby grid, J. Pediat. 29:439-454, 1946.
893. White House Conference on Child Health and Protection: Addresses and Abstracts of Committee Reports. New York, The Century Co., 1931.
894. ————: Growth and Development of the Child, Part I. New York, The Century Co., 1932.
895. ————: Growth and Development of The Child, Part III. Nutrition. New York, The Century Co., 1932.
896. White House Conference on Child Health and Protection: Special Education. New York, The Century Co., 1931.
897. White House Conference Report; Children in a Democracy. Washington, D. C., Superintendent of Documents, 1940.
898. Whiting, J. W. M., and Child, I. L.: Child Training and Personality: A cross-cultural study. New Haven, Yale University Press, 1953.
899. Wickes, F. G.: The Inner World of Childhood. New York, D. Appleton-Century Co., Inc., 1928.
900. Widdowson, E. M.: Mental contentment and physical growth, Lancet 1: 1316-1318, 1951.
901. ————: Reproduction and obesity, Am. J. Clin. Nutrition 3:391-396, 1955.
902. Wiegand, E.: Use of Time by Full-Time and Part-Time Homemakers in Relation to Home Management. Memoir 330. Ithaca, N. Y., Cornell University Agricultural Experiment Station, 1954.
903. Wiehl, D. G., and Tompkins, W. L.: Size of babies of obese mothers receiving nutrient supplements, Milbank Mem. Fund Quarterly 32:125-140, 1954.
904. Wilkins, L.: The Diagnosis and Treatment of Endocrine Disorders in Childhood and Adolescence. ed. 2. Springfield, Ill., Charles C Thomas, Publisher, 1957.

905. Wilkinson, J.: Relation of Parental Behavior to Social and Emotional Adjustment of Children in Nursery School. Master's Thesis, Purdue University, 1950.
906. Williams, R. B., and Matson, M.: Effect of social groupings upon language of preschool children, Child Development 13:233-245, 1942.
907. Williams, R. J.: Biochemical Individuality. The Basis for the Genetotrophic Concept. New York, John Wiley and Sons, Inc., 1956.
908. Willis, R. S., et al.: Clinical observations in treatment of nausea and vomiting in pregnancy with vitamins B_1 and B_6; preliminary report, Am. J. Obst. & Gynec. 44:265-271, 1942.
909. Wilson, B. A.: The Development and Evaluation of a Speech Improvement Program for Kindergarten Children. Doctoral Thesis, Purdue University, 1952.
910. Wilson, J. G., and Barch, S.: Fetal death and maldevelopment resulting from maternal vitamin A deficiency in rat, Proc. Soc. Exper. Biol. & Med. 72:687-693, 1949.
911. Wilson, J. G., and Warkany, J.: Cardiac and aortic arch abnormalities in the offspring of vitamin A deficient rats correlated with similar human anomalies, Pediatrics 5:708-725, 1950.
912. Wilson, J. G., et al.: Analysis of syndrome of malformations induced by maternal vitamin A deficiency. Effects of restoration of vitamin A at various times during gestation, Am. J. Anat. 92:189-217, 1953.
913. Winstel, B.: Use of controlled play situation in determining certain effects of maternal attitudes on children, Child Development 22:299-311, 1951.
914. Witkin, H. A., et al.: Personality through Perception: An Experimental and Clinical Study. New York, Harper and Brothers, 1954.
915. Witmer, H., and Kotinsky, R. (editors): Personality in the Making: Fact Finding Report of Midcentury White House Conference on Children and Youth. New York, Harper & Brothers, 1953.
916. Witty, P.: The Gifted Child. Boston, D. C. Heath & Co., 1951.
917. Wolf, A.: Parents Manual. New York, Simon & Schuster, Inc , 1941. Also in Popular Library edition. New York, Popular Library, Inc.
918. Wolf, K. M.: The Controversial Problem of Discipline. New York: Child Study Association of America, 1953.
919. Wolff, W.: Personality of the Preschool Child. New York, Grune & Stratton, 1946.
920. Wolman, I. J.: Does milk between meals hamper the appetite or food intake of the child? J. Pediat. 28:703-712, 1946.
921. ———: Major motility patterns of the child's digestive tract; a review, Am. J. M. Sc. 207:782-804, 1944.
922. Woodcock, L.: Life and Ways of the Two-Year-Old. New York, E. P. Dutton & Company, 1941.
923. Woodhill, L. M., et al.: Nutrition studies of pregnant Australian women. Part II. Maternal diet and the duration of lactation, Am. J. Obst. & Gynec. 70:997-1003, 1955.
924. Woods Schools: Helping Parents Understand the Exceptional Child; Proceedings of Annual Spring Conference on Education and the Exceptional Child. Langhorne, Pa., May, 1952.
925. ———: The Exceptional Child in Infancy and Early Childhood; Proceedings of Annual Spring Conference on Education and the Exceptional Child. Langhorne, Pa., May, 1950.
926. Wooley, H. T.: David—A Study of the Experience of a Nursery School in

Training a Child Adopted from an Institution. Child Welfare League of America, Case Studies, No. 2.

927. Worcester, D. A.: Mental development from birth to pre-adolescence, Rev. Educ. Research 20:345-350, 1950.

928. Yamazaki, J. N., et al.: Outcome of pregnancy in women exposed to the atomic bomb in Nagasaki, Am. J. Dis. Child. 87:448-463, 1954.

929. Yerushalmy, J.: Neonatal mortality by order of birth and age of parents, Am. J. Hyg. 28:244-270, 1938.

930. ———: On interval between successive births and its effect on survival of infant; indirect method of study, Human Biol. 17:65-106, 1945.

931. Ziskin, D. E., and Hotelling, H.: Effects of pregnancy, mouth acidity and age on dental caries, J. Dent. Research 16:507-519, 1937.

932. Zubek, J. P., and Solberg, P. A.: Human Development. New York, McGraw-Hill Book Co., 1954.

Index

(Numbers in *italic* type refer to pages containing illustrations.)